PLATE 1

MAJOR PHYSICAL REGIONS OF MIDDLE NORTH AMERICA

INTRODUCTION TO PHYSICAL GEOLOGY

Chester R. Longwell & Richard F. Flint

EMERITUS PROFESSOR OF GEOLOGY, YALE UNIVERSITY   PROFESSOR OF GEOLOGY, YALE UNIVERSITY

SECOND EDITION

INTRODUCTION TO
PHYSICAL GEOLOGY

John Wiley & Sons, Inc., NEW YORK, LONDON

Title page photograph by *Andreas Feininger*

Maps by *Vaughn Gray*

Drawings by *Sy Barlowe*

THIRD PRINTING, APRIL, 1963

Library of Congress Catalog Card Number: 62–8779
Printed in the United States of America

PREFACE

In preparing this thorough revision, we have had the benefit of suggestions from numerous teachers and students who used the first edition, published early in 1955. Little change has been made in the general order of treating major subjects, but most parts of the text have been reorganized, rewritten, and considerably amplified to make the presentation clearer, more effective, and up-to-date. Improvement of the illustrations also has been a main objective. Many diagrams and halftones have been replaced, and the total space given to illustrations has been increased by more than 50 per cent. Final copy of all line drawings has been prepared by skilled draftsmen under central supervision to insure uniformly clear execution.

Two features introduced in this revision call for special mention and explanation. One is a scheme of brief, "dictionary-style" definitions, not in a separate glossary but within the body of the text. Concise definitions of technical or unusual terms often are useful, but commonly they require some amplification for full understanding. The chief merit urged for a glossary is its convenience for quick reference. This advantage is matched by the scheme adopted here. A term defined in the text appears in *boldface italic* type, the defining phrase or clause, in *lightface italics*. The page on which the term is defined is indicated by boldface italic type in the general index; thus the reader is guided to his objective without loss of time. If the bare definition does not fill his need, he has additional information at hand in the related text and perhaps in one or more adjoining illustrations. Definitions isolated in a glossary lack this advantage.

Actually the primary purpose of having succinct definitions in the text is not to give aid in casual reference but to help the student focus on basic meanings in his reading. Care has been taken to avoid a sameness of pattern in wording the definitions, which are set apart from the associated text only by the use of distinctive type.

A second special feature of this revision is a brief summary at the close of each chapter. Beginners have difficulty in digesting the volume of description and analysis required for presenting the many facets of a new and complex subject. We believe that a concise statement of the essential points covered and conclusions reached in a chapter will be a direct and effective aid to students. Such a helpful digest is the aim of the chapter summaries.

Teachers of elementary geology have differing views on the most effective order of subjects to be discussed and on the proper balance between classroom and laboratory work. Whatever order of subjects may be chosen, the relations of geologic features and processes do not permit independent and final treatment of any major topic. Understanding of processes requires some acquaintance with the basic materials, minerals, and rocks. But only a superficial knowledge of these materials is possible until the student knows something about processes involved in their formation. Although he may learn at an early stage to identify common kinds of sedimentary rocks, he can not grasp their full meaning until he has some knowledge of weathering, erosion, the distribution of modern sediments, and their conversion into rock by physical and chemical agencies.

For these reasons a textbook should have some flexibility to be useful in more than one kind of approach. We have aimed to insure such flexibility that an instructor can rearrange the order of study of the geologic processes to suit his own preference.

We thank especially the following persons and organizations for generous help not acknowledged elsewhere in this edition: F. M. Bullard, C. O. Dunbar, R. V. Dietrich, M. L. Jensen, Adolph Knopf, P. A. Reitan, J. E. Sanders, Kurt Servos, A. L. Washburn, Horace Winchell, U. S. Geological Survey, and Geological Survey of Canada. Members of the staff of John Wiley and Sons who were charged with processing the book for publication gave many constructive suggestions.

In acknowledging the help, we exempt the givers from blame for errors or other weaknesses in the finished volume. Margaret Flint and Irene Longwell helped greatly to make parts of the text smoother and clearer.

C.R.L. *and* R.F.F.

Palo Alto, California
New Haven, Connecticut
October 1961

CONTENTS

Chapter 1 The science of the Earth   1
2 A general view of the Earth   13
3 Materials of the Earth's crust   27
4 Geologic time   49
5 Field study and geologic mapping   65
6 Igneous geology   79
7 Weathering and soils   113
8 Mass-wasting   133
9 Running water   153
10 Sculpture of the lands by streams and mass-wasting   177
11 Ground water   197
12 Lakes and basins   213
13 Glaciers and glaciation   227
14 Deserts and wind action   253
15 The sea: submarine geology   281
16 Waves, currents, and the sculpture of coasts   303
17 Sedimentary rocks   323
18 Deformation of the Earth's crust   347
19 Metamorphism   375
20 Earthquakes: the Earth's interior   391
21 Origin and history of mountains   413
22 Geology in industry   441

Appendices A How to identify common minerals   468
B Identification of common rocks   476
C Maps   483
D Symbols and conversion tables   488
E The elements   492

Index   493

CHAPTER 1. THE SCIENCE OF THE EARTH

Geology defined   Scientific and practical aspects   Growth of ideas about the Earth   Uniformity of process through time   Record in the rocks   Change through conflict of forces   Physical and historical geology

Stromboli Volcano, Italy, in action. (Underwood & Underwood)

What geology is

Plans for exploring outer space arouse interest, but there is much we do not know about the Earth beneath us. Wherever we may live or travel—in mountains, on plains, or at the seashore—we meet problems that have puzzled thinking people over the centuries. What holds the continents above the much wider ocean basins? What forces have raised mountain chains such as The Himalaya and the Andes? What is the meaning of volcanoes and earthquakes? We want to know about the history of living things. How long has life existed on the Earth? Is there firm evidence for the view that progressive changes have occurred in forms of plants and animals down through the ages? How long has man been part of the earthly scene?

Geology (Gr. *Ge,* "earth," and *logos,* "discourse"), *the science of the Earth,* gives answers in part to some of our questions. It is a science that uses all available knowledge in a continuing effort to learn the secrets the Earth still holds. The chief aim of this effort is not just to assemble facts but, more important, to work out principles that will explain the facts. Essential help toward this goal is given by related sciences: physics, which deals with the laws of energy and with atomic structure; chemistry, concerned with compositions and interactions of materials; biology, the science of living matter. Questions that involve our place in the universe keep us in close touch with astronomers.

Interest in studying the Earth is not rooted entirely in human curiosity, though this has been a strong incentive. Many of our basic resources are parts of the Earth: the soil, which produces food and other necessities; the mineral fuels—coal, oil, and natural gas; and metals and other mineral products essential to industry. These materials are the lifeblood of our civilization. Problems of developing and conserving available supplies, as well as competition for their control, play a significant part in shaping policies of nations. There is need for the best skills in finding and utilizing these basic resources, and naturally there has grown up a profession of geology which makes practical use of knowledge gained from scientific study and in turn contributes much to the science. At present the largest number of trained geologists in North America is engaged in the petroleum industry (Chap. 22). Many are connected with various kinds of mining, and others give their attention to engineering projects, such as the construction of aqueducts, tunnels, dams, road grades, and similar works that involve large-scale excavation (Fig. 1–1). Several states and provinces employ geologists to work with highway engineers in examining and reporting on proposed routes for highways and selecting sites for bridges. The vital program of soil conservation enlists geologists in considerable numbers (p. 149).

Because basic resources are of great importance to the general public, every country of considerable size has a government bureau staffed with geologists. The Geological Survey of Great Britain has been in continuous operation since 1835 and has made the geology of that country exceptionally well known. The United States Geological Survey, organized in 1879, has grown to impressive proportions and employs hundreds of geologists. In addition, nearly every state has its own geological survey. A fundamental duty of these organizations is the making of maps that show the kinds of rock beneath the land surface (p. 66). Study and mapping of surface features and the underlying rocks in the United States are going forward rapidly, though the task is so enormous that at the present rate several generations of geologists will be occupied with it. The Geological Survey of Canada is also a vigorous organization, with a vast field for its work, including the sparsely settled lands that extend from Hudson Bay and Great Slave Lake northward to the Arctic Ocean (Fig. 1–2). Mexico and several other Latin American countries maintain programs of study that contribute to knowledge of geology in the Western Hemisphere.

In large parts of every continent very little geological work has been done, and study of ocean floors, which comprise nearly three-fourths of the Earth's surface, is hardly more than well started (Chap. 15). Opportunities for discovery, therefore, are inviting, and the science of geology is in some respects still in an early stage of development.

Beginnings and progress of the science

Early ideas. Several ancient scholars did remarkably accurate reasoning about some geologic problems, but their efforts were individual and led to no sustained progress. The most influential of these

Fig. 1–1. Preliminary surveying at site of Hoover Dam, Arizona-Nevada. In selecting this site for the highest dam of its day, engineers had to decide whether (a) the rocks were strong enough to withstand great pressures from a large artificial lake, (b) no serious leaks would develop from fractures in the rocks, (c) the rock would not be dissolved by water under continuous pressure. Geologists who were consulted approved the site on all these counts. Results justify this verdict. (U. S. Bureau of Reclamation.)

Fig. 1–2. Air view north of Yellowknife and Great Slave Lake, Northwest Territory, Canada. In vast areas of eastern and northern Canada the rocks are visible at the surface because glacier ice removed the cover of soil only yesterday in geologic history (Chap. 13). The dark areas are surfaces of lakes (Royal Can. Air Force, courtesy A. W. Jolliffe.)

thinkers was Aristotle (384–322 B.C.), whose observations and speculations about natural features and laws were accepted and quoted without question during the long intellectual stalemate of the Middle Ages. Scattered signs of a real awakening of interest in the Earth appeared early in the Renaissance. Leonardo da Vinci, the famous Italian artist and engineer (1452–1519), had a remarkably modern point of view in reasoning about the forms of shells in rocks at high altitudes in the Apennine Mountains (Fig. 1–3). His intellectual stature is appreciated against the background of beliefs regarding fossils that were prevalent in his time. One of these quaint doctrines, dating back to the ancient philosopher Theophrastus, regarded fossils as imitative forms, produced by a "plastic force" within the Earth. Da Vinci observed that the forms common in the rocks of the Apennines have all the essential details of modern sea shells, including scars where muscles of the animals were attached, and that they are imbedded in material resembling the muds and sands spread out near the mouths of modern rivers, though the material is now firm rock. In his reasoned view, the wide distribution

Fig. 1–3. Forms of marine shells, generally similar to those in present seas but different in important details, are abundant in rocks of all continents. These forms are from a sandstone in eastern New York. (Courtesy C. O. Dunbar.)

of the old shells, in layers of rock that now are steeply tilted and at varied heights, must mean great uplift of an area that once was part of the sea floor.

Da Vinci's method of attack, by explaining features formed in rocks in the light of processes now operating, is the very essence of modern geology. The method must start with careful observation of all evidence to be found in the rocks themselves. This essential first step was emphasized in 1571 by an exceptional Dane, Peter Severinus, when, apparently impatient with the repetition of half truths and unfounded speculations in textbooks, he told his students: "Go, my sons . . . burn your books . . . buy yourselves stout shoes, get away to the mountains, search the valleys, the deserts, the shores of the sea, and the deepest recesses of the earth. . . . In this way, and no other, will you arrive at a knowledge of things and of their properties."

Key to the past. During many centuries all real progress in understanding the natural things around us was blocked by general acceptance of the teaching that only a few thousand years have gone by since the Earth was formed. Under this assumption, every major feature, such as a deep canyon or a great volcanic mountain, was supposed to be the result of an exceptional event, a *catastrophe*. Those who held this view, the *catastrophists*, were in the ascendancy until late in the eighteenth century, when an increasing number of men began to be impressed with evidence that features of the Earth reflect the operation of familiar processes working through immensely long intervals of time. This point of view was expressed by an able Scot, James Hutton of Edinburgh (1726–1797), in the maxim "The present is the key to the past." Hutton formulated *the principle of **uniformity of process**,* which *assumes that the forces now operating to change the face of the Earth have worked continuously and rather uniformly through a large part of the Earth's history* (p. 24). His concept of an immensely long history is indicated in his statement that he had found "no vestige of a beginning, no prospect of an end." His view, strongly supported by all later studies and discoveries, is recognized as a major principle in modern geology and an outstanding contribution of geology to scientific thought. This principle is cited again and again in later pages of this book.

Fig. 1—4. Eruption at the summit of Mauna Loa Volcano, Island of Hawaii. Continued activity of numerous volcanoes provides a key to the history of vast quantities of older rock. Mauna Loa and Kilauea erupt at frequent intervals (Chap. 6). (Sawders from Cushing.)

Hutton was followed shortly by a host of vigorous workers in Britain and other countries, whose co-ordinated efforts established the science of geology on a firm basis.

Rocks, the primary documents of geology

Any understanding of the Earth must start with some knowledge of the materials that compose it. As only a thin rind of the globe can be examined directly, information about the vast interior must be based on indirect evidence. Our most active interest, however, lies in the outer zone, and this part provides an almost limitless field of study. It is a zone composed of rocks and their constituent minerals. These materials, best exposed in cliffs or in road cuts and other artificial excavations, appear highly varied, and casual observers may suppose that only students with intensive special training can gain any adequate acquaintance with rocks. Actually, only a few general kinds of rock make up the greater part of the Earth open to view, and therefore any interested person can without great difficulty learn to read parts of the record offered by geologic displays that he may

see in his travels. A thorough study of rocks and minerals involves complexities and problems that must be left to those specially trained for the task.

A visitor to the slopes of Vesuvius or of Mauna Loa sees masses of dark, slaggy rock. Even if no eruption is in progress, the ropy forms suggest that the rock was once liquid and flowed as a white-hot stream (Fig. 1—4). Continued observation would convince the traveler that the "fire-made" or *igneous* rocks are common in many lands and have been formed at many dates (Chap. 6). Thoughtful observers of volcanic action reason logically that the floods of ejected material must have their source in deep-seated molten masses which eventually will cool and solidify. This reasoning is supported by studies in mountain lands where running water, acting through a great length of time, has cut deeply beneath remnants of old volcanic fields, revealing bodies of igneous rock that cooled and crystallized far below the land surface of that time. Rocks of this kind, as well as those formed by volcanic action, are exposed over great areas of the present lands.

Fig. 1–5. Sedimentary layers in Spring Mountain Range, southern Nevada. All rocks within this view contain abundant fossil forms of animals that lived in seas, yet these rocks extend to more than 11,000 feet above present sea level. (Josef Muench.)

Fig. 1–6. Fossil fish from sedimentary rocks formed on sea floor. Delicate features preserved in outline by carbonaceous residue. West Indies. (Courtesy American Museum of Natural History.)

Rocks in another major class, the sedimentary rocks, occur in layers, one above another, with exposed thicknesses in some wide areas totaling thousands of feet (Fig. 1–5). In some layers the forms of shells, bones, and parts of plants appear on exposed surfaces or on freshly broken pieces of the rock. Delicate patterns of some forms are preserved in astonishing perfection (Fig. 1–6). Clearly the materials in these rocks have their counterparts in the sands and muds found along present-day streams or dredged from the floors of lakes and seas. Three-fourths of the land area of the Earth is underlain by sedimentary rocks, which have particular value in geology because they preserve abundant remains of plants and animals and also many physical features that record conditions under which the rocks were formed (Chaps. 3, 17).

The *metamorphic rocks,* making a third major class, show by vestiges of earlier composition and structure that they were formed by physical and chemical alteration of rocks which originally were either igneous or sedimentary (Chaps. 3, 19). Strong pressures, probably with some increase in temperature, caused growth of new minerals in a parallel arrangement; as a result, many metamorphic rocks, notably slates, split into regular slabs that transect patterns of the original rock (Fig. 1–7, **A**). Other rocks have been intensely crumpled (Fig. 1–7, **B**). Deep burial seems essential for large-scale development of metamorphic rocks, as they are best displayed in cores of old mountain belts from which large thicknesses of rock have been removed through long ages by running water and other agents.

Another important unit must be considered with the three major types of rock in the visible part of the solid Earth. Over wide areas in each continent, particularly on the flat and gently rolling land surfaces devoted to agriculture, exposures of solid rock are exceptional. Wide stretches of prairie in central Illinois have no natural exposures, and in many land areas continuous rock is visible only on hillsides, in cliffs bordering the larger valleys, or in the beds of exceptionally swift streams. Numerous artificial pits and drilled wells demonstrate that *continuous solid rock,* commonly known as **bedrock,** is everywhere beneath the concealing cover, at varying depths. The *assemblage of loose material, consisting chiefly of*

A

B

Fig. 1–7. A. Slate, with cleavage plates oblique to original layering. Hammer handle is parallel to the sedimentary layers. Desert Range, southern Nevada. (C. R. Longwell.) **B.** Old sedimentary layers, changed chemically and crumpled. (J. W. Ambrose, Geol. Survey of Canada.)

rock particles, that commonly mantles the bedrock at the Earth's surface is **regolith** (rĕg'ō-lĭth; Gr. *regos*, "blanket," and *lithos*, "rock"). In some places the regolith has been formed by breakup and chemical change of the local bedrock (Fig. 1–8); but in many other places the regolith has been transported, by any of several processes, and deposited in its present position. Regolith has large significance, as it is an important source of materials that go into formation of the sedimentary rocks (Chap. 17).

Varied histories of rock materials

Water sweeps clay, sand, and coarser rock particles from land areas and spreads these materials on the floors of valleys, lakes, and seas. With compaction and cementation, layers of such deposits now visibly building up may become sedimentary rocks of the future. World-wide studies have established that sediments of varied kinds have been laid down continually through long ages, though the sites of accumulation have shifted from place to place. Some thick sections of the resulting sedimentary rocks have

Fig. 1–8. Bedrock beside a graded highway in southern California is partly decayed and broken into fragments, large and small. The resulting loose rock material forms a cover of regolith, thin at right of view, much thicker at left. (John S. Shelton.)

been buckled and raised to high altitudes in the growth of mountain belts (Fig. 1–9). Many of these deformed sections also contain large thicknesses of volcanic materials that were erupted while the sediments were being deposited. Under high pressures and rising temperatures in deep parts of the growing mountains, both the sedimentary and the volcanic rocks were transformed into metamorphic rocks. Locally, temperatures rose above the melting point, fusing rocks of all kinds and thus starting new episodes of volcanic activity. This general history, with variations, is revealed by relationships in complex assemblages of igneous, sedimentary, and metamorphic rocks exposed to view by the wearing down of old mountain systems.

Thus the several kinds of rock reflect conditions under which they were formed. The making of sedimentary and igneous rocks is still in active operation, as we can see in the large-scale movement and deposition of sedimentary materials and in the continued activity of volcanoes. Study of these visible processes gives a highly effective key to much of the older record. As metamorphic rocks have been formed at some depth, probably for the most part at rates too slow for human perception, we lack direct evidence that such rocks are now developing on a large scale, although reasoning from the available evidence implies that they are.

The record we read in the rocks indicates clearly that processes now operating in the outer part of the Earth have performed in much the same way through long ages. These processes reflect incessant conflict between two sets of forces. One set, involving solar energy, water, air, and the pull of gravity, tends to break up exposed rocks and to reduce all surface irregularities; this tendency is evident in the making of sedimentary rocks. The opposing set of forces, operating within the body of the Earth, causes uplift and depression of surface areas, thus defeating or retarding the persistent tendency toward leveling. The internal forces, whose origin is not yet understood, cause uplift of mountains and have an important connection with igneous activity and large-scale metamorphism. Continued operation of these forces has supplied potential for the age-long production of sedimentary deposits from which we read a significant part of Earth history.

Fig. 1—9. Layers of sedimentary rock formed on ancient sea floor, now much deformed and exposed in high ranges in southern Nevada. (Spence Air Photos.)

Physical and historical geology

A study of the Earth starts logically with the visible materials, their compositions and relationships, and the processes now operating on and beneath the surface. Such a study is basic for reading the history recorded in the rocks. In a general way we can separate preliminary study of the Earth's physical features from a systematic study of the historical record. The present volume is devoted to the basic subject matter of the science. Geology, however, deals fundamentally with a record of the past. Many materials and features in the visible part of the Earth can have adequate explanation only within the framework of a long history. Accordingly, the story recorded in the rocks is repeatedly emphasized, and a brief outline of Earth history is presented in Chapter 4. A

detailed and systematic presentation of historical geology is the function of a later systematic treatment in which the physical evidence seen in the relations among bodies of rock is supplemented by the record of organisms, both plant and animal. The evidence bearing on organic evolution, including the early history of man, is logically a part of historical geology.

Geology and the citizen

Scientific and professional concern of the geologist merges with the general interest people have in many aspects of the Earth. They want to know why soils differ radically, why and how petroleum occurs underground. Natural scenery has its basis in geologic features, and many people in viewing landscapes are not satisfied with vague impressions of

Fig. 1—10. Grand Canyon of the Colorado River. View west from Lipan Point, Arizona. In forming this valley, the river carried away hundreds of cubic miles of rock. (Josef Muench.)

beauty or grandeur; they wonder about the origin and history of such exhibits as the Carlsbad Caverns, the Grand Canyon, and the fiords of Norway, about the mechanism of a geyser or of a volcano. This kind of interest is stimulated by increased opportunity to visit national parks and other scenic areas where geologic features are exceptionally well displayed.

Intelligent laymen find much of interest in geologic reports and maps, though they may have to struggle a bit with some technical terms that geologists use habitually in communicating with each other. Every science develops a vocabulary that expresses its facts and ideas with the greatest possible precision and brevity. It is possible, however, to describe and discuss the common geologic features and problems in simple English, and geologic literature in nontechnical language is on the increase. Publications of some government agencies are setting a good standard in this kind of writing. Colleges could perform a real service by offering well-designed courses in the effective use of English for clear and accurate presentation of scientific facts and concepts.

In his reasoning about geologic matters the average layman at first finds the element of time the most difficult to grasp. Instinctively we think in terms of our own experience and try to explain large results by great forces and fast action. It is not surprising that during the infancy of geologic science catastrophism was a convincing doctrine. After their first look at the Grand Canyon many people feel that it must represent a cataclysmic tearing apart of the Earth's crust (Fig. 1—10). Yet a careful study of the detailed evidence will bring conviction that Hutton's principle is sound and that the immensity of the Grand Canyon represents the cumulative effects, in a very long lapse of time, of processes we see operating today at an unimpressively slow rate.

SUMMARY

1. Study of the Earth has scientific, professional, and general-interest incentives.

2. Geologic concepts now accepted have developed in large part since the middle of the eighteenth century, though exceptional glimpses of some principles came earlier.

3. The key to an understanding of geologic features and relations is found in processes now operating.

4. Rocks hold a record of changes on the Earth through ages inconceivably long.

5. All geologic study involves history. Analytic study of physical features and processes lays a foundation for systematic reconstruction of geologic history, including the complex record of animals and plants.

REFERENCES

Study of well-chosen extracts from the writings of pioneers in geology gives an appreciation of the great strides in development of the science through four centuries. An assemblage of carefully selected quotations from 125 authors is available in the book by Mather and Mason listed below. Though some of the earliest writings may now seem quaint in expression and concept, generally they represent constructive thought in a period of rapid growth of the science. In relation to points discussed in this chapter, the following pages of the book, quoting authors named in parentheses, are recommended: pages 1–6 (Da Vinci), 7–11 (Agricola), 33–39 (Steno), 92–100 (Hutton), 131–135 (Playfair), 138–142 (Werner).

The book by Playfair, first published in 1802 and now available in a recent reprinting, interprets in clear and lively fashion the constructive thoughts which in Hutton's own writing are partly obscured by clumsy phrasing.

Mather, K. F., and Mason, S. L., 1939, A source book in geology: New York, McGraw-Hill.
Playfair, J., 1802, Illustrations of the Huttonian theory of the Earth: Reprinted 1956, Urbana, University of Illinois Press.

CHAPTER 2. A GENERAL VIEW OF THE EARTH

Spheroidal form   Atmosphere, hydrosphere, crust   Continents and oceans   Gravity and solar energy   The hydrologic cycle   Conflict between internal and external forces   Scientific method of study   Coordination of research efforts

A model of the Earth. (Courtesy A. N. Strahler, Physical Geography, John Wiley and Sons, 1960)

Shape and size

A number of ancient scholars realized that the Earth has a generally spherical form, and possibly this thought came even to some prehistoric men when they saw the curved shadow advance across the full Moon during an eclipse. Today no informed person can have any doubt that the Earth is "round"; its curved form is registered clearly in a high-level photograph (Fig. 2–1). But how is the circumference measured precisely, and how is it known that each of the poles is somewhat closer to the center than are points on the equator?

The general method of finding answers to these questions is shown in Figure 2–2. Astronomers estimate our distance from the Pole (or North) Star as about 500 light years, or 3,000 million million miles. As this distance is almost infinite in relation to our small planet, lines from all points on the Earth to the star are, in effect, parallel. At the north pole the Pole Star is directly overhead; that is, the line of sight to the star is at 90° to a horizontal plane.[1] To an observer traveling south from the pole, the star appears lower and lower in the northern sky, and at E, on the equator, the star is seen exactly on the horizon. At each point south of the pole along the north-south line the star has a precise *altitude*, which is the acute angle measured in the vertical plane between the line to the star and the horizontal. Each of the points also has its own *latitude*, which is the value of the angle between the Earth's radius at the point and the plane of the equator. At every place north of the equator the angle of latitude is equal to the altitude of the Pole Star. Take, for example,

[1] Not precisely true, but the necessary correction is small and is known exactly.

the point P at 60° north latitude (Fig. 2–2). The angle V^2PS and the angle A are equal, because these angles lie between a common side R and parallel lines. But $A = 90°$ minus $60° = 30°$; hence the angle H^2PS (altitude of the Pole Star at P) $= H^2PV^2$ (90°) minus V^2PS (30°) $= 60°$, the same as the latitude.

Surveyors with proper equipment, therefore, can determine the latitude at any point in the Northern Hemisphere by measuring at that point the altitude of the Pole Star. By finding values of latitude at many points along a north-south line and measuring precisely the distances on the ground between points, surveyors find that near the equator the distance corresponding to 1° of latitude is 68.70 miles and that this value increases gradually northward to 69.41 miles near the pole. Closely similar results are found in the Southern Hemisphere (where, however, other points in the heavens are used for fixing latitudes). Hence, a meridian, followed around the Earth, is not a circle; it is an ellipse with the "flatter" parts of its curvature in polar latitudes (Fig. 2–3). The degree of flattening, though measurable, is so slight the eye can not detect it in a scaled model or diagram. But an ellipse is a mathematical form, and from the exact measurements along a meridian the length of the polar radius is computed to be about 3950 miles, or 13.3 miles shorter than the equatorial radius. Thus, whereas the circumference following the equator measures about 24,903 miles, the circumference through the poles is some tens of miles less.

This polar flattening of the Earth, to a form known as an *oblate spheroid*, is a logical result of rapid rotation (p. 19). Minor departures from the simple

Fig. 2–1. Part of the Earth photographed from an Atlas rocket. View generally southwest across Caribbean Sea to northern part of South America. (Wide World.)

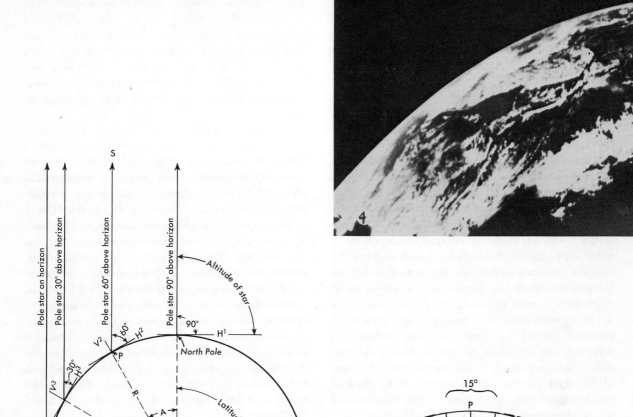

Fig. 2–2. The form and size of the Earth are found by observations on the Pole Star and precise measurements on the Earth's surface. If the reader doubts that the lines to the star are essentially parallel, let him try to compute the angle subtended by the Earth's radius, 4,000 miles long, at a point 3,000 million million miles away. (Modified from S. J. Shand.)

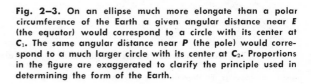

Fig. 2–3. On an ellipse much more elongate than a polar circumference of the Earth a given angular distance near **E** (the equator) would correspond to a circle with its center at **C₁**. The same angular distance near **P** (the pole) would correspond to a much larger circle with its center at **C₂**. Proportions in the figure are exaggerated to clarify the principle used in determining the form of the Earth.

geometric form are being detected by sensitive mechanical devices; for example, the behavior of a small artificial satellite, revolving in a polar orbit, has indicated small differences in shape between the north and south polar segments of the Earth. Knowing the form of the globe as precisely as possible is important in making exact maps, which represent parts of the curved surface projected onto planes (App. C).

Major divisions and features

Air, water, rocks. The part of the Earth we know directly consists of air (gases), water (liquid), and rocks (solids). Water and air form two distinct envelopes around the solid body of the Earth, and, although geology deals basically with rocks, the air and water claim a good deal of the geologist's attention because they change rock material continually and on a large scale. The *atmosphere* (Gr. "vapor sphere") extends in detectable quantity hundreds of miles above the Earth's surface, though in the outer part the gases are extremely thin; more than half of the gaseous matter, by weight, is in a zone 6 to 10 miles thick directly above the Earth's surface. Within this lower zone, the *troposphere* ("sphere of change"), is all the Earth's weather (Chap. 7). Although the matter in the atmosphere makes up only a tiny percentage of the entire Earth, it is one of the chief geologic agents because of its physical and chemical activity. Oxygen, carbon dioxide, and a variable content of water vapor are the most active ingredients; nitrogen, although it makes up more than three-fourths of the total, is comparatively inert chemically.

The other envelope, the *hydrosphere* ("water sphere"), is not continuous, although the oceans cover nearly three-fourths of the Earth's surface, and water is widespread on the lands also, forming lakes and streams and filling openings in soil and bedrock. So large is the volume of water that if all surface inequalities of the globe were leveled off there would be a world-wide ocean more than a mile and a half deep. Water, with the aid of the atmosphere, has been one of the most powerful agents in causing changes on the surface of the lands through geologic ages.

In general, the light gases of the atmosphere overlie the denser hydrosphere, which in turn lies above the much denser rock of the solid Earth. There is, however, considerable intermingling of the three major units. Great quantities of water vapor are carried aloft temporarily, as we can see in clouds, and large amounts of air are dissolved in the hydrosphere. Both air and water circulate through openings in rock material. The outer zone of the solid Earth is known as the *lithosphere* ("rock sphere"), but commonly the outer part of this zone is called the *crust*, a term inherited from an old and now discarded concept that all the Earth within a thin outer shell is molten. In spite of its dubious origin, "crust" is a popular and convenient term, and we shall use it with the understanding that it does not suggest the condition and origin of the Earth's interior. The modern scientific concept of the crust is explained in Chapter 20.

Continental masses and ocean basins. Of the 197 million square miles that make up the surface of the Earth, nearly 71 per cent is covered by the

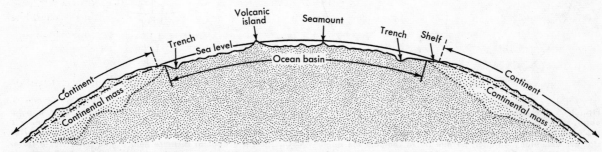

Fig. 2–4. The major features of relief on the Earth appear distinctly on a segment drawn with the vertical scale about 15 times the horizontal scale. Continental masses appear as gigantic icebergs. Further detail is shown in Figure 20–21.

interconnecting bodies of sea water (Pl. 2, inside back cover); the Pacific Ocean alone covers fully a third of the globe and averages about 14,000 feet deep. The *continents*—Eurasia, Africa, North America, South America, Australia, and Antarctica—are *the parts of the continental masses that are above sea level* (Fig. 2–4). The high stand of continents above ocean floors is not accidental. As suggested in Figure 2-4, the continental masses are distinctive bodies; their average density is less than that of the crust generally, and thus, like icebergs, they stand higher than the denser material beneath and around them. Evidence for this important conclusion is explained in Chapter 20. The submerged borders of the continental masses are the continental shelves, beyond which lie the ocean basins.

The greatest depths, 25,000 to more than 35,000 feet, are not in the central parts of the oceans but in a number of long and narrow troughs called sea-floor trenches (Chap. 15), which, especially in the Pacific and Indian oceans, tend to lie near the continental masses. These positions suggest that the trenches are of fairly recent origin; otherwise they would have been filled with waste derived from the lands. In fact, some of the trenches may be developing now, since they are sites of earthquakes which indicate strong movements of the crust (Chap. 20).

New information about the surface forms of ocean floors is building up rapidly through use of echo sounding and other recently perfected methods of study (Chap. 15). Surveys of the Atlantic floor, begun about 1920, have revealed many details of the Mid-Atlantic Ridge (Fig. 15–4), a formidable submarine mountain range extending from the latitude of Iceland southward, about midway between Europe-Africa on the east and the Americas on the west, with high points projecting as islands and island groups. A somewhat similar but lower submarine range, the Mid-Indian Ridge, runs generally southward from near India through the Indian Ocean. Many high and abrupt ridges are hidden beneath the Pacific. Before the development of modern devices for submarine study, the sea floors were known only from widely spaced soundings made laboriously by lowering weighted cables. It was concluded from such meager information that the floors were in general monotonously smooth. Now we know, from many continuous lines of soundings, that many parts of the ocean floors are as rugged as mountainous areas on land (Chaps. 15, 21).

The continents stand on the average slightly more than half a mile above sea level. The lowest is Europe; despite its Alps and other commanding mountain chains, it averages little more than 1,000 feet. Asia, the highest and most rugged continent, averages about 3,200 feet; the Tibetan Plateau and the great Himalayan chain, with Mount Everest reaching above 29,000 feet in altitude, have earned the title "top of the world." Africa is in large part a plateau, with prominent mountain chains at the extreme northern and southern edges only. Australia consists largely of monotonous plains and plateaus relieved by a mountain chain of moderate height in the eastern part. North America, averaging about 2,400 feet, has in the west the high Cordillera[1] (Rocky Mountains and the ranges farther west), with much lower ground eastward to the moderate heights of the Appalachian chain (Pl. 1, inside front cover). In South America the great Cordilleran belt includes the Andes and the high plateau of Bolivia; to the east, much lower ground extends to the stumps of older mountains in eastern Brazil. Antarctica has high mountain ranges protruding through a thick ice sheet that conceals much of the continental surface. The major surface features of the continents are outlined on Plate 2.

All these surface irregularities, enormous from the "worm's-eye" point of view of the men who toiled to the top of Mount Everest (Fig. 2–5), may seem out of accord with the concept that the equator is essentially a circle and that a circumference through the poles is a nearly perfect ellipse (p. 14). Viewed to scale, however, the highest mountains and the greatest deeps are almost negligible. On a globe with a 16-inch diameter Mount Everest, to scale, would be about 0.01 inch high—almost microscopic.

Forces acting on the Earth

In geologic study we see clear evidence that during a very long history the Earth has undergone many changes and that these changes have come about through a conflict of forces still in operation. One set of forces, deriving energy from outside the Earth

[1] This word, pronounced either kôr-dĭl-yā′ra or kŏr-dil′ĕr-ă, is Spanish for "string."

Fig. 2—5. Mount Everest in the Himalayas, "the last adventure." The summit is 29,000 feet—5½ miles—above sea level. Layers of sedimentary rock are clearly visible, though partly covered with snow. The glacier in foreground is one of several that flow outward from the high mass. (Ewing Galloway.)

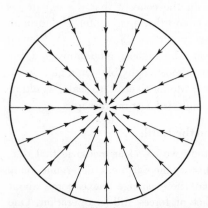

Fig. 2—6. At every point along each radius of the Earth the force of gravity pulls constantly toward the center of mass, tending to create a spherical form. Irregularities in form of surface result from differences in density between continental masses and ocean floors. (Figs. 2—4, 20—21).

and therefore grouped as *external* forces, includes heat from the Sun and gravitational pull from other astronomic bodies, especially the Sun and the Moon. One of the chief *internal* forces is *gravity*, which is gravitation within the Earth itself—the attraction of all solid, liquid, and gaseous particles toward the Earth's center. The centrifugal force of rotation subtracts very slightly from the pull of gravity. Also acting within the body of the Earth are the physical and chemical reactions that give rise to volcanic and related activities and to large-scale movements of the crust such as the uplift of mountain masses. Some of the forces acting on the Earth tend to upset equilibrium which others strive to establish; taken together, they provide motive power for geologic processes that have shaped the outer part of the Earth

Fig. 2–7. El Capitan, a mass of granitic rock, rises precipitously more than 3,000 feet from the floor of Yosemite Valley, California. The vertical fractures, dividing the mass into crude columns, are the chief element of weakness in the mass. (Knoop from Monkmeyer.)

as we now see it. Surprising as it may seem, these processes appear to be as vigorous today as they have been at any time in the Earth's long history.

Gravity, the leveler. All our lives we strive against and take advantage of the pull of gravity. This force, which urges everything toward the center of the Earth (Fig. 2–6), seeks to make our planet a perfect sphere and would nearly succeed were it not for rotation, which results in a little bulging in the equatorial belt and a little flattening in polar regions. Because of rotation, the pull of gravity is slightly but measurably less in low than in high latitudes; a man tipping the scales at 200 pounds on the equator would weigh about 201 pounds at the poles. Gravity shapes the sea water to a nearly spherical form, *sea level,* which is disturbed only by tides and winds; it

makes water run down slopes and thereby provides energy for stream erosion; it pulls persistently on rock material beneath slopes and does enormous work in moving such material to lower levels. The force of gravity is strong enough to prevent the escape of active gases that make our atmosphere and to compress the greater part of these gases into a zone a few miles thick directly above the solid Earth (p. 16). In this zone water vapor is carried to form clouds, which provide the water that flows, because of gravity, as streams on the lands.

We think of rock as a symbol of strength, and at first sight a cliffy mass of granite such as El Capitan (Fig. 2–7) seems unchangeable. Yet such a mass is under constant strain from the pull of gravity. A component of gravity rolls a ball down a very gentle

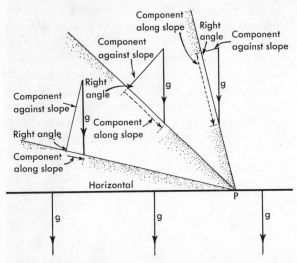

Fig. 2—8. The steeper the slope of a land surface the stronger the tendency to failure under the pull of gravity. The component of gravity perpendicular to the slope creates frictional resistance to sliding. Note that this component is small on a steep slope.

Fig. 2—9. A characteristic lunar landscape. The largest crater is 50 miles across, 6,000 feet deep. The Apennine Mountains have extremely steep slopes, and the highest points are about 18,000 feet above the dark-colored plain. Space men who may visit the moon will find the scenery fascinating but bleak.

slope, and the effective pull along the surface increases steadily as the slope is steepened (Fig. 2–8). Large angular blocks of rock go hurtling down a steep hillside. Precipitous masses much like El Capitan have broken off and have slid down under their own weight, probably along hidden surfaces of weakness (Fig. 8–1). Even fresh, strong rock becomes weakened if exposed to the air for a long period. Gravity bides its time and smooths out irregularities bit by bit.

Role of solar energy. In its effort to level the Earth's surface, gravity has a strong ally, the Sun. Light and heat from the Sun play on the face of the Moon but have no visible effect in changing the Moon's surface features. Great, steep crater rims and rugged mountains, interspersed with wide, smooth plains (Fig. 2–9), supposedly date from the early history of our small sister planet. The Moon has no detectable atmosphere or water. If there were appreciable water, it would be vaporized by high solar temperatures during the Moon's long day and could be seen as obscuring clouds; but all details of the lunar landscape are sharply defined whenever our own atmosphere allows good visibility. We conclude, therefore, that the Moon lacks a medium, such as the Earth's air and water, for harnessing the Sun's energy as an aid to gravity in leveling the surface; and because the Moon's mass is only about one-eightieth that of the Earth, gravity on the Moon is from our point of view very weak, so that precipitous lunar mountain masses of great height have endured through the ages.

Air and water on the Earth, reacting to the Sun's rays, maintain a continuous circulatory system on a vast scale. This system, the *hydrologic cycle,* is generally as follows: *water in the oceans is evaporated by solar energy; it is carried as water vapor over lands, precipitated as rain or snow, and returns to the oceans by flowing on and beneath the surface of the lands* (Fig. 2–10). Actually, the system is much more complex than this general outline suggests. Only a small percentage of the water vapor carried over land areas is precipitated there. Much water that reaches land surfaces is again evaporated from streams and lakes, from the soil, and from vegetation. *Transpiration, the passing of water vapor through pores of plant tissues,* also returns much water from the ground to the atmosphere (Fig. 2–10, **A**). Some of the vapor returned to the air is again precipitated, and thus we may picture small cycles within the major system. For a given large area an average amount of water completes the full cycle within a year, as represented in Figure 2–10, **B** for the entire United States.

Erosion. Much geologic work is accomplished in the course of the hydrologic cycle. Moisture and air together react with rock materials and slowly break them up. The resulting debris, saturated and lubricated by water, is urged downslope by gravity. Running water picks up quantities of rock particles and rolls them or carries them in suspension toward the sea. At high altitudes and in polar climates, snow is compacted into masses of ice, which move slowly downslope as glaciers and add their energy to that of running water in wearing down the land.

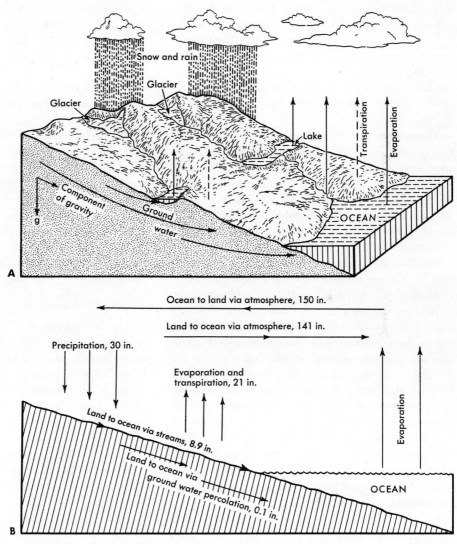

Fig. 2–10. The hydrologic cycle is not a simple system. Much of the water, once it is vaporized and carried over the land, is kept in nearly perpetual motion. Some details of the complex circulation are shown in diagram A. The over-all annual water economy for the United States, represented in B, has been worked out over a period of years by pooling the results of studies by individuals and large organizations. (Based on publications of U. S. Dept. of Agriculture.)

Much water makes its way underground and slowly moves seaward, dissolving rock material as it goes. Winds and waves also join in the attack on the lands. These varied activities make up *erosion,* a *composite of all processes by which rock materials are loosened or dissolved and moved from place to place.*

Gravity, therefore, aided by solar energy transmitted by air and water, strives continually to establish equilibrium at the Earth's surface by leveling out all irregularities. Another external force, the gravitational pull of the Moon and Sun, disturbs the spherical form of sea level by generating tides. The resulting rise and fall of sea water, twice daily, extends the erosive action of waves to more than one level and thus makes it more effective in reducing the lands (Chap. 16).

Forces that disturb equilibrium. At the present rate of erosion, which is reasonably well known, the continents would be worn almost to sea level within a small fraction of the time that has elapsed since life on the lands began. This calculation in itself suggests strongly that something must be at work to offset the tendency to reduce the surface to a monotonous level. Actually, there is abundant evidence that the lands have been elevated repeatedly and on a large scale. Every great mountain chain consists partly of rock layers that evidently were formed on sea floors because they contain abundant shells and other fossils of marine animals. In many places these old layers lie thousands of feet above the sea and are inclined at all angles up to the vertical (Figs. 3–1, 21–9). On some plains and high plateaus the layers of rock arch very gently across areas hundreds of miles wide, indicating broad upwarping of the Earth's crust after the layers were formed. Locally the rocks broke under the strain, and blocks tens of miles long were lifted hundreds or thousands of feet higher than adjacent blocks (Fig. 2–11). *Fractures* of this kind, *along which movement has occurred, are faults.*

Some broad land surfaces are now rising at slow but measurable rates, and along many large faults movement of blocks is still going on (Figs. 18–1, 2). The Earth, then, is not an inert mass that merely holds a record of past activities; it has within it forces that renew its highlands and make rugged landscapes which the forces of erosion strive continually to smooth out and destroy. This renewing tendency is fortunate for us, since without it the seas would have spread over the Earth and we and all other forms of life on the lands would long ago have lost our dwelling place. What are these renewing forces that continue to interrupt the work of gravity and its allies?

Surely part of the answer is suggested by volcanoes. During the Earth's tremendously long history, great quantities of molten rock have been poured out, much of it in regions in which no present volcanoes exist. The piling up of volcanic rock over wide areas has in itself helped offset the leveling work of erosion. Melting of rock deep within the Earth's crust implies reactions there, probably both chemical and physical, that raise the temperature. Rock expands when heated, and expansion in a great body of rock may cause considerable uplift of the overlying surface. But the problem is far from simple and can not be discussed satisfactorily until after more of the essential evidence has been presented (Chaps. 18, 21). When we look at the clear evidence that in a long history mountain chains have risen repeatedly and continents have enlarged, we realize that there are mighty forces within the Earth, hidden though they may be.

Zones of the Earth's crust

The deepest mines go down more than a mile and a half, and a few wells drilled for oil reach depths exceeding 4 miles. Such openings are classed as "deep" from a human viewpoint, but they are only pinpricks in comparison with the 4,000-mile radius of the Earth. Most of what we see directly is at or barely below the present surface. In mountain lands, lifted high and deeply eroded, rocks that once were miles deep in the crust are now exposed to direct view. In effect, therefore, we can "see" down through the crust several miles and compare rock materials at the various depths. Striking differences in the rocks indicate that conditions change with depth. On the basis of these differences we divide the Earth's crust into shallow and deeper *zones,* just as we recognize climatic zones on the Earth's surface. Like climatic belts the depth zones are not sharply separated but grade one into another.

Fig. 2–11. West edge of the Colorado Plateau, in air view looking south from Hurricane, a town in southwestern Utah. The abrupt scarp marks the location of a great fault along which the plateau block moved up. Remnant of a higher part of the plateau surface at upper left. Dark volcanic rocks make the blackish areas on both sides of the scarp. The layers of sedimentary rock are essentially horizontal. (John S. Shelton.)

Under long exposure to the weather, rocks of nearly all kinds are changed chemically and broken up. A land area that has been for a long time at low or moderate altitude normally has a thick cover of soil and other loose products of rock decay which represent an approach to equilibrium among the forces operating in this surficial zone. Quantities of rock particles carried by streams and ground up by wave action are spread in layers along coasts and on sea floors, and in sinking areas these deposits reach thicknesses of several miles (Chap. 21). The deposits become compacted and the particles are slowly cemented to form new rocks. In such zones, then, the tendency is *constructive* and therefore in contrast to the *destruction* of rocks at higher levels. At still greater depths all rocks are under high pressures; a cubic foot of average rock weighs about 175 pounds, and 10 miles beneath us each square foot of area has above it the equivalent of 52,800 such blocks, with total weight about 4600 tons. Temperatures also increase with depth, and in many places the deep-seated rock materials have at some time been melted and again cooled to the solid state (Chap. 6). Even without melting, rocks under high pressures and temperatures slowly undergo important changes (Chap. 19).

Conditions of equilibrium, therefore, change with depth. If no force acted on the crust except gravity, a state of equilibrium might eventually be reached at each level. Continued uplift and erosion keep much of the continental crust in a condition of slow but continual change. The changes now going on, and the record of past changes, make up the subject matter of physical geology.

The scientific method in geology

The importance of learning *facts* about the Earth, as a basis of further study, is self-evident. Before the nineteenth-century, philosophers were in the habit of announcing sweeping conclusions on geologic matters—but their conclusions were based largely on assumptions rather than on the truths that can be learned only by field study. As a result, there arose rival schools of thought, each devoted to some speculative concept. A prominent school in Germany taught confidently that common rocks now known to be of igneous origin were formed as chemical precipitates on the floor of an ancient universal ocean. Gradually it came to be realized that speculations have lasting value only if they continue to hold good each time they are tested by a newly discovered fact. Early in the nineteenth century many students of the Earth set about the laborious task of mapping and describing the vast array of features on its surface. This was an outstanding epoch of fact finding, an extremely important stage in the growth of geology. But science is not a mere collection of facts; it searches for logical relations among facts, and its goal is the discovery of principles that will explain the relations.

The scientific attack on any problem follows an orderly procedure in a succession of steps about as follows: (1) we set down the facts known in the problem; (2) we consider how these facts may be related and how the relationship may be explained; (3) we search for new information that will test the assumed explanation. At the start there may be only scattered facts, doubtfully related. Intelligent guesses, or *hypotheses,* are set up in trying for an explanation. It then becomes clear that certain specific information, if it can be found, will either strengthen or weaken one or another hypothesis. Thus the scientific guessing game stimulates further search and results in more facts which may eliminate some of the hypotheses and require changes in others. After a considerable body of new information has been built up, any hypothesis that still survives may graduate to the more respectable status of *theory.* As evidence favoring a particular concept becomes ever more convincing, this concept may emerge from the realm of theory as an established natural law.

Development of a vague hypothesis to the status of a major scientific principle is seldom if ever carried out by one person. Progress in such matters usually has required the efforts of many workers in more than one generation. Kepler, Galileo, and others had grasped parts of the truth about gravitation nearly a century before Newton was able to state the law in the form of a precise mathematical equation (page 405). Another illustration, in the field of biology but of much interest also in geology, concerns the idea of organic evolution. In the late eighteenth and early nineteenth centuries numerous descriptions of modern and fossilized animals and plants had focused attention on relationships and differences among living forms, and more than one scientist came to suspect that species have appeared successively by evolutionary development. The French scientist Lamarck in 1815 published his well-known suggestion that structural changes in animals have come about slowly through special use of certain bodily parts and that characters thus acquired by individuals are inherited and carried forward in their offspring. According to this view, the giraffe's neck became elongated by stretching, through many generations, in efforts to reach the foliage on which these animals depend for food. This hypothesis has not stood up under tests of further study. Darwin later developed the rival concept of evolution by *natural selection* of types best fitted to survive under given conditions. This view, in modified form, became well established in biologic theory, though the exact mechanism by which evolutionary changes arise is not yet understood. Evidence that such changes have occurred is now overwhelming, and organic evolution has long been accepted as natural law.

Major problems in geology are in various states of solution, but none can be put aside complacently as solved in all its aspects. Hutton's principle, "the present is the key to the past," has so far stood up under all major tests, but we are still on the lookout for facts about the Earth that may not be explained in terms of processes now active. All tests used so far convince us that rocks under the ocean floors are heavier than average rocks in continental masses, but how this came to be so is still a matter for speculation. Powerful forces within the Earth announce their presence by continued uplifts of the lands and by the crushing of rocks in mountain belts, but the exact nature of these forces remains a great mystery. Like any other growing science, geology extends far beyond the lighted zone of proved fact; it has also a large twilight zone of inference and probability and beyond this a region of darkness, relieved only by flashes of speculation. Thus a fascinating field for future exploration awaits those who have the zeal and the proper equipment for the venture.

Attack on a major geologic problem must make use of all information supplied by observations in the field. Every geologic feature—a large lake basin, a cliff made of chalk, a widespread layer of coal, or a rich deposit of metallic minerals—presents a question as to its origin: when and by what means was it formed? The answers are to be sought (1) by thorough examination of the feature itself and (2) by a close study of processes, still known to be active, which may have played a part in fashioning the feature as we see it. Geology is often called the *historical science* because its major goal is to work out the complete history of every geologic feature and ultimately of the Earth itself.

Cooperation in research

To a layman it may appear that each major field of science is self-sufficient, independent of all others. No concept could be farther from reality. Interdependence of workers in the several sciences has led to growth of "hybrid" fields of study with the names *physical chemistry, biophysics,* and *biochemistry.* Students of the Earth encounter problems that can be solved only by use of principles and techniques developed by physicists, chemists, and biologists. These overlaps of interest are evident in three outstanding scientific disciplines: *geophysics, a discipline that applies physical principles in attacking ma-*

jor problems of the Earth; geochemistry, concerned with geologic problems that involve chemical change; and *paleontology, the science devoted to fossil animals and plants.* Continued broadening and deepening of geologic study make it impossible for any one student to be fully competent in all aspects of his subject. Particular problems may be referred to men equipped in one of the three fields defined above or to *mineralogists (special students of minerals), petrologists (special students of rocks), structural geologists (students of rock deformation), geomorphologists (students of land forms), or economic geologists (specialists in mineral resources).*

Thus geology, like modern medicine, calls increasingly for the services of specialists. Just as in the field of medicine, however, geology has need also for "general practitioners." Problems worked out by specialists lead to recognition of principles that add to the broad base of the science.

SUMMARY

1. Shape and size of the Earth have been determined to close approximations.

2. Though air and water make up a very small percentage of the Earth's mass, they are major agents of mechanical and chemical change in the outer zone.

3. The hydrologic cycle, powered by solar energy and gravity, operates continually to reduce surface irregularities created by persistent forces within the Earth.

4. Geologic problems are in various stages of solution. Scientific attack on the major problems considers all plausible hypotheses, which are tested for survival as directed studies produce critical evidence.

5. Advance in geologic research enlists the help of specialists in several basic sciences.

REFERENCES

Chamberlin, T. C., 1897, The method of multiple working hypotheses: Jour. Geology, vol. 5, pp. 837–848.

Lyell, Charles, 1875, Principles of geology, 12th ed.: London, John Murray. (Out of print but available in many college libraries.)

CHAPTER 3. MATERIALS OF THE EARTH'S CRUST

Loose and solid rock materials   Nature of minerals   Atomic structure   Minerals a geologic alphabet   Igneous rocks, surficial and deep seated   Sedimentary rocks as historical documents   Profound changes in rocks

A cluster of calcite crystals.

Bedrock and regolith

Nearly everywhere we see at the surface of the ground some kind of loose material: soil in fields, sand and gravel in the beds or banks of stream courses, yellow clay in road cuts. Deep pits are dug into such "dirt," as construction workmen call it, by power shovels on road grades and at many building sites; in other places firm rock is found at shallow depths and has to be blasted for removal in construction work. Deep wells and mine shafts go through whatever loose "overburden" there may be and continue downward into solid rock. In many mountain districts and in cliffy slopes of arid lands, such as parts of Arizona and Nevada, soil cover is thin or absent and great masses of bare rock are in plain view (Fig. 3–1). We are confident, therefore, that bedrock underlies the land surface everywhere, though commonly it is hidden beneath regolith, a sheet of varied loose materials (p. 8).

Masses of bedrock that are *not covered are exposures* (Fig. 3–2). Pieces of fresh bedrock vary greatly in general appearance, and in a close view we also find differences in detail. A broken surface of white marble shows close-set grains with flashing faces, all much alike. A piece of granite is made up of definite grains (Fig. 3–3, **A, B**), some of which are light-colored and others dark, some that flash in the light and others that have no luster; we can distinguish perhaps four or five distinct kinds of grains, intimately mixed, some more abundant than others. In a handful of sand we may recognize, with an ordinary magnifying glass, grains similar to some of those in granite. Even soft clay, which under a common microscope appears as a formless mass, is resolved by an electron microscope into flat particles with regular form, the images enlarged by a factor of tens of thousands (Fig. 3–4, **A, B**).

In general, then, rocks and regolith in the visible parts of the Earth's crust are aggregates of simpler units known as *minerals*. The word *mineral*, in common with some other terms, is used both in a loose, general sense and with a more precise meaning. An economist speaking of *mineral resources* has in mind all substances in the Earth's crust that are valuable to man. Petroleum and coal are high on such a list, although, as we shall see, these materials are of organic origin; coal has developed from plant tissues, petroleum from plants or animals or both. The minerals of geology are inorganic constituents of rocks, with fairly definite characteristics. As some knowledge of common minerals provides a key to the study of the entire crust of the Earth, a brief examination of these definite characteristics should precede a "dictionary definition" of the term *mineral*.

Minerals

General properties. Repeated testing of the grains in granite with the point of a knife blade convinces us that most of the constituents of this rock are harder than good steel because the grains are not scratched and the knife point becomes blunted. If a rough surface of the rock is rubbed against a window pane, permanent scratches are made on the glass. However *mica*, a flaky mineral that is common in granite, is easily cut with a knife point. It is common knowledge that *diamond* is the hardest of all natural substances; on the other hand, several common minerals are easily scratched with the fingernail. Thus there is a wide range in the *hardness* of minerals.

In a close look at a freshly broken piece of granite we find that light is reflected from smooth, plane surfaces of gray or pinkish grains of common minerals in a group known as the *feldspars*. If we break one of the larger grains, the pieces also have bright, mirror-like faces. Other grains in the rock that look like dull glass are seen to have very irregular surfaces; these are grains of the mineral *quartz*. Thus some minerals *cleave* along definite planes which other minerals lack. ***Cleavage, the capacity to break in preferred directions along plane surfaces***, is a conspicuous property of some common minerals such as mica, which splits readily into extemely thin, flexible sheets or flakes (Fig. 3–5).

Not uncommonly we find minerals in the form of nearly perfect *crystals* bounded by faces as plane and

Fig. 3–1. South end of the Sheep Range, southern Nevada. High points on the range are more than 9,000 feet above sea level; altitude of slope in foreground about 2,500 feet. Bedrock in the range, continuously exposed, consists chiefly of limestone and dolostone containing marine fossils. Regolith in foreground is made up of rock fragments, coarse and fine, that have been washed out from the range. (Spence Air Photos.)

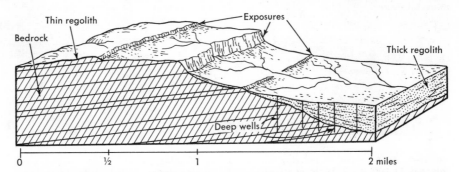

Fig. 3–2. Relation of loose rock materials to bedrock commonly found in humid areas with irregular topography and plentiful soil. Regolith varies in thickness from zero to hundreds of feet. Bedrock is everywhere beneath the surface; it is revealed by deep wells that penetrate the thickest cover of regolith. Bedrock is exposed in steep cliffs.

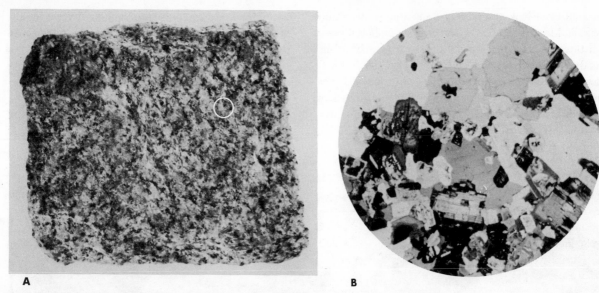

A   B

Fig. 3—3. Mineral grains in granite are visible, but for precise study the rock is sliced and ground to make a *thin section* about one-thousandth inch thick. This section is placed in a *petrographic microscope* and studied, with any desired magnification, in light transmitted through *nicol prisms*. Minerals can be identified by their appearance in this light. **A.** Hand specimen of granite. **B.** View of mineral grains as seen in thin section, magnified 14 diameters by petrographic microscope, in light transmitted through nicol prisms. Small circle on **A** shows size of this area without magnification.

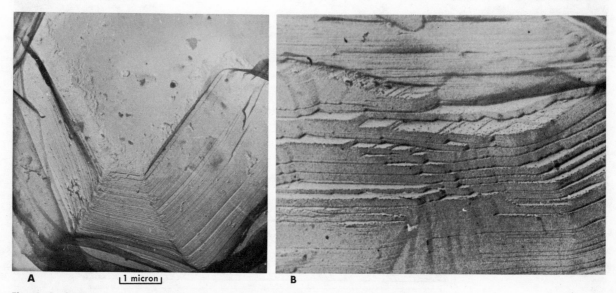

A   ⌊ 1 micron ⌋   B

Fig. 3—4. A. A crystal of the clay mineral *dickite* revealed by the electron microscope, enlarged 11,100 times. Edges of cleavage plates appear clearly on the crystal faces. The scale on the photograph, 1 *micron*, is 0.000001 *(one-millionth) meter*. One inch with this enlargement would be more than a sixth of a mile long. **B.** Face of the same dickite crystal enlarged 37,500. (Courtesy Thomas Bates, Penna. State University.)

smooth as if they were artificially shaped by a machine. Moreover, each kind of mineral has its own distinctive crystal forms (Fig. 3–6). Quartz occurs in six-sided prisms that end in pyramids; a common brass-colored mineral known as *pyrite* forms cubes, either separate or in intergrown clusters; a typical *garnet* crystal has twelve similar faces, each of them a parallelogram. Clear crystals with perfect form reflect light with exceptional brilliance; it is an old jest among students of minerals that "the beauty of a crystal depends on the *planeness* of its faces." The angles between adjacent crystal faces are characteristic and constant for each mineral species. What principle underlies these perfect geometric patterns in minerals? To this question we shall return.

Chemical composition. All substances known on Earth are composed of chemical *elements,* of which 92 that occur in nature have been determined. The name seems to imply that an element is the basic identifiable constituent of matter.

Most of the elements occur in comparatively small quantities. According to careful estimates from all available analyses, the ten most abundant elements are listed in the following table.

Thus oxygen, which makes up a large fraction of the hydrosphere and atmosphere, is nearly twice as abundant as any other element in the outer part of the Earth. It forms more than 46 per cent of the known rocks in the Earth's crust, where it is combined with other elements. Only eight elements form more than one per cent each of the outer Earth, and all of the several dozens not listed in the table make a total of less than one per cent of the crust. In this large list of comparatively scarce elements are the important metals: copper (Cu), lead (Pb), zinc (Zn), manganese (Mn), and uranium (U). Percentages of silver, gold, and platinum are vanishingly small.

The elements that make up a mineral are determined by laboratory analysis: *quartz* (SiO_2) is found to contain silicon and oxygen in definite proportions; *galena* (PbS) consists of lead and sulfur. Such analysis helps to identify minerals and is an essential step toward an understanding of rock materials.

Internal structure. The term *element* is in some respects a misnomer, since chemical elements are divisible into still smaller units. Some Greek philosophers, in reasoning that was wholly speculative, thought of matter as made up of invisible basic building blocks which they called *atoms.* Early in the nineteenth century this general concept was revived in a working hypothesis, and the *atomic structure* of chemical elements is now firmly established. Wide popular interest in practical aspects of this abstruse subject was aroused by development of the atomic bomb during World War II.

In striving to picture atoms, we grope for the infinitesimal. By ingenious devices, physicists find precisely the diameters of these tiny bodies, expressed in a unit of measure known as the **angstrom**, which

Fig. 3–5. A 6-sided crystal of mica cleaves into very thin, plane flakes that suggest leaves of a book. Nearly perfect specimens like this, found in pegmatite masses, have cleavage plates a foot or more in width. (Ward's Natural Science Establishment.)

Table 3–1. Average composition of the outer part of the Earth

Element	Chemical symbol	Weight per cent of total	
		Crust alone	Crust, hydrosphere, and atmosphere
Oxygen	O	46.60	50.02
Silicon	Si	27.72	25.80
Aluminum	Al	8.13	7.30
Iron	Fe	5.00	4.18
Calcium	Ca	3.63	3.22
Sodium	Na	2.83	2.36
Potassium	K	2.59	2.28
Magnesium	Mg	2.09	2.08
Hydrogen	H	0.14	0.95
Titanium	Ti	0.40	0.40
Total of 10 elements		99.13	98.59

is *a hundred-millionth part of a centimeter,* or about one 4-billionth part of an inch. The smallest atoms have diameters measuring less than one such unit, the largest more than three units (Fig. 3–7). But tiny though it is, each atom is made up of far smaller particles. A hydrogen atom, the simplest of all, has one *electron* carrying a negative electric charge revolving around a *proton* with a positive charge (Fig. 3–8, **A**). Nuclear physicists even weigh these atomic parts and tell us confidently that the proton is 1845 times as heavy as the electron. Other elements have atoms with more complex makeup; the calcium atom has 20 electrons distributed in four "orbits" or energy

levels, commonly called *shells,* and the uranium atom has 92 electrons distributed among seven shells. For each electron with its negative charge there is a proton with an equal positive charge; thus an atom is electrically balanced, or neutral.

The protons are grouped together as a nucleus, around which the electrons revolve in orbits that suggest tiny planets in motion around a sun. Many of the atomic neuclei have particles called *neutrons* grouped with the protons; a neutron has nearly the same mass as each associated proton, but it is without an electric charge (Fig. 3–8, **B**). The number of positive charges—that is, *the number of protons in*

Fig. 3–6. A. This *quartz* crystal **(1)** is hexagonal; the form is a 6-sided prism terminated at both ends by hexagonal pyramids. Cubic crystals of *pyrite* **(2)** are commonly intergrown in this fashion. Note small cubes on the larger face. The crystal of *garnet* **(3)** has 12 faces (6 visible here), all alike in shape and size. (Ward's Natural Science Establishment. Black lines have been added in **1** and **3** to emphasize boundaries between crystal faces.) **B.** Microcrystals of quartz, enlarged 120 times. The characteristic hexagonal forms persist even below limits of visibility. (Courtesy Carl Struwe.)

B

A

an atomic nucleus of each element is **the atomic number** of the element. For hydrogen the number is 1; for oxygen, 8; for uranium, 92 (App. E). Ten elements not known to occur naturally have been produced in the laboratory. These have atomic numbers 93 to 102, inclusive.

Each element has one or more **isotopes**, *alternate forms that differ only in the number of neutrons in the nucleus.* Ordinary hydrogen, which has one proton and no neutron, unites with oxygen to make ordinary water. **Deuterium**, *the isotope of hydrogen,* has one neutron paired with a proton; when this isotope unites with oxygen, *heavy water* results. Iso-

topes of uranium and carbon have particular interest, as explained in Chapter 4.

Formation of minerals. Elements with chemical affinity for each other combine to form minerals. A few elements, among them copper, gold, and carbon, are self-sufficient, so to speak, since each can form crystals made up exclusively of its own atoms; thus we have *native* (pure) copper and gold and the diamond which is pure carbon. In general, however, a mineral is a combination of two or more elements. The union occurs by electric attraction. As atoms normally are in a neutral electric state, one atom can attract another only if both become electrically unbalanced. The sodium atom has in its outer orbit only one electron, whereas chlorine has seven. Eight electrons in an outer orbit give maximum stability. By giving up its one, sodium acquires a positive charge; by taking up this one, chlorine acquires a negative charge. *Each electrically unbalanced atom is an* **ion**. The two join and are held together by electrostatic force to form a *molecule* of sodium chloride,

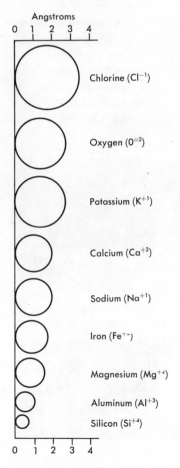

Fig. 3—7. Ionic diameters of 9 common elements. Note contrast in size between ions of chlorine and silicon. Calcium and sodium, with ions nearly the same size, commonly replace each other, as in plagioclase feldspar.

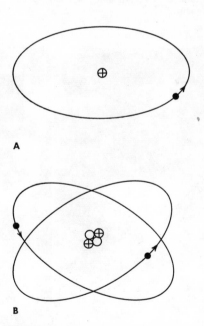

Fig. 3—8. Hydrogen and helium atoms, shown schematically. Hydrogen is the simplest atom with one proton (positive) electrically balanced with one electron (negative). Helium has 2 electrons in orbit around a nucleus with 2 protons and 2 neutrons. The *atomic number* of helium is 2 (the number of protons); its *mass number* is 4 (the sum of protons and neutrons).

which is *halite,* or common salt. Such *a tendency of different kinds of atoms to join* in strong combination is called *chemical affinity.*

Sodium ions and chlorine ions become arranged in cubic patterns, as shown in Figure 3–9. The model used to picture the combination is, of course, diagrammatic, but it shows the general relation and the

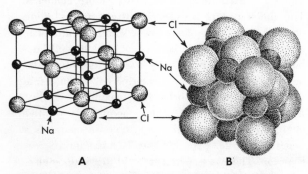

Fig. 3–9. Schematic arrangement of sodium (Na) and chlorine (Cl) ions in the mineral halite. The cubic pattern internally is reflected in the cubic form of a crystal and the tendency to cleave into cubic fragments.

relative sizes of the two ions. Under favorable conditions, the ions in a water solution may continue to unite in the simple pattern of the diagram until a large cubic crystal with smooth faces is built up. Crowding during growth may result in a mass of halite with irregular form; but, when such a mass is broken, it separates along cleavage planes that intersect at right angles. Galena (lead sulfide, PbS), has similar cubic cleavage (Fig. 3–10, **A**). A crystal of *calcite* (calcium carbonate, $CaCO_3$) cleaves into perfect rhombs, which reflect the atomic pattern of this mineral (Fig. 3–10, **B**). In quartz and some other minerals the groups of ions interlock, no natural planes for easy separation are provided, and crystals break on surfaces that are curving or irregular.

The *arrangement* of atoms also controls the hardness of a mineral; hardness is not a property of atoms themselves. The element carbon, with atoms grouped in one pattern, forms diamond, the hardest of minerals; with its atoms grouped in another pattern, carbon forms *graphite,* one of the softest minerals.

How do we know the arrangement of these ultramicroscopic "bricks" that are built into the varied

Fig. 3–10. A. Cubic cleavage fragments of galena have mirror-like faces; the smaller pieces are reflected in the large piece behind them. (Adolph Knopf.) **B.** Cleavage planes in three directions divide calcite into perfect rhombs. The dark appearance in parts of the rhombic pieces is caused by refraction of light in a way peculiar to calcite. (Ward's Natural Science Establishment.)

architecture of minerals? Chiefly through the use of X rays, which vibrate with wavelengths far shorter than those of light. Because of their short vibrations X rays perform feats that seem magical, such as giving clear photographs of bones, though they are covered with flesh. They can also penetrate the invisible spaces between atoms in a mineral, and on emerging they will portray, on suitably placed photographic film, a characteristic *diffraction pattern* (Fig. 3–11). Study of a series of such patterns given by a crystal held in various positions reveals the geometric spacing of atoms that is characteristic of the mineral. So penetrating X rays provide a "seeing eye" that enables us to explore the ultramicroscopic world, to measure accurately particles that seem infinitesimally small, and to appreciate that a law of order and symmetry extends far below the limits of ordinary vision.

Silicate minerals. Oxygen and silicon, the two predominant elements in the Earth's crust (Table 3–1), are combined with a number of other elements to form numerous minerals known as *silicates*. In these minerals, which make up the greater part of known rocks in the Earth's crust, the ionic pattern is distinctive. Four ions of oxygen, arranged in the form of a pyramid, surround a much smaller ion of silicon (Fig. 3–12). These units, known as *silica tetrahedra*, are grouped in chains or sheets. Quartz, the simplest silicate mineral, consists wholly of these tetrahedra. Ions of other elements, implaced among the tetrahedra, complete the compositions of numerous minerals that are common in igneous and metamorphic rocks.

Prominent among them are the feldspars, a group of related silicates. One kind, abundant in granite, is **orthoclase** (ôr′thō-klāz; Gr. "right breaking" or cleaving at right angles), *a combination of the elements potassium, aluminum, silicon, and oxygen* (as written by the chemist, $KAlSi_3O_8$). Another common feldspar is **plagioclase** (plăj′ĭ-ō-klāz; Gr. "oblique breaking" or cleaving at oblique angles), *a group of feldspars in which the key element is either sodium or calcium, and commonly both are present.* Sodium and calcium, both abundant elements, have atoms nearly equal in diameter (Fig. 3–7); hence they can substitute for each other in the framework of a min-

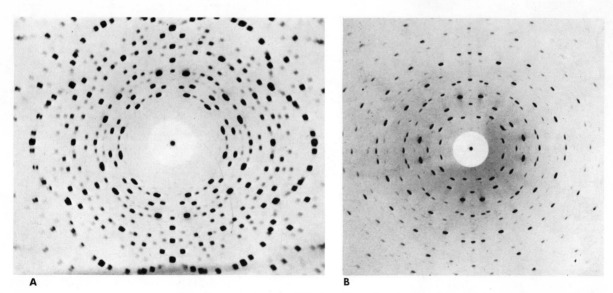

Fig. 3–11. X-ray diffraction photographs of (A) beryl (beryllium aluminum silicate) with 6-sided symmetry; (B), *wulfenite* (lead molybdate), which occurs in crystals that have 4-sided prisms. (Courtesy C. S. Hurlbut, Harvard University.)

eral, provided there is some adjustment also between aluminum and silicon. The sodium "end member" of plagioclase has the formula NaAlSi₃O₈, the calcium "end member," CaAl₂Si₂O₈. For various combinations of the two elements the first term in the formula is written (Na, Ca). In the same way iron and magnesium are "twin" elements that may substitute for each other in all proportions. Minerals in which they play an important role are known as *ferromagnesian minerals.*

Thus not all minerals have fixed chemical composition such as that of quartz or halite. The most dependable characteristic of a mineral species is its internal structure, which under conditions favorable to growth is expressed in crystal form. This tendency in each kind of mineral to take on its own geometric shape is as insistent as the growth habit of a species of plant or animal.

Basic importance of minerals. Mineralogy, *the science of minerals,* is in itself a vast and growing subject. Only a few decades ago the total number of minerals known was hardly more than 1,000. New techniques and interests have led to many new discoveries, and complete lists now include more than 2,000 kinds of minerals. Attention focused on ura-

nium in the present century has led to recognition of dozens of minerals that contain this element. Rapid development of geochemistry, equipped with X-ray instruments, the electron microscope, and other modern devices has opened a new world in mineralogy.

Records of past events are inscribed in rocks of the Earth's crust. Rocks are made up of minerals, just as words are made by combining letters. Minerals, then, are in a real sense the alphabet of geology. This is not to say they are simple or easy to learn; but the common kinds are basic, and study of them must come first. We recognize granite only if we can identify its essential minerals—feldspar and quartz.

Fortunately for our beginning study, only a few dozens of the large list of minerals are abundant in the rocks of the crust. We can become familiar with them only by studying typical specimens in the laboratory. The more common rock-making minerals, and also some of the minerals most important in ore deposits, are listed in Appendix A, with criteria for their identification. Direct acquaintance with these basic materials is essential for an understanding of rocks.

Let us now set down the essential points that be-

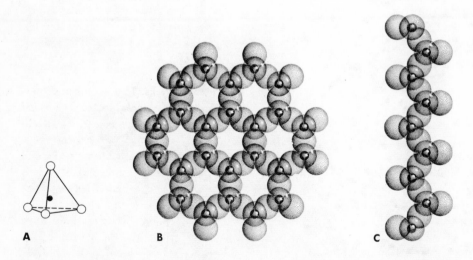

Fig. 3–12. Atomic pattern of silicate minerals. **A.** Single tetrahedron made up of oxygen ions at the four corners and equidistant from a silicon ion. **B.** Tetrahedra grouped in a sheet, as in mica. The view is directly down on the linked tetrahedra, in each of which the upper oxygen ion is represented as transparent, with the silicon ion directly beneath it. **C.** Tetrahedra grouped in a chain, as in pyroxene. (Courtesy C. S. Hurlbut, with permission of John Wiley and Sons.)

long in the definition of a mineral:

1. *A **mineral** is an inorganic solid substance that occurs naturally.*

2. *It is built up of atoms or ions, representing one chemical element or more than one, arranged in a definite pattern that is characteristic for each mineral.*

3. *Physical properties and chemical composition are constant in some minerals; in others there are variations as ions of one element are replaced by those of another.*

Well-formed crystals of a mineral hold much interest and are helpful in making identifications. Six general systems of crystal form are recognized, and within each system there are many variations in external form. Thus in Figure 3–6, **A** the crystals of pyrite (2) and garnet (3) belong in the *isometric* ("equal-measure") system, though details of form are strikingly different. Quartz (1), which belongs in the hexagonal ("six-cornered") system, occurs in six-sided prisms with ends shaped like pyramids. This system also has many variations in form.

Detailed discussion of mineral crystals has no logical place here for two reasons: (1) most specimens of minerals lack the crystal form; (2) the subject, forming part of the special field of study *crystallography*, is involved and technical. Although specimens for laboratory study ordinarily include some crystals, identification depends chiefly on other physical properties. Much detailed information, which is of practical value only in connection with study of actual specimens, is given in Appendix A for use in laboratory study.

Rocks

Engraved stone tablets left by ancient Egyptians have supplied valuable information on an early civilization in the Nile Valley. Many of the tablets, inscribed with strange characters known as hieroglyphics, gave up their secrets only after the discovery of a key, the famous Rosetta Stone on which a message in hieroglyphics is repeated in the language of old Egypt and again in Greek. The records of Earth history also remained largely undeciphered until the eighteenth century when a few exceptional men, including the Scot James Hutton (p. 4), found keys to the meaning of some critical features in rocks. Discoveries that resulted supplied new keys which led to more discoveries, and this kind of "chain reaction" has continued to our time.

To an observant traveler who watches road cuts in many parts of the country, rocks may appear hopelessly diverse and complex. Here he sees rocks in thin sheets that sparkle with flakes of mica; there, layers varied in color and thickness, some flat-lying, others inclined or vertical; in other places, massive, coarse-grained granite or dark cliffs of what is locally called "trap rock." All kinds, however, fall into three general groups according to mode of origin. These major groups are known as *igneous, sedimentary* and *metamorphic,* as explained briefly on pages 5 to 7.

Satisfactory understanding of the rocks in any group comes only after some study of the processes by which these rocks have been formed. This is particularly true of sedimentary rocks, which are products of long-continued and complex changes at the Earth's surface. A considerable share of this book is devoted to these processes of change, but the detailed explanation of sedimentary rocks is reserved for Chapter 17. Similarly, a full appreciation of igneous and metamorphic rocks must await the explanation of igneous and metamorphic processes. Rocks, however, are the essential materials in geology, and an introduction to the major kinds is required at an early stage in the study of the Earth. A fuller appreciation of rock types will come as the study unfolds. *The scientific study of rocks* is **petrology** (Gr. *petros*).

Igneous rocks

Volcanic or extrusive rocks. *Igneous* means "pertaining to fire," and ***igneous rocks*** are *rocks formed by cooling of molten silicate materials.* Early dwellers in the Mediterranean region witnessed the eruption of such material from several volcanic vents and were aware that the fiery fluid, on cooling, hardens to form the slaggy rock near eruption centers. The word *volcano* has come to us from *Vulcan,* the Roman god of fire. The ancient observers may have noted, too, that the ashy dust and the irregular fragments spread over the countryside during an explosive eruption need only be compacted and somewhat cemented to become identical with much of the bedrock in the Mediterranean lands. Although they had no organized science, some individuals had strong scientific curiosity. Pliny the Elder lost his life in trying to observe at close quarters the destructive eruption of Vesuvius in A.D. 79.

Active volcanoes are widely distributed around the Earth's surface, and at any one of them we can see igneous rocks in the making. These *extrusive rocks*—so called because they *consist of igneous material extruded from the Earth's crust*—are of various kinds, all of them highly distinctive. In one general class are the heaps and layers of fine *volcanic ash* and clinkery fragments that have rained down at times of violent outbursts; these are the *fragmental* products of the igneous factory. The other general class of extrusive rocks consists of *lava flows, rocks made of molten materials, that flow over the ground as hot streams or sheets* and on cooling form rock masses with a wide range in color and other properties. Some flows solidify quickly to *natural glass, or obsidian;* there is no opportunity for atomic arrangement to form mineral grains, and glass is a solid in which the atoms are mixed at random. Other flows, particularly those of large extent and thickness, require months or even years for complete cooling; the resulting rock consists largely or entirely of definite mineral grains, though generally they can be identified only under a high-power microscope (Fig.

3–13). With few exceptions, surfaces of hardened lavas are somewhat porous and irregular because of innumerable holes made by escaping gas held in solution under high pressure while the molten material was underground. Sheets of obsidian commonly have thick caps of whitish *pumice, volcanic rock consisting of a hardened froth created by rapidly escaping gases.*

In spite of wide diversity among themselves, therefore, volcanic rocks have unmistakable characteristics by which students in the field can identify them. Anyone who has seen a modern lava flow on Mount Etna in Sicily, on Mauna Loa in Hawaii, or on one of numerous peaks in Central America realizes that each of these great mountain masses consists of volcanic rock and must have been built up by successive eruptions (Fig. 6–15). Even more important, anyone who has studied modern volcanoes is equipped to recognize old rocks of volcanic origin in the Columbia Plateau of Washington, in central Connecticut, in northern Ireland, and in many other parts of the world far from any volcanoes now active. Thus volcanic activity of the present is a key to important records of past events.

Intrusive igneous bodies. Each of numerous vol-

A   **B**

Fig. 3–13. A. Specimen of gray andesite, an aphanitic rock. **B.** Thin section of the andesite as seen in petrographic microscope with about 20 times magnification. Small circle on **A** shows size of the area without enlargement.

canoes, such as Mount Etna, has built up many cubic miles of volcanic rock, chiefly lavas. Such persistent outpouring suggests a reservoir of molten rock at some depth, and we may suppose that a volcano becomes extinct when all the molten material remaining in its reservoir has cooled and solidified. If we could slice down through a volcano, as a zoologist dissects one of his specimens, what would be seen at depth? Fortunately, nature has performed many "autopsies" by erosion to give a large part of the answer. Moderate erosion of many old volcanic mountains shows in each an elongate *plug* of igneous rock filling the conduit through which molten rock reached the surface (Fig. 6–21). Commonly some of the hot liquid was squeezed out from the conduit along nearly vertical fractures and on cooling became sheets of igneous rock, large and small, cutting across the older rocks (Fig. 6–22). Much deeper erosion in some old mountainous areas has laid bare great bodies of granite and other coarse-grained igneous rocks. Comparative studies of many igneous bodies indicate clearly that those of large size and with coarse grain were formed far below the land surface, and have been exhumed by the slow downcutting of streams and other agents through long ages. Although much of the direct evidence has been removed by these destructive agents, the comparative studies indicate that some of the large igneous bodies now exposed were deep-seated reservoirs that supplied materials for ancient volcanoes.

Molten rock material is **magma.** *Lava* is *magma that flows out on the land surface* in a volcanic eruption. All *igneous bodies formed below the Earth's surface* are classed as **intrusive bodies** because they represent magma that *intruded* older masses of rock.

Texture of igneous rocks. *The **texture** of a rock is the pattern determined by size, shape, and arrangement of grains composing it.* Generally, the grains of igneous rocks are angular and very irregular because during their growth the mineral particles crowded against each other and became interlocked. There is wide variation in size of grain. Intrusive rocks that formed at great depth commonly are coarse-grained because cooling was very slow and individual grains had opportunity for continued growth (Fig. 3–3). Conversely, the volcanic rocks tend to be fine-grained; many have **aphanitic** (ăf-ăn-ĭt′ĭk; Gr. "in-

Fig. 3–14. Huge crystals in a large pegmatite mass, Black Hills, South Dakota. Single crystals of the lithium-bearing mineral *spodumene* quarried at this locality were 20 feet or more long. (C. R. Longwell.)

visible") *texture, made up of grains visible only with some magnification.* Because of extremely rapid cooling, some volcanic rocks are glassy—no mineral grains have formed. Intrusive bodies formed at shallow depth generally have moderate size of grain, though there is considerable range.

A rock of exceptionally coarse grain is *pegmatite,* sometimes called "giant granite," which occurs in masses of tabular or irregular form near the borders of large intrusive bodies. Pegmatite is made up chiefly of the minerals feldspar and quartz, with individual grains a foot or more across. Some pegmatites in the Black Hills of South Dakota contain individual crystals that resemble logs tens of feet long (Fig. 3–14). Nearly all pegmatites yield large "books" of mica (Fig. 3–5). The large sizes of crystals in pegmatite bodies indicate exceptional freedom for growth, probably in highly fluid magma in

39

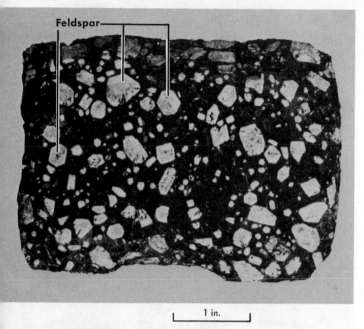

Feldspar

Fig. 3–15. Andesite porphyry, with large phenocrysts of feldspar in an aphanitic groundmass. Henry Mountains, Utah.

1 in.

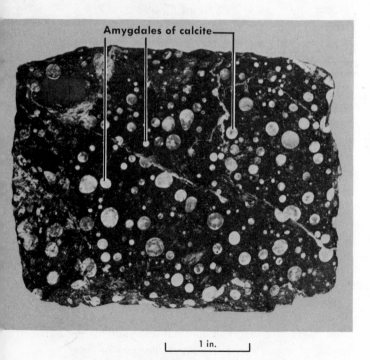

Amygdales of calcite

Fig. 3–16. Amygdaloidal basalt has a superficial resemblance to porphyry, but the rounded amygdales are unmistakable.

1 in.

the outer part of a large intrusive mass. This interpretation is favored by the common location of pegmatites in or somewhat outside the marginal parts of large intrusive bodies.

Some masses of pegmatite contain crystals of minerals rich in uranium and other uncommon elements.

Igneous rock, whether extrusive or intrusive, *with grains of exceptional size scattered through a finer-grained groundmass* (Fig. 3–15), is **porphyry,** and *its texture* is described as *porphyritic.* A plausible explanation of such texture is movement of a magma mass into a cooler environment after scattered crystals had grown to appreciable size; with more rapid cooling, the remainder of the magma formed rock of finer grain size. The *isolated crystals in the finer-grained groundmass* are **phenocrysts** (fēn′o-krĭsts; Gr. "visible crystals"). As they grew without interference in a fluid, these crystals commonly have perfect forms.

Some volcanic rocks have a superficial resemblance to porphyries, but the scattered spots of mineral are roundish, not angular. This pattern is found in the upper parts of some dark lava sheets. *Small openings formed by escaping gas as the lava cooled are* **vesicles.** Circulating water later deposited mineral matter to fill the cavities; the *roundish fillings of vesicles* are *amygdales* (ă-mĭg′dāles), and the rock is given the ponderously attractive name *amygdaloidal basalt* (Fig. 3–16).

Fragmental materials blasted from a volcano become compacted and cemented into firm rock. *Consolidated powdery volcanic material* is **volcanic tuff.** *Rock made up of the coarser angular volcanic fragments* is *volcanic breccia* (brĕtch′ĭ-ah).

Composition of igneous rocks. In all igneous rocks the most abundant chemical elements are oxygen and silicon, combined in the silicate minerals. Oxygen and silicon unite to form quartz (*silica,* SiO_2), but if certain other elements are present the tendency is to form more complex combinations, such as the feldspars. Granite, a coarse-grained intrusive rock, consists chiefly of feldspar but also contains an abundance of quartz grains. Hence we can say that granite has an *excess* of silica, and, in fact, the silicon and oxygen in granite may amount to as much as 75 per cent of the rock. Extrusive igneous material with chemical composition like that of granite forms *rhyo-*

lite, in which mineral grains generally can be distinguished only with strong magnification, and yet some grains of quartz may be visible to the unaided eye. All these *high-silica* rocks are comparatively light-colored; shades of gray and pink are most common in granites and rhyolites. At the opposite end of the scale are rocks averaging somewhat below 50 per cent in silica, most of them dark in color; examples are *basalt,* common among the lavas, and its coarse-grained intrusive equivalent, *gabbro.* These are classed as *low-silica* rocks, although silica totals nearly half their composition. Intermediate between the high-silica and low-silica groups are many types of rocks that appear in a detailed classification but only a few general kinds that are abundant in the visible part of the Earth's crust.

Figure 3–17 indicates graphically the mineral composition of rock types that range from high-silica content at the left to lowest in silica at the right. The critical minerals are arranged in logical order, with quartz (pure silica) at the upper left, olivine (lowest in silica) at lower right. Potassium feldspar, abundant in the granitic rocks, gives way toward the right to plagioclase (soda-lime feldspar), which in turn almost disappears at the right. Ferromagnesian minerals (biotite, hornblende, pyroxene, olivine) make up a small percentage of the silica-rich rocks at the left but increase toward the right, where olivine is dominant. In the area representing plagioclase feldspar sodium exceeds calcium in the left-hand portion. Amounts of the two elements are essentially equal near the vertical broken line, to the right of which calcium is predominant. Thus we have graphic expression of the role played by feldspars in the compositions of igneous rocks: with decrease in content of silica, the feldspars that contain the element potassium are superseded by those combining sodium and calcium, and with large increase in content of ferromagnesian minerals the dwindling amount of feldspar is progressively richer in calcium.

Modern studies in specially equipped laboratories have determined the order in which the several minerals crystallize from a magma, attended by a sequence of chemical changes. *Geochemistry* plays an increasingly important role in solving major geologic problems.

General classification. Specialists in the study of rocks (petrologists), using refined mechanical and chemical equipment, have an elaborate classification which recognizes dozens of igneous-rock types distinguished by rather small differences in composition. A chart representing such a classification, far more detailed than Figure 3–17, might have firm vertical lines to indicate the exact differences. For a general introductory study such detail is more confusing than helpful. Our chart has comparatively few names of rocks, and absence of vertical boundaries emphasizes that these rocks are gradational, one into another, not rigidly separated. To estimate the approximate mineral composition of granite, we scan the vertical area below the name, and, using the percentage scale at the left, we estimate the proportions of quartz, potassium feldspar, sodium-calcium feldspar, and ferromagnesian minerals. In a study of hand-specimens, unaided by precise equipment, such estimates must be rough. A common practice in general studies is to lump together as "granitic rocks" all coarse-grained specimens in which feldspar and quartz are conspicuous. Such an assemblage would include granodiorite and several other types recognized and named by petrographers.

For exact classification of aphanitic and glassy igneous rocks the precise petrographic skills are required even more than in study of coarse-grained types. Names of aphanitic rocks are reduced to a minimum on our chart, and equivalences indicated between coarse-grained and aphanitic types can be only approximate.

Common kinds of igneous rock are described, with specific information for use in identifying them, in Appendix B.

Sedimentary rocks

Early views. Sedimentary rocks are the most common at the surface of the Earth, and in many regions sedimentary layers are strikingly exposed in mountain sides and in walls of canyons. Such layers must have drawn the attention of many observant men, even in ancient times. Surely some of the more thoughtful of those early observers put two and two together and realized that many are fragments of other rocks, spread out as loose sediment, then compacted and cemented to form new rock. This realization is implied in written documents left by Greek philosophers long before the time of Christ; and later it was stated explicitly by Leonardo da Vinci. We find in his notebook that he perceived the close similarity between sedimentary rocks high in the mountains of northern Italy and the sands and muds of the seashore. He inferred that the layers of rock now high in the mountains are sea-floor deposits that have been lifted high above sea level.

Perhaps subconsiously, Leonardo had used his observation of a process actually going on—the laying down of sediments in and near the sea—in his

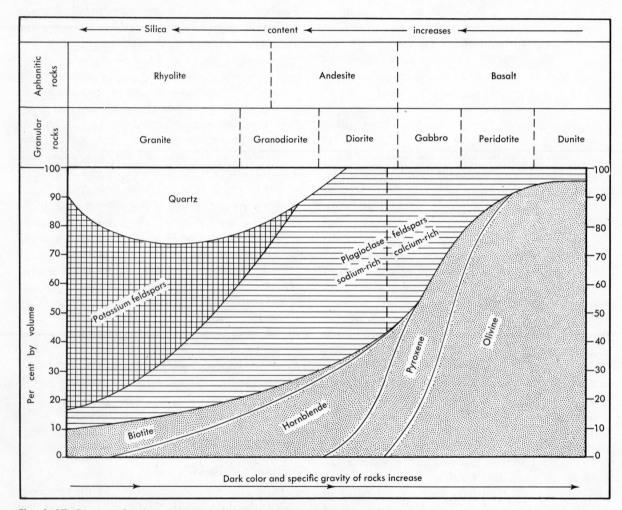

Fig. 3–17. Diagram showing proportions of the principal minerals in the common igneous rocks for use in study of specimens with no greater magnification than is given by a hand lens. Boundaries between kinds of rock adjacent in the table are not abrupt but gradational, as suggested by broken lines. Note the wide range in proportions of minerals in different granites, for example: some that have nearly 75 per cent potassium feldspar belong at the left side of the diagram; others with only 20 per cent are near the boundary with granodiorite. To see the general range in composition for any granular rock, project vertically downward the broken-line boundaries, then estimate percentage of a given mineral component by means of figures at right and left edges of the diagram. Only three kinds of aphanitic rocks are included. Without considerable magnification it is not possible to estimate proportions of minerals in these rocks. Differences in color and other criteria are used for identifying such rocks, as explained in Appendix B. Table B-1 can be used to advantage in connection with this figure. (Modified from R. V. Dietrich, Virginia Minerals and Rocks, Va. Polytech. Inst.)

interpretation of rocks: these rocks must be the product of a similar process that acted long ago. He was helped to this inference by the fact that the rocks he examined contained forms of shells similar to those of shellfish now found living in the sea. Later it was realized, by the same method of observation and comparison, that not all sedimentary rocks are of marine origin; clearly some of them are deposits of streams, lakes, glaciers, and winds.

Concept of today. By the end of the eighteenth century sedimentary rocks were being examined systematically, in a study which brought recognition of the great principle we call uniformity of process (p. 4) and which actually was the basis of Leonardo's inference 200 years earlier. The concept that has evolved from wide and intensified study may be summarized as follows:

1. The sedimentary rocks were formed by processes that are still continuously active on the Earth.

2. Great thicknesses of sedimentary layers represent accumulations over vast periods of time.

3. Pebbles, sand grains, and smaller particles in loose deposits, together with materials of chemical and organic origin, have in the course of time been compacted and cemented into firm, strong rock.

4. Large parts of the Earth's surface have been alternately sea floors and land areas because of slow downward and upward movements of the crust. Sedimentary layers formed in low-lying basins have been uplifted and deformed by such movements. These layers hold our best records of geologic history.

Kinds of sedimentary material. *An accumulation of loose rock particles that have been transported is sediment.* This word comes from the Latin *sedimentum* ("a settling") and was first used when all transported rock particles were supposed to have been deposited from suspension in the fluids water and air, which indeed are the most obvious agents of transport. Pebbles, sand grains, and smaller particles, carried along by currents, settle in quieter water to form layers on stream bed, lake bottom, or sea floor. After muddy flood waters withdraw from a wide valley, we find a new layer of mud made by settling of fine particles. A wind storm leaves coatings of dust, which settles wherever the flowing air is slowed down. Vast quantities of material, much of it the product of inorganic and organic chemical activity,

is settling continuously on the floors of oceans, seas, and lakes.

We realize, however, that although most sediment is accumulated by these processes of settling, there are other kinds of transport and deposition. Regolith can slide, creep, or flow down slopes without settling from suspension, and a pebble can be rolled or pushed along a stream bed without being lifted by the stream. Accordingly, the definition of sediment has been broadened to take account of particles moved in any way. It may be difficult to distinguish between regolith formed essentially in place and sediment that has been moved only a short distance down a slope. This is merely an example of the gradational series that are common in nature.

We recognize pebbles and sand grains as pieces of rocks or minerals, more or less rounded. We shall see that most of the fine particles in dust and ordinary mud also were derived from broken-up rocks, usually with some chemical change. All sediment of this kind is known as *clastic sediment* (Gr. *klastos,* "broken"), *accumulated particles of broken rocks (or fossils).* There is, of course, an insensible graduation in size from the largest boulder to ultramicroscopic dust particles; but to insure some precision in use of terms the classification below (Table 3–2) has been adopted.

A typical clastic sedimentary rock contrasts strongly with an igneous rock in shapes and arrangement of grains, as shown by comparison of **A** and **B** in Figure 3–18.

Close study of sediments now accumulating on

Table 3–2. Definition of clastic particles and aggregates

Name of particle	Limiting diameters		Name of loose aggregate	Consolidated into rock
	mm.	in. (approx.)		
Boulder	more than 256	more than 10	gravel	conglom-
Cobble	64 to 256	2.5 to 10	gravel	erate and
Pebble	2 to 64	0.09 to 2.5	gravel	breccia
Sand grain	1/16 to 2	(not of prac-	sand	sandstone
Silt particle	1/256 to 1/16	tical use)	silt	siltstone
Clay particle	less than 1/256 (about 2 microns)		clay	shale

(From Wentworth, C. K., Jour. Geol., vol. 30, p. 377-, 1922)

lands and in water supplies numerous clues for translating the records preserved in exposed sedimentary rocks. Thus we are made aware of radical changes in geography in geologic time. Distinctive old deposits mark the locations of former lakes, floodplains, deltas, and swamps. Deposits on sea floors of past ages underlie vast areas of present lands. Great quantities of these old deposits are clastic, similar to the materials now derived from land and spread over the continental shelves and slopes. Mingled with these clastic materials, or in places comprising entire layers, are shells, stems, and other hard parts of marine animals and plants. But a large fraction of the exposed rocks made of deposits in former seas consists of fine-grained, in part crystalline, calcium carbonate[1], analogous to material now slowly accumulating on vast areas of oceanic floors (Chap. 17). Consolidated deposits made up chiefly of the mineral *calcite* are *limestone*. In many old deposits the element *magnesium* has combined with *calcium* to form *dolomite*, and the resulting rock is *dolostone* (Table 17–1).

In summary, intensive studies long under way, and continuing at accelerating pace, demonstrate that sediments now accumulating, and those recognized as ingredients of sedimentary rocks, consist of (1) clastic materials, ranging from coarse to fine, (2) chemical deposits, both inorganic and organic, and (3) purely organic materials, such as beds of coal formed of plant materials on land and layers

[1] Commonly called "lime," but, strictly, lime is calcium oxide, CaO.

made chiefly of hard parts of marine invertebrate animals.

Principal kinds of sedimentary rocks

We can appreciate fully the important place of sedimentary rocks in geologic study only after we have analyzed the processes now active on the Earth's surface. But, because these activities affect the rocks formed in past ages by the same processes now in operation, the foregoing advance summary, with brief descriptions of some rock types, will help us to understand the processes themselves.

A study of the common sedimentary rocks, using good specimens in a laboratory, is advisable in connection with class work and reading. The brief descriptions of rock types presented in this chapter may be consulted during the laboratory study. More precise definitions of the common sedimentary rocks are given in Chapter 17.

Conglomerate. Gravel, coarse or fine, becomes cemented to form *conglomerate*. The pebbles, cobbles, and boulders have been more or less rounded during transport by streams or glacier ice or in buffeting by waves along a shore. They consist of any kind of rock but most commonly of the kinds rich in the durable mineral quartz. Usually the spaces between pebbles contain sand, cemented with silica, clay, iron oxide, or calcium carbonate.

Breccia. Sedimentary breccia resembles conglomerate, but most of the fragments are angular instead of rounded. We find all graduations between the two kinds of rock, and some specimens with partly worn

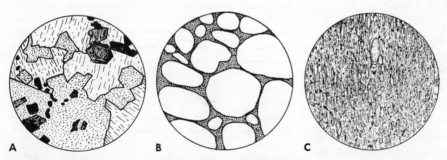

Fig. 3–18. Characteristic textures of **A,** igneous, **B,** sedimentary, and **C,** metamorphic rocks as seen under a microscope. All are enlarged to 15 times natural size. **A.** *Diorite;* mineral grains have generally angular outlines, fit snugly together. **B.** *Sandstone;* grains of quartz sand were more or less rounded, spaces between were filled later with cementing material. **C.** *Phyllite;* mineral grains elongate, with long dimensions parallel.

fragments may be called by one name or the other, according to individual judgment.

The term breccia should always be used with a modifier to indicate whether it refers to rock of sedimentary, volcanic, or other origin. Fault breccia records the breaking of rock in movements on faults.

Sandstone. *Sandstone* is made of cemented sand grains. With progressive change in size of grain, coarse sandstone grades into conglomerate, fine sandstone into siltstone. In many rocks grain sizes are mixed, and we speak of conglomeratic sandstones and sandy siltstones and shales.

In many sandstones the grains consist almost entirely of quartz, a durable mineral abundant in most sandstones. The cementing material varies, as in conglomerates; calcium carbonate is common, but silica makes a more durable stone. Color in sandstone, produced partly by the grains, partly by the cementing material, varies within a wide range.

Arkose is a variety of sandstone with a large proportion of feldspar grains. A composition of feldspar and quartz suggests granite, and some fresh arkose may be mistaken for it. In an arkose the grains do not interlock; they are separated by fine-grained cementing material.

Shale. *Shale*, made of compacted clay and silt, is so fine-grained it seems homogeneous to the unaided eye or even under ordinary magnification. It is soft and generally has a smooth, greasy feel, though some admixed fine sand or coarse silt may make it gritty. Shales generally split into thin layers or flakes. Rocks of similar composition but with thick, blocky layers are termed *mudstone*. Rocks in this group consisting largely of silt rather than clay are termed *siltstone*. Surfaces of such rocks are somewhat rough in contrast to the smoothness of typical shale.

Color in these fine-grained rocks ranges through shades of gray, green, red, and brown. Some layers that contain considerable carbon are black.

Limestone and dolostone. *Limestone* consists chiefly of calcite but has many impurities and varies greatly in appearance. Some limestones that are uniformly aphanitic probably were formed as chemical precipitates, aided more or less by tiny organisms. Some of the oozes on present sea floors probably represent an early stage in formation of aphanitic rock. By contrast, many limestones are coarse-grained, either from crystallization of the calcium carbonate or because they are made largely of shell fragments. All limestone effervesces freely in dilute hydrochloric acid.

Chalk, a weakly cemented limestone, usually contains many very small shells. *Marl* is a mixture of calcium carbonate and clay.

Dolostone is much like limestone in appearance, but it is slightly harder and effervesces with acid only on a scratched surface or in powdered form. The rock is made chiefly of the mineral dolomite, which has magnesium as well as calcium in its composition.

Peat and coal. *Peat,* made of partly decomposed plant tissues, represents an early stage in the formation of coal. The parts of plants are easily recognized in the brownish, lightweight mixture. *Lignite*, or *brown coal*, is much more compact than peat but usually shows some recognizable plant tissues. *Bituminous* (soft) coal is black, firm, breaks into blocks, and has a mixture of dull and bright bands. *Anthracite* (hard coal) breaks with conchoidal fracture and has a high luster. Anthracite represents an early stage in metamorphism (Chap. 19), but it is inclosed in unmetamorphosed rocks.

Salt and gypsum. Both halite (rock salt) and gypsum occur in large deposits. In pure form they have their distinctive mineral properties (Table A–1). Even with impurities, salt keeps its unmistakable taste and gypsum its characteristic hardness.

Importance of sedimentary layers

World-wide studies have established that sediments now being laid down in stream valleys, at the bottoms of lakes, and on sea floors are spread out in layers generally almost horizontal. When the loose particles are immersed in water they are easily moved, and water in motion tends to spread the particles evenly and so to fashion a nearly level surface. Therefore at the end of each stream flood, and of each storm offshore, a new sedimentary layer is deposited almost horizontally over the one beneath. Locally, some layers of limited extent are laid down with an inclination (Figs. 9–26, 17–23), but these represent special conditions and so are exceptions to the general rule. It is, then, an observed fact that most layers of sediment are nearly level at the time they are formed. This establishes a principle of major importance. In mountain lands we find large thicknesses of old deposits containing marine fossils in layers that now are sharply bent and steeply tilted (Fig. 18–9); this must mean that after they were deposited on the sea floor and consolidated the layers were deformed and uplifted by powerful forces.

Many widespread lava flows also are nearly horizontal at the time they are formed, and in some mountain zones strong deformation is recorded in the buckling and tilting of old lava sheets. Not uncommonly, however, lavas are viscous and the flows come to rest on steep slopes (Fig. 6–15). Therefore, they are less trustworthy than sedimentary layers in giving a measure of deformation (Chap. 18).

Metamorphic rocks

Metamorphism. "Nothing is constant but change." Formation of both igneous and sedimentary rocks involves radical changes in pre-existing rock material—in one case complete fusion, in the other breaking up by mechanical and chemical processes, moving, sorting, and spreading out of particles, followed by compaction or cementation. But the term *metamorphism*, which means transformation, is reserved for further changes in form and mineral content of any igneous or sedimentary rock mass after its formation. In mountain belts such as the Alps and the Appalachians, where old sedimentary layers have been strongly buckled and crumpled, we find a closely spaced slaty parting cutting across the layers. Many of the slaty surfaces glitter with flakes of mica, all in parallel arrangement; and commonly there is a gradation into rock made up largely of mica mixed with quartz grains. This radical change in the sedimentary rock probably was caused by high stress—which also buckled the layers—deep beneath the Earth's surface where temperatures also are fairly high. Hot igneous material intruded between or across sedimentary layers has caused growth of new minerals, such as garnet, by raising the temperature and sometimes by adding new elements carried in hot solutions.

The texture of a characteristic metamorphic rock, as revealed by magnification, is shown in Figure 3–18.

Metamorphic rocks are exposed over wide areas, particularly in mountain belts that have undergone repeated uplift and much erosion. The metamorphic processes are explained more fully in Chapter 19.

Principal kinds of metamorphic rocks

Slate is a *fine-grained metamorphic rock that splits into very thin plates*. Cleavage planes separating the plates commonly cut across layering of the original rock (Fig. 19–4, **A**). Although surfaces of the cleavage slabs have considerable luster, mineral grains can be seen only with very high magnification. A common color is dark bluish gray, generally known as slate color, but many slates are red, green, or black. Thin slabs of slate ring when they are tapped sharply.

Phyllite (fill′īte) is an *exceptionally lustrous rock representing a higher stage of metamorphism than slate*. The mica flakes responsible for the luster can be seen only with magnification, but some phyllites have visible grains of garnet and other minerals. The cleavage plates commonly are wrinkled or even sharply bent. Phyllite grades on the one hand into slate, on the other into schist.

Schist, a well foliated rock in which the component flaky minerals are clearly visible, represents a higher stage in metamorphism than phyllite. Mica schist is rich in mica—biotite, muscovite, or both together. Chlorite schist and hornblende schist also are common. Quartz is abundant in all kinds. Many schists are studded with garnets and other minerals that grew in the rock during metamorphism.

Gneiss (nīce) is a *coarse-grained metamorphic rock, commonly banded and with imperfect cleavage*. Many gneisses have a streaky, roughly layered appearance, caused by alternating lenses that differ in mineral composition. Feldspar, quartz, mica, hornblende, and garnet are common minerals in gneisses. *Granite gneiss* is a *distinctly banded rock with the mineral composition of granite*.

Metamorphism of limestone has caused growth of the calcite grains until the entire rock mass is granular. This is marble. Dolomite marble has been made in the same way from beds of dolostone. *Marble*, then, is just *crystalline limestone or dolostone* and responds to the tests for those rocks. Impurities in the original rock have gone into the formation of pyroxene, serpentine, and other minerals, which in many marbles make striking patterns.

Some commercial "marbles" are actually unmetamorphosed limestones and dolostones that take a good polish.

Quartzite is *a metamorphic rock developed from sandstone by introduction of silica into all spaces between the original grains of quartz.* When quartzite is broken, the fracture passes through the original quartz grains, not around them as in ordinary sandstone.

In some situations ground water has filled the pore spaces of sandstone with silica, thus producing a rock that imitates closely a metamorphosed sandstone. Microscopic study reveals differences that can not be seen in hand specimens. We accept as quartzite any rock that has quartz grains fully cemented with silica, whether or not they have resulted from metamorphism.

Quartzites usually have no patterns of foliation. Quartzite and marble are examples of nonfoliated metamorphic rocks, in contrast to gneiss, schist, phyllite, and slate.

Anthracite and graphite are formed by metamorphism of coal (Chap. 19). Near intrusive igneous bodies some of the invaded rock is greatly altered by high temperatures. Shale and some other fine-grained rocks are thus changed to *hornfels, a very hard, nonfoliated metamorphic rock, commonly studded with small crystals of mica and garnet.*

Other products of metamorphism are discussed in Chapter 19.

Rock cycles

Geologic history has been long and complex, and rock materials in many parts of the crust have passed

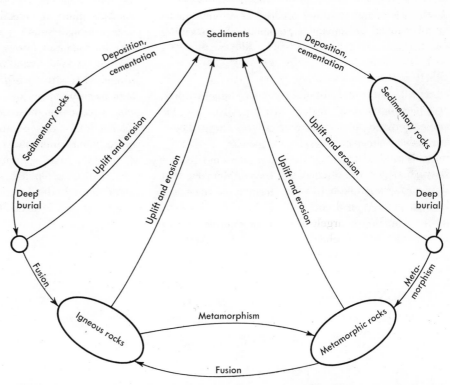

Fig. 3–19. Diagrammatic representation of "rock cycles," indicating that materials in the Earth's crust may pass through the igneous, sedimentary, and metamorphic states repeatedly and in several possible sequences. The diagram might show additional variations; for example, magma might form either volcanic or intrusive igneous rocks, and rocks in either group might be metamorphosed, reduced to sediments, or fused again to start new generations of igneous bodies. Rocks in an active mountain zone are subject to most frequent and radical changes.

through varied cycles of change. Rocks of all kinds exposed at the surface have been broken up, mechanically and chemically, and resulting materials have been deposited in sedimentary layers. Thick sections of the resulting rocks have been crushed and deformed in belts of growing mountains. Deep in the deformed zones some of the sedimentary layers are metamorphosed by pressure and rising temperature; locally, fusion occurs, and parts of the sedimentary section become magma which later solidifies into igneous rock. In some mountain zones that have been deeply eroded the three related rock types—including old sedimentary layers that are in part metamorphosed and elsewhere grade into igneous bodies—are being worn away and the resulting debris is carried by streams to be deposited in the building up of new sedimentary deposits.

Surely much rock material has passed through cyclic changes of this kind. The *rock cycle* may start with rock of any kind and proceed along any one of several paths, as shown diagrammatically in Figure 3–19.

SUMMARY

1. All matter is made up of submicroscopic atoms. Each atom has a nucleus with positive electric charge, about which revolve negatively charged electrons. The atom is in electric balance.

2. With loss or gain of electrons, an atom becomes an ion, electrically unbalanced. Ions of elements that have chemical affinity join to form molecules of a chemical compound.

3. A mineral consists of atoms of one element or ions of two or more, in an arrangement that forms a crystalline structure peculiar to each mineral.

4. Nearly all rocks consist of mineral assemblages. Exceptions are glassy rocks in which atoms are without orderly arrangement.

5. Rocks belong in three classes known as igneous, sedimentary, and metamorphic rocks.

6. Igneous rocks are formed by solidification of molten silicate material, either on or beneath the Earth's surface.

7. Erupted igneous materials form extrusive rocks, which are in part solidified lavas, in part fragmental products compacted or cemented.

8. Igneous materials cooled within the crust form intrusive rocks, many of them coarse grained. Both intrusive and extrusive rocks have wide range in chemical composition.

9. Sedimentary rocks are made of clastic materials, chemical deposits, and organic products. The ingredients accumulate on continents, on ocean floors, and in transitional zones.

10. Sedimentary rocks, because of orderly superposition of layers, significant physical features, and contained fossils, have great value as records of geologic history.

11. Igneous and sedimentary rocks have been changed by pressure and temperature into several types of metamorphic rock, some of them with secondary cleavage.

12. During geologic history much rock material has gone through the igneous, sedimentary, and metamorphic states in cyclic fashion.

REFERENCES

Hurlbut, C. S., 1959, Dana's manual of mineralogy, 17th ed.: New York, John Wiley and Sons.

Bragg, W. L., 1937, The atomic structure of minerals: Ithaca, New York, Cornell Univ. Press.

Mason, Brian, 1958, Principles of geochemistry, 2d ed.: New York, John Wiley and Sons.

Williams, H., Turner, F. J., and Gilbert, C. M., 1954, Petrography: San Francisco, W. H. Freeman and Co.

CHAPTER 4. GEOLOGIC TIME

General reasoning about time   *Qualitative estimates of geologic age*   *Isolated exact measurements*

Revolution in geochronometry   *Absolute and relative time values*   *Scale of geologic time*

View of the starry heavens, including the spiral nebula in Cepheus.
(By permission of California Institute of Technology.)

Concepts of space and time

Surely every thinking person has more than once wrestled with the puzzle of infinity. We gaze into the heavens on a clear night and try to imagine an outer limit to space as we conceive it. If we leap in fancy to our planetary neighbor Jupiter, then to distant Sirius, and on into and beyond the Milky Way, an innate sense seems to demand somewhere a final destination; the stars and galaxies, so intuitive reason says, must end somewhere. Yet as we try to picture an outer boundary, at once comes the question "What lies beyond that?" Thus our reasoning, schooled by practical, earthly experience to require finite bounds, finds the concept of infinite space appalling but apparently inescapable.[1]

Astronomers have confirmed that the universe is immense, but they have found no hint of its outermost limits. The planets of our Solar System are dispersed through billions of miles, yet this entire assemblage is a mere speck in our galaxy of stars, in which distances between neighboring bodies are measured in multiples of the *light year*, the inconceivable span traversed in a full year by light moving at the rate of 186,000 miles per second—roughly 6 million million miles. Telescopes, penetrating space beyond our starry system, reveal myriads of similar galaxies; those brought to view by the 200-inch lens at the Palomar Observatory in California are numbered in hundreds of millions, and those at the outer limit of vision are about 2 billion light years from us. The new radio telescope now coming into use extends the astronomer's horizon at least a billion light years farther. Space extends beyond, but how far?

[1] The suggestion of some scholars that "space is curved" does not clear up the great puzzle for most of us.

Attempts to conceive limits of time lead to a similar impasse. The Earth, so we reason, must have had a beginning; it was born, went through a youthful period, and is now at some stage in a finite life-cycle. So, too, we can imagine a birthtime of the Sun or of any other star within our galaxy. But if we project backward and try to imagine a starting hour for all things, we are faced with the query, "What was before that?" If we carry fancy into the far future, to a possible ending of the cosmos, we begin to wonder, "And after that, what?" Thus the human mentality seems to have reasoned viewpoints that are utterly contradictory: on the one side we see everything as necessarily finite, with beginning and end, birth and death; on the other, we look backward and forward into endless time.

Beliefs and teachings regarding the origin of the Earth and of man have been curiously varied. At one extreme the Brahmins of ancient India were convinced that the Earth, as well as time, is eternal. Priests of old Chaldea, on the other hand, held that our planet emerged from chaos about 2 million years ago. We have no clue to the source of that figure, but perhaps it reflects an intelligent perception that rocks and landscapes suggest a very long history. Astrologers of Babylon said that man appeared on Earth about 500,000 years ago. So far as we know, this date rested on pure guess, yet by coincidence it seems actually to be the right order of magnitude according to modern scientific chronology.

Champions of a much shorter time scale include Zoroaster of Persia, who about 600 B.C. taught that the Earth was 12,000 years old and would last another 3,000 years, at which time a new prophet, descendant of Zor, would be born, the dead would

Fig. 4–1. North side of the Grand Canyon, Arizona, as seen from the air. The suspension bridge for the Kaibab Trail is at lower right, lower part of Bright Angel Canyon at left. Letters *T* to *K*, corresponding to those in Figure 4-2, mark the units of sedimentary rock. The Inner Gorge, with nearly vertical walls, has been cut into Precambrian rocks. Erosion has dissected the layered sedimentary rocks, leaving large remnants of the units *C* and *H* in isolated buttes. Airline distance from foreground to the far rim is about 7 miles. (Spence Air Photos.)

come to life, and a new incorruptible state of existence would begin. Our own era has fostered the concept of a still shorter chronology, built on literal acceptance of statements in ancient Hebrew writings. In the seventeenth century one Anglican divine won a kind of fame by announcing that the Earth was created in the year 4004 B.C., or less than 6,000 years ago.

What is the truth about the age of the Earth? Since reason suggests that time is eternal and the universe is ageless, why should anyone shrink from the concept that our planet, and with it the Solar System to which it is delicately geared, dates from the remote past? Perhaps the answer is twofold: the viewpoint of the individual is closely limited by his experiences in finite time and space; and we are still emerging from the long spell cast by generations of leaders to whom our puny Earth was the center of the universe, and our twenty-four-hour day a significant unit of time.

The only way to a real appreciation of geologic time is in careful study of landscape features, of the rocks beneath them, and of processes we can see in operation now. It will also help to examine methods used in measuring time and to have a preliminary look at some of the results. Evidence brought together by geologic studies of several generations indicates clearly that the Earth is very old. Much of the evidence is qualitative and serves as a basis for only rough estimates of time measured in years. Within the present century, however, precise methods of age determination have been developed, and we now know that even the most generous of the "intelligent guesses" based on general evidence were gross underestimates.

General evidence on geologic time

Physical evidence. At the Grand Canyon of the Colorado River in Arizona (Fig. 4–1) we see at a glance sedimentary beds more than 4,000 feet in total thickness. These layers, consisting of sandstone, siltstone, shale, and limestone, are nearly horizontal and so have been little deformed since they were made. Simple analysis convinces us, however, that the vast accumulation of deposits, exposed over thousands of square miles, was not formed in its present setting. Scattered through layers in the lower half of the canyon wall are many shells and other parts of animals like many now living only on the floors of the seas. Above these is a large thickness of sandstone and siltstone layers without marine fossils but inclosing many fossilized plants of kinds that live only on land; from this evidence, and from certain peculiarities of the sediments, we reason that these layers represent deposits made by ancient streams (Chap. 17). Still higher lie limestone layers hundreds of feet thick in which marine shells are abundant. Thus the great thickness of deposits accumulated partly below and in part somewhat above sea level. Since we find every unit in the north wall matched on the opposite side (Fig. 4–2, *T* to *K*), each layer was once continuous across the area of the canyon. After the deposits now seen in the canyon walls became compacted and cemented into firm rock, uplift of a wide region carried the top of the section more than 7,000 feet and its base about 3,000 feet above sea level. Since uplift began, erosion by running water has removed thousands of cubic miles of rock in fashioning the Grand Canyon and its surrounding landscape.

Studies of sediments now being deposited on sea floors give a basis for crude estimates of the minimum time required for laying down the beds in the Grand Canyon section. Limy deposits accumulate at an extremely slow rate; it is estimated that each foot in thickness of a widespread limestone layer represents several thousand years. At that rate, laying down the 1,500 feet of nearly pure limestone in the canyon walls required many millions of years. Thus without any pretense to accuracy, and by focusing on only one element in the complex record, we glimpse the order of magnitude in the measure of time. The sample used in our rough check represents only a fraction of the total thickness of beds exposed in the wide plateau crossed by the Colorado River. North of the Grand Canyon the land surface mounts in a succession of broad steps (Fig. 4–2). The topmost beds (*K*) exposed in the canyon disappear beneath the first step, and each cliff brings to view the edges of sedimentary layers that formerly extended southward across the canyon until erosion removed them from large areas. Some of these beds contain marine fossils; others have the characteristics of deposits now being formed by streams and in broad lakes. The total thickness of all layers preserved in the steps is about 10,000 feet, or more than twice the thickness of all layers forming the walls of the Grand Canyon. Thus the impression of antiquity given by study of limestones in the walls gains force when we ponder the growth of the full plateau section of sedimentary beds, nearly 3 miles thick, and its partial destruction by erosion after widespread uplift.

Biologic evidence. Remains of animals and plants found in the thick sedimentary sections bear eloquent testimony to the passage of time. These records of former life are found at many levels in the full sec-

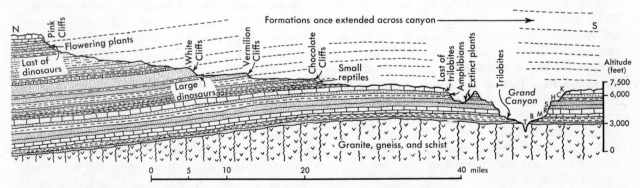

Fig. 4–2. Section representing a vertical slice across the Grand Canyon and the great cliffs north of it. The vertical scale is about 6 times the horizontal; but the inclinations of rock layers are shown less steep than this difference in scale would require, to avoid undue distortion. Letters on walls of Grand Canyon correspond to those on sedimentary units in Figure 4–1. Only a few of many significant fossil locations are indicated.

tion north of the Grand Canyon (Fig. 4–2). Although in general character the fossils show relationships to modern forms, no fossil in the entire section belongs to any living species or genus, and nearly all are in still larger biologic groups that are now extinct. Moreover, in progressively lower (that is, older) layers the fossil forms are less like the modern and in general more primitive. In the lowest shaly layers of the section are fossils of invertebrate animals only, and the dominant type is the *trilobite* (Fig. 4–3), a strange extinct marine animal distantly related to our horseshoe crab. Remains of primitive fishes are found considerably higher, and, progressively upward, appear diverse types of fishes with more modern appearance. In the upper part of the canyon wall are records of salamander-like amphibians, and somewhat higher are remains of small reptiles. In some of the layers that form steps north of the canyon there are tracks of large reptiles known as dinosaurs, which dominated the animal kingdom of their day. Still higher, the evidence of dinosaurs disappears, and the highest sedimentary layers contain numerous bones of primitive mammals.

Fundamental changes in plants also are recorded in the thick succession of layers. In the lowest nonmarine layers, midway in the canyon wall, are abundant remains of primitive ferns and other small land plants. North of the canyon, in the rocks containing bones of small reptiles, are numerous petrified logs of extinct relatives of modern pine trees. Through the upper part of the section are distributed fossils of many kinds of flowering plants related to modern forms. Thus the entire biologic record shows unmistakably a progressive development of new types and a dying out of old types.

We have no way of measuring with assurance the rate of evolutionary changes, but there is no firm evidence that during all of written human history any new species of animal or plant has appeared through natural development. Man himself, by methods of crossbreeding and artificial selection, has developed many contrasting varieties of grains, fruits, and domestic animals and probably a few actual species of plants. But the process of evolution by natural selection seems to have been extremely slow. In studies of changes recorded in animal fossils, and by using modern methods of reckoning time, research

Fig. 4–3. The trilobite was the most highly developed animal of its time, about 500 million years ago. These specimens, found in marine shale exposed in British Columbia, are exceptionally well preserved. Legs, antennae, and segments of each carapace are clearly outlined, and curved markings made by movements of the animals on the muddy sea floor are well defined on the slab of shale. (Courtesy The American Museum of Natural History.)

workers suggest that the average period required for the appearance of a persistent new species has been of the order of a million years. All known evidence indicates that organic evolution is very slow and that the time elapsed since deposition of the oldest sediments in the Grand Canyon has been enormously long.[1]

Fragments of exact chronology

Annual sedimentary layers. Each yearly overflow of the Nile presents to agricultural Egypt a new layer of soil. Herodotus and other ancient scholars noted this annual increment in the upbuilding of the Nile Valley floor, as indicated in the historic pronouncement, "Egypt is the gift of the Nile." Successions of such yearly layers that reflect stable conditions over extended periods are recognized also in the ancient sediments that now are firm bedrock. One of the best examples is in Germany, where a large body of old marine shaly rocks has remarkably uniform layers

[1] A fuller appreciation of evidence bearing on the age of the Earth is given by a study of historical geology, which treats the entire succession of sedimentary rocks and the fossils contained in them.

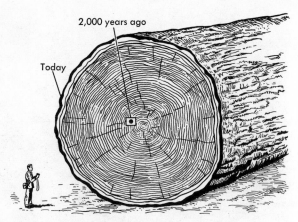

2,000 years ago

Today

Fig. 4-4. The annual rings of growth on a section of a redwood tree record a long span of years. The greatest age reported for an individual tree, 4,600 years, is on a section of a bristlecone pine tree in eastern California.

Fig. 4-5. Petrified stump of an ancient tree, near Florissant, Colorado. Many ancestors of the living redwoods were buried in volcanic ash and sediments, and the wood was gradually replaced with mineral matter. (H. N. Andrews, Jr.)

that average a small fraction of an inch in thickness. Thorough study has revealed in the layering an alternate thinning and thickening in a recurrent cycle averaging a little more than eleven of the layers and thus corresponding accurately to the sun-spot "cycle," in the course of which the energy received from the sun varies enough to affect weather conditions on Earth. This systematic arrangement confirms an obvious suggestion that the regular thin layers represent yearly increments of sediments. Altogether about a million layers, representing an equal number of years, are exposed, and thus another fragment of the total geologic record gives strong support to general qualitative evidence that the Earth is very old.

Fossil trees. The rings of annual growth displayed on the smooth cross section of a tree trunk are counted to determine the age of the tree (Fig. 4-4); some of the great redwoods of California are thus found to be more than 3,000 years old. Ages up to 4,600 years are reported for specimens of bristlecone pine trees now living in the White Mountains of eastern California. In favorable specimens of the large trees an alternate thickening and thinning of growth layers apparently corresponds to the sun-spot cycle of about 11 years, just as in some sections of sedimentary layers. Growth rings are clearly marked on many petrified tree trunks, and in Yellowstone National Park petrified logs of primitive redwoods as old as 1,600 years have been found. Large numbers of petrified trunks and stumps, many standing as they grew, record the overwhelming of entire forests by great eruptions of volcanic ash (Fig. 4-5). The wall of Yellowstone's Lamar Canyon, which rises steeply more than 2,000 feet, reveals twenty-seven such forests, one above the other, to record a succession of widely spaced volcanic catastrophes (Fig. 4-6). The minimum life of each forest has not been determined; but if we assume for each a single redwood generation of just over 2,000 years, the whole succession represents a period of more than 50,000 years. Probably this is only a fraction of the time involved, since after each major eruption a soil had to be developed before the next forest could flourish, and at least some of the forests may well have lasted through several life spans of individual trees. Yet from matching up the sedimentary layers (Fig. 17-24) the entire record of the Yel-

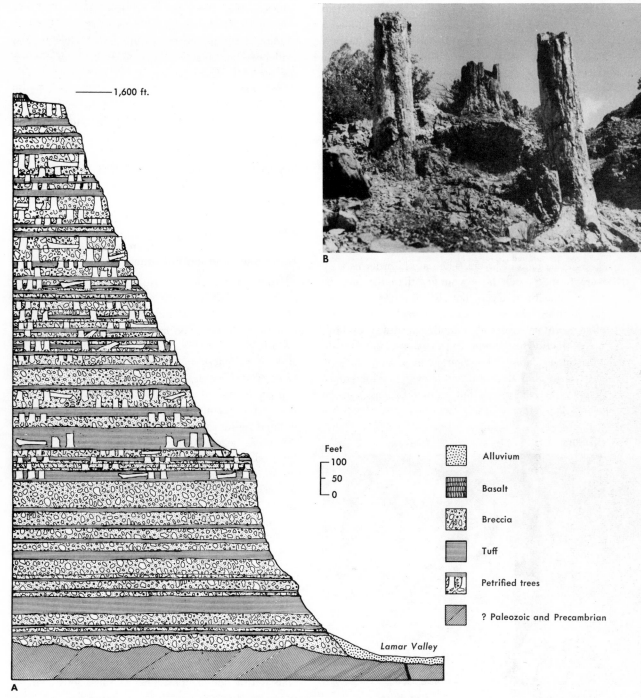

— 1,600 ft.

Feet
100
50
0

Alluvium

Basalt

Breccia

Tuff

Petrified trees

? Paleozoic and Precambrian

Lamar Valley

A

B

Fig. 4–6. A. Section of a cliff beside the Lamar River, Yellowstone National Park. Twenty-seven successive forests were buried by volcanic ash and breccia, and many trunks were petrified in a standing position. Individual trees were as much as 500 years old, as shown by annual rings of growth. **B.** Characteristic appearance of the petrified trunks, partly exposed by erosion. (Erling Dorf.)

lowstone fossil forests is known to be much later than the uppermost beds shown in Fig. 4–2, and thus in a comparative sense it is a part of late geologic history. From a human point of view, however, it belongs far back in prehistory, since it antedates the shaping of the present land surface, including the Yellowstone Canyon, and occurred long before any records of man himself.

Relative versus absolute dating. Study of some annual sedimentary layers and rings of fossil trees may give accurate measurements of time for limited and isolated episodes in the history of the Earth. A more continuous general record is supplied by the thick section of sedimentary layers almost perfectly exposed in the Grand Canyon and a wide adjoining region. In this section there can be no question about the *relative ages* of layers. They are in order as they were formed, each layer younger than the one directly beneath it. Even though exposures are interrupted in a wide region, we can *correlate* one group of sedimentary layers with another far away by finding distinctive fossil forms in the two sections (Chap. 17). Such "dating," however, is in a relative sense only; it establishes the *order* in which sedimentary layers were laid down but cannot fix any ages in years. The urge to learn the exact age of earthly

things, and of the Earth itself, has long been an incentive to efforts of scientific workers.

Late in the nineteenth century, with the kinds of evidence then available, geologists were estimating the age of the Earth as at least 100 million years. The British physicist Lord Kelvin considered this figure extravagantly large; following theories in vogue at that time, he calculated that not more than 40 million years could have gone by since the crust of a once-molten Earth had formed. Since Kelvin's time, revolutionary discoveries have supplied a quantitative basis for some age determinations and theories have changed radically. Though we cannot yet state confidently the exact age of the Earth, we now have good information on the ages of many rocks in the crust.

Exact measurements of time

Uranium provides a yardstick. In 1896 Becquerel discovered that uranium at ordinary temperatures emits an invisible radiation that will affect a photographic plate screened by thin plates of metal. This historic discovery was a step in revealing the principle of *radioactivity, the spontaneous disintegration of certain elements, with emission of radiant energy and production of some other elements.* Shortly after Becquerel established this milestone and the Curies isolated radium as a product of the radioactive process, there began an era of research that has revolutionized concepts of physics and chemistry and has profoundly affected ideas about the Earth and the universe. There is no better illustration of the fact that all fields of science are interdependent. One of the results is the growing use of radioactive minerals in dating rocks.

Several elements are now being used for age determinations; but uranium was used in the earliest work on age values, and the results are regarded as among the most dependable. Combined with oxygen in the mineral *uraninite*, uranium is not abundant but is widely distributed in small amounts. Crystals of uraninite occur locally and exceptionally in pegmatite veins (Fig. 4–7). Uranium breaks down slowly with emission of helium ions. Loss of these ions changes uranium atoms into a different substance, also unstable; and emission of helium continues until lead results as a stable end product. For the predominant isotope of uranium the *mass number—the number*

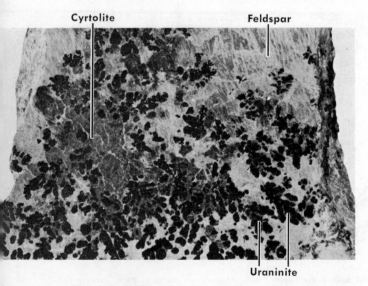

Cyrtolite

Feldspar

Uraninite

Fig. 4–7. Black grains of uraninite (uranium oxide) are characteristically intergrown with feldspar and other minerals. The specimen is from a pegmatite vein. (Ward's Natural Science Establishment.)

given by the sum of all protons and neutrons in the atomic nucleus—is 238. Hence the isotope is known as uranium 238 (written U^{238}). Helium (H^4) has mass number 4. In successive steps of disintegration U^{238} gives off eight helium ions. Thus the resulting lead (Pb^{206}) has mass number $238 - (8\times4)$, or 206. The entire process is expressed diagrammatically as follows:

$$U^{238} \to 234 \to 230 \to 226 \to 222 \to 218 \to 214 \to 210 \to Pb^{206}$$
$$\downarrow \quad \downarrow \quad \downarrow \quad \downarrow \quad \downarrow \quad \downarrow \quad \downarrow \quad \downarrow$$
$$He^4 \ He^4 \ He^4 \ He^4 \ He^4 \ He^4 \ He^4 \ He^4$$

Each unit represented by a mass number in the diagram has a technical name, but only radium (226) is widely known to laymen. With passage of time the quantities of both helium and lead increase and the amount of uranium decreases. The gas helium tends to diffuse, and part of it may leak away, whereas the solid lead remains where it is formed. Therefore, when a crystal of uraninite is analyzed accurately, the ratio of lead to uranium (known as the *lead-uranium ratio*) should reveal the age of the crystal, provided (1) the rate of change, uranium to lead, is known precisely and (2) the rate of change has been constant since it began. The present rate is known with a high degree of accuracy; repeated measurements have determined that one gram of uranium yields $\frac{1}{7,500,000,000}$ gram of lead per year. Furthermore, research during half a century has established that the rate is invariable under all known conditions of temperature, pressure, and chemical environment.

Several troublesome complications delayed satisfactory development of the lead-uranium method for accurate determination of age. Uranium 238 is accompanied by small quantities of uranium 235, the isotope used in making atomic bombs. This isotope also emits helium, but, with loss of seven ions, produces lead (Pb^{207}) with mass number $235 - (7\times4)$, or 207. Moreover, thorium, another radioactive element, is commonly associated with uranium; the mass number of thorium is 232, and loss of six helium ions results in another lead isotope, Pb^{208}. Many test specimens also contain some original or "common" lead, which includes an isotope with mass number 204. These difficulties are resolved by the *mass spectrometer, an instrument that determines precisely the amount of each isotope present in a mineral specimen*. It is actually desirable (and not uncommon) to have both uranium and thorium in a test sample, since independent determinations can be made for each element and the results used to check each other.

Much of the usable radioactive material is in igneous rocks. A mineral containing uranium or thorium started its existence when the igneous body containing it solidified from a fluid condition and so is like a clock set at zero at that critical hour; the time we now read on the clock gives the exact age of the igneous body. But our greatest interest is in a sedimentary deposit that was formed at a critical time, during or just following a great crustal disturbance. Commonly, we must search for igneous rocks that contain favorable minerals and that have a determinable relation to the sedimentary layers we wish to date.

An occurrence that would be considered very favorable is represented in Figure 4–8. The oldest sedimentary layers (*a*), containing marine fossils, were deformed by folding and were invaded by magma that solidified into the igneous bodies (1). Uplift occurred, and much of the rock mass was cut away by streams. The region slowly subsided, and another series of marine layers (*b*), containing a different assemblage of fossils, was laid down. The igneous bodies (2), transecting both sets of deposits, record a second episode of igneous activity. In a second regional uplift the layers (*b*) were tilted; and after they were partly worn away a third set of sedimentary deposits, containing fossil trees and bones of land animals, accumulated. If analyses of radioactive minerals give the age of the oldest igneous bodies as 110 million years and of the later dikes as 72 million, we know that the oldest sedimentary layers are older than 110 million years, the second marine series is between 72 and 110 million, and the nonmarine beds are less than 72 million years old.

As indicated by the small measure of disintegration year by year, uranium has a very long life, hence is suited to recording very ancient dates. Use of the radioactive method is accelerating, and results have dispelled all doubt that the Earth is very old. Rocks tens of millions of years old are comparatively young, values in hundreds of millions of years are commonplace, a number of the best determinations indicate ages between 2,000 and 3,000 million years, and dates in excess of 3,000 million years are appearing in the record.

Growing use of other elements. As the studies proceed, the methods become more refined and the results more dependable. Use of several radioactive elements not only serves as a check on results but also extends the field of investigation to rock masses in which uranium and thorium are not found. Thus potassium (K), abundant in many common minerals, disintegrates slowly with production of argon (A). Ages based on ratios of these two elements are regarded as accurate, not only for the older rocks but also for many that are geologically young. Because of its double advantage, the potassium-argon method is meeting widespread favor, and announcements of "K-A dates" are accelerating. Another method makes use of strontium (Sr) and rubidium (Rb). Ratios in some old rocks between potassium (K) and argon (A) and between strontium (Sr) and rubidium (Rb) give reliable values. As the campaign moves on a broad front, some minerals that occur in sedimentary rocks are being analyzed with promising results. Direct dating of sedimentary deposits is highly desirable, for igneous bodies with the relationships shown in Figure 4–8 are exceptional, and at best they can indicate only between certain limits the ages of the rocks they transect.

Some investigators, using astronomical data, radioactive analyses of minerals in meteorites, and studies of "common" lead, suggest about 4,500 million years as the probable age of the Earth. This is a matter of much general interest; but geologists are more concerned with increasing the number of accurate analyses for dating sedimentary deposits that are critical in the time scale of Earth history (Table 4–2).

In the literature dealing with exact dates in geologic history the expression "absolute time" is commonly used. *Absolute time* is *geologic time reckoned in years,* in contrast to *relative* dating by assigning events to their proper places in a chronological sequence. A chronological tabulation is, of course, required for an orderly record of geologic history. Ideally, a table should list in sequence the distinctive periods in the Earth's history, with absolute dates for as many critical parts of the record as possible. This is a desirable goal in modern geologic study.

Special role of radiocarbon. Because of their slow rates in radioactive disintegration, uranium and thorium have no value in dating events that occurred only a few thousands or tens of thousands of years ago. This later part of geologic history holds particular interest because it involves our human forebears. How far back, in actual years, can the record of early man be traced? And what firm dates can be fixed in the record of the glacial ages (Chap. 13)?

A technique developed about 1950 makes use of a carbon isotope for determining dates as old as 60,000 years before the present. Carbon dioxide in

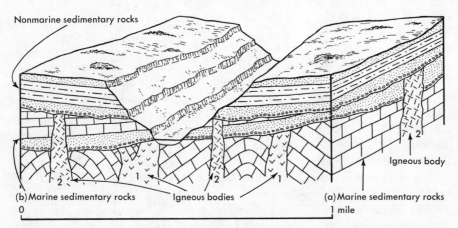

Fig. 4–8. A common arrangement of units in bedrock that makes possible the dating of sedimentary layers in relation to associated igneous rocks containing radioactive minerals. The igneous bodies shown here represent two episodes of intrusive activity; the sedimentary layers record three chapters of history.

the atmosphere contains, chiefly, ordinary carbon with mass number 12 and a small proportion of an isotope that has mass number 14. This isotope, known as *radiocarbon,* emits radiant energy. It is generated continually in the upper atmosphere by bombardment of nitrogen by cosmic rays and is carried down into the lower atmosphere where it maintains a nearly constant ratio to ordinary carbon. Tissues of living organisms absorb the C^{14} in this ratio, and at the time of death the tissues have a known *specific activity* of radiation. This activity decreases at a constant rate that is accurately known. Therefore, measuring the radiant energy in organic carbon gives a measure of the time since death occurred.

Accuracy of the method is checked against samples of known date, such as corn and wooden beams from ancient human tombs and pieces from the hearts of large redwood trees (Fig. 4–4). One of the most significant investigations by this technique used wood from trees that were overrun by the latest ice sheet to invade the Great Lakes region. The dates of many wood samples show that the glacier reached its greatest extent in the Ohio-Indiana-Illinois region not more than 18,000 years ago; then retreated before making a conspicuous readvance of lesser extent that culminated less than 11,000 years ago.

Growing program in geochronometry. A number of laboratories in several parts of the United States and in other countries are rapidly enlarging and refining the list of geologic dates, extending from the immediate past to the remote history of the Earth. These workshops are known as *geochronometric laboratories: geochronometry is the process of measuring geologic time.* Inevitably there is much "trial and error" in the early stages of a study involving the testing of new methods and techniques, some of which prove to be unsatisfactory and are discarded. Objective checking, one against another, of dates indicated by different methods is essential for dependable results. This campaign, enlisting the best skills in geochemistry, is still in an early stage but has great promise as an aid to giving quantitative solutions to many problems in geology.

A few years ago there was a "no man's land" between recent dates based on radiocarbon determinations and much older dates given by uranium-lead ratios. No dependable method was known for measures of absolute time within a range of several million years beyond the low brackets cared for by radiocarbon analyses. This gap is being closed by the potassium-argon method, which appears to give dependable absolute age values ranging from much less than a million years to the greatest ages so far determined.

The geologic record

The analysis of historical records has two main objectives: (1) to determine what events occurred, and in what order; (2) to fix the exact date of each event. Discoveries in modern human history are announced frequently, as obscure records are brought to light. Piecing together a connected account of early man proceeds slowly, as source materials are discovered by accident or through diligent search. Basic information on the history of the Earth is stored in rocks of the crust, but efforts of several human generations have been required to search out and interpret parts of the critical evidence. Now a general order of major events has been established. The fixing of actual dates in years has made a promising start, though some of the results can be accepted as only approximate.

The geologic column and scale of time. Late in the eighteenth century and in the early years of the nineteenth some geologists in Europe began to see evidence of law and order in the complex array of sedimentary rocks that underlie much of the land surface. Although they had no such clean-cut exhibit of superposed layers as that in the Grand Canyon region, the general order of the principal units was becoming clear. British geologists recognized that in the western part of their island a thick sequence of sedimentary beds had been severely folded and much eroded before the laying down of another set of deposits in which the layers are tilted uniformly toward the east (Fig. 4–9). The older, folded series they designated *Primary,* the younger series, *Secondary.* They saw, furthermore, that a distinctive thick sequence in southern England overlies the "Secondary" layers and generally has been less tilted; this third major group was called *Tertiary.* In more recent years the latest deposits, largely unconsolidated alluvium above the "Tertiary" rocks, were grouped under the designation *Quaternary.*

As field studies proceeded, it became clear that definite groups of layers in each of the major divisions of rocks could be recognized by distinctive assemblages of fossils found in these layers. This discovery focused attention on the importance of the record left by animals and plants, and gradually the terms *Primary* and *Secondary* became supplanted respectively, by *Paleozoic* (Gr. "pertaining to ancient life") and *Mesozoic* ("pertaining to Medieval life"). *Tertiary* and *Quaternary* have persisted, not as names for major divisions of rocks and of time but to designate subdivisions of a third major unit, the *Cenozoic* ("pertaining to recent life"). Furthermore, it was found that each major group of rocks could be divided into distinctive units, also on the basis of their fossil content; each unit is known as a *system* and the time of its formation a *period* (Tables 4–1, 4–2). The largest time units—Paleozoic, Mesozoic, Cenozoic—are *eras*. As in human history, much more is known about the recent than about the older past, and accordingly for the younger periods there are world-wide subdivisions called *epochs,* each with a name to indicate the degree of its recency (e.g., *Pleistocene* = most recent, *Miocene* = less recent, *Eocene* = dawn of the recent). The group of sedimentary beds formed during an epoch is a *series*. As field studies become more detailed still smaller divisions, known as *stages,* can be traced widely in a continent. A number of stages (and corresponding ages) defined in Europe have been recognized in parts of North America also. Moreover, with continued study, the Mesozoic and Paleozoic systems and periods are being divided into series and epochs, with further subdivisions into well-defined stages and ages.

Because the names applied to divisions of rocks are attached also to divisions of time, the logic of the two tables, 4–1 and 4–2, is evident. Table 4–1 shows diagrammatically a column of sedimentary rocks as they might be exposed in the wall of a deep canyon. Of course, such a column is pieced together from studies of exposures in many places. Age relations of the units are determined in part from physical evidence, in large part by distinctive fossils of animals and plants. No pretense of actual scale is represented in the diagram—only the correct sequence. A columnar section to show relations in detail would indicate kinds of rock, with deformation at many horizons. Only the general structural break between Precambrian and younger rocks is included here. Space allows brief notes on a few significant highlights in the fossil record of animals and plants to illustrate the kind of evidence used in geologic dating.

Table 4–2 gives the main divisions of geologic time and lists a few dates in years determined by analyses of radioactive materials. Some published tables give figures for the duration of each division of time. Such figures can be estimates only and are subject to change because the exact positions of specimens used for analysis, in relation to boundaries of the time units they represent, are not known exactly. Moreover, the age values given by some of the methods now in use are subject to error up to 10 per cent or more. Not all *absolute* ages that are published can be accepted as *exact* ages.

Estimated values for the age of the Earth range from 4,500 to 5,000 million years. Ages of some rocks as high as 3,000 million years have been determined. Ancient rocks underlie a vast area in eastern and northern Canada (Fig. 4–10). The time elapsed since the start of the Paleozoic Era is short by comparison with Precambrian time, as shown by the scale at the right side of Table 4–2.

As usual in a study that builds up slowly through generations, the geologic terms that have become fixed by usage do not conform to a consistent scheme. *Cretaceous* is derived from the Latin *creta,*

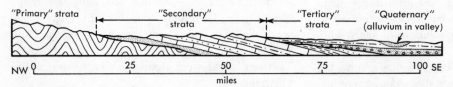

Fig. 4–9. This section (vertical slice) across part of Wales and southern England shows the relations among four great groups of sedimentary rocks. Layers of the oldest group are much deformed, and there is progressively less deformation in the younger groups.

Fig. 4—10. Airview of large exposures of bedrock northwest of Yellowknife, Northwest Territory, Canada. The light-colored areas are on bodies of granite that are intrusive into older metamorphic rocks. Radioactive minerals in the granite give absolute dates much older than the beginning of the Paleozoic Era (Table 4—2). The metamorphic rocks (Precambrian) are older still. We have no basis for dividing these ancient rocks into groups that represent successive eras and periods of time. (Royal Canadian Air Force, courtesy A. W. Jolliffe.)

chalk, a common kind of marine limestone deposited during that period. Each Paleozoic system is named for the geographic area in which the unit was defined; *Mississippian* and *Pennsylvanian*, however, are names given in the United States to subdivisions of the original *Carboniferous* (period of coal formation). As all rocks earlier than Paleozoic contain few fossils, and in large part have been metamorphosed, no logical scheme for subdividing them into units with world-wide correlation has been devised; hence they are commonly lumped together as *Precambrian*. Yet the accumulating evidence indicates that these rocks represent at least 85 per cent of geologic time. The complex record in these ancient rocks will provide research materials for future generations of geologists.

Although the classification of rock units and time

Table 4—1. Standard geologic column

Records in rocks		System	Series	Stage	Distinctive records of life
Cumulative column of sedimentary deposits, marine and continental	**C E N O Z O I C**	Quaternary	(Recent) Pleistocene	More than twenty widely recognized	Development of man
		Tertiary	Pliocene		Dominance of elephants, horses, large carnivores
			Miocene		Development of whales, bats, monkeys, horses
			Oligocene		Grazing animals widespread, grasses abundant
			Eocene		Primitive horses
			Paleocene		Rapid development of mammals
	M E S O Z O I C	Cretaceous	Two or more series in each system. Not standardized world-wide	About thirty widely recognized	Extinction of dinosaurs and ammonites. Development of flowering plants
		Jurassic			Climax of dinosaurs Earliest record of birds
		Triassic			First primitive mammals Conifers and cycads abundant Appearance of dinosaurs Rapid development of reptiles
	P A L E O Z O I C	Permian		Many recognized. Wide correlation improves as evidence accumulates	Development of conifers Spread of reptiles
		Pennsylvanian (Upper Carboniferous)			Earliest primitive reptiles Abundant insects Coal-forming forests widespread
		Mississippian (Lower Carboniferous)			Echinoderms abundant Spreading of fish faunas
		Devonian			Appearance of amphibians Earliest forests
		Silurian			Earliest record of land plants and animals
		Ordovician			Primitive fishes, the first known vertebrates
		Cambrian			Marine invertebrate faunas abundant. Trilobites predominant

PRECAMBRIAN
Complex assemblage of rocks, largely meta-morphosed. No systematic subdivisions that are widely recognized

Wide distribution of simple marine plants

Table 4–2. The scale of time

Relative dates				Absolute dates (in millions of years before the present)*	Relative lengths of major time divisions, to actual scale
Eras	Periods	Epochs	Ages		
CENOZOIC	Quaternary	(Recent) Pleistocene		— 1 —	⊢ Cenozoic
	Tertiary	Pliocene		— (13) — — —	Mesozoic
		Miocene		— (26) — — —	Paleozoic
		Oligocene		— (40) — —	
		Eocene		— — — —	
		Paleocene			
				— 70	
MESOZOIC	Cretaceous			(100) — — —	
	Jurassic		An epoch for each recognized series in the geologic column. Names of epochs and corresponding series are identical		
			An age for each recognized stage of geologic column	(190) — — —	
	Triassic				
				— 220 —	Precambrian time (Approximately 4,000 million years)
PALEOZOIC	Permian			— — —	
	Pennsylvanian			(290) — —	
				— — —	
	Mississippian			(340) — —	
	Devonian			— (400) — —	
	Silurian			— — —	
	Ordovician				
	Cambrian			(510)	
				— 550 —	

PRECAMBRIAN TIME

No systematic subdivisions

Canada { (1,100)
{ (1,400)
{ (2,750)

Rhodesia (2,910)

* Figures for absolute dates shown in parentheses are among the most reliable determinations from radioactive minerals. Figures without parentheses are approximate dates for the beginnings of the three eras and the Pleistocene Epoch.

63

divisions is accepted generally, some disagreements on matters of detail persist. National geological surveys continue to use the names *Tertiary* and *Quaternary* for divisions of the Cenozoic Era, but some individuals insist that these terms have outlived their usefulness and should be supplanted. Commonly, the record and time interval following the Pleistocene is designated the *Recent,* a series and epoch in its own right. Some geologists argue, however, that the Pleistocene probably is not ended and that widespread glaciation may be renewed after a brief geologic interval. From a human point of view this is not an attractive possibility.

In using tables of geologic history, we must keep in mind that subdivisions are in final analysis artificial. Time runs continuously; we divide it into hours, years, and geologic periods only for convenient reference. Passage from one geologic period to another was gradational, just as in our analysis of human history there is an insensible blending from ancient to medieval to modern.

SUMMARY

1. General reasoning favors the concept that the solar system is very old.
2. Rocks exposed in and near the Grand Canyon hold records of tremendous physical changes and of progressive radical development of plants and animals. This record suggests an immensely long history.

3. Isolated fragments of history recorded in thick sections of annual sedimentary layers and in fossil forests suggest a great total length of geologic time.

4. Disintegration of radioactive elements provides an accurate clock for measuring geologic time. Ages of the oldest rocks dated by this method exceed 3,000 million years.

5. Different minerals and methods are used for dating very old and comparatively recent geologic events. The isotope Carbon 14 has yielded dates through the last 60,000 years.

6. Relative ages indicated by the sequence of sedimentary strata provide a useful check on radiometric dates.

7. A scale of geologic time, developed and tested over more than a century, divides the known history of the Earth into major and minor segments that have world-wide significance. Each division is identified by a record of distinctive living forms.

8. Numerous rock masses that have been dated radiometrically have places in the scale of time, though it is not yet possible to state absolute age brackets for any division of the scale.

REFERENCES

Darton, N. H., 1917, Story of the Grand Canyon, Grand Canyon, Arizona: Fred Harvey.

Dunbar, C. O., 1960, Historical geology, 2nd ed.: New York, John Wiley and Sons.

Holmes, Arthur, 1937, The age of the Earth: London, Thomas Nelson and Sons.

Knopf, Adolph, 1949, The geologic records of time, Time and its mysteries (Ser. 3): New York Univ. Press.

————, 1957, Measuring geologic time: Scientific Monthly, vol. 85, p. 225–236.

Libby, W. F., 1956, Radiocarbon dating: American Scientist, vol. 44 p. 98–112.

CHAPTER 5. FIELD STUDY AND GEOLOGIC MAPPING

Importance in geology   *Units for mapping*   *Geologic dating*   *Structure of bedrock*

Earliest geologic maps   *Continuing revisions*   *Cooperative efforts*

Sedimentary formations perfectly exposed on north side of Lake Mead, 5 miles west from mouth of Grand Canyon, Arizona.

(Courtesy A. G. Boynton, U. S. Bureau of Reclamation.)

Purpose of field study

The basic materials of geology are the rocks in the Earth's crust. These materials are out-of-doors or, as phrased by geologists, "in the field." Geologic study of an area begins with field work, to determine the kinds of rocks present, forms and sizes of masses of each kind, and relations of these masses to each other. Ordinarily, a thorough study also requires laboratory examination and analyses of critical samples collected in the field. A first requirement, however, for accurate interpretation by the field worker himself, and to serve as a permanent record of his results, is a map showing the essential geologic features in as much detail as possible. Large numbers of publications issued by geological organizations contain accurate geologic maps, and the eventual goal is to provide maps of this kind for the entire land surface of the Earth.

Geologic field equipment

A first essential for accurate field study and mapping is a *base map* of the area to be studied, preferably one that shows altitudes of the land surface. Such maps, known as *topographic maps,* are explained in Appendix C. For different areas the available maps vary widely in scale, in spacing of contours, and in detailed representation of accurately located surface features, for example, stream courses, hilltops, roads, and buildings. The geologist makes use of such details for accurate mapping of critical geological features such as exposed contacts of adjacent rock masses. Even if his base map is quite accurate, he must have some instrumental aid for entering his critical data on the map.

Finding precise locations on the map commonly requires both horizontal and vertical measurements and determination of directions. Generally, two geologists divide the duties and join efforts in some operations such as measuring with a steel tape. An indispensable instrument is *a specially designed magnetic compass and clinometer* known as a **brunton** (from the name of its designer), which is used to determine directions and to measure angles of inclination (Fig. 5–1). Instruments commonly used for checking altitudes and for measuring thicknesses of rock units are a *hand level* (Fig. 5–2) and an **altimeter** (ăl-tĭm′ĕ-tĕr), the latter *a highly accurate barometer.*

Vertical air photographs, available for large parts of North America, are useful either as a substitute for base maps or as a supplementary aid in locating detailed features (Fig. 5–3). For especially accurate mapping, or to provide control in areas not supplied with good base maps, the *plane table* and *telescopic alidade* may be necessary. This kind of mapping requires one man to operate the instrument and sketch the map, and at least one other to select critical points on the ground and to hold a *stadia rod* for instrumental determination of map locations and distances.

What a geologic map shows

Geologic formations. Bedrock units chosen for representation on the map are shown by distinctive colors or patterns. These basic map units are *formations.* A *formation is the basic unit of geologic mapping, consisting of a persistent sequence of strata of one kind of rock or of closely related rocks.* Thus in Figure 5–4 two of the sedimentary formations are the Tapeats Sandstone and the Bright Angel Shale. The first part

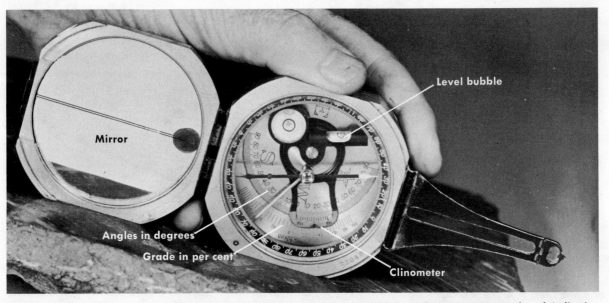

Fig. 5–1. With a brunton ("pocket transit") a geologist measures angles of inclination. When the level bubble is centered (by using a lever on the back of the case), the angle is read in degrees on the inner semicircular arc, in per cent on the shorter scale below. Compass directions are read on the large outer scale when the instrument is held face up and level. The adjustable mirror is an aid in sighting on selected points.

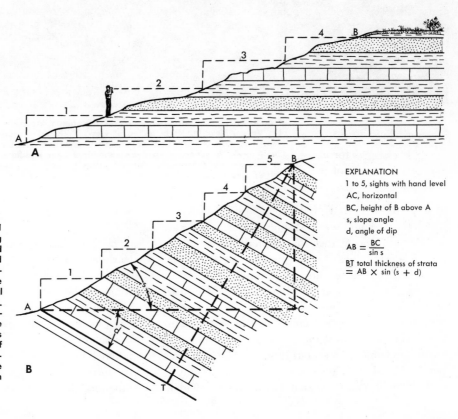

Fig. 5–2. A hand level is used in measuring heights along slopes and thicknesses of layered rocks. In **A** thicknesses are found directly. In **B** a simple trigonometric computation uses the angle of dip and the vertical distance between critical points. The observer determines accurately the height of his eye above the ground, and multiplies this figure by the number of "sights." If he carries an altimeter instead of a hand level, he computes differences between readings at critical points.

EXPLANATION
1 to 5, sights with hand level
AC, horizontal
BC, height of B above A
s, slope angle
d, angle of dip
$$AB = \frac{BC}{\sin s}$$
BT total thickness of strata
$= AB \times \sin (s + d)$

Fig. 5–3. Vertical air photograph of Frenchman Mountain and associated ridges, east of Las Vegas, Nevada. North at top of view. Thick sedimentary formations are inclined steeply east-southeast. Note distinct offsetting of formation boundaries by large faults. The largest fault marks a generally east-west boundary near middle of view, with an abrupt change in structure and topography. Highest points in area more than 2,000 feet above lowland at left of view. Scale, 1.5 in. = 1 mile. (U. S. Geological Survey.)

of each name is that of the geographic locality in which the rock unit was first studied; the second part signifies the kind of rock that is predominant in the unit. If several types of rock—for example sandstone, shale, and limestone—are interlayered to make up a mappable unit, the term *formation* is used instead of a rock-type designation; the Supai Formation in the area of Figure 5–4 consists of sandstone and shale. This general rule for formation names is standard in the United States, but in some other countries purely descriptive names are common; for example, in England a sandstone that has been used widely

for making large grinding stones is called *Millstone Grit*.

The formations represented in Figure 5–4 are clearly exposed (Fig. 5–5, **A**). Regolith covers large parts of the land surface, and in mapping a given formation the geologist may see actual bedrock only in widely separated valleys (Fig. 5–5, **B**), in artificial pits, or in drill cores. He must then infer from all available evidence the continuity of a given formation between known exposures. Where sedimentary formations are nearly horizontal and exposures numerous, as in the Colorado Plateau, the problem

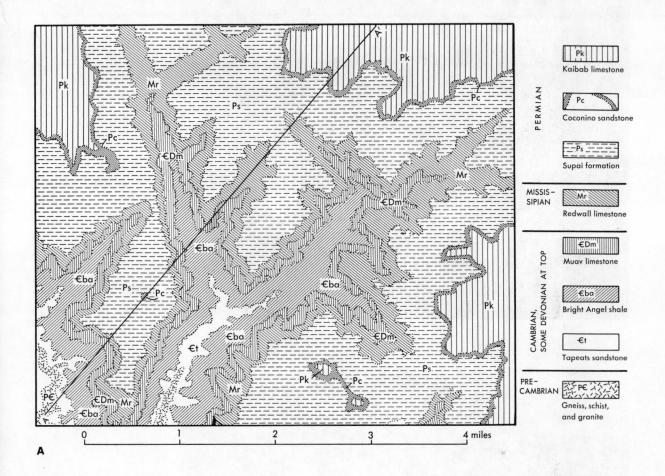

A

		Pk — Kaibab limestone
		Pc — Coconino sandstone
	PERMIAN	Ps — Supai formation
	MISSISSIPPIAN	Mr — Redwall limestone
		€Dm — Muav limestone
	CAMBRIAN, SOME DEVONIAN AT TOP	€ba — Bright Angel shale
		€t — Tapeats sandstone
	PRE-CAMBRIAN	P€ — Gneiss, schist, and granite

0   1   2   3   4 miles

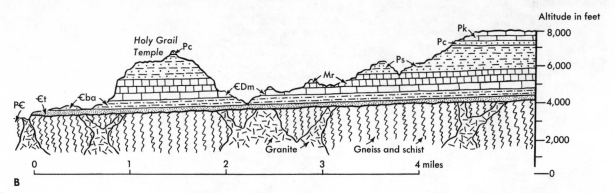

B

Altitude in feet — 8,000 / 6,000 / 4,000 / 2,000 / 0

Holy Grail Temple — Pc, Pk, Ps, Mr, €Dm, €ba, €t, P€, Granite, Gneiss and schist

0   1   2   3   4 miles

Fig. 5—4. A. Geologic map of an area on the north side of the Grand Canyon, Arizona. The original map is on a topographic base, with contour interval 50 feet. Contours are omitted here to avoid confusion of lines. Patterns of the older formations outline the principal valleys, which open to the south and southwest. No symbols showing strike and dip are entered because the formations are nearly horizontal. This area is part of the Shinumo Quadrangle, studied and described by L. F. Noble. (From Bulletin 549, U. S. Geological Survey, 1914.) **B.** Structure section along the line A-A' on the map. Vertical scale same as horizontal. The deep gorges, with nearly perfect exposures of bedrock, reveal the complete section of sedimentary rocks. Average dip of sedimentary layers in the section is about 3°.

Fig. 5–5. **A.** Almost continuous exposure of rock formations in the cliffs bordering the Grand Canyon. The view, from Point Sublime on the North Rim, shows in foreground a spur north of the canyon with Bright Angel Shale at the base, remnants of Coconino Sandstone and Kaibab Limestone at top (see Fig. 5–4). Top of view shows south side of canyon, with Kaibab Limestone beneath the even plateau surface. (Josef Muench.) **B.** In this soil-covered area in Monterey County, California, bedrock is exposed only in scattered cliffs and beds of streams. Layers of rock inclined to the left are partly exposed at upper right. (Courtesy A. N. Strahler and U. S. Forest Service.)

is simpler than in wide areas that have a nearly continuous cover of soil. *The area on a geologic map shown as occupied by a given rock unit* is known as the **outcrop area** of that unit. Under this definition, an outcrop area is the area in which a given rock unit forms the highest part of the underlying bedrock, whether or not it is visible. A part of the bedrock not hidden by regolith is an exposure.

Geologic age of formations. An important objective in the geologist's field work is good evidence of the geologic date of each rock unit shown on his map. In Figure 5–4 the column headed *Explanation* shows the proper position of each formation in the scale of geologic time (Table 4–2). Evidence for this important part of the mapping was given by fossil remains of extinct animals and plants. Such evidence is much more plentiful in some formations than in others. The Kaibab Limestone, the uppermost—and therefore youngest—formation shown in Figure 5–4, records a wide spreading of the sea during the Permian Period, near the close of the Paleozoic Era. Little effort is required to find proof that the limestone is of marine origin. Abundant forms of shells, representing animals of kinds now found only in the sea, are conspicuous in almost every large exposure of the formation in the Colorado Plateau, throughout an area measuring thousands of square miles. Specialists in paleontology, the scientific study of ancient life, recognize in the Kaibab Limestone an assemblage peculiar to Permian rocks in North America and other continents.

Satisfactory dating of the Supai Formation has been more difficult. Deposits making up this unit consist of sand, silt, and clay, in layers like those now being spread out by running water in lowlands. The hard parts of animals and plants that die on land decay completely unless they are buried quickly under water-soaked deposits, as in a stream bed. Fossils found in the Supai Formation, chiefly petrified parts of plants, are not abundant, and many of them are fragmentary. Continued field research and study of the plant remains by expert students of *paleobotany—the study of ancient plants*—has been required for assigning the formation to its proper place in the scale of time.

Formations lower in the section contain marine fossils distinctive of older Paleozoic systems.

Structure of bedrock

Normally, sedimentary layers are almost horizontal when they are formed, and in much of the Grand Canyon district the original altitude of layers has been little disturbed. In many areas, however, especially in mountain belts, layers have been bent and tilted to all degrees up to the vertical. Thus in Figure 5–6 the layers exposed in a prominent ridge are inclined at a 30° angle from the horizontal. An important function of a geologic map is to indicate the attitudes of the formations represented.

Dip and strike. In the language of geology the layers shown in Figure 5–6 have an eastward *dip*. A *dipping* layer is an *inclined* layer, and **dip** is *the angle of inclination of an inclined surface measured downward from the horizontal*. In his work of mapping a geologist measures many dips, using the clinometer of his brunton (Fig. 5–1). In recording these measurements, he sets down not only the amount but also the *direction* of dip. Let us examine the steps in this operation.

If an inclined layer, or group of layers, has superior resistance to erosion, it stands up as a ridge, like that in Figure 5–6. Such a crest of uniform height represents the **strike,** defined as *the direction of the line of intersection between an inclined surface and a horizontal plane*. This is a logical term because the up-

Fig. 5–6. Edges of resistant sedimentary layers with steep dip make a *narrow-topped, asymmetric ridge* (**hogback**). Weaker layers on either side have been eroded to form the lower surface. View northward, near Denver, Colorado. (Courtesy of Karl M. Waagé.)

standing edges of beds strike across country. If an inclined layer extends along the shoreline of a lake, the horizontal line at the intersection of the water surface with the dipping layer gives accurately the direction of strike. Any other horizontal line drawn on the inclined layer is, of course, parallel to the shoreline, and the compass direction of such a line is the value of the strike. If this direction is 20° east of north, the value is recorded as N 20° E.

The direction of dip is exactly at right angles to the strike, as an inspection of Figure 5–7 makes clear. A line on the inclined surface through d^1 and oblique to the strike is inclined, but the *maximum* inclination on the surface is along the line perpendicular to the strike and passing through d. The inclination of the line through d^1 is a *partial dip*. If the bedding surface is perfectly plane, the full value of the dip is the angle between the bed and the surface of the lake, as measured in a vertical section at right angles to the strike. The front of the diagram (Fig. 5–7) is such a section, and the measured dip is 32°.

The water surface in our illustration is, of course, just a convenient device for showing relations of lines and angles. With his brunton a geologist measures strikes and dips wherever the bedding is well exposed and plots each value in the proper position on his map. If the values are those given in Figure 5–8, **A**, he determines the location on his map and with a protractor draws through the point a short line with the direction of strike (N 20° E). At right angles to this line he draws an intersecting line point-

ing in the direction of dip, as shown in the figure. This direction need not be measured with the brunton; it is 90° clockwise from the strike, or 70° east of south (S 70° E). We say, then, that the beds dip 32° S 70° E: 32° is the angle of dip, measured in the vertical plane downward from the horizonal, in the compass direction 70° east of south.

The method commonly used in the United States and Canada for describing and recording the directions of lines is shown in Figure 5–8, **B**; it is the *quadrant* method. Each quarter of the full circle is graduated 0 to 90°, laid off to the right and left of

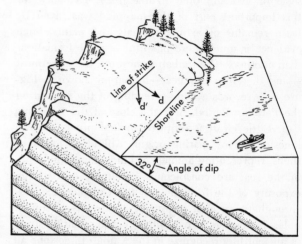

Fig. 5–7. Strike and dip of layers are defined by a surface of standing water. Arrows show directions of the full dip, *d*, and a partial dip, *d'*.

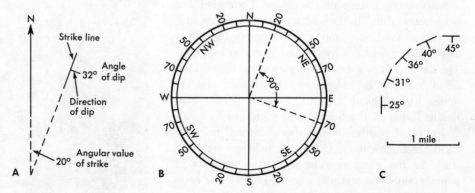

Fig. 5–8. A. Explanation of the map symbol for strike and dip. **B.** Graduations of the four quadrants of the compass. The strike and dip values of **A** are indicated by broken lines. Some compasses are graduated through the full circle, 360°, to the right from N. On such a compass the direction of dip would be 110° (equivalent to S 70° E by the quadrant method). **C.** Readings on a layer with changing strike and dip.

true north in the upper quadrants, to the right and left of true south in the lower quadrants. In the diagram (Fig. 5–8, **A**) dashed lines show the directions of strike (N 20° E) and dip (S 70° E). Direction of strike is always stated in relation to north, not south.

Some compasses are graduated through the full circle, 0 to 360°. A direction from such an instrument is the full angle read clockwise, with north at 0°.

This explanation is made step by step, at the risk of seeming technical, because the strike and dip of rock surfaces are fundamental to an understanding of geologic features in the field and their representa-

tion on maps. The pattern of strike-and-dip symbols on a good map gives at a glance a general picture of the structure in sedimentary beds. Several readings on the top of a sandstone bed, as plotted in Figure 5–8, **C**, show that within a mile the outcrop curves from north to east and the dip steepens by 20°. If this bed had beneath it a continuous layer of valuable coal, this information about the structure of the rocks would have large practical as well as scientific interest.

Reflection of structure on maps. In addition to information given by dip-and-strike symbols, patterns

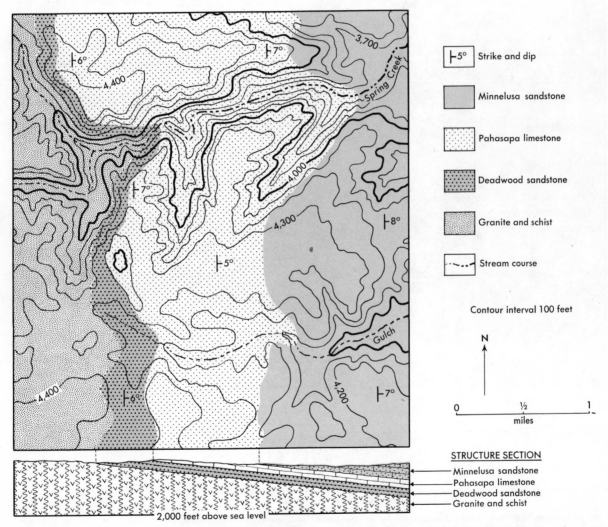

Fig. 5—9. Geologic map of an area near Rockerville, South Dakota. The structure section is along the south border of the map. (Modified from Black Hills Folio, No. 219, U. S. Geological Survey.)

73

on maps made by boundaries of formations reveal general types of structure. When the layers are nearly horizontal the formation boundaries are essentially parallel to contours; along valleys, the older formations come into view progressively downstream and boundaries between formations wedge out upstream, as shown in Figure 5–4. Uniform dip of layers parallel to the slope of the ground, but at a somewhat steeper angle, presents a different pattern; as shown in Figure 5–9, the boundaries between formations cross contours and outline wedges that point *downstream*. A localized uplift in the form of a dome, with some removal of rocks by erosion, results in a circular or oval pattern (Fig. 5–10).

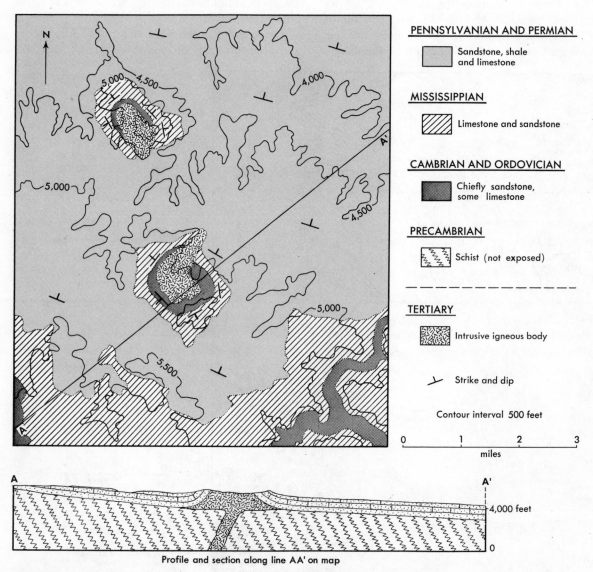

PENNSYLVANIAN AND PERMIAN

Sandstone, shale and limestone

MISSISSIPPIAN

Limestone and sandstone

CAMBRIAN AND ORDOVICIAN

Chiefly sandstone, some limestone

PRECAMBRIAN

Schist (not exposed)

TERTIARY

Intrusive igneous body

Strike and dip

Contour interval 500 feet

0   1   2   3
miles

Profile and section along line AA' on map

Fig. 5–10. Geologic map and section northwest of the Black Hills, near Spearfish, South Dakota. Two intrusive igneous bodies are well exposed at the surface, and around the margins of the exposures the sedimentary layers have been turned up steeply. This structure indicates that the upper part of each igneous mass is dome-shaped; but the form at depth, as represented in the structure section, is speculative. Symbols indicate directions but not values of dips. (From Folio 219, U. S. Geological Survey.)

Structure sections. A map represents the uppermost part of the bedrock in an area. If the surface is rugged, as it is along the Grand Canyon, bedrock is exposed locally to considerable depth. The third dimension has large importance in geology, and geologic maps are usually accompanied by one or more vertical sections. *A structure section represents what would be seen in the wall of a deep, straight trench running in any desired direction.*

The general method of constructing geologic sections is illustrated in Figure 5–11 by ideal examples. Four identical hills are represented by the oval-shaped areas in *A*, *B*, *C*, and *D*. Contours at 20-foot intervals show altitudes up to 80 feet. A distinctive layer of sandstone, represented by the pattern, is horizontal in *A*, dips oppositely in *B*, and *C*, and is offset along a vertical fracture in *D*. How would the edge of this layer appear in the wall of a vertical east-west trench across each hill? Below the map we construct a grid of horizontal lines, spaced to represent the contours. Dashed vertical lines are drawn from each contour on the map to corresponding lines on the grid. By connecting the points of intersection, we construct an east-west profile of the hill. Next we draw dash-dot lines from borders of the outcropping layer to intersect the profile on the grid. By connecting points on the profile that represent, respectively, the top and bottom of the layer, the structure section of the layer is completed.

Since the hills have identical form, construction lines for making the topographic profile are shown for *A* only. On the identical profiles for *B*, *C*, and *D*

the lines dropped from lower and upper boundaries of the outcropping layer give points required for completing the structure sections.

The structure section with the map in Figure 5–4 is drawn confidently. Deep canyons expose all the formations in many parts of the general area, showing that each maintains essentially uniform thickness and nearly horizontal attitude. Likewise, in constructing the section shown in Figure 5–9, there is no reasonable doubt that the layers extend downward with uniform dip, since the dip of all layers is essentially the same in the entire width of their outcrop. In some regions with low relief and few exposures of bedrock the construction of a structure section may involve considerable speculation. Records kept in drilling numerous deep wells, as in the oil-producing areas of Illinois, Oklahoma, and Texas, give information for reliable structure sections.

Mapping igneous and metamorphic rocks

Rocks of sedimentary origin are most satisfactory for mapping because generally they have regular layering and are divisible into distinctive formations with wide distribution. Moreover, these units usually contain fossils by which they are dated geologically; thus they may be correlated with other formations far away, even in other continents.

Some volcanic rocks occur in widespread sheets that superficially resemble sedimentary layers (Fig. 5–12). These sheets consist in part of lavas, in part of volcanic ash and breccia. In some districts it is possible to map these units separately, just as sedi-

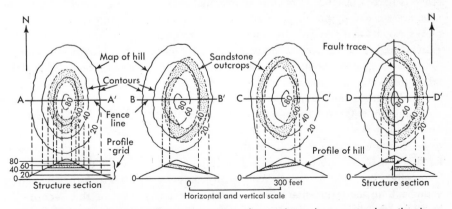

Fig. 5–11. Geologic map and structure section of a sandstone layer exposed on the slopes of a rounded hill. Four possible attitudes of the layer are shown. **A.** Layer horizontal. **B.** Layer dipping east. **C.** Layer dipping west. **D.** Layer horizontal, but broken and offset.

Fig. 5–12. Thick section of volcanic rocks in southern Nevada. View looking northeast. Beds of lava, tuff, and volcanic glass, all dipping about 30° east. The small butte on skyline, right of center, is about 4 miles from camera. These volcanic rocks are like sedimentary formations for mapping. (C. R. Longwell.)

mentary formations are mapped. Exceptionally, the layers of ash contain distinctive fossils, but usually volcanic rocks can be dated geologically only by their relation to associated sedimentary units. In many volcanic fields the lavas and fragmented materials, erupted from a number of centers at irregular intervals, are mixed in hopeless confusion. Such complexes can be mapped only as general assemblages, without regard to the various kinds of volcanic rock.

Intrusive igneous bodies exposed at the surface are highly varied in form and in their relation to associated rocks. Commonly, they cut across some older sedimentary units and have areas of outcrop that range widely in shape and in size. Those large enough to be shown clearly to the scale of the map are outlined and marked with distinctive colors or patterns. Generally, they can be dated geologically only as younger than the sedimentary formations transected by them and older than any deposits of known date

that were laid down on them. Many intrusive bodies contain radioactive minerals from which *absolute dates* have been determined (p. 57).

Metamorphic rocks commonly are the oldest rocks in the areas in which they are exposed. Usually they have complex structure, are not divisible into distinctive units, and so are represented on a map by a uniform color or pattern. In many mountain zones the "basement complex," consisting of metamorphic rocks intermixed with small bodies of granite or other intrusive rock, is mapped as a unit (Fig. 5–9).

Some structure sections show inferred relations at depth, with an aim to explain features that are visible. Thus Figure 5–10 represents a channel through which molten igneous material supposedly moved from a deep source to form an intrusive body of granitic rock that is seen at the surface. Only the upper part of this section is based on what can be seen within the immediate area; the lower part is based on evidence found some miles to the east, where, in the broad Black Hills uplift, all sedimentary formations have been swept away by erosion and the deep-seated "basement" rocks are widely exposed.

Progress in geologic mapping

Pioneering efforts. The concept of geologic mapping, first expressed near the start of the nineteenth century, developed quickly after it was realized that distinctive sedimentary units could be recognized over wide areas by study of the fossil asemblages in them. Two French naturalists, Cuvier and Brongniart, used this principle in making the first map of central France, published in 1810. During the same period an English surveyor, William Smith, discovered that a sequence of sedimentary rocks, exposed in the banks of canals in southeastern England, could be correlated over a wide area by means of distinctive fossils in each of several units. After many years of labor he completed the first geologic map of England, published in 1815. This accomplishment marks a major advance in geologic science.

A geologic map of eastern United States, by William Maclure, was published in 1809 and thus antedates the early French and English contributions. Maclure's map, however, was much more generalized and less accurate than the first maps of Cuvier and Smith.

Early reconnaissance mapping. During most of the nineteenth century great areas of the United States were unknown geologically, and much field work was necessarily of an exploratory nature. Attention of geologists was devoted to the larger and more obvious features and relationships. Most mapping was of small scale and without benefit of base maps with contours. Even today large fractions of some states have not been surveyed topographically or have only maps of small scale, each sheet covering a full degree of latitude and longitude (nearly 4,000 square miles). This situation is being improved rapidly by the development of new techniques in making contour maps with the aid of air photographs.

Even with the best equipment, the making of good geologic maps proceeds slowly, and for large areas of the country available maps are much generalized. A published geologic map of the entire United States has the scale 1:2,500,000 (about 40 miles to the inch). A map with this scale can display only the major geologic features and relations.

Continuing revision. A geologic map, like any other human product, is always subject to improvement. Bedrock is complex, and some significant features may escape notice even in a careful survey. Moreover, some interpretations are changed in the continual advance of geologic science. Therefore, no geologic map can be accepted as wholly accurate or complete. Figure 5–4 is part of a map that illustrates this point. Published in 1914, this map was the earliest to present in detail the geology of a part of the Grand Canyon. The precipitous slopes make field work difficult, and in thick successions of layers that look much alike it is not easy to find the fossils critical for dating every part of the section. Readers will note that three Paleozoic systems listed in Table 4–1 are not represented in Figure 5–4; these are the Ordovician, Silurian, and Devonian systems. In later field work some fossils of Devonian age were found in a small thickness of limestone between the Muav and Redwall Limestones. No rocks dated as Ordovician or Silurian have yet been reported, after intensive search, from the Grand Canyon district. Their absence may mean either that the sea did not cover this area during those periods or that deposits laid down in that long interval of time were removed by erosion before the marine invasion in the Devonian period.

Other changes in details of the map have come about from later studies of fossils in the higher formations of the section. Explanation of these changes would only emphasize the point that geologic maps are subject to change.

Team work in geologic research

No one geologist, however able and well trained he may be, can solve all the problems he encounters in the field. Cooperation of men with varied training and the aid of modern equipment are required for most effective results. A large organization, such as the United States Geological Survey or a company engaged in mining or oil production, is manned and equipped to help a field geologist make the best use of his materials. Certain minerals and rocks may require analysis by specialists; fossils of two or more types may be studied most effectively by experts in different aspects of ancient life. Moreover, some geologic problems go much deeper than the superficial zone that is open to direct inspection. Techniques

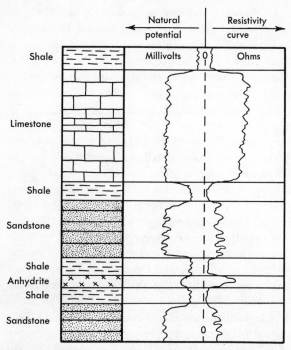

	Natural potential			Resistivity curve	
Shale		Millivolts	0	Ohms	
Limestone					
Shale					
Sandstone					
Shale					
Anhydrite					
Shale					
Sandstone			0		

Fig. 5—13. Two electric logs (*right*) of a drilled well, made by different methods. Both logs show a close relation to kinds of rock determined by examination of the drill core from the well. The variations are distinct enough to justify correlation from one well to another, on the basis of similar electric logs, where no drill cores are available. (Modified from K. K. Landes, John Wiley and Sons.)

have been developed for getting certain kinds of information about the rocks deep underground. The *seismic* (sīs′mĭk) method, based on principles worked out in the study of earthquakes, is used successfully in choosing some locations favorable for oil and gas production (Chap. 22). Companies devoted exclusively to the practice of this method may be employed to make tests in aid of geologic studies. Other companies specialize in the use of the *gravity meter, a delicate instrument that reveals slight differences in the pull of gravity* from place to place, which may suggest concealed bodies of rock that are exceptionally heavy, such as iron ore, or exceptionally light,

such as rock salt. Another technique in common use employs the *magnetometer* (măg-nĕ-tŏm′ĕ-ter), *an instrument that detects areas with abnormal magnetic attraction.* With a "flying magnetometer" mounted in an airplane, skilled operators can make preliminary surveys of large areas in a short time. Oil companies make extensive use also of *electric logging* in studies of deep wells; varying resistance to an electric current indicates differences in the kinds of rock penetrated by a well, and from a graphic record made by an ingenious mechanism the operator can determine the kind of rock present at every level (Fig. 5–13).

These technical devices are in no way magical. At best, they serve only as aids in exploring the bedrock beneath us; but their value is increasing as more sensitive instruments are developed and as experience points out new ways to apply them. A number of important oil fields have been located and known fields extended from information supplied by the seismic and gravity techniques, and these methods will no doubt be used extensively in further exploration for oil offshore under the continental shelves (Chap. 22).

SUMMARY

1. The making and use of geologic maps are fundamental in geologic study.

2. A geologic map depicts important units of bedrock and indicates their geologic dates.

3. Structure of bedrock is shown by standard symbols on the geologic map and by vertical sections.

4. Construction of geologic sections is based on visible evidence and on reasonable inference.

5. The first geologic maps were made near the start of the nineteenth century.

6. Geologic maps are subject to constant revision as new evidence becomes available.

7. Study of visible geologic features and relations is supplemented by devices that detect some physical conditions deep in the crust.

REFERENCES

Dutton, C. E., 1882, Tertiary history of the Grand Canyon district, with atlas: U.S. Geol. Survey, Monograph 2.

Lahee, F. H., 1961, Field Geology, 6th ed.: New York, McGraw-Hill Book Co.

CHAPTER 6. IGNEOUS GEOLOGY

Volcanoes in action   Varied types of eruption   Records of past volcanism   Exposed roots of volcanoes   Plutonic igneous bodies   Thermal waters and gases   Puzzles of igneous geology

Attempt to divert a flow of lava from the village of Kapoho, Hawaii.
(Underwood & Underwood.)

Volcanoes and volcanic rocks

A newborn volcano. In February 1943 people living in the mountain land 200 miles west of Mexico City were alarmed by frequent earthquakes. Each day for more than a week the number of tremors increased, and on February 19 about 300 were counted. Next day a farmer, Dionisio Pulido, while he worked in his field heard noises like thunder, though the sky was clear. He saw that a crevice had opened in the ground, and from this narrow opening arose a small column of "smoke"—actually vapor and fine dust—with an odor of sulfur. That night strong explosions began at the vent, and coarse rock debris was thrown up, some of it red-hot. At daybreak the vent was marked by a cone-shaped mound, more than 30 feet high, through which in violent bursts large fragments of rock were hurled high into the air. Successive explosions came only a few seconds apart, and a great cloud of fine rock dust mixed with vapor arose continuously to a great height (Fig. 6–1). The coarser particles rained down on the flank of the cone and built it up at the rate of tens of feet in a day.

At night the young volcano presented to Pulido and his neighbors an awesome spectacle. Much of the rock material blasted upward was incandescent. In their rapid trip through many hundreds of feet upward and down again, the small particles cooled, but the larger masses kept their glow, curved over in their courses like giant Roman candles, and on striking the steep surface of the cone came bounding and sliding down in great streaks of flame. Large numbers of these masses measured as much as 3 to 5 feet in diameter, many others, 10 to 15 feet, and exceptional blocks, 40 to 50 feet. With bursts coming at short intervals, particles from several explosions were in the air together, in various stages of

upward and downward flight, and inevitable collisions added to the turmoil.

As the conical hill grew visibly in height and width, a new actor entered the drama. Liquid rock broke through the ground near and beneath the growing cone to form swelling lava flows that moved slowly outward along small valleys. Where it emerged, the hot glowing liquid flowed like molten steel from a blast furnace; but, as it moved away, rapid cooling formed a crust of dark rock with a rugged surface. Continued movement of live lava beneath broke this crust into large blocks, between which the red fluid gushed out in local streamlets. As it advanced, the forward part of each main flow became entirely solid and piled up in a jumble of blocks as it was pushed along slowly by pressure of the flowing liquid. These moving dams caused the crusted streams to deepen and widen into veritable lakes. As successive streams broke forth at intervals of several weeks or months, those of earlier date cooled to sheets of dark rock that became partly or wholly covered by later flows (Fig. 6–2). The largest lava flow, which spread to widths greater than a mile, advanced six miles by a roundabout path to overwhelm the largest town in the district (Fig. 6–3).

Pulido's farm and many others were now gone forever; but with machine-like rhythm the young volcano continued its heartless way. Close-spaced explosions kept a great cloud boiling up, and although outpourings of lava breached the cone and made changes in its form, the unending shower of rock particles mended these wounds and ensured rapid growth. Within a month the height was more than 550 feet, and on its first birthday the vigorous infant was about 1,000 feet tall. The diameter in-

Fig. 6—1. Day and night at Parícutin Volcano in 1943, a few months after its birth. The lava flow was moving slowly, though in the view its top and front appear solid. (Otto Brehme and W. F. Foshag.)

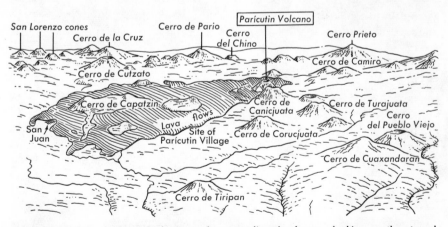

Fig. 6—2. Sketch showing Parícutin and surrounding landscape, looking southeastward. Cones of extinct volcanoes similar to Parícutin are distributed over a wide region. The area covered by lava flows from Parícutin up to August of 1947 is indicated. (Modified from Howel Williams, U. S. Geological Survey.)

Fig. 6–3. A. San Juan Parangaricutiro, the largest town near Parícutin Volcano, was completely overridden by lavas except for the towers of the church. (Tad Nichols.) B. Rubble front of a slowly advancing flow from Parícutin Volcano. (Fred M. Bullard.)

creased steadily with the height, but the steepness of slope remained almost constant. With this over-all expansion of the cone, the particles blown upward came down on a larger and larger surface area, and, although in its second year the volcano was as active as in its first, it had gained only 100 feet in height. But desolation of a wide surrounding territory was intensified. Fine rock particles carried by changing winds slowly settled into a layer of volcanic ash, thickest in an area around the cone (Fig. 6–4) but in suffocating amounts over many hundreds of square miles. Numerous towns and villages and great numbers of country houses became uninhabitable. All vegetation, including forest trees, within a radius of several miles from the cone, was killed.

Parícutin Volcano, so named for the closest of the villages buried by its lava and ash, performed zealously for about nine years and became an active laboratory for geologists. All written human history records the beginnings of only a few volcanoes, and information about most of those earlier than 1943 is meager. Skilled observers were in the vicinity of Parícutin from the third day after its birth through several years, setting down every significant event, measuring temperatures of lavas and rates of lava movement, noting changes in intensity of explosive activity, and even recording, by mechanical devices, the frequency of the explosions and the variety of noises coming from the cone. All these facts, added to the store of information already in hand from the study of older volcanic centers, helped to outline the full case history of a volcano and to clarify the meaning of all igneous activity.

In studying Parícutin, geologists learned that hundreds of closely similar cones, all now extinct, dot the surface of a surrounding area 300 miles long and 50 to 60 miles wide. One of these older cones, Jorullo, born in 1759, was explosively active, gave forth lava flows much like those of Parícutin, and grew to about the same size. The active career of Parícutin seems to be at an end, but other volcanoes like it can be expected to appear in its general neighborhood in future centuries. A comparative study of cones in the group suggests that Parícutin acted as the most recent safety valve over a great chemical cauldron in which energy has been generated slowly for a long period of time.

Nature of volcanic action. Every volcano has individual traits, and several classes of volcanoes are recognized. Yet, basically, there are only two kinds of volcanic action: uprush of gases under high pressure, and outflow of liquid rock. Both kinds of action have been important in Parícutin and in the large majority of known volcanoes; but at some volcanic centers one or the other action predominates. Abundant evidence indicates that molten rock below the surface is highly charged with gases, which stay in solution as long as the mass is held under strong pressure, just as gas remains unnoticed in a sealed bottle of carbonated water. Probably molten rock working its way upward beneath the site of Parícutin began moving blocks of the solid crust and thereby caused the warning earthquakes. The magma carried gases in solution, and its heat turned to steam any water in the overlying rocks. Fractures in these "roof rocks" allowed some of the gases to escape upward and to form the thin column of "smoke" seen by the Mexican farmer. Gas crowding into pockets in the fractured rock built up bursting pressures, and explosive activity began, first blowing out fragments of the solid rock but soon including masses of the molten material. Gases rushing to the escape hatch dominated the early activity; but they cleared the way for the liquid rock, and the lava flows started. Gases still held in the liquid continued to separate out while the liquid cooled, as evidenced by gas cavities or vesicles that make the surface of the solid lava spongy. The term lava flow does double duty;

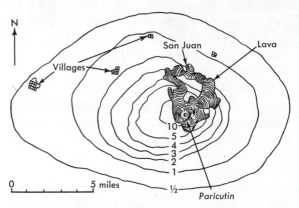

Fig. 6–4. Distribution of ash around the Parícutin cone after two years of activity. Numbered lines show thicknesses in feet. Lava flows cover shaded area. (Modified from Howel Williams and Adán Pérez Peña.)

it is applied to the flowing sheet of liquid, and to the resulting layer of solid rock. We speak of "old lava flows" that are recognized in Connecticut, in northern Ireland, and in many other lands now entirely free from volcanic activity.

The difficulty of defining exactly some terms in common use is illustrated by the word *volcano* itself, which to many people suggests primarily a conical mountain. Yet Parícutin surely was a full-fledged volcano the first day it operated, before any appreciable cone was built; the essential part of it is the system of *vents* or pipes leading from an underground reservoir of molten rock to the Earth's surface. The lavas, which form a large share of the new rock brought to the surface at Parícutin,[1] came in considerable part from openings near but outside the base of the cone. This volcano, therefore, has a number of vents, through one of which rock fragments were thrown up to build a conical mountain; through the same vent and other openings poured a vast amount of liquid rock that spread out widely in nearly flat sheets. Each of many other volcanoes has several vents, close together and clearly related in their action; we suppose that they branch from one central pipe at some depth or lead separately from one body of magma.

A *volcano,* then, is *a vent or a group of closely spaced vents, through which hot gases and rock materials pass from a deep-seated source to the Earth's surface*. Commonly, but not invariably, the rock materials passed through a vent have built up a *volcanic cone,* or *mountain,* which then is the conspicuous part of the volcano. Mount Etna in Sicily is a high mountain built by a volcano that is still active; Mount Rainier in the State of Washington is a somewhat higher mountain built by a volcano now either extinct or dormant. Every well-developed volcanic cone has near its top a *volcanic crater, a funnel-shaped depression out of which fragments are thrown during explosive eruptions*. Some lava flows emerge through the crater; others break through the side of the cone or emerge from fissures beyond its base.

Volcanic products. The volcanic factory turns out a wide variety of products, but these are included in

[1] The total weight of cinders, blocks, and ash erupted during nine years was estimated at about 2,500 million tons; the weight of lava, at about 1,500 million tons.

a few general classes. Materials come from the vents in the form of gases, liquids, and solids. Samples of gases, taken with special equipment at Parícutin, Vesuvius, the Hawaiian volcanoes, and other stations, contain 60 to more than 95 per cent superheated steam. Surely a large part of this steam comes from the ground water contained in pore spaces of the rocks (Chap. 11) through which the magma slowly works its way upward. But some free hydrogen among the volcanic gases speedily unites with oxygen in the air to make water vapor. Probably, too, some *water* that had been *joined with other mineral matter deep in the crust is brought up in the magma to become part of the hydrosphere for the first time;* this is *new* or *juvenile water* (p. 110). The total quantity of water released by an active volcano is enormous; it was estimated that Parícutin, at the height of its activity in May 1945, gave off 16,000 tons of water daily, along with 100,000 tons of lava. Rapid condensation of water vapor during violent eruptions has caused destructive floods, which were added to the other woes of the occasion for all living things in the neighborhood.

Second in abundance to steam among volcanic gases is carbon dioxide. Sulfur, combining with oxygen of the air, makes some of the gases deadly. Some volcanoes emit chlorine and its kindred element fluorine, and others yield boron, the essential element of commercial borax.

Liquids flowing from volcanic vents are the hot lavas that have made vast quantities of rocks. Except for loss of gases, the lavas are samples of the parent magmas, and as such they merit particular attention in a general study of volcanic rocks. There is great diversity in chemical composition, but a general classification of lavas recognizes (1) those high (65 to more than 75%) in content of silica, such as rhyolite (p. 42); (2) those with low (50% more or less) silica content, the basalts; and (3) those with intermediate (55 to 60%) content of silica, of which andesite is typical. Some volcanoes specialize in one or another of the three general kinds of lava, but at many vents there have been radical changes in composition from one eruption to another.

Solid materials thrown out by volcanoes include blocks and finer particles torn and blasted from the older rocks through which the vents pass. The large, angular pieces of such rocks are easily identified among the fragments making a volcanic cone or included in lava flows. But fine particles of the older bedrock are hopelessly mixed with those made of the liquid rock blasted into the air by violent explosions in a vent. Much of the material that has come down solid directly on a cone, or as fine ash carried afar by winds, started as liquid or semiliquid rock, was blasted to bits, and cooled to the solid state in its rapid flight through the air. Sizable clots of such material, whirled rapidly through the air like pinwheels, have become *volcanic bombs,* which are *rounded, spindle-shaped masses of hardened lava* (Fig. 6–5). Their twisted forms indicate rapid rotation in the air while the material was plastic. No doubt many of them, while still luminous, made part of the night display over Parícutin.

Standard terms are used for the ejected volcanic particles. *Volcanic fragments more than 32 mm. (1¼ in.) in diameter* are either *blocks* or *bombs.* Angular forms of *volcanic blocks* suggest that they are *fragments of lava that was almost or wholly congealed when it was blasted from the vent.* Exceptional blocks and bombs range up to 60 tons or more in weight. *Volcanic fragments between 32 and 4 mm. in diameter* are *cinders; smaller fragments* are *ash particles.* The terms *cinders* and *ash* reflect a widespread early belief that volcanoes mark sites of underground combustion. Now we know that both terms are illogical, but we accept them as fixed by long usage.

Mediterranean volcanoes. Historical records through the centuries tell us that Stromboli, a volcano on one of the Lipari Islands north of Sicily, has performed much as it does now since the days of ancient Rome. Moderate explosions occur at intervals of 10 to 15 minutes, hurling lumps of red-hot lava into the air above the crater; the glow from these masses, appearing with regularity and visible afar to men on ships, has earned for this volcano the friendly title "Lighthouse of the Mediterranean." In strong contrast is the behavior of a famous neighbor, Vesuvius, on the Bay of Naples about 140 miles to the north. The ancestor of Vesuvius was Monte Somma, which until the first century A.D. was thought to be extinct. Starting in the year 63, frequent strong earthquakes shook the surrounding country, and 16 years later the historic eruption that destroyed Pom-

Fig. 6–5. Pile of eight volcanic bombs, ranging in size, gathered within a radius of 100 feet on the slope of a cone in Hawaii. The twisted spindle-shaped form is best displayed in the third bomb above the base of the pile. (C. K. Wentworth, U. S. Geol. Survey.)

peii and other communities blew away a large part of the old mountain, including the southern rim of its great crater (Fig. 6–6, **A**). In the following fifteen centuries Vesuvius erupted strongly only ten times, with long intervening periods of quiet. After a violent outbreak in 1631, the volcano took on its modern habit of nearly continuous mild activity, interrupted at intervals ranging from 10 to 40 years by spectacular outbursts, the latest in 1944. Each of these major eruptions has yielded vast quantities of fragmental materials and large lava flows.

The sustained regularity of Stromboli is exceptional; the highly irregular activity of Vesuvius is generally more characteristic of known volcanoes. Parícutin began with the rhythmic precision of a drum beat, but after a few years its activity became varied and erratic. The underground mechanism of a volcano is no doubt complex and unstable and may be thrown out of adjustment by the violence of its own explosions. Also the physical and chemical conditions that generate the gas-charged magma may be changed during a major eruption, and after a long time they will reach equilibrium, with extinction of the volcano.

Vesuvius has been studied longer than any other volcano; an observatory high on its slope has been manned by trained observers for many decades and is provided with all essential equipment, including precision instruments for recording and analyzing earthquakes related to eruptions (Chap. 20). The bedrock of a large surrounding area has been mapped in detail, and it is known that thick sedimentary lay-

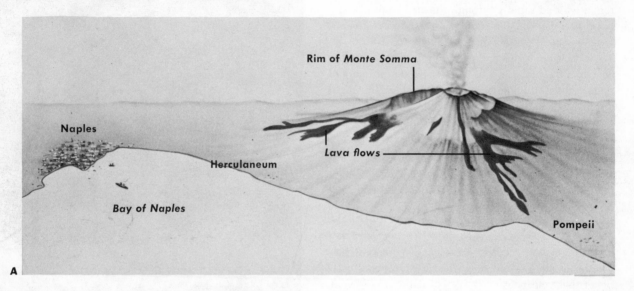

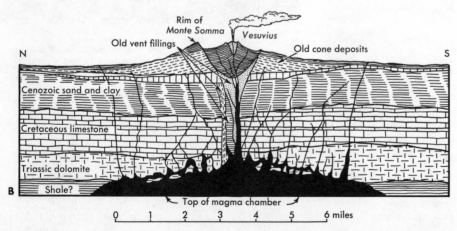

Fig. 6–6. A. Idealized view of Vesuvius and its surroundings. Pompeii and Herculaneum, near the base of the mountain, were buried by the eruption of Monte Somma in A.D. 79. **B.** Vertical section showing general relation of Vesuvius to the older volcano. The sedimentary formations are known accurately from regional geologic studies. Depth to the magma chamber has been determined instrumentally at the observatory. (After A. Rittmann.)

ers, including much limestone, are steeply inclined on the flank of the Apennine Mountains several miles to the east but are nearly horizontal beneath the volcanic rocks around Naples. Blocks of these limestones and other well-known sedimentary rocks are thrown up in great numbers by explosive activity and extruded in the lavas of Vesuvius. Evidence of several kinds indicates that the top of the magma chamber is in the limestone, about 3 miles below the base of the volcano (Fig. 6–6, **B**). Dissolving of limestone ($CaCO_3$) in the hot magma would explain the exceptionally high content of carbon dioxide (CO_2) in the gases of Vesuvius. Accumulation of CO_2 over the years may have turned the upper part of the magma chamber into a gigantic bottle of soda pop, with high explosive potential.

Two other Italian volcanoes illustrate the varied behavior of individual vents. Vulcano, in the Lipari Islands south of Stromboli, was the supposed chimney of the forge tended by the Roman god Vulcan. It is intermittently active, and between eruptions the stiff lava in its crater becomes entirely solid, as if the volcano were dead. The next outbreak comes abruptly as a violent explosion that blasts the old lava crust to pieces and hurls them into the air along with masses of stiff new lava which descend as bombs.

Etna, in the eastern part of Sicily, has the largest of the Mediterranean cones; it is more than 10,000 feet high, and its base, nearly circular, is more than 25 miles in diameter. The lower part of the cone, with its gentle slopes, was built up almost entirely of lavas. Higher and steeper parts of the mountain have increasing proportions of fragmental materials, but in its long history the cone has not grown entirely by eruptions from the central crater; its slopes are dotted with about 200 secondary vents, many of which have built up sizable cones of their own. These vents occur along great fractures that radiate out from the central part of the mountain. Many recorded eruptions have broken through the flanks at various heights. In 1928 explosions, with "smoke" clouds, started on the northeast slope, and lava streams broke out from twelve centers at successively lower levels along a line that extended from altitudes of 9,200 feet down to 3,700 feet; these streams merged and flowed many miles into the lower country, overwhelming a good-sized town and smaller communities. Altogether, the lavas

Fig. 6–7. Nuée ardente from Mont Pelée, in 1902, flowing to the sea. Vent is concealed in right background. Height of cloud is about 2.5 miles. (A. Lacroix.)

covered an area of 2 square miles, and their total volume is estimated at about 200 million cubic yards, or 1/27 cubic mile. The total volume of Etna's cone is about 215 cubic miles; hence the flows of 1928, vast though they seem to us, represent only 1/58 of one per cent of the entire mountain.

Nuées ardentes. The explosive violence of Vulcano and Vesuvius has been exceeded in the eruptions of several other volcanoes. Mont Pelée, on the island of Martinique in the West Indies, after more than 50 years of quiet came to life in 1902 with a succession of major explosions that continued for several months. With each burst, a great cloud of superheated vapor and incandescent rock material rushed forth and flowed down the mountain slope at estimated speeds as high as 2 miles per minute (Fig. 6–7). This incandescent material was lava blasted to bits but retain-

Fig. 6–8. A small sample of the utter ruin in the city of St. Pierre after it was swept by a nuée ardente in 1902. All vegetation was destroyed on surrounding hills. (Underwood and Underwood.)

ing enough heat to give the clouds a bright glow and to melt all glass[1] in their paths. One cloud swept through St. Pierre, capital of Martinique, on the shore 5 miles from the volcano (Fig. 6–8). All buildings and all but two of the 28,000 people in the town were destroyed; one of the fortunate survivors was a prisoner in a dungeon. In the harbor ships were turned over in a churning sea that literally boiled. Great numbers of fishes and other marine animals died in the hot water.

Since 1902, students of volcanoes have applied the term nuée ardente ("fiery cloud") to the kind of volcanic pall that swept over St. Pierre. During the eruptions the crater of Pelée was choked with a plug of stiff lava, and the explosions shot either obliquely upward or were almost horizontal; this accounted for the high speeds of the clouds along the ground. Ash from ordinary eruptions either settles quickly to the

[1] Glass is softened enough to flow at a temperature near 700° C.

ground or floats upward and disperses. But the Peléan cloud, heavily charged with hot particles of rock, was much denser than air, and therefore the lower part of the mass, where the density was greatest, hugged the ground like a flowing liquid. Turbid masses of this kind flowing through water are called *turbidity currents* (p. 292), and this term may well be extended to include fiery volcanic clouds.

The front of a moving nuée ardente is indeed turbulent. Witnesses have described the forward part of the cloud as a billowing mass, its base hugging the ground as the higher parts swirl upward, with a boiling motion, to heights more than 10,000 feet. A logical explanation is the continuous entrapment of cold air by the advancing front. This air, rapidly heated, expands, and thus supplies energy for the continued turbulence. Testimony to high energy in the moving cloud is given not only by the volume of total load spread along the path but also by the large size of some components of the load. Individual blocks 10 to 25 feet in largest dimension have been moved as far as 10 miles. Probably such masses have been urged along, in a hopping, sliding fashion, by the billowing forward part of the cloud.

Ten years after the great outbreak at Pelée, Mount Katmai, on the Alaskan Peninsula, erupted in similar fashion and on a much larger scale. There, as at Pelée, the ash and larger rock fragments consisted of frothy pumice, indicating that the magma under the volcano was excessively charged with gas. Fortunately, no large settled community was in the path of the Katmai cloud. Dust from this eruption was carried high in the air and settled on lands around the globe. After the Katmai eruptions, a large surrounding area in which countless columns of vapor continued to rise was named the Valley of Ten Thousand Smokes. This area is now the largest of our national monuments.

Another volcano of the Peléan type, in the Philippine Islands, has the double name Hibok Hibok; it erupted in 1951. Widespread deposits around a number of extinct volcanic centers are strikingly similar to the products of these modern eruptions; one excellent older example is Crater Lake, Oregon, described in a later paragraph. Thus this kind of volcanic action has been fairly common, not exceptional. Moreover, the materials erupted are not closely restricted in composition; they range from high silica content, like that of rhyolite, to a silica content almost as low as that of basalt. The essential condition seems to be an exceptionally high build-up of gas in the magmatic chamber when eruption occurs.

A nuée ardente, then, is *a very hot cloud of magmatic material blasted at a low angle from a volcanic vent, from which it rushes downslope, with intense turbulence in its frontal part.*

Calderas. Crater Lake in Oregon occupies an enormous pit, almost circular in plan, inside the steep circular rim of a blunt, conical mountain (Fig. 6–9, **B**). Rocks bordering the lake are lavas and layers of ash, inclined steeply outward. Remnants of small valleys on the steep outer slope of the mountain bear clear testimony that they were once filled with glacier ice moving from heights vertically above the present lake. A wide surrounding area is covered with ash and larger fragments of pumice. This is convincing evidence that a great volcanic mountain similar in form and height to Rainier in Washington and Shasta in California once towered above the site of the lake (Fig. 6–9, **A**). After tremendous eruptions, the summit of the mountain collapsed, leaving a pit nearly 5 miles in diameter and 3,000 feet deep, inclosed by precipitous walls (Fig. 6–9, **C** and **D**). A volcanic crater enlarged to this general form is a *caldera;* the

type, La Caldera, is the great circular pit in the Canary Islands. We define a *caldera* as *a volcanic crater enlarged to a diameter of several miles.* Characteristically, the nearly circular pit is bounded by a high, precipitous cliff, as at Crater Lake.

A wide area around Crater Lake has thick deposits consisting of pumice in unassorted fragments, large and small. Some of the largest, up to 14 feet in diameter, are 20 miles from the caldera. Apparently the great volcano ended its activity with a phenomenal outburst of nuées ardentes, accompanied or followed by subterranean withdrawal of magma from the feeding chamber (Fig. 6–9, **D**). Wizard Island in the present lake is a cone representing final weak volcanic activity after the upper part of the mountain collapsed (Fig. 6–10, **A**).

Aniakchak Caldera, Alaska, is remarkably like the basin of Crater Lake in form and size. A valley has been cut through the rim of Aniakchak, and therefore it does not contain a deep lake (Fig. 6–10, **B**).

Shield volcanoes of Hawaii. The islands of the Hawaiian archipelago, rising out of the deep Pacific basin, are made almost entirely of basaltic lavas, with only minor amounts of fragmental material. These rocks are well exposed in high wave-cut cliffs and on the flanks of high volcanic domes, many with old

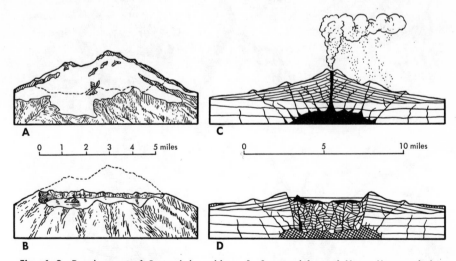

Fig. 6–9. Development of Crater Lake caldera. **A.** Supposed form of Mount Mazama before the collapse. **B.** Present appearance, with former profile in dotted line. **C.** Ideal section through entire mountain during final period of activity. **D.** Section after mountain collapsed and underlying magma cooled (A and B modified from W. W. Atwood, Jr.; C and D after Howel Williams.)

A

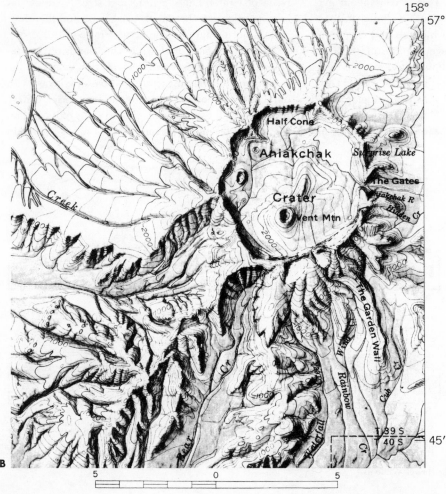

B

Fig. 6–10. A. View east across Crater Lake, Oregon. Wizard Island, in foreground, is a cone built after the caldera was formed by collapse of Mount Mazama. (John O. Sumner, Monkmeyer Press Photo Service.) **B.** Aniakchak Crater, on the Alaskan Peninsula, is a caldera similar in form and size to Crater Lake, though a valley breaching the rim prevents formation of a deep lake. Note the two small interior cones similar to Wizard Island. (Part of the Chignik, Alaska, topographic map, U. S. Geological Survey.)

vents at their tops and scattered over their slopes. The Island of Hawaii, largest of the group and at the southeast end of the long chain, has the only volcanoes now active: Mauna Loa, with its summit 13,680 feet above the sea, and Kilauea at about 4,000 feet (Fig. 6–11).

The Hawaiian Islands, consisting of eight large and dozens of small islands, lie in a remarkably straight chain, nearly 1600 miles long, trending northwest-southeast (Fig. 6–12). Although many small islands in the northwestern part of the group are in their visible parts coral reefs, doubtless these also, be-

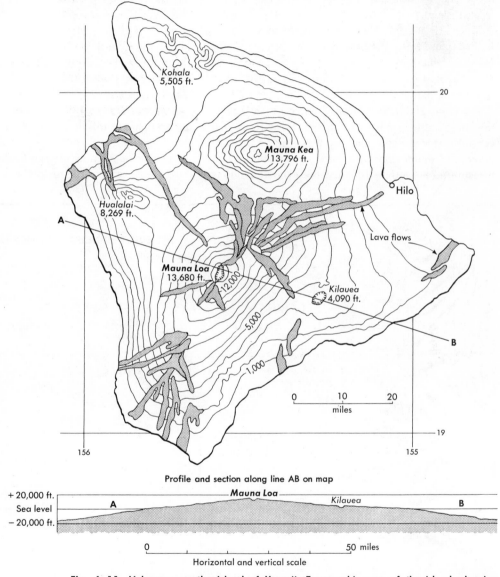

Profile and section along line AB on map

Fig. 6–11. Volcanoes on the Island of Hawaii. Topographic map of the island, showing the five major volcanic centers and the principal lavas erupted between 1750 and 1950. Contour interval 1,000 feet. (*Below*). Profile and section along the line *A-B*. This volcanic mass, which extends much farther below sea level than shown in the diagram, has an estimated volume of about 10,000 cubic miles. (After H. T. Stearns and G. A. MacDonald.)

low the superficial reef caps, are piles of volcanic rock. Suggestion is strong that the islands represent a chain of volcanoes along a zone of weakness in the floor of the Pacific Ocean. Geologic study indicates that the building up of the islands was, in general, progressive from the northwest to the southeast end of the long chain. As shown in Figure 6–11, **B**, the ocean depth is nearly 20,000 feet around Hawaii, the largest island, and high points on the island reach to nearly 14,000 feet. Therefore this volcanic pile is higher than Mount Everest. The gentle slopes of the Hawaiian mass carry down to a very broad base, and thus its total volume is enormously greater than that of the part above sea level.

No large Hawaiian volcano, active or extinct, is marked by a steep-sided cone. Slopes away from each central crater are long and gentle, outlining a broad dome. Maximum slopes on the flanks of Mauna Loa measure no more than 10°, and the average angle is considerably less (Fig. 6–11, **B**). Mauna Loa, therefore, has not built a mountain but a wide plateau gently convex upward, in a form suggesting a shield. The term *shield volcano* is appropriate in the Hawaiian Islands, Iceland, and Samoa, where this form of volcanic structure is common. The basaltic lavas that have built up the broad domes are exceptionally fluid when they emerge and therefore spread out in thin sheets before they harden. Many flows of Mauna Loa have not issued from the central crater but from vents far out on the flanks (Fig. 6–11, **A**); the result has been further broadening of the dome.

A ***shield volcano,*** then, is *a volcano that emits fluid lava which spreads to build up a broad edifice, convex upward, with a surface slope of only a few degrees.* This term, like some others applied to volcanoes, actually relates only to land forms resulting from volcanic action and not to the eruptive apparatus. A pile of volcanic rock, always impressively visi-

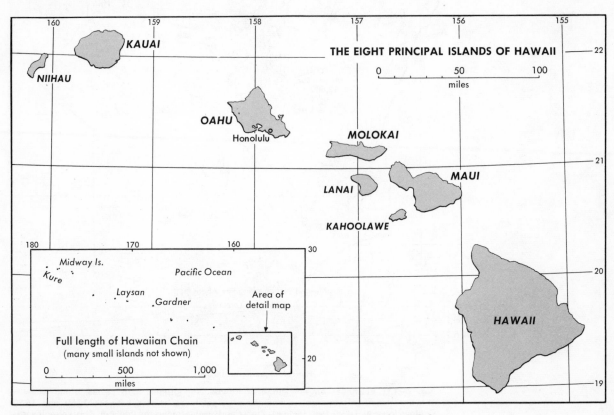

Fig. 6–12. The principal islands of the Hawaiian Chain, with outline of entire chain. Only a small part of the basaltic lava making these islands is visible. A far greater part is below sea level, as shown in Figure 6–11, **B**.

ble, is in popular parlance *a volcano*, even if there is no longer any evidence of volcanic activity.

Mauna Loa and Kilauea have large calderas with almost vertical walls, as shown in Figure 6–13, which were formed by the dropping of great blocks along fractures. The behavior of Kilauea, continuously recorded at an observatory in operation since 1912, indicates that a body of magma beneath the volcano sometimes presses upward and at other times is lowered. Strains from these movements break the over-

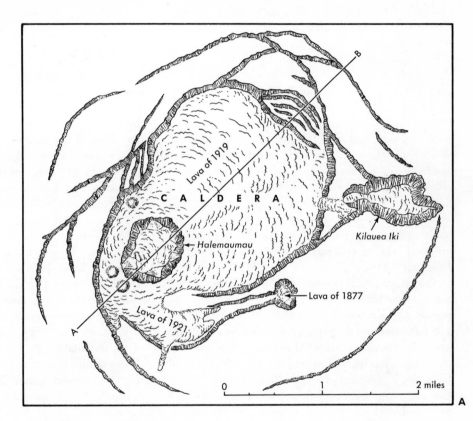

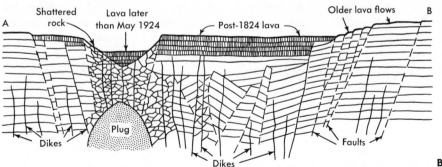

Fig. 6–13. Kilauea in plan and section. **A.** Diagrammatic view from above showing the main caldera and related pits. The deep pit Halemaumau was formed mainly by a great explosive eruption in 1924. The pit Kilauea Iki was a scene of much activity during the eruption of 1959-1960. **B.** Vertical section along the line *A-B*, showing general structure of successive lavas and suggesting the location of a plug beneath Halemaumau. (After H. T. Stearns and G. A. MacDonald.)

lying rocks, and when the magma goes down considerably the unsupported blocks directly above it drop tens or hundreds of feet (Fig. 6–13, **B**). Abrupt lowering may occur when magma is drained out as lava flows on the slopes of the volcanic dome far below sea level. An important recording instrument is a *tiltmeter*, which indicates accurately the uplifts and depressions within the area on which the observatory is located.

The main caldera at Kilauea has in its floor a much deeper pit, Halemaumau, the center of nearly all recent activity at this volcano. In 1919 lava welled up to the brim of Halemaumau and poured out over the floor of the caldera (Fig. 6–13, **A**). The column of lava then sank, and for some years the floor of the pit was a boiling lake of liquid rock. In 1924 this lake was suddenly lowered several hundred feet; water held in cracks in the surrounding rock drained down into the hot pit, and the resulting steam caused a tremendous explosion which blasted out quantities of rock in the walls and greatly enlarged the pit. This explosive eruption was exceptional in the known history of Kilauea.

Two other pits connected with Kilauea have been active since 1868 (Fig. 6–13, **A**). One, Kilauea Iki, played a prominent part in the strong eruption of 1959–60. Because these pits and the caldera itself are generally circular or elliptical in plan, we reason that the magma has worked its way up, at each of several locations, in the form of a cylindrical column. Mauna Loa also has a main caldera and a number of related pits, and each of the five volcanic centers on the island is on a long belt marked by dozens of old calderas and smaller pits that now seem to be extinct. Probably these belts lie along vertical fractures, each tens of miles long, up which magma has been working its way for a long time, with shifts in positions of vents for outflow of lava.

Kinds of volcanic cones. The steep cone of Parícutin is made wholly of rock fragments, large and small, which lie at the angle of repose for this material. Thousands of such cones are known, nearly all of which are small or of moderate size. Many that stand on the flanks of large volcanic mountains represent temporary "leaks" of magma along fractures that soon became filled and never again operated as vents. At the opposite extreme, in substance and in form, is the immense lava shield of Mauna Loa (Fig. 6–14, **A**). Vesuvius has a **composite cone;** this is *a cone made partly of fragmental materials from explosive eruptions, partly of lava flows*, as we know from the record of its activity since the new cone was started in A.D. 79. Many other major volcanoes have had similar histories, and large numbers of old cones, in various stages of destruction by erosion, display flows alternating with layers made up of cinders, bombs, and ash (Fig. 6–21).

Slopes of a typical composite cone are steepest near the summit and decrease outward to the base (Fig. 6–14, **B**). This form is determined largely by the fragmental materials. During an explosive eruption most of the coarse blocks and bombs and the large cinders fall near the vent to form a stable slope as steep as 40°. Some of the smaller cinders are carried somewhat farther out, whereas ash settles in a large radius but in decreasing amounts outward (Fig. 6–4). Lavas that emerge from the central crater flow down the steep upper part of the cone. If they are highly fluid, they continue to move until a large part of their volume spreads out on the lower slopes; viscous lavas congeal on the steeper upper slopes (Fig. 6–15). Much of the lava breaks through the flanks of the cone at various levels, as in the 1928 eruption of Etna, and so adds nothing to the steep upper part of the mountain.

The addition of lavas makes a steep volcanic mountain stronger and more resistant to erosion than cones built wholly of fragmental materials. Ash and cinders make smooth, steep slopes, and excavations show remarkably uniform layering in flanks of a cone built of these small fragments (Fig. 6–16). But without reinforcement by addition of some lavas, these materials are subject to rapid erosion.

Wide differences in the forms of cones are not accidental; they reflect, in part, differences in composition of magmas, especially in their content of silica and gases. Molten rhyolite, high in silica, is stiff and often resists movement through vents until it is blasted out by accumulating gas pressure. Basaltic magmas are low in silica and usually produce lavas that flow freely. A majority of the great volcanic cones are composite, and the rocks in them are predominantly andesite, containing only average amounts of silica. At high temperatures molten andesite flows readily,

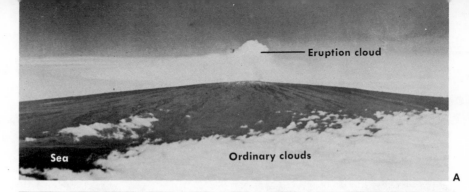

Eruption cloud

Sea   Ordinary clouds

A

Fig. 6—14. Contrasting forms of volcanic mountains. **A.** Gentle slopes of the Mauna Loa shield, as seen from the air. The part of the shield in view is about 30 miles across. Summit is nearly 14,000 feet above sea. (U. S. Army Air Force.) **B.** Mayon Volcano is an exceptionally symmetrical composite cone in the Philippine Islands. Width of base about 15 miles, altitude of summit 7,916 feet. (Courtesy American Museum of Natural History.)

B

Fig. 6—15. Atitlan and Toliman Volcanoes, Guatemala. Lake Atitlan in foreground. Composite cones, with flows of stiff andesite lava on slopes in foreground. Note forms of superposed flows at right and flow near center bordered by conspicuous "levees." (U. S. Air Force, courtesy Howel Williams.)

Fig. 6–16. Volcanic ash as deposited in the flank of a cone near Cerro de Camiro, Mexico. This material is subject to rapid erosion. (K. Segerstrom, U. S. Geol. Survey.)

but with cooling it stiffens; therefore, temperature and the content of gases probably determine whether an andesite volcano at a given time will erupt explosively or with outflow of lavas. Even basalt, if highly charged with gases, becomes explosive and builds up *cinder cones, small to moderate-size cones made of clinkery volcanic debris* (Fig. 6–2). Material erupted at Parícutin, all of it basalt, emerged partly as quiet flows and partly as fragments blasted out to build a sizable cinder cone.

Fissure eruptions. Iceland, which has an area of more than 40,000 square miles, is made entirely of volcanic rocks, nearly all basalt. Several shield volcanoes, some of which lie along great fractures, resemble those of Hawaii. In 1783 lava poured out along a fracture about 20 miles long, extending generally northeast to southwest. Immense lava streams flowed as much as 40 miles from one side of the fracture and nearly 30 miles from the other side. This lava covers an area of 218 square miles, and its estimated total volume is about 3 cubic miles; it represents the greatest volcanic eruption recorded in human history.

A volcanic outburst along an extensive fracture is

a *fissure eruption.* Possibly some of the Hawaiian eruptions started in this way, and later the outflows became restricted to separate vents.

Plateau basalts. Several continental tracts of vast extent have been flooded with basaltic lavas. One of these, covering parts of five states in our Pacific Northwest (Fig. 6–17, **A**), has a total area of about 200,000 square miles. The Snake and Columbia rivers have cut deep canyons that expose lava thicknesses as great as 4,000 feet. Individual flows average only 15 to 40 feet thick but have very wide extent; therefore, the molten basalt must have been highly fluid and very hot when it was poured out. The lavas buried a rugged old land surface, filling deep valleys and covering all but the highest ridges and peaks and producing a vast plateau that is now being dissected by streams. *Basaltic lavas that accumulate to form a wide plateau* are called *plateau basalts.*

Another great accumulation of basalt flows covers 250,000 square miles in India (Fig. 6–17, **B**), and remnants scattered over a wide area suggest that this plateau was twice as large before erosion destroyed much of it. Plateau basalts on a similar scale lie in Basutoland, Africa, and in the Paraná Basin of South America. Probably much of the lava in each of these great plateaus came not from central vents but from long fissures. The upbuilding was a slow process. Fossils found at many levels show that soils were formed, forests grew, and animal life flourished between successive episodes of eruption.

Kinds of volcanic rocks. The record of past volcanic activity is written in rocks that are highly distinctive. Ash and coarser fragments have become cemented into firm rock masses, commonly after some sorting and spreading out by running water. Lavas assume varied forms. The forward part of a long flow cools and hardens but is broken into blocks by pressure of the moving fluid farther back (p. 80); later these blocks may be cemented together. Escaping gases commonly make the upper part of a flow porous or frothy, perhaps to a depth of several feet; this characteristic feature is one of the best for recognizing an old flow. Surfaces of some cooling basaltic lavas are made very rugged by gas action, others are smooth, with local ropelike ridges (Fig. 6–18)

Many old basalt flows have separated into rounded bodies shaped like and known as *pillows.* Some spaces between adjacent pillows are filled with ma-

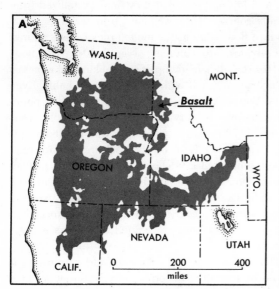

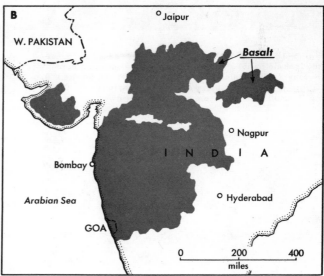

Fig. 6–17. Two great fields of basaltic lavas. **A.** Plateau basalts in northwestern United States. (From Geol. Map of United States, U. S. Geol. Survey) **B.** Plateau basalts in India. (After H. S. Washington.)
Original areas of exposed basalt have been much reduced by erosion and by concealment under a cover of younger sedimentary deposits.

A

B

Fig. 6—18. A. Lava of the smooth variety known as *pahoehoe* (pah-hō′ ā-hō′ ā). On some parts of the surface it hardens in ropy folds. (Miller, Monkmeyer Press Photo Service.) B. Surface of rough, porous lava known as *aa* (ah′ ah′). (G. A. MacDonald.) Both views are on Island of Hawaii.

Fig. 6—19. Upper part of a basalt lava, covered by layers of younger limestone. The pillows indicate that the flow entered water, probably shallow sea, and the sedimentary layers were deposited on the uneven surface. Note that some of the white deposit filled spaces between pillows. Aleutian Islands, Alaska. (Harald Drewes, U. S. Geol. Survey.)

terial like that in underlying sedimentary layers, and layers containing fossils of animals that lived on floors of seas or lakes lie directly above some pillows (Fig. 6–19). Flows that entered the sea from Pacific islands in recent years have been seen to divide into typical pillows. Hence we conclude that pillows result from immersion of hot lava in water and that old lavas with pillow structure flowed into water bodies or across swampy ground. Basaltic lavas have been erupted on ocean floors in immense quantities, and doubtless the flows there are replete with pillows.

Less than 200 years ago it was widely believed and taught that all basalt was deposited in the sea, as a chemical precipitate. This concept seems ludicrous to us now, with our heritage of observations and reasoning by generations of careful workers; but the most influential teacher of his day, A. G. Werner (1749–1817) of the still famous Freiberg Mining Academy in Germany, was convinced that nearly all rocks, including granite, were precipitated from a "primitive universal ocean." He was especially sure that basalt was formed in this way because sheets of basalt commonly are divided into columns that tend to be six-sided. Werner accepted these as huge hexagonal crystals shaped like those of quartz (Fig. 3–6, A), and he supposed that they had crystallized from a water solution. Now we know, from watching modern lava flows, that as the molten rock cools it shrinks and divides into columns (Fig. 6–20). We know, too, that basalt is made up of several kinds of minerals in tiny grains, each with its own crystal habit. Even while Werner's theory was at the height of its popularity, a quiet, observant Frenchman, Nicolas Desmarest (1725–1815), published the results of his long geologic study of the bedrock in the Auvergne region, now cited as a classic example of the plateau basalts. On evidence that has stood up under all later research, Desmarest concluded that the Auvergne, known also as the Central Plateau of France, had gone through a long and varied history as a great volcanic field.

Though we may find Werner's ideas amusing, it would be repeating his error to assume that we now have most of the answers. Surely students of the future will smile at some geologic theories that today are published widely and looked on with much favor. Trial and error are essential in a growing science.

A

B

Fig. 6–20. A. A flow of basalt, vesicular and uneven at the top, columnar in lower part. This flow, south of Hoover Dam on the Arizona side of Colorado River, lies on unconsolidated sediments, geologically young. (C. R. Longwell.) **B.** Part of the Giant's Causeway, in Northern Ireland. An extensive, thick sheet of columnar basalt is exposed to erosion by waves. (British Information Services.)

Distribution of volcanoes. Scenes of volcanic activity have shifted widely during the Earth's history. Ancient volcanic rocks are well exposed in many parts of eastern Canada and in other continental areas now thousands of miles from any active vents. Nearly all modern volcanoes, in company with large numbers that seem to be extinct, occur in long and rather narrow belts. The most conspicuous of these belts occur around the borders of the Pacific Ocean, both on the marginal parts of the continents and on long island archipelagoes. Many high peaks of the Andes Mountains are cones of active volcanoes, including Cotopaxi (19,498 feet), the world's highest volcanic mountain that still erupts. The common rock *andesite* got its name from this belt. Central America and Mexico have numerous volcanoes, and in western United States several lofty peaks, notably Shasta and Rainier, may be slumbering before renewed action, though only Lassen Peak in California has a record of eruption in the present century. From Alaska the great Aleutian chain of volcanoes reaches toward Asia, and the western part of the Pacific teems with active vents as far south as New Zealand. An old saying that "the Pacific is rimmed with fire" has much to support it.

A great majority of the volcanoes now active or recently extinct lie in belts subject to frequent earthquakes (Fig. 20–15). These belts also include the great mountain systems that formed late in the Earth's history, some of them still actively growing. Mountain making involves dislocations of the crust, a prime cause of earthquakes (Chaps. 20, 21). We infer, from the geographic distribution of volcanoes, that igneous activity is in some way associated with large crustal movements.

Exceptional volcanic centers that are isolated present special problems of origin. One of these is the San Francisco field south of the Grand Canyon, Arizona (p. 101), in an area far from any mountain system and showing no exceptional disturbance. Réunion, an island in the Indian Ocean east of Madagascar, is a similar example at sea.

More than 500 volcanoes are classed as active. Many thousands more, with cones that are slightly or moderately damaged by erosion, are either dormant or became extinct very recently. If the present is assumed as an average sample of the Earth's history, we cannot wonder that during hundreds of millions of years volcanic rocks have built up to vast areal distribution and total volume on land. Probably the oceans hide several times more than can be seen on the continents.

Intrusive igneous bodies

Source of information. We learn many things about volcanoes by watching eruptions; but a close student of Vesuvius or of Mauna Loa sometimes wishes he could slice down through cone and vent to the underlying roots and have a direct look at the whole mechanism. Fortunately, there is a partial substitute for direct anatomical dissection of a living specimen. Generations of volcanoes have lived and died, and erosion, working relentlessly through long ages, supplies information on individual volcanoes

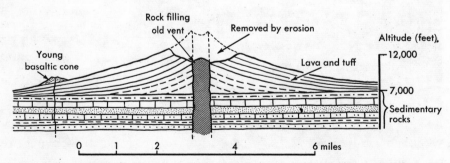

Fig. 6–21. Generalized section through San Francisco Peak, near Flagstaff, Arizona, showing structure of the composite cone. Though the peak has been considerably eroded, local eruptions have made sizable cinder cones since primitive human dwellings were built in the area.

Fig. 6–22. Shiprock, a volcanic neck in northwestern New Mexico, with three long attached dikes. The neck is 1,300 feet high. Air view, looking southwest. Erosion has removed the volcanic mountain that presumably stood here. Several other similar volcanic necks are in this general area. (John S. Shelton.)

and volcanic fields in all stages of dissection, from slight breaching of cones to exposure of rocks made at great depths by cooling of the parent magmas. Comparative study of these old exhibits along with modern activity may be called the comparative anatomy of volcanoes. Such a study gives us respect for the great energy, the endless variety, and the long-continued operation of the igneous processes.

Records of extinct vents. Several large volcanic cones stand in a group on the Colorado Plateau south of the Grand Canyon. All appear to be extinct, and the largest, San Francisco Peak, is well on its way to destruction. A deep valley is cut into the northeastern flank, and the head of this valley occupies the entire central area of the cone, which clearly has been reduced thousands of feet below an earlier summit (Fig. 6–21). The valley walls reveal alternating lavas and layers of volcanic fragments, all inclined steeply outward. In a central position, and dividing the valley, a vertical rock mass with nearly

circular cross section appears to cut across the inclined layers. Such a mass, known as *a volcanic neck, is a cylindrical filling of the central vent of an extinct volcano.*

The diagram, Figure 6–21, shows the neck extending downward through the older bedrock on which the cone stands. This diagram is not imaginary but is based on analogy with numerous ancient volcanoes, representing many stages of destruction, in a wide region east of San Francisco Peak. Some cones have been cut away until at each of them only small remnants of lava and ash remain on the older bedrock around the neck, which is the one durable element marking the old vent. Necks are so distinctive they are identified with confidence even if all other evidence of a former cone has disappeared. Shiprock, in New Mexico, is a great column of igneous rock with nearly circular ground plan, and its top is 1,300 feet above surrounding layers of shale and sandstone that underlie a wide plateau surface (Fig. 6–22).

101

A

Fig. 6–23. **A.** Outcrops of large dikes in the Spanish Peaks area resemble great artificial walls because the adjacent sedimentary rock is eroded more rapidly than the dikes. This view shows some of the rugged topography on and near the stocks. West Spanish Peak in background (G. W. Stose, U. S. Geological Survey.)

B. Area around Spanish Peaks, southern Colorado. The peaks are local mountains on stocks of irregular shape, exposed by erosion of overlying and surrounding sedimentary rocks. The dikes are of several ages and varied composition. Many radiate out from the stocks; others apparently had a deeper source. Many are precisely straight through several miles. This map does not represent nearly all the dikes exposed in the area. Topographic contours and stream courses are omitted, to avoid confusion with pattern of dikes. (From Folio 71, U. S. Geol. Survey.)

Long ridges of the igneous rock extending out from Shiprock remind us of the radiating fractures in Mount Etna, from which lavas pour out on the slopes of the cone (p. 87). Rock samples from the outer parts of Shiprock are very fine grained; samples taken some tens of feet inside the margin are much coarser grained and have porphyritic texture. This textural gradation is characteristic of volcanic necks. While the magma was moving up through a vent, it became chilled at contact with the surrounding rocks, but inside the column the molten rock cooled slowly, allowing time for growth of moderately coarse grains.

The sum of evidence is convincing that Shiprock and many features of its kind correspond in origin to the plug in the old bedrock below the base of the San Francisco cone. Commonly, the igneous rock filling a former vent is more resistant to erosion than the rocks that are transected; hence many necks have come to tower above their surroundings.

Most volcanic necks are deceptively simple in appearance. The central rock mass of San Francisco Peak consists of at least five distinct parts made of different kinds of rock. This is not surprising when we review the histories of the best known composite volcanoes. Monte Somma seemed dead before A.D. 79, and no doubt its central vent was filled with solidified magma. Centuries between the infrequent eruptions of Vesuvius before 1631 must also have

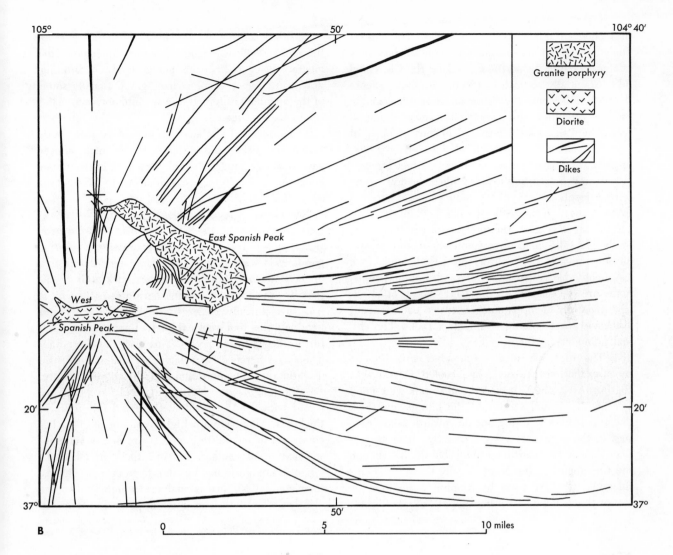

105°

50'

104° 40'

Granite porphyry

Diorite

Dikes

East Spanish Peak

West
Spanish Peak

20'

20'

37°

37°

50'

B

0   5   10 miles

allowed the vent to be sealed. Magma coming up for each great renewal had to make its way either by remelting or blasting out the earlier plug or by making a new passage. Study of old dissected cones shows clearly that successive new vents were opened alongside the earlier fillings, and in this way many necks grew to large size. The compound plug of the San Francisco cone is more than half a mile in diameter, and some others are as much as a mile.

Dikes and sills. Each of the long ridges that extend out from Shiprock, shown in Figure 6–22, is on a *dike, a tabular intrusive body that cuts across the older bedrock*. Dikes are common features in areas of former igneous activity. Great dikes in the Colum-

bia Plateau of the Pacific Northwest represent fillings of the fissures through which much of the widespread plateau basalt was erupted. Dikes of large size and extent form a conspicuous pattern in the Spanish Peaks area of Colorado (Fig. 6–23). Such networks suggest that the bedrock in wide belts was fractured as a result of stresses set up by emplacement of large masses of magma.

A tabular intrusive body similar in form to a dike, but parallel to inclosing layers instead of transecting them, is a sill. Commonly dikes and sills are closely associated, either type of body branching from the other (Fig. 6–24). Both dikes and sills range widely in size; the largest dimensions of some are measured

103

in inches, of others in tens of miles. The largest known bodies of either kind are made of dark rock related to basalt. In northern England the Cleveland dike, essentially vertical, is traced continuously more than 100 miles, and the Whin sill, nearly horizontal, extends 80 miles with average thickness about 90 feet. The Palisades sill, exposed in tens of miles of high cliffs along the west side of the Hudson River, opposite Manhattan, is as much as 900 feet thick.

Sills and buried flows. Many old lava flows were buried deeply under younger sediments and later became exposed in the walls of valleys cut by streams. Lavas that have gone through this history look generally like sills. In central Connecticut and Massachusetts several large sheets of dark igneous rock are included between layers of sandstone and shale. Some are recognized as buried lava flows, others as sills, by study of the contacts between each igneous sheet and the adjoining sedimentary rocks. The critical points are as follows:

1. The upper part of a lava flow has vesicles made by gases that escaped as the lava cooled. Deep cracks that formed as the rock cooled and shrank were filled later with silt and sand, and the fillings now look like small dikes wedging out downward. Some pebbles in the sedimentary layer directly above the igneous sheet are made of spongy basalt like that in the upper part of the sheet; locally these sediments fill gullies that were cut by running water into the top of the flow while it was exposed (Fig. 6–25, **A**).

2. When a sill was emplaced, the upper part of the molten rock was chilled against the cooler sedimentary layer and became fine-grained rock grading downward into rock of coarser grain. Locally some of the magma was forced upward into cracks to make small dikes (Fig. 6–25, **A**). Heat of the intrusive mass hardened the adjacent sedimentary rock, both above and below the sill, and by chemical effects caused some change in color. Bleaching is a common effect in dark-colored rocks adjacent to a large sill (Fig. 6–25, **B**).

Laccoliths. A *laccolith* is *a lenticular intrusive igneous body above which the layers of invaded bedrock bend upward as a distinct dome, circular or elliptical in plan* (Fig. 6–26). The name, descriptive of the form, means literally "cistern rock" (Gr.). Apparently the injected magma became so stiff that it was mechanically easier to thicken the mass and bend up the roof rocks than to force the material further between the layers. This brings our attention again to differences in behavior of magmas because of variations in composition and also in temperature. Basaltic magmas are highly fluid and have been injected widely to form sills with remarkably uniform thickness. Magmas with higher content of silica become stiff at moderate temperatures and so offer resistance to movement. Igneous rocks in laccoliths range in composition from diorite to granite; that is, their content of silica is medium to high.

A large laccolith is as much as several miles in di-

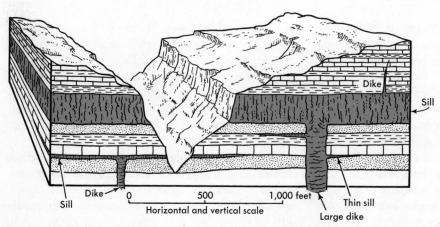

Fig. 6–24. These dikes and sills, intruded into sedimentary layers beneath a former land surface, are now partly exposed by erosion.

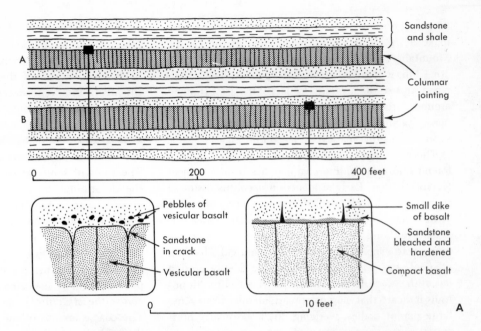

Fig. 6–25. A. A lava flow *A* and a sill *B*, inclosed in the same section of sedimentary layers exposed in a cliff, are much alike in general appearance. Features shown enlarged in the lower drawings tell us that *B* was intruded between layers, whereas *A* was erupted as a thick lava flow and later buried by the upper layers of sediment. **B.** A thick sill of dark igneous rock is exposed in a high cliff in Glacier National Park, Montana. Layers of limestone, wedged apart by the hot intruding magma, were changed chemically. The altered rock appears as irregular white bands along the top and base of the sill. (Spence Air Photos.)

ameter and thousands of feet thick; several in a group make a sizable mountain mass, such as the La Sal Mountains in Utah. In the Henry Mountains of southern Utah, where bodies of this type were first recognized and studied, groups of laccoliths are arranged around larger intrusive masses like chicks around hens. Each of the large bodies probably was the source of magma for several laccoliths.

The exact mechanism by which magma has been forced into a laccolithic chamber has been a subject for speculation. Early students of laccoliths assumed that the fluid rock "drilled" its way vertically to a critical level, where the upward pressure was sufficient to bend the roof rocks, thus allowing the magma to spread laterally. The vertical "feeding channel" has not been found in any deeply eroded laccolith. More recent studies in the Henry Mountains indicate that magma spread laterally from some large parent bodies, wedging apart the nearly horizontal layers of the invaded sedimentary rock. As the magma became stiff from loss of heat, the overlying layers were bowed up, and the advancing magma wedged out abruptly.

The two concepts of feeding channels for emplacement of laccoliths are indicated in Figure 6–26.

Many laccoliths, partially exposed by erosion, have irregular shapes that differ considerably from the ideal form. With decrease in the ratio of vertical to horizontal dimensions, there is insensible gradation from laccolith to sill. Both types are known as *concordant intrusive bodies* because *typically* they *conform to the layered structure of the rocks they invade*. The roofs of some laccoliths, however, broke under the deforming stresses of intrusion, and the transgressing magma took on irregular discordant shapes.

Stocks and batholiths. Many intrusive igneous bodies have at the present land surface large lateral dimensions, and they increase in size downward to undisclosed depths. All such bodies are at least in part *discordant intrusive bodies;* that is, they *cut across the structural grain of the invaded bedrock.* The coarse texture of the rock in these bodies, and their relations to the surrounding bedrock, show convincingly that they were formed deep underground and have been exposed by age-long erosion in belts of strong uplift.

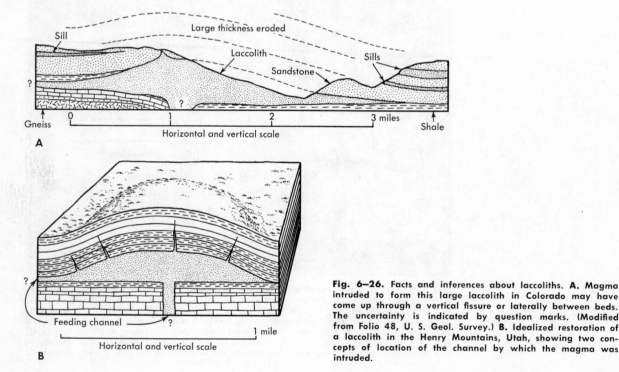

Fig. 6–26. Facts and inferences about laccoliths. A. Magma intruded to form this large laccolith in Colorado may have come up through a vertical fissure or laterally between beds. The uncertainty is indicated by question marks. (Modified from Folio 48, U. S. Geol. Survey.) B. Idealized restoration of a laccolith in the Henry Mountains, Utah, showing two concepts of location of the channel by which the magma was intruded.

These major intrusive masses are arbitrarily put into two classes on the basis of size and general form. *A stock is an intrusive igneous body, roughly circular or elliptical in ground plan, with an exposed area of less than 40 square miles.* Characteristically, the borders of such a body go down steeply, and the name was suggested by the roughly cylindrical form, similar to that of a tree trunk. Actually, the diameter of a typical stock seems to increase downward, and

some stocks probably are dome-shaped protuberances from larger intrusive masses. Perhaps some stocks, when they were active, fed magma upward to the vents of volcanoes.

The greatest of the exposed igneous intrusive bodies is the *batholith* (Gr. "deep rock"), *a deep-seated igneous mass, generally discordant, with known surface exposure greater than 40 square miles.* Batholiths and stocks consist of granitic rocks, that

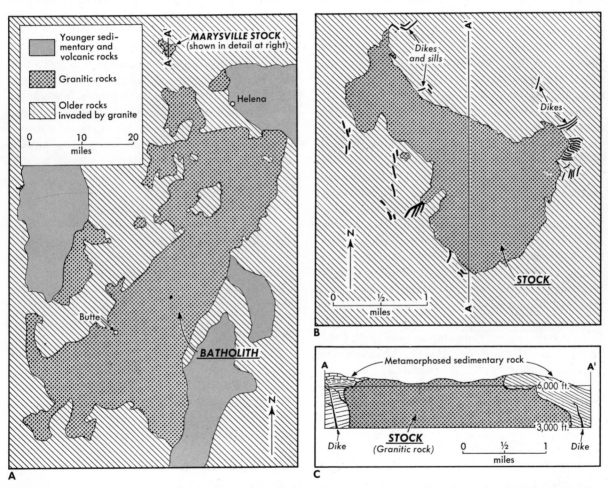

Fig. 6–27. Intrusive bodies of granitic rock, formed far below the land surface of their time. **A.** The Boulder batholith, in the Rocky Mountains, Montana, partly unroofed by erosion. *Several nearby stocks probably rise as offshoots from parts of the batholith that are still covered.* (From Geologic Map of Montana, U. S. Geol. Survey 1955.) **B.** Enlarged map of the Marysville stock, which has been closely studied and mapped because of valuable mineral deposits associated with it. **C.** Vertical section through the Marysville stock, along line *A-A'* on map, constructed with the aid of mining shafts and tunnels (B and C after J. Barrell, Prof. Paper 57, U. S. Geol. Survey, 1907.) Note the different scales in **A**, **B**, and **C.**

is, granite, granodiorite, and related granular rocks in which the chief minerals are feldspar and quartz. As we see them at the surface, these bodies differ widely in size, partly because some are eroded more deeply than others; many batholiths enlarge downward, and the area of one classed as small might be doubled if an additional mile or so of its thickness were stripped off. The exposed part of the Boulder batholith in western Montana is about 60 miles long and 20 miles wide (Fig. 6–27, **A**). The Idaho batholith in central Idaho, with an exposed area of 16,000 square miles—nearly twice the size of the State of Massachusetts—is the largest known batholith in the United States, but it is far exceeded by the Coast Range batholith in western Canada and southern Alaska, more than 1,000 miles long and 25 to more than 100 miles wide. Masses of comparable size are exposed along the western border of South America.

The general term pluton. Known igneous bodies of deep-seated origin are exposed at the surface in varied degree, dependent on the amount of regional uplift and the length of time erosion has been active in a particular area. If the outcrops within a large area are chiefly of sedimentary or volcanic rocks, scattered exposures of coarse-grained granite within a considerable part of the area will indicate a partly concealed igneous mass that was formed at depth but may reveal nothing about the size and form of the mass. A *pluton is any large intrusive igneous body, regardless of form.* Batholiths, stocks, laccoliths, and other large masses made of granular igneous rock are covered by this general term, in fanciful reference to Pluto, the Roman god of the nether regions. *Plutonic rocks are igneous rocks formed far below the Earth's surface.*

Relations among igneous bodies. Information about igneous rocks that were formed underground has been built up slowly in wide study of exposures made by age-long erosion. Old mountain zones yield the best evidence for two reasons: igneous activity has been most pronounced in mountain zones; and erosion has gone to greatest depths in belts of persistent uplift. In exposing great plutons such as the Idaho and Coast Range batholiths, erosion has, of course, destroyed nearly all igneous bodies that were formed at less depth directly above these great plutons. Only some remnants spared by erosion give in-

formation about shallower zones of the crust. The most favorable locations for such remnants are in belts of moderate uplift along the borders of exposed batholiths. A reasonable concept of general relations among the various kinds of igneous masses is given by evidence assembled from many mountain belts.

These relationships probably are less simple than they are represented in some published diagrams. Laccoliths in the Henry Mountains seem to be offshoots of stocks, though evidence suggests that the feeding channels may have a pattern very different from that commonly assumed (p. 106). Many dikes and sills made of rock with high silica content are reasonably connected with laccoliths and stocks, but some diagrams that are widely circulated represent fissure eruptions fed by channelways from batholiths. Since such eruptions, as far as is known, produce only basaltic lavas, they cannot originate in chambers of high-silica magma. Moreover, a large majority of volcanoes erupt materials of andesitic composition, and many that give forth materials rich in silica have also erupted andesitic and even basaltic lavas. The enormous volume of basalt under the Columbia Plateau (Fig. 6–17, **A**) probably came up from a deep zone beneath the continental mass (Fig. 2–3). Volcanoes that alternate between high- and low-silica products may be fed from deep-seated reservoirs in which there has been *magmatic differentiation, a slow physical-chemical process by which a magma divides into high-silica and low-silica fractions.*

Outflow of hot gases and water

Kinds and source of gases. In every active volcanic field and in many areas of extinct or dying igneous activity hot gases are leaking upward to the surface. "Smoking" cracks and larger openings are common around the volcanoes of Italy, where the term *fumarole* was first applied. Gases that emerge have temperatures as high as 700° C and carry in solution iron, copper, lead, and other metals which no doubt had their source in the magma. The elements chlorine and fluorine appear to combine in the vapor state with these metals, which then are deposited as metallic minerals on the walls of the fumarole vents. Hematite formed in this way at Vesuvius many years ago first led to the idea that we owe our ore deposits primarily to igneous processes (Chap. 22)

The superheated steam in fumarole fields in northern Italy and in Iceland has been harnessed for power generation on a considerable scale. Utilization of volcanic energy is being studied also in Indonesia, and this conversion of wasting power to man's use will probably grow to much larger proportions.

Hot springs and geysers. As magmatic gases rise through the crust, they heat underground water, part of which comes to the surface as hot springs at or near boiling temperature. More spectacular is a *geyser* (Fig. 6–28), a *spring equipped with a system of plumbing and heating that causes intermittent eruptions of water and steam.* Nearly all the world's true geysers are in Iceland, Yellowstone National Park, and New Zealand; the term geyser comes from an Icelandic word meaning *to gush.* No volcanic activity has been known in the Yellowstone region since this country was settled, but some volcanic rocks within the area of the Park look very recent, and the vast heat energy required for continuous functioning of the hot springs must be supplied by a mass of hot rock at depth.

No two geysers behave alike, and we can not map the system of underground passages supplying any one of them. The basic principle of the intermittent action must lie in the relation between pressure and the boiling point of water. As pressure increases, the boiling point rises, and in a vertical tube full of water the pressure increases rapidly downward. Hot gases rising in the tube heat the lower part first, and, if the tube were fairly straight, convection would be set up to equalize the temperature, as in a kettle of boiling water. But effective convection is prevented by crookedness of the passage, so that water at each level eventually approaches the boiling point. Rise of steam bubbles throws some water out at the top; this is seen in the preliminary spurts that herald a full-scale performance. Loss of water from the column reduces the pressure slightly below the critical point, and water flashes into steam throughout a large part of the tube, causing eruption (Fig. 6–29)

Problems of igneous geology

Source of heat. During the Earth's history the sites of volcanic action have shifted; therefore, we reason that the temperature of a region in or below the crust

Fig. 6–28. The Pohutu Geyser, Whakarewarewa, North Island, New Zealand (Underwood & Underwood.)

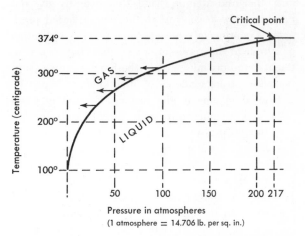

Pressure in atmospheres
(1 atmosphere = 14.706 lb. per sq. in.)

Fig. 6–29. This curve shows rise in boiling point of water with increasing pressure until the critical temperature, 374° C., is reached. In a tortuous geyser tube full of water pressure increases downward from 1 atmosphere at top to, say, 100 atmospheres at depth 350 feet. If when temperature at each depth is near boiling point some water is forced out at top, reduction in pressure causes water at many levels to pass instantaneously from liquid to gas, as indicated by arrows. The geyser then erupts.

rises to a critical point, igneous activity starts and runs its long course, and the excess heat is finally dissipated. As we have no direct information on chemical and physical conditions at depth, the source of the heat energy beneath a great volcanic field is a mystery. Possibly at least part is supplied by the continual breakdown of radioactive elements which we know are present in very small amounts in all rocks of the crust. We can not expect that this major problem will be solved quickly.

Variations in magmas. On the continents there are many kinds of igneous rocks, and lavas given forth by any one volcano may differ widely from one period of activity to another. The earliest eruption at San Francisco Peak was of basaltic lava; later there was much andesite, and after that rhyolite, the igneous rock highest in silica. Is there some mixing process in a deep magma chamber? Some scientists suggest there is an "unmixing," the separation of a magma body into two or more very different fractions, much as cream rises on standing milk, and that eruptions come now from one, now from another part of the *differentiated* magma. This concept is supported by extensive laboratory study.

Volcanoes on the floors of oceans (those on the Hawaiian and many other Pacific islands, the Azores and other mid-Atlantic islands) consistently give out basaltic lavas in contrast to the highly varied products of continental volcanoes. This direct indication of a radical difference in composition between continental and oceanic parts of the Earth's crust is supported by strong evidence of other kinds (Chap. 19).

Rise of magma to the surface. Expanding gases blast rock fragments through a vent, and conceivably the gas pressure also makes some lavas flow out, just as warm champagne or beer is forced from an uncapped bottle. But plateau basalts are not rich in gas, yet they flood the surface in record quantities. Perhaps the weight of the solid crust forces fluid magma to rise through fissures opened to great depth. In growing mountain chains the forces that buckle the crust may also squeeze magma from deep reservoirs (Chap. 21). However, this whole problem is still in a speculative stage of study.

The "room problem." What becomes of the older rock that must have filled the space now occupied by an immense batholith? Two suggestions are offered. (1) As the igneous mass came into place, slow-

ly and over a long period of time, large masses of older rock were displaced upward, to be removed by erosion. (2) Much of the older rock was engulfed and slowly *assimilated* by the magmatic fluids and so is now a part of the igneous mass. This promising suggestion, in more than one form, is still highly controversial. A concept in much favor holds that granitic bodies have been formed by granitization, a subtle chemical transformation of older bedrock into granitic rock. This important problem is discussed further in Chapter 19.

Effects on hydrosphere and atmosphere. Of the water released from volcanoes, at least a small percentage probably is "new"; and through the ages the amount of water at the surface may have been greatly increased (p. 84). Likewise, some of the carbon dioxide from volcanoes may be newly added to the atmosphere. Since both water and carbon dioxide play a critical role in the development of soils (Chap. 8) and in sustaining plant and animal life, igneous processes may play a major role in the over-all economy of nature.

Volcanoes and man. Java, the most densely populated country on Earth, has a number of active volcanoes. The slopes of volcanic mountains are intensely cultivated because the soils produced on volcanic materials commonly are very fertile; and although repeated eruptions bring great destruction and loss of life, the inhabitants return persistently to these dangerous neighborhoods. People of Japan, Italy, and other volcanic lands show the same fatalistic attitude toward their volcanoes.

Explosive eruptions, with their showers of ash, affect wide areas, but the most relentless and dreaded invader is the advancing lava flow, which crushes the works of man in its path and covers fertile ground beyond repair. In Hawaii attempts have been made to divert threatening lavas by well-placed bombs dropped from planes; and the Japanese are learning that massive concrete walls built in strategic positions are effective as a long-range measure in the protection of some of their towns. In the struggle with natural forces there will always be a frontier.

SUMMARY

1. Study of active volcanoes provides a key to the meaning of older volcanic records. Parícutin Volcano was studied through its life cycle.

2. Volcanic action varies between violent explosions that produce rock fragments, and quiet flows of liquid rock.

3. Magmas with high silica content are generally involved in explosive eruptions. Low-silica magmas commonly issue as large flows, but with high content of gases they also become explosive.

4. Some steep volcanic cones consist wholly of rock fragments; others are composites of fragmental products and lava flows.

5. Fissure eruptions of basaltic magma have built up wide plateaus on continents.

6. Erosion, to greatest depths in old mountain belts, has exposed many kinds of intrusive igneous bodies.

7. The largest intrusive bodies—batholiths, stocks, and laccoliths—consist of rocks with high content of silica. Dikes and sills represent a wide range in lithology.

8. All known volcanic rocks in ocean basins have low to moderate content of silica.

9. Geysers and hot springs in some areas mark dying phases of volcanism.

10. Among many problems of igneous geology, the origin of granite is outstanding. The great size of granitic batholiths gives emphasis to this problem.

REFERENCES

Daly, R. A., 1933, Igneous rocks and the depths of the Earth: New York, McGraw-Hill Book Co.

Foshag, W. F., and Jenaro Gonzàlez, 1952, Birth and development of Parícutin Volcano, Mexico: U. S. Geol. Survey Bull. 965-D.

Hunt, Charles B., 1953, Geology and geography of the Henry Mountains region, Utah: U. S. Geol. Survey Prof. Paper 228.

Stearns, H. T., 1946, Geology of the Hawaiian Islands: Honolulu, Hawaii Division of Hydrography, Bull, 8.

Tyrrell, G. W., 1931, Volcanoes: London, Thornton Butterworth, Ltd.

Williams, Howel, 1942, Geology of Crater Lake National Park: Washington, D. C., Carnegie Institution of Washington.

CHAPTER 7. WEATHERING AND SOILS

Break-up and decay of rocks   *Varied response of rock materials*   *Climate a strong influence*

Roles of land forms and time   **Soils the outstanding product**   *Records of climate in soils*

Over-all results of weathering

Relics of an old civilization at Chichen-Itza, Yucatan, Mexico, have been etched by weathering through about eight centuries. (Sawders from Cushing.)

Effects of weather

The weather is a matter of daily concern and comment. In common speech many things are described as weather-beaten: a frame house that has gone for years without protective paint; a gravestone on which we make out with some effort an inscription two or three centuries old; or a stone building that is crumbling visibly (Fig. 7–1). A piece of bright steel left in the damp outdoors soon becomes coated with yellowish-brown rust as some of the iron unites with oxygen and water. If the exposure continues for months or years, scales of rust fall from the steel, and the entire piece finally can be crumbled to brown powder. New copper stays "clean" longer than steel, but in time it takes on a thick green coating from chemical union with carbon dioxide. The stamp made by the weather is varied but sure. As one writer has phrased it, we spend our lives at the bottom of a great sea of air, which is essential to our existence but is also an agent of unending changes, many of which we regard as destructive.

Presumably the air, which is the vehicle of weather, is as old as the solid Earth. If gravestones and buildings made of the strongest rock have begun to crumble within a few centuries, what must have happened to materials exposed to the weather through thousands or even millions of years? Study of bedrock in many places gives at least a strong lead toward a general answer. In Hawaii a sheet of fresh black basalt, formed a few years ago from liquid lava, partly covers older basalt that is generally similar but in its upper part (where the later sheet does not cover it) grades into soil in which plants are growing. Take, as another sample, a granite quarry near Washington, D. C. Fresh rock suitable for buildings is found only in the man-made pit, tens of feet below the original surface of the ground. In its upper half the quarry wall is much discolored, and near the top the rock is so rotten it can be crumbled with the fingers. The most noticeable change is in the feldspar grains, which in the fresh rock have glistening cleavage surfaces between the dull grains of quartz. Higher up in the wall these surfaces are lusterless and stained, and near the top the grains of quartz, still distinguishable, are separated by soft, earthy material that has no resemblance to the former feldspar, which has literally rotted away. In many man-made cuts beside highways we may study gradations upward from decaying bedrock to soil (Fig. 7–2). We infer that in exposed bedrock effects of weather, like those shown by old buildings, accumulate with time until the rock breaks up and parts of it decay. This process, called *weathering,* is highly complex and poses problems that call for the best skills not only of geologists but of chemists, physicists, and biologists as well.

Weathering is the alteration of rock materials during exposure to air, moisture, and organic matter.

Kinds of weathering

Weather is variously classified, but we speak of it particularly as warm or cold, wet or dry. Temperature and moisture, then, are among the prime elements of weather. Warmth and moisture favor chemical action, and the rotting of feldspar in granite represents chemical change on a large scale. But we see in many places heaps of broken rock that is either fresh or only slightly decayed. Blocks forming sheets of *sliderock* match the bedrock in adjacent cliffs (Fig. 7–3), from which they must have been displaced. Hence, in addition to chemical decay there

A

Fig. 7–2. Gradation upward from partly decayed gneiss, through clay intermingled with rock fragments, to soil in which plants are growing. Beside U. S. Highway 40, west of Denver, Colorado. (John S. Shelton.)

B

Fig. 7–1. A. The columns beside a doorway of Durham Castle, in England, are made of porous sandstone. Exposure for 263 years damaged the stone noticeably. **B.** This monument in a cemetery at Salzburg, Austria, bears the date 1547. The inscription, on fine-grained, resistant stone, is clearly legible after exposure to the weather for more than 400 years. (C. R. Longwell.)

Dolerite sheet

Layers of sedimentary rock

Sliderock

Fig. 7–3. A sheet of jointed dolerite overlies layers of sedimentary rock. Top of cliff is 325 feet above water. Blocks of dolerite have tumbled down, building up piles of slide-rock. Northwest Territories, Canada. (A. L. Washburn.)

is a natural process of rock breaking, and we speak of *mechanical weathering* as distinct from *chemical weathering*, though the two processes work in close coordination, and often their effects are inseparably blended.

Disintegration, the *mechanical break-up of rocks*, exposes additional fresh surfaces to air and water. Therefore, disintegration aids *decomposition,* the *chemical alteration of rock materials*. On the other hand, some chemical changes are directly responsible for mechanical disruption on a large scale. Let us look first at some of the chemical effects.

Chemical weathering

Nature works subtly, and many of her devices have been discovered only by patient detective work and the pooling of results gained by many individuals in more than one generation. Gradual changes in feldspar from the bottom to the top of a granite quarry convince us that chemical weathering has progressed from the surface downward. But just what chemical reagents have been used in nature's laboratory, what reactions have occurred, and what are the resulting materials?

Effects on granitic rocks. Rainwater brings to the ground with it small amounts of the carbon dioxide present in the air. This gas combined with water makes carbonic acid, which to the chemist is H_2CO_3. The reaction is as follows:

$$H_2O \text{ (water)} + CO_2 \text{ (carbon dioxide)}$$
$$\rightarrow H_2CO_3 \text{ (carbonic acid)}$$

Water that enters openings in the regolith and in bedrock is therefore a weak acid, a chemical reagent; wherever plants grow, the strength of the solution is increased many times by addition of carbonic acid from decaying vegetation. The feldspar minerals, which make much more than half the bulk of a granitic rock, are attacked slowly but persistently by this acid, with a result shown by the following chemical equation:

$$2KAlSi_3O_8 + H_2CO_3 + H_2O =$$
(orthoclase) (carbonic acid) (water)

$$K_2CO_3 + Al_2Si_2O_5(OH)_4 + 4SiO_2$$
(potassium carbonate) (kaolinite) (silica)

Of these products, the kaolinite is one of the common minerals in clay. Its crystal form, visible only with very high magnification, is shown in Figure 7–4. Another of these minerals, dickite, is pictured in Figure 3–4. Clay is highly insoluble and much of it accumulates below the surface of the ground as part of the regolith; the silica is partly soluble, but some of it remains in the clay; the potassium carbonate, most soluble of the three products, is largely taken away by water, but some is held in the clay and may become a valuable food for plants.

In the weathering of plagioclase, the other abundant feldspar, the reactions are complex because the proportions of calcium and sodium vary; but the essential products are soluble bicarbonates of those two elements and clay minerals. In plain English, then, chemical weathering of feldspars, the most abundant rock-making minerals, produces clay, one of the most common materials in regolith. Clay, however, is by no means a simple substance. There are several distinct clay minerals, all of them made up of submicroscopic grains. The use of X-ray equip-

Fig. 7–4. Crystals of the clay mineral kaolinite, enlarged 26,900 times by an electron miscroscope, resemble plates of mica (see Fig. 3–4). (Paul F. Kerr.)

1 micron

ment and of the electron microscope reveals some of the properties of these minerals; but much remains unknown in spite of the most ingenious modern techniques. Without an intimate acquaintance with clays, we can not have a full understanding of soils, of which clay and other products of chemical weathering form an essential part (p. 126). Soils supply us with food, and therefore we should re-examine the concept that weathering is a *destructive* process (p. 114). Both weathering and the operation of gravity cause us some inconvenience, but we could hardly do without them.

Quartz, next in abundance to the feldspars among the minerals that make up granite, stubbornly resists chemical change. As the feldspars rot, gradually forming clays, the quartz grains are loosened like bricks in a wall when mortar decays. The loose quartz grains can then be picked up by running water, carried far away, spread out in layers, and eventually cemented to form sandstone (Chaps. 9, 17). If this sandstone is later exposed to erosion and broken up, the quartz grains will slowly grow smaller with abrasion by water and wind but will persist without chemical change for long ages. Much of the sand now on beaches or in desert dunes consists of quartz grains that doubtless were set free by the weathering of granitic rocks in remote geologic periods.

Effects on ferromagnesian minerals. Granitic rocks usually contain some grains of biotite or hornblende or both. These and other ferromagnesian minerals are abundant in diorite, gabbro, and basalt. Under chemical weathering the ferromagnesian minerals, all with complex compositions, yield varied products. The most conspicuous are hydrous iron oxides, for which the general term *limonite* is commonly used. This is not a single mineral, though an important part of it consists of the mineral *goethite,* $FeO(OH)$. Hematite, Fe_2O_3, with more or less absorbed water, is also a common constituent.

The rusty-brown color of limonite is distinctive. Clay making the greater part of decomposed rock contains varied shades of yellow-brown from admixed fine particles of limonite. This coloring is most pronounced in clays formed by weathering of the dark-colored rocks, such as basalt, of which ferromagnesian minerals are an important fraction. The effects are most conspicuous in warm, moist climates.

Light-colored clay, free from iron and suitable for making high-grade porcelain, is formed in large quantities only under exceptional conditions and is therefore a valuable commercial product.

Solution. Pure water will dissolve quantities of common salt and a few other minerals, but it is not an effective solvent for any of the common rocks. Calcite, $CaCO_3$, the chief mineral in ordinary limestone, is very slightly soluble in pure water. But nearly all the water that percolates through crevices in rocks has taken up CO_2, partly from the air, but more abundantly from decaying plants, and so is equipped with carbonic acid which greatly speeds the dissolution of calcite. Vast quantities of limestone have been dissolved and carried away by water underground (Chap. 11). All large bodies of limestone, however, contain material other than calcite, much of which is insoluble. Laboratory analysis reveals as much as 10 per cent of clay and particles of silica in limestone that from casual inspection might be passed as "fairly pure." As the calcite is dissolved, this included matter is set free, and much of it accumulates at the surface of the ground to form **residual soil,** which is *soil overlying its parent bedrock.*

The solubility of any rock material depends on its chemical composition and on the nature of the fluids with which it comes in contact. Even silica, generally resistant to solution, is dissolved in alkaline fluids.

The continued removal of soluble material by water percolating through regolith or through openings in bedrock is **leaching.**

Processes and effects in weathering. The aim of this discussion is first to make clear the chief chemical *processes* that operate in weathering. Full explanation of weathering *effects* must await a more complete discussion of processes, some of which are classed as mechanical. As stated on page 116, some results of chemical action lead to mechanical break-up of rocks, and therefore in the discussion of processes those that involve chemical changes are given priority. Let us now consider the operation of mechanical agencies in weathering. We have by no means completed an analysis of the role played by chemical changes. The most profound chemical effects in weathering are seen in the development of soils under varied climatic conditions. This large aspect of the subject is considered in later pages, together with the place of weathering in the complex interplay of agencies responsible for continual change on the Earth through long ages.

Mechanical weathering

Frost wedging. Ice is unique among minerals; it has a larger volume than the liquid from which it crystallizes. Laboratory tests show that water, in freezing, expands about 9 per cent and that in a closed vessel the bursting pressures from this expansion reach thousands of pounds per square inch. Freezing of water held in the open spaces of rocks and regolith is commonplace in all temperate and colder regions and has been repeated countless times in the Earth's history. Although most cavities in rocks are open to the air, preliminary freezing in the upper parts of water-filled crevices may form closed systems in which further freezing will set up bursting pressures. This mechanism is aptly called *frost wedging*. Its action is confined to a rather shallow zone and is most noticeable near the edges of cliffs where poorly supported blocks are sent tumbling down into heaps of sliderock (Fig. 7–3). The process is most effective in high mountains, where bedrock is widely exposed on steep slopes and where freezing at night occurs during much of the year (Fig. 7–5). Probably the wedging apart of minute rock scales and mineral grains is as important in the long run as the more spectacular loosening of large blocks.

Mechanical work of plants and animals. Tree roots gradually extend into crevices of bedrock, and in their growth they wedge apart the adjoining blocks. Shrubs and smaller plants also send their rootlets into tiny openings and slowly enlarge them. The total amount of rock breaking done in this way must be large, but much of it is obscured by chemical decay of the rock which takes advantage of new openings as they are formed.

Burrowing animals, large and small, bring quantities of partly decayed rock fragments to the surface, where they are exposed more effectively to chemical action. Lowly worms and ants, toiling in countless numbers, one generation after another through long epochs of time, have done incalculable work of this kind. Charles Darwin made close observations in his English garden and calculated that worms brought particles to the surface at the rate of more than 10 tons per acre every year. After a study in the Amazon basin, the geologist J. C. Branner wrote that the soil "looks as if it had been literally turned inside out by the burrowing of ants and termites."

Effects of changing temperature. The heat of forest and brush fires breaks large flakes from exposed surfaces of bedrock. Rock is a poor conductor of heat; fire heats only a thin outer shell, which expands and is disrupted. Forest fires set by lightning must have been common during long ages before man came to disturb nature's economy, and doubtless fire has been an agent of considerable importance in breaking rocks at the Earth's surface.

Possibly heating by the Sun, followed by cooling at night or during exceptional downpours of rain, has caused some breaking of exposed bedrock, at least in arid regions in which there are large daily ranges in temperature. This theory has been tested by laboratory experiments involving temperature changes greater and more abrupt than the daily ranges recorded in deserts. By the use of an automatic mechanism, these extreme changes have been repeated thousands of times without any detectable fracturing of the rock. Although these results do not favor the theory, conceivably some fracturing may result from diurnal changes over a long time interval. Slow chemical changes, discussed below, probably are more effective even in deserts than are changes in temperature.

Mechanical effects of chemical weathering. The development of clay minerals is accompanied by increase in volume. The outer surface of exposed rock dries rapidly after wetting, but moisture that penetrates into minute crevices stays until some decay is started. Slow increase in volume at slight depth sets up strains that break off flakes of rock. *Separation, during weathering, of successive thin shells from massive rock* such as granite is *exfoliation* (Fig. 7–6). This form of weathering is conspicuous only where there is appreciable moisture. Under the arid climate of Egypt, ancient stone monuments appear unchanged by weathering except for parts that were repeatedly submerged by flood waters (Fig. 7–7). In regions that have cold seasons frost wedging plays an important part in further loosening the shells produced by exfoliation.

Separation of curved shells is not confined to rocks exposed at the surface. Some of the best examples

Fig. 7–5. Freezing of water in countless openings wedges blocks from this massive granitic rock in the high Sierra Nevada, California. The location, above timberline, favors frost wedging during much of the year. (Photo Researchers.)

A

Fig. 7–6. Exfoliation of massive granitic rock exposed to weathering in the Sierra Nevada, California. This location is at a much lower altitude than the location represented in Figure 7–5. (G. K. Gilbert, U. S. Geol. Survey.)

B

Fig. 7–7. A. Colossus in Amun Temple, Karnak, near pylon No. VII, Egypt. The statue and base are of red granite. Exceptional floods of the Nile have reached as high as the ankle of the statue. Note the exfoliation below that point. Higher parts of the statue and monument, exposed in the arid climate of Egypt, are almost unaffected by weathering. B. Granite on the east side of Roger Playa, Mohave Desert, California. Exfoliation affects the lower part of the exposed rock, which occasionally is moistened. The upper part of the exposure stays fresh and firm in the dry climate. (Eliot Blackwelder.)

are found several feet or even tens of feet underground, in massive rock blocked out by sets of fractures (Fig. 7–8, **A**). Within blocks that are nearly cubic the concentric shells are almost perfect spheres. We reason that water, supplied with CO_2, circulated through the fractures on all sides of a block, and the chemical action rounded off each corner, where the attack came from three sides with equal intensity (Fig. 7–8, **B**). Separation of shells proceeded inward, and we now find an outer zone of thorough weather-

A

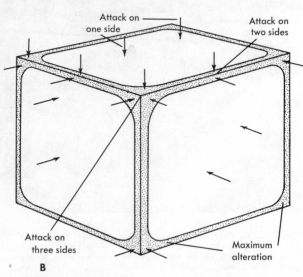

Attack on one side

Attack on two sides

Attack on three sides

Maximum alteration

B

Fig. 7–8. A. Granite divided into blocks by intersecting fractures, one set nearly vertical, another set nearly horizontal. Weathering has proceeded inward from the fractures, producing almost spherical forms. Roadbed at base of view suggests the scale. **B.** Solutions circulating in fractures around a nearly cubic block attack corners and edges most effectively, eventually reducing the block to forms shown in **A.** (Eliot Blackwelder.)

ing, although the central core may still be very little altered. Formation of the shells tens of feet below the Earth's surface must be wholly the result of chemical action; in temperate regions frost action does not extend so deep.

In coarse-grained rocks, such as granite, blocks separated by steep joints are characteristically rounded by weathering (Fig. 7–9).

Influence of climate

Weather is a day-to-day matter, the condition of the air for a short time. *A composite of weather conditions over a period of years* determines the **climate** of a region. **Meteorology,** *the science of weather and climate,* deals with many variable and unknown quantities. The atmosphere is part of the Earth, but geology is concerned primarily with the rocky crust, which offers problems enough for one major science. Yet because the air affects the solid Earth in very important ways, we must give attention to some general principles that determine climates.

Solar energy. The Greeks noted that in warm lands such as Egypt the Sun at noon is high in the heavens, and in going northward into cooler regions they found progressive lowering of the Sun's track toward the southern horizon. They reasoned, correctly, that the solar rays strike the Earth's surface more and more obliquely toward the north (Fig. 7–10); their explanation was that the surface *slopes* away from the equatorial belt. Doubtless they pictured the slope as curved, because Greek scholars from an early date taught that the Earth is round. Their word for slope or incline (*klima*) is the basis of our word *climate,* and they divided the Earth into climatic zones bounded by parallels of latitude.

Further weakening of solar energy in polar regions results from its absorption by air in the longer path of the Sun's rays through the atmosphere as compared with the equatorial belt (Fig. 7–10).

Movements of air. A major pattern of circulation in the atmosphere operates under two controls: (1) unequal heating between equatorial and polar latitudes and (2) rotation of the Earth. The primary differences in temperature divide the atmosphere into northern and southern cells that are mirror images of each other (Fig. 7–11). In the Earth's rotation movement of the surface is fastest at the equator, progressively slower toward each pole. Therefore, the surface

Fig. 7—9. Characteristic rounded forms produced by weathering of granitic rocks. Sierra Nevada, California, near Lone Pine. (Photo Researchers.)

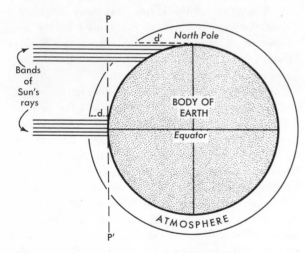

Fig. 7—10. This relationship of the Sun's rays to the Earth's surface is an average for a full year. Sunshine equally distributed on a plane P-P' at right angles to the equator is spread unequally on the curved surface of the Earth. Rays reaching the polar region travel much farther through air (*d'*) than those reaching the equator (*d*). (Modified from Finch and Trewartha, courtesy McGraw-Hill Book Co.)

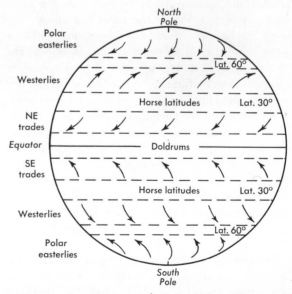

Fig. 7—11. General directions of prevailing winds at the Earth's surface in three major belts within each hemisphere. (After C. G. Rossby.)

121

"gets ahead of" an air current moving toward the equator. As a result the *trade winds, the prevailing winds in the tropical zone,* move generally from the northeast in the Northern Hemisphere and from the southeast in the Southern Hemisphere. On the other hand, in middle latitudes, where air currents tend to move poleward, the surface of the Earth "lags behind" the moving air because of decreasing velocity in rotational movement at higher latitudes. Therefore the *prevailing westerlies, the prevalent winds in middle latitudes,* move generally from the southwest in the Northern Hemisphere and from the northwest in the corresponding southern belt. In the polar regions, where cold air tends to flow equatorward, the effect of increasing rate of rotational movement with decrease in latitude again has its effect. The *polar easterlies, common winds in polar regions,* move generally southwestward in the Arctic zone, northwestward in the Antarctic zone (Fig. 7–11).

The general system of air circulation does an enormous amount of work as a conditioning apparatus for modifying temperatures at the Earth's surface. But the simplicity of the ideal system is disturbed in many ways, especially by the irregular extents and heights of land masses. Lands are heated and cooled more rapidly than adjoining seas, and special cells of circulation result, usually not in keeping with the main planetary system. Violent tornadoes that afflict some areas are but one example of disturbance within a large circulation. High mountain ranges change the directions of some large air currents and may even dissipate them by turning the moving air sharply upward, perhaps into conflicting winds at a higher level.

A general understanding of atmospheric movements is of interest in geology because weather and climate play major roles in profound changes of rock materials in the outer part of the Earth. In our introduction to geologic study, however, we cannot go beyond some basic facts about the atmosphere to a lengthy analysis of the intricate mechanism of weather. Such an analysis is within the province of meteorology.

Movements of ocean water. Ocean currents have been charted accurately during the long history of navigation. Prevailing surface winds, by frictional drag on the water, cause the important surface currents in the oceans. Thus broad equatorial currents flow westward in the trade-wind belts and divide at the west margin of each ocean, completing the circulation generally in the belts of prevailing westerlies (Fig. 15–8). The resulting over-all pattern of circulation is clockwise in the Northern Hemisphere, counterclockwise in the Southern.

The continental masses, of course, deflect and control the circulation in the oceans more effectively than in the atmosphere. A conspicuous example of diverted flow is the North Atlantic current (or *drift*), a branch of the Gulf Stream, which is responsible for exceptional warmth in the British Isles and western Norway. At the same latitudes in eastern North America, Labrador and adjacent areas have cold climates, made bleaker than normal by a current flowing southward past Greenland. Ocean currents affect the climates of many lands.

World precipitation. Movements of air govern the *precipitation* of moisture as rain, snow, sleet, or hail. In general, there is abundant precipitation wherever air flows strongly upward because the cooling that results condenses the contained moisture. On the other hand, rapid descent compresses and heats air and so causes it to absorb moisture. The areas with heaviest precipitation, then, should be near the equator and latitude 60°, and the most arid belts should be the horse latitudes and the polar regions.

To a large extent this is true, but many irregularities in the expected pattern are caused by the arrangement of land masses and seas (Fig. 7–12). Masses of cold heavy air flow from the Arctic zone far to the south over the low interior of North America, and the front of such a mass forces up the warm moist air from the Gulf of Mexico and the nearby Atlantic Ocean, causing widespread precipitation; hence there is no arid belt in the horse latitudes of the midwestern and eastern states. In Asia the high Himalaya chain causes heavy seasonal rainfall near latitude 30°, and the belt of deserts is displaced northward into central Asia. High mountain chains that extend generally north-south, as in North and South America, break the normal east-west trends of climatic belts. In western United States the westerly air currents, forced up by the Sierra Nevada and the Cascade Mountains, lose much of their moisture on the western slopes and summits. As it flows down the eastward slopes, the air becomes heavier and drier; hence our most arid belt extends nearly north-south in this region (Fig. 7–12). In many areas precipi-

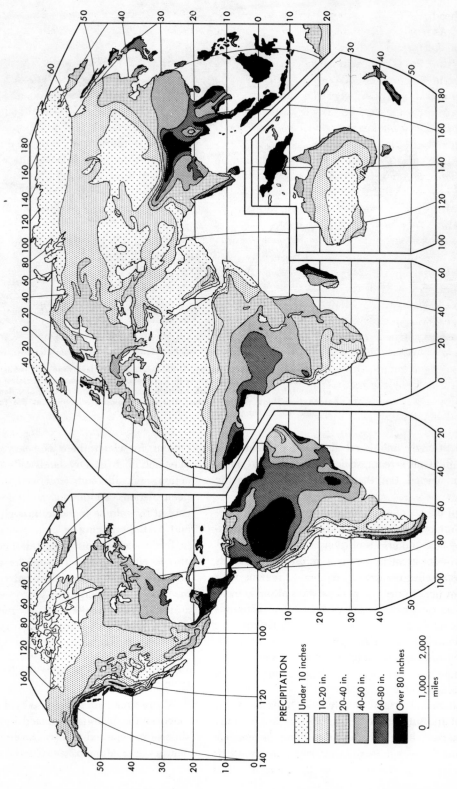

Fig. 7–12. This map shows average annual precipitation on all continents except Antarctica. The north-south relations of land masses are correct, but to save space the continents are pushed together laterally. Resulting elimination of seas justifies the somewhat jocular term "dehydrated" map. (After Finch and Trewartha, courtesy McGraw-Hill Book Co.)

PRECIPITATION

Under 10 inches
10-20 in.
20-40 in.
40-60 in.
60-80 in.
Over 80 inches

miles
0   1,000   2,000

arroyo - wadis

Fig. 7–13. Monument Valley, Utah-Arizona, with less than 10 inches of precipitation per year, has a barren landscape with large exposures of bedrock. Massive sandstone, hundreds of feet thick, overlies a weak formation consisting largely of shale. Remnants of the sandstone form high mesas, buttes, and some isolated columns that are fantastically tall and slender. (C. R. Longwell.)

tation is strongly influenced also by ocean currents, such as the Gulf Stream, which carry heat and moisture far beyond the theoretical limits of climatic zones.

Varied effects of climate on weathering. Rock decay is promoted by warmth and humidity and is hindered by cold and arid conditions. Chemical weathering reaches to greatest depths in moist tropical lands but is very effective also in temperate regions with abundant rain. In dry Egypt the details of many monuments and inscriptions are distinct after thousands of years. The large areas of nearly fresh bedrock exposed in arid and Arctic landscapes (Figs. 7–13, 7–3) contrast with the thick cover of weathered material mantling even the steep slopes in most humid regions (Fig. 7–14).

The abundant litter of nearly fresh broken rock on much of the surface in deserts and in Arctic lands might suggest that mechanical weathering is more effective in those regions than in temperate or warm regions in which there is heavy rainfall. But this may not be true. Dry lands lack moisture for frost action, and, although frost wedging is important in polar regions, continuous and widespread break-up caused by volume increase through chemical change and by the wedging of plant roots is most effective in fairly warm, moist climates. There rock breaking also is effective, but the results are in large part obscured by unending chemical changes. Although mechanical weathering may proceed more slowly in arid and Arctic regions, broken rock accumulates in deceptively large quantities because the rate of chemical decay is comparatively slow.

Importance of topography, rock composition, time

Where slopes are steep, gravity is in command, and much of the material loosened by weathering falls, slides, or is washed to lower levels; in this way fresh bedrock is continuously exposed to attack. In moist

Fig. 7–14. In western Pennsylvania, where the annual precipitation is about 40 inches, the land surface consists largely of smooth, soil-covered slopes. Some strips of grass parallel to contours on cultivated slopes serve to check erosion of soil. Note strong contrast between this landscape and that shown in Figure 7–13. (Ewing Galloway.)

regions the lower, gentler slopes of mountains are covered with regolith. Rolling topography at moderate altitude offers the best opportunity for weathering to extend deep below the surface, for vegetation protects the soil from rapid erosion, and as the upper part of the regolith decays the chemical reagents extend their work downward. There is a limit to this penetration because below a certain depth, even in rugged country, all openings are filled with water in which there is little free oxygen or carbon dioxide (Chap. 11).

Rocks vary greatly in their resistance to weathering. Quartzite, and sandstone that is made chiefly of resistant quartz, yield very slowly and so tend to form steep ridges. Granite breaks down much more easily in any climate; in a moist region the feldspar decays to form clay, and in a desert the mineral grains fall apart, probably because of strains set up by slight chemical weathering of the feldspar. But the actual rate at which these changes occur is slow from a hu-

man point of view. Granite has a long life in buildings and monuments, and in the Sierra Nevada some surfaces on granite still keep the polish and scratches formed long ago by glacier ice (Fig. 7–15).

In regions with plentiful rainfall limestone is dissolved, leaving only a residue of clay and other impurities. Hence in a moist climate lowlands tend to form on limestone bedrock; in arid lands, such as southern Nevada, solution is negligible, and thick limestone masses make the highest peaks and ridges (Fig. 3–1). Shale, consisting chiefly of clay made by chemical decay in earlier geologic periods, is changed in composition only very slowly by further weathering; generally, it breaks down mechanically to form soft clay.

Examination of land surfaces in regions covered by ice sheets in the latest glacial age (Chap. 13) gives a general appreciation of the slow rate at which weathering of fresh rock proceeds. In New England and northern Europe we find granite and other kinds of

Fig. 7–15. Granitic bedrock high in the Sierra Nevada was smoothed and polished by movement of glacier ice thousands of years ago. Although there may have been a covering of debris that has been removed by erosion, certainly the bedrock at this locality has been exposed for a long time. Yet weathering has destroyed only parts of the polished surface. (G. K. Gilbert, U. S. Geol. Survey.)

bedrock exposed over large areas and still bearing the marks made by the moving ice thousands of years ago (Fig. 13–24). From this kind of evidence we infer that weathering effects, extending tens of feet below the surface, as is common in the southern Appalachian region, the Coast Ranges of California, and other lands that were not glaciated, required a vast lapse of time as measured by human standards.

Soils

If the weathering of rocks merely changed lifeless matter from one form to another, it would not be an exciting subject to most of us. A final product of rock decay, soil, "is the great bridge between the inanimate and the living." Soil is our greatest natural resource, and its proper use and protection require knowledge of how it is formed. There is a special field of study, *pedology,* or *soil science,* which makes intensive use of the principles of chemistry, physics, and biology. We can examine only a few general

contributions from this large and growing science.

Development of soil. The term *soil* is used in more than one sense. To an engineer it is a synonym for regolith; that is, the aggregate of all loose rock material above bedrock. In geology we adopt the definition used in soil science and agriculture: *soil is that part of the regolith that will support rooted plants.* Chemical changes that occur in the formation of clay make some mineral substances available to the simpler plants, which then add carbon from the air and start a complex chain of reactions. There is no real soil without organic matter. **Humus,** the *decomposed residue of plant and animal tissues,* gives the dark color that is common in the upper parts of soils. Humus provides food for more plants and with water forms acids that percolate downward to carry on chemical change. Bacteria multiply, and some kinds take nitrogen from the air, combining it with other elements to make foods essential for some kinds of plants, notably clover, alfalfa, and peas. Plant roots strike down, some to considerable depth, admitting air and helping circulation of water; more work of this kind is done by worms and other small animals, which also help chemical changes by passing great quantities of soil through their bodies. One of the best indications of a productive soil is the presence of well-nourished earthworms.

Soil profiles. Unless it is washed away as fast as it forms, a soil slowly grows thicker and becomes divided into rather distinct layers that have important differences in composition. *The succession of distinctive layers in a soil, from the surface down to unchanged parent material,* is the **soil profile.** (Fig. 7–16, **A**). In standard practice the upper layer, containing most of the organic material, is called the *A* horizon; the layer below this, poor in organic content and rich in clay, is the *B* horizon; below it is an irregular layer, the *C* horizon, which contains remnants of the parent material and grades downward into the unaltered parent rock. In everyday speech the *A* layer

is the topsoil, the *B* layer the subsoil. A *soil in which the full profile has developed* is **mature soil.**

The organic matter in the upper part of the soil leads to chemical activity, which in a warm temperate region is intensive. Acid solutions percolate downward, dissolving materials that are either carried away with movement of ground water or redeposited in layer *B*. Calcium carbonate is leached out, and the abundance of carbon dioxide supplied by plant decay makes the soil acid; farmers find it necessary to offset this acidity by spreading powdered limestone on the surface at intervals to condition the soil for certain crops. Iron also is dissolved out and, in part, is added to layer *B*. Clay minerals are slowly carried downward, making the *B* layer clay-rich. A thriving forest, especially one of conifers, adds abundant organic matter to the topsoil, creating strong acids that leach the lower part of layer *A* and make it light colored, in some places almost white.

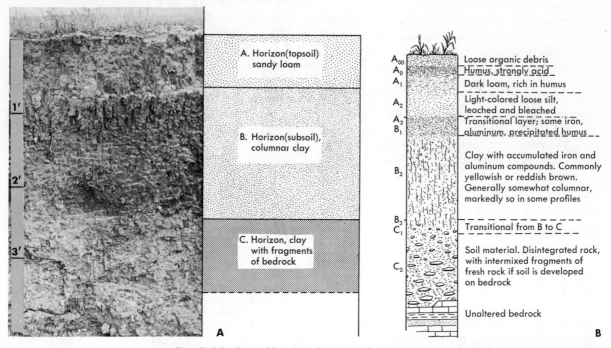

Fig. 7–16. A. Freshly exposed section of soil developed on bedrock consisting of shale and sandstone. The three horizons of the soil profile are clearly distinguished. The scale shows thickness in feet. (U. S. Soil Conservation Service.) **B.** Ideal soil profile showing all horizons commonly developed under a moist, temperate climate. Boundaries of adjacent units are gradational. A_{00} and A_0 are present in forests, usually not on grass lands. The transitional unit A_3-B_1 is commonly but not universally recognized in well-developed profiles. The B_3-C_1 gradational zone generally is distinct but varies in width. (Modified from T. L. Lyon and H. S. Buckman, *The Nature and Properties of Soils*, The Macmillan Co., 1943, p. 264.)

The several horizons of a soil profile vary considerably with differences in topography, drainage, kinds of vegetation, and other items. Commonly, each horizon is divisible into two or more distinct fractions (Fig. 7–16, **B**). The soil on a treeless slope differs in important details from neighboring soils in forested areas or in swampy lowlands.

The parent material from which a soil is developed may be any kind of bedrock or a thick cover of sediment moved to its present position by streams, glaciers, or some other agent of erosion. In the "bottom lands" of large valleys the soil is exceptionally rich and thick because the parent material itself is in considerable part topsoil washed from uplands (Chap. 9). In many of our northern states and in much of Canada soils are being developed on loose materials that were moved, well mixed, and redeposited thousands of years ago by the great ice sheets. Because of this history, the soils of New England and in states near the Great Lakes are *immature,* and their profiles differ radically from those of soils farther south in areas not disturbed by glaciation.

Climatic types of soils. Kinds of parent materials differ widely and have strong influence on the resulting soils, especially in early stages of development. We often hear such terms as *granite soils* and *limestone soils.* An abundance of quartz grains, inherited let us say from sandstone, will keep a soil loose textured because quartz resists chemical change. A soil formed on bedrock consisting chiefly of shale tends to be "tight"; it forms a hard crust when it is dry, sticky mud when it is wet. But over a long period of time climate has an even stronger influence than bedrock in determining types of soil. Under given climatic conditions the profiles of mature soils developed on widely different kinds of rock are surprisingly alike.

Rainfall is one of the most effective elements of climate, and in a very general way the soils in the United States are divided into two types on the basis of the degree of leaching by circulating water. The most effective leaching is found in areas with average annual rainfall of more than 25 inches. A somewhat irregular line extending northward from central Texas to the western part of Minnesota divides the more humid eastern district from the drier western states. East of this line the upper horizons of mature soils have lost, by leaching, large fractions of the calcium

and magnesium carbonates that were in the parent material. Moreover, the B horizon of such soils has received much iron and clay carried down from the A horizon. These effects reflect not only a good supply of circulating water but also an abundance of organic acid furnished by plants. West of the critical line, where circulating solutions are in shorter supply and chemically weaker, carbonates accumulate in the upper part of the soil, making it strongly alkaline in contrast to acidic soils of humid regions. An important part of the accumulation results from evaporation of water that rises in capillary channels, bringing dissolved salts from a lower zone. In large areas of western Texas and adjoining states the carbonates deposited in this way have built up a solid, almost impervious layer, which halts the development of a mature soil profile. Such *a layer of calcium carbonate developed in a soil profile* is **caliche** (kă lē′che).

A soil that has calcium-rich upper horizons is a **pedocal** (pĕd′ō-kăl; Gr. *pedon,* soil, and the first syllable of *calcium*). *A soil in which much clay and iron have been added to the B horizon* is a **pedalfer** (pĕd-ăl′fer; symbols for aluminum and iron— Al and Fe— added to the root). West of the general dividing line shown in Figure 7–17 there are, of course, many limited areas that have rainfall higher than the average for the region. In some such areas the soils belong in the pedalfer group. Many mountainous parts of the continent as a whole, especially in areas of luxuriant conifer forests, have *podsols,* which are

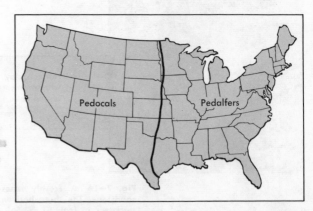

Fig. 7–17. A general division of soils in the United States into two major classes determined by climate. West of the dividing line many variations in kinds of soil are found in mountainous districts. (Courtesy of A. N. Strahler, after C. F. Marbut.)

pedalfer soils strongly leached by solutions rich in humic acids. These acids have removed most of the calcium and iron, and commonly the upper part of the soil profile is light gray to nearly white.

In Arctic regions soils are generally immature and stony because their development is disturbed and chemical changes are slow. Large desert areas, whether warm or cold, are almost without real soil, and a large share of the little that has formed is stony, lacking in organic matter, and alkaline.

Most soils developed at moderate altitudes in humid tropical lands are conspicuously different from those found in cooler parts of the temperate zones. The basic cause of this difference seems to be organic. In temperate regions organic matter accumulates, but under higher temperatures certain bacteria destroy much of the humus, except in swampy areas. Hence in many tropical soils the acids from decaying vegetation are ineffective in leaching out iron, which accumulates steadily. Large areas in southeast Asia, Brazil, Cuba, and other parts of the tropics with seasonal rainfall are covered with thick red crusty regolith called *laterite* (lăt'ĕr-īte) from the Latin word *later,* brick; the hard crust has been cut and used as building bricks, as in the famous ruins of Cambodia in southeast Asia. In very old laterites this oxide is so concentrated and plant food is so deficient that even with a high rainfall the vegetation grows poorly. In some laterites the concentration and volume of iron oxide make valuable ore deposits.

Laterite, then, is *a reddish residual product of moist-tropical weathering, rich in oxides of iron and aluminum.* Commonly, these red crusty deposits are 20 feet or more thick. Manganese and nickel, as well as iron, are metallic concentrates in some laterites. No doubt these varied products reflect differences in composition of the parent rocks. The peculiar composition of a laterite is indicated by the analyses quoted in Table 7–1.

Other deeply weathered regoliths in the humid tropics contain little iron but have large volumes of hydrous aluminum oxide, used widely as an ore for metallic aluminum. This material is known as **bauxite,** which is not a distinctive mineral but *a mixture of hydrated oxides,* usually *expressed by the generalized chemical formula* $Al_2O_3 \cdot nH_2O$. The parent material was probably a rock made largely of feldspar.

Rate of soil formation. Development of good soil requires a much longer time than a human generation, and we have little definite evidence on which to base any convincing estimate of the rate. Soil scientists are sure that acid soils of humid regions are developed as rapidly as any, and from their studies they hazard the guess that on sandy material with a dense forest cover a fair soil might develop in 100 to 200 years. But this seems to assume that the forest, to furnish abundant organic acid, would be there before the soil in which trees could grow. This is a situation to which the old adage "the first hundred years are the hardest" may aptly apply. Probably

Table 7–1

	Earth's Crust	Average of 18 representative soils		Laterite, India depth below surface	
		A Horizon	B Horizon	2 ft.	19 ft.
Silicon oxide	61.28	76.46	76.46	2.70	4.70
Aluminum oxide	15.34	9.97	11.77	23.75	8.20
Iron oxide	6.26	3.59	5.74	73.50	87.05
Magnesium oxide	3.90	0.60	0.85	—	trace
Calcium oxide	4.96	1.04	1.01	—	—
Total	91.74	91.66	95.83	99.95	99.95

Remaining constituents are oxides of potassium, sodium, manganese, titanium, phosphorus, and sulphur

Average percentage composition of 18 good agricultural soils, compared with a laterite in India and with the mean composition of the crust. All analyses show inorganic oxides, water-free. Sources: Column 1, F. W. Clarke, U.S. Geol. Survey Bull. 770, 1924; Columns 2 and 3, U.S. Dept. of Agriculture Yearbook, 1938, p. 917; Columns 4 & 5, J. S. Joffe, Pedology, Rutgers Univ. Press, 1936 (recomputed, water-free).

more time is required for the early rock decay and some accumulation of organic material than for any later stage in the process. Once plant growth is well started, the development of soil must accelerate.

We have examples of weathered buildings that give us some measure of the process, but they leave important questions unanswered. If the sandstone in the pillars of Durham Castle (Fig. 7–1) had lain on the ground instead of standing upright during those centuries, would they have decayed more or less? We hear of soil on venerable towers, long abandoned, but there is no assurance of the date at which soil development started, and conceivably the old inhabitants had a roof garden to which soil was carried. Wherever man's activities are involved, special caution must be used in weighing evidence because human beings tend to complicate nature's records.

Quantities of good soil have been lost to erosion because of bad farming practices (p. 149), and vigorous remedial measures have within comparatively few years restored some of this ruined farm land to partial usefulness. But the rebuilding started with subsoil and parts of the upper layer A (Fig. 7–16), not "from scratch," and even so the task has taken much labor and expense, not to mention the barren years with no return from the soil. Whatever length of time is necessary for soil development or partial restoration, from a human point of view the time is long and soil should not be wasted.

Broad appraisal of weathering

Its part in erosion. Weathering of rocks is not an isolated process; it is closely related to other activities at the Earth's surface, all of which are working toward the same end, the wearing away of lands. Weathering attacks exposed bedrock, and as particles are loosened they are washed off by rain or blown away by wind. Larger pieces fall to the ground, where weathering agents continue to break them up as gravity urges them down slopes. Beneath gently sloping surfaces weathering proceeds until considerable thicknesses of soil accumulate, but, as this cover forms, it creeps, flows, or slides to lower levels. Continually the water soaking through the soil robs it of soluble materials. Surface water forms gullies and washes loose material into larger streams, and, as the moving regolith arrives at the margins of valleys, these streams take their toll directly (Chap. 9).

Weathering and moving of rock materials proceed together; *weathering is a part of erosion.*

Some of the rock particles in transport are dropped temporarily at the bases of mountains, on the floodplains of streams, on beaches, or in sand dunes; but in the upper parts of these deposits break-up and chemical decay continue. There is no escape from the unrelenting attack until the debris is deeply buried on land or spread out in lakes or on ocean floors and there enters into the formation of new sedimentary strata.

Nature's complex laboratory. In the chemical weathering of rocks minerals are broken down and elements enter into new combinations, some of them more or less soluble in water. The role of carbonic and humic acids in redistributing materials during the development of soil profiles has been outlined (p. 127). But much of the dissolved material is carried away by water which makes its way into streams directly or by devious courses underground (Chap. 11). During its slow movement through tiny underground passages, water deposits dissolved mineral matter between sand grains and larger sedimentary particles, thus converting loose sediments into strong sedimentary rocks (Chap. 17).

Vast quantities of dissolved mineral matter are carried by streams into the oceans. World-wide studies of the water in major streams give a basis for reliable estimates of quantities of various salts added to the ocean water year by year. Two of the dissolved salts in which we are most interested are sodium chloride and calcium carbonate. Ocean water contains only a small fraction of its capacity for dissolving sodium chloride, and at one time this fact was made the basis for estimating the age of the Earth. The reasoning was as follows: all sodium in ocean water has been contributed by water from land; all sodium thus contributed is retained in the ocean water; dividing the total sodium content of the oceans by the present yearly increment will give the length of time the process has operated.

Now we see several serious flaws in this argument. (1) The volume of ocean water probably has increased steadily by additions of juvenile water (p. 84). (2) Sodium ions react with clay, and therefore an unknown but sizable quantity is concealed in deposits on ocean floors. (3) Large quantities of sodium chloride have been precipitated in shallow seas under arid or semiarid climatic zones and are buried under younger sediments. (4) Much sea water, containing sodium, is locked in the pores of marine sediments that now lie beneath the surfaces of continents. (5) A considerable part of the sodium now carried by streams is derived from old marine deposits that contain beds of salt or sea water that was trapped in pore spaces of marine sediments.

Thus the economy of nature is highly complex. Land erosion makes large contributions to the oceans, but this is not a one-way procedure, as emphasized by the vast quantities of limestone and dolostone deposited on sea floors but now comprising important parts of mountain blocks on land (Figs. 1–5, 3–1).

Aside from the soluble products, the weathering in past ages is recorded amply in the sedimentary rocks. Shales, which consist chiefly of clay minerals produced by chemical weathering, make up much more than half the volume of these rocks now exposed on continents. Clay and quartz sand resist chemical attack, and in large part these materials have no doubt passed through repeated histories of uplift, erosion, and deposition.

Close study of weathering and its products reveals the large role of chemical agents in geologic activities. Geochemistry is a branch of geology of growing importance.

SUMMARY

1. Rocks exposed to weather are subject to breakup and decay.

2. Mechanical breaking of rocks speeds chemical attack, and some chemical changes cause mechanical rupture.

3. Carbonic acid, supplied in part by the air but chiefly by plants and animals, is a prime factor in chemical weathering.

4. Kinds and rates of weathering are strongly affected by climatic conditions. Warmth and moisture are essential for thorough chemical changes.

5. Rugged topography favors rapid weathering. Thorough decay to large depth requires much time, but some kinds of rock respond more quickly than others.

6. Soils are a major product of weathering. The nature of a mature soil is determined partly by the parent material but chiefly by climate.

7. Distinctive zones in the vertical section of a soil determine its profile. Profiles of mature soils in moist temperate climates are strikingly alike.

8. Under a moist temperate climate, iron, carbonates, and much clay are leached from the upper soil zone by humic acids. Some soils of this type are excessively acidic.

9. With deficient rainfall, carbonates accumulate in the upper part of a soil, making it alkaline, impervious, and unproductive.

10. Laterite, a product of weathering in many tropical areas, has excessive iron and aluminum. Destruction of humus by bacteria is largely responsible.

11. Weathering plays a major role in land erosion, and is an essential link in a great chain of chemical activities on land and in the sea.

REFERENCES

Climate and man, by numerous authors: U. S. Department of Agriculture, Yearbook for 1941, especially p. 265–287, 599–613.

Keller, W. D., 1957, Chemistry in introductory geology: Columbia, Missouri, Lucas Brothers.

Lyon, T. L., Buckman, H. O., and Brady, N. C., 1952, The nature and properties of soils, 5th ed.: New York, The Macmillan Co.

Reiche, Parry, 1950. A survey of weathering processes and products, revised edition: Albuquerque, Univ. of New Mexico Publications in Geology.

Soils and men, by numerous authors: U. S. Department of Agriculture, Yearbook for 1938, 1,232 p.

CHAPTER 8. MASS-WASTING

Shifting of rock and regolith   Varied rates of movement   Sliding and flowing debris

Widening of valleys   Importance in erosion   Practical problems

Polygons formed by freezing and thawing of regolith in Arctic lands. Northeast Greenland. The complete polygon within the view is about 10 feet across.
(A. L. Washburn.)

Definition

Frank, a small coal-mining town in western Alberta, lies at the foot of Turtle Mountain, which has a steep front 3,000 feet high. No doubt the people in the valley thought of their mountain as strong and changeless, but one morning in the early spring of 1903 their faith in terra firma was rudely shaken. With a great roar, a mass of rock half a mile square and hundreds of feet thick rushed from the highest peak down the mountain front, wiped out a large part of the town and many of its people, and spread onward in a wide sheet of broken rubble. Momentum carried the front of the sheet about 2 miles across the valley from the base of the mountain and 400 feet up the opposite side. In less than 2 minutes 40 million cubic yards of rock was moved from mountain to lowland and thoroughly shattered.

The occurrence at Frank is by no means unique. Every year there are similar movements, small or large, in the world's mountainous districts. A little observant study convinces us that these sudden events are only the most conspicuous examples of downslope movements, for the most part slow but almost continuous, by which the lands are being lowered. Because these movements under the direct pull of gravity affect large masses of regolith and bedrock as units and because they are part of the general wasting to which all the lands are subject, the entire process is called *mass-wasting, the en masse downslope movement of rock debris*.

A highly important part of mass-wasting goes on at an imperceptibly slow pace. Between this extreme and the explosive violence at Turtle Mountain there are many rates and kinds of movement. Let us proceed from the swift and most obvious kinds, to those with intermediate speeds, thence to movements so slow that they are detected only by indirect evidence.

Rapid movements

Bedrock masses. After the Frank disaster, geologists studied Turtle Mountain to determine if possible whether another avalanche of rock might be in the making. They found that numerous fractures, steeply inclined toward the valley, cut across the limestone beds that make the mountain ridge (Fig. 8–1). A large mass under North Peak appears to be unstable and in danger of collapse, though there is no way to predict how soon this may happen. If the fractures crossing the layers of limestone extend almost continuously under the peak, as suggested by the broken line S-S' in Figure 8–1, then little besides frictional resistance on the base of the mass holds it from sliding under ceaseless pull by a large component of gravity. Even if the fractures do not now connect, forces are at work to extend them. Water percolates from the top along many openings, enlarging them by solution. During a considerable part of each year melting snow supplies abundant water, and with repeated freezing and thawing some fractures are enlarged by frost wedging. Probably, too, the mining of coal near the base of the mountain was removing some support from the weakened mass. The geologists suggested moving the townsite from the vicinity of North Peak and shifting the mining operations from that critical zone.

A *landslide is a perceptible downslope movement of a mass of bedrock, regolith, or a mixture of the two*. The term *rockslide* is sometimes applied to *the sliding of a mass consisting chiefly of detached bed-*

rock. The nature of motion in the Turtle Mountain slide must have been complex. If the North Peak mass should be released, at the start all parts of its base would actually slide on the bedrock beneath. But, on reaching the irregular surface below S′ (Fig. 8–1), it would have such velocity that the mass as a whole would continue on a nearly straight course as a giant projectile, and much of it would pass above the concave surface between S′ and X. On striking the ground lower down, the block would be shattered into countless pieces. Although the momentum would carry all fragments in the same general direction, there would be friction of the particles against each other and a rolling, turbulent motion within the mass with some resemblance to the flowage of a liquid. At the base there would be sliding over the uneven ground against enormous frictional resistance.

Related to the landslide is a movement known as *rockfall, the descent of a rock mass either vertically from a cliff or by a series of leaps along an irregular slope*. An event illustrating this kind of movement occurred in 1881 in the Swiss Alps, where steep to-

pography favors rapid mass-wasting. Near the village of Elm a large slate quarry was cut obliquely into the steep mountain slope, high above the valley floor. Continued enlargement of this quarry pit took away more and more support from the bedrock above, and suddenly a great block nearly a quarter of a mile long sheared off and slid steeply to the quarry floor. The impact broke the mass into innumerable pieces that traveled in flat paths through the air until they struck obliquely against the opposite valley wall. This glancing blow broke the pieces further and turned the flying mass down the valley. These fragments then settled into a sheet that moved with decreasing speed along the valley floor until its front was more than a mile from the quarry site. Because of the long flight of blocks through the air, this event has been called the Elm rockfall, though actually the total movement was of complex nature, as was that at Turtle Mountain. The Elm disaster has especial interest because it probably was touched off by human activity, the quarrying operation.

Some rapid mass movements of bedrock are properly called slides in their full extent. Such a move-

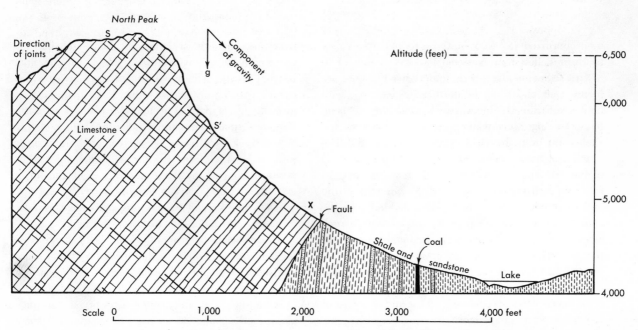

Fig. 8–1. Vertical section across Turtle Mountain, Alberta. This section is directly north of the 1903 slide area. S-S′, base of mass now in danger of sliding. (Modified from Geological Survey of Canada, Dept. of Mines, Memoir 27, 1912.)

135

A

ment occurred in 1925 in the Gros Ventre Valley south of Yellowstone National Park, Wyoming (Fig. 8–2, **A**). Sedimentary beds underlying the area are inclined about 20° to the north (Fig. 8–2, **B**), with clay shale directly below thick sandstone. During heavy spring rains water percolated down to the shale, and by thorough wetting of the clay the frictional resistance was much reduced along the base of the overlying sandstone, on which was a cover of soil with a large growth of forest. A wide strip of the sandstone finally broke away and skidded into the valley, where it piled up as a mass of broken rock mixed with soil that effectively dammed the river to make a sizable lake. A farmer in his field with a team heard the initial roar, saw the mountainside rushing at him, and galloped away just in time to escape burial. His cattle, slower of wit and less fleet of foot, were overwhelmed.

Rapid movements of regolith. In the sliding of masses detached from bedrock, quantities of the overlying regolith are carried along and become thoroughly mixed with broken blocks in the final heap of rubble. The moving mass also plows up and carries with it any soil or other loose material that may lie in its path. But many masses of regolith, large and small, move independently of the bedrock. When thick rock waste on a steep mountainside is saturated with water from exceptional rainfall or rapid melting of snow, the added weight and lubricating effect may cause a large body of the wet material to break from its mooring and move, rapidly or slowly and haltingly, to lower ground.

All downslope movements of regolith in large bodies is complex, though to the average citizen all are landslides. Much actual sliding occurs at the base of some masses, especially of those that move directly over bedrock. Generally, uneven frictional resistance along the base and sides causes the material at some depth to flow, whereas the upper part, containing less water, is broken locally into rough blocks bound-

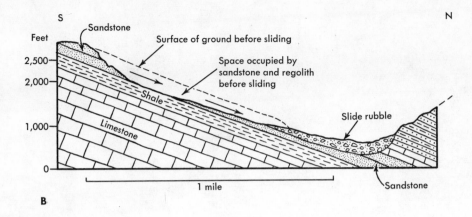

S   N

Fig. 8–2. A. Scar and rubble heap made by the landslide in the Gros Ventre Range, Wyoming, in 1925. View from the air, looking SSW. Top of scar is 2,200 feet vertically above valley. Lake formed as a result of the slide extends about 3 miles upstream (left). (John S. Shelton.) B. Profile and section along the course of the Gros Ventre slide. Arrows indicate movement of the sliding mass. The amount of rubble shown in section appears too little because much of the material spread up and down the valley at the front of the slide. (After W. C. Alden, American Institute of Mining and Metallurgical Engineers, Transactions, vol. 76, 1928.)

ed by low scarps. As the front of the mass moves onto a gentler slope, it is slowed by friction, and material from the rear piles up by flowage and by formation of new slip surfaces to form a hummocky ridge. The upslope portion of the mass is thinned and broken as some material moves away from parts held back by friction. Usually a scarp marks the upper limit of the displacement. Movements of this kind, started on steep slopes in California by the earthquake of 1906, differed according to the kind of regolith affected and the nature of the slope.

Some geologists who have studied these rapid movements of regolith closely have set up a detailed classification, in which special terms express the varied nature of materials and kinds of movement. It will serve our purpose to recognize *debris slides and flows, mudflows,* and *earthflows,* with the understanding that many combinations of flowage and sliding are represented in any one mass of varied loose rock materials.

Debris slides and flows. A high, steep ridge generally has along its flank a thick accumulation of rock debris (Fig. 8–3). Much of this material consists of blocks that have fallen and rolled from cliffs; finer rock waste is added partly by running water, partly by chemical weathering on the slope. Under a humid climate, soil is developed on such steep slopes, which commonly are covered with vegetation and tend to be stable. In mountains near timberline, and in regions that are arid or semiarid, loose debris on many slopes lies near the angle of repose and is set in motion by a moderate disturbance, such as the fall of a large block from a cliff. Movements of loose materials on these slopes occur frequently; some are so massive and swift they are reported as *avalanches.*

A rapid downslope movement of a mass consisting of regolith of varied texture is a **debris slide.** These movements occur even on steep forest-covered slopes in rugged mountains but are more common where vegetation is scarce. In arid parts of our southwestern

Fig. 8–3. View west from Mount Evans, in the high Rocky Mountains of Colorado. Loose rubble covers slopes below high cliffs of bedrock. Debris in right foreground lies near the angle of repose for coarse blocks. (Ewing Galloway.)

states exceptional heavy rains precipitate sliding by the added weight of water and by wetting the finer debris, thus providing lubrication. Slides move from steeper onto gentler slopes, partly under momentum but in many cases by flowage of a muddy matrix inclosing rock fragments of many sizes. Thus a debris slide may pass into *debris flow,* which *is downslope movement in water-saturated rock waste, of varied texture* (Fig. 8–4, **A**). Masses of debris that have moved by sliding and flowage are recognized from their characteristic form and composition, even after much dissection by running water (Fig. 8–4, **B**).

The coarseness of debris in some masses that have moved several miles is surprising (Fig. 8–5). Large bodies of extremely coarse blocky waste build up only adjacent to high steep ridges. Downslope movement of such material over several miles is explained by (1) momentum gained in a swift start on the steep slope, (2) thorough wetting of fine materials that form a considerable part of the debris, and (3)

opportunity for spreading on a wide area that has continuous slope of moderate degree. Forward movement of the mass may continue for some distance by imperceptible creep after the rapid flow stops.

Mudflows. *Fast movement of a mass of regolith that has the consistency of mud* is a **mudflow.** The ease of movement depends on the proportion of admixed water; there are all gradations from mud so stiff it barely moves under its weight to a thin, soupy mixture just beyond what would be accepted as muddy water. In fact, many mudflows start, after heavy rains in mountain valleys, as muddy streams that continue to pick up loose material until the front portion of each stream becomes a slowly moving dam of mud and included rubble, extending to each steep wall of the valley and urged along by the pent-up water behind it. On reaching open country at the mountain front the dam collapses, the flood water pours around and over it, and thin mud mixed with blocks of rock is spread in a wide sheet, with destruc-

A

B

Fig. 8–4. A. A large debris slide that started in the steep upper part of a valley became a debris flow as it moved to a lower gradient. Resistance to movement is indicated by the steep front of the mass. Stream channels in the larger valley were covered and the drainage diverted by the invading mass of debris. Lost River Range, southern Idaho. (John S. Shelton.) B. Coarse rubble representing an old debris slide and flow in the Mohave Desert, southern California. The source of the material was the steep mountain front, upper right of view. The sheet of debris is several miles long, more than 2 miles wide. It has been much dissected by running water, an indication that the movement occurred long ago from a human point of view. (Robert C. Frampton.)

Fig. 8—5. A sample of coarse, blocky material in a debris slide. At lower right the slide overrode a section of water-laid gravel. Note contrast between this older deposit and the unassorted blocks in the slide. (John S. Shelton.)

tive effects to farms and villages. Local floods in canyons on the steep western flank of the Wasatch Range in Utah have brought disastrous mudflows to communities near the base of the range within the last century.

A mudflow is especially destructive because of its high density, which enables it to move large, heavy objects. Houses and barns in the paths of some mudflows have been carried from their foundations, and blocks of rock many feet in diameter are pushed along, rolling and sliding in the slimy mixture, some of them finally coming to rest on gentle slopes far out from a mountain front.

Mudflows are most common in semiarid regions, where cover of protecting vegetation is scant (Fig. 8–6). Temporary streams from exceptional floods pick up quantities of weathered material that has accumulated during years without heavy rainfall. Nearly all the available water becomes mixed with this material, and the resulting thin mud moves from

slopes and small stream courses into large valleys, which may become partly filled as the water evaporates or soaks into the underlying regolith and the mud becomes too stiff for further motion.

Earthflows. The ease and rapidity of movement in a typical mudflow is made possible by excess of water beyond the amount required to saturate the loose materials. With less abundant water, a mass of wet regolith moves slowly and unevenly, as indicated by small scarps near the margins where some parts of the moving mass pull away from others. This *sluggish, halting flowage in a body of water-soaked regolith* is *earthflow*. Some high mountain areas in which bedrock is very weak and easily weathered are afflicted with large earthflows. One of the best known examples is the Slumgullion flow (Fig. 8–7) of Colorado, in a region of old volcanic rocks, including thick ash beds that weather to clay and silt. As we see it today, the Slumgullion occupies a large valley in 6 miles of its length and most of its width and

Fig. 8–6. Marginal part of a fresh mudflow after drying. Note the coarser slope debris beneath the flow. East base of Stillwater Range, Nevada. (Eliot Blackwelder.)

Fig. 8–7. The Slumgullion earthflow near Lake City, Colorado, impounding Lake San Cristobal. Chief source of material in the flow is in white areas high on mountain side. (U. S. Geol. Survey.)

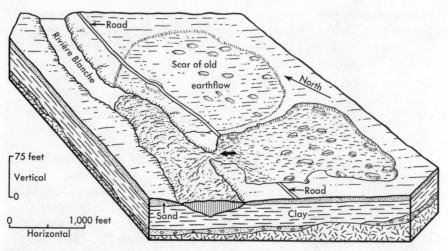

Fig. 8–8. Earthflow in valley of Rivière Blanche, Quebec. Flowage of the saturated soil took place on a very low gradient. (Modified from C. F. S. Sharpe, Columbia University Press.)

Fig. 8–9. Slump and flowage on a steep, grass-covered slope after thorough saturation by rainfall. Note the downslope bulge, compensating the depression made by slumping farther upslope. Berkeley Hills, California. (G. K. Gilbert, U. S. Geol. Survey.)

keeps much of the typical form it had while it was in motion, which in the final stage must have been almost imperceptible. The front of the flow spread across a river valley and still serves as a dam to impound a large lake.

In general, earth flowage occurs only on fairly steep slopes; but large-scale flowage of saturated clay may take place on slopes of less than 1°. The best known example is reported from eastern Canada, where just after a spring thaw clay from layers in ground slightly above a river valley poured slowly through a narrow channel and filled the valley along 2 miles of its length to a depth of 25 feet (Fig. 8–8). The large depression left in the upland was similar to others close by that record older flows of the same kind. Whether or not this exact kind of earthflow is common, it illustrates the ease of movement in clay that is thoroughly wet.

Movements in thick soil on steep slopes, starting abruptly when the ground is water soaked and recurring intermittently, are illustrated in Figure 8–9. The flowing mass leaves a steep scarp in the rear and builds a compensating bulge downslope. Such movements have a wide range in scale, and in some examples actual sliding is as important as flowage (Fig. 8–10).

Slow movements

In a classification of downslope movements there is vague transition between those described as *rapid* and *slow*. On many mountain slopes large bodies of regolith move haltingly and unevenly year after year. Surfaces of such masses have large hummocks, undrained depressions, and large open fissures that mark areas of recent movement. Thawing in early spring, with abundant water from melting snow or exceptional rainfall, starts some creeping movements that strongly tilt or prostrate large trees. These recurrent movements in regolith have been called slow-motion landslides. Probably the movement is a combination of earthflow and soil-creep.

Soil-creep. There is abundant evidence, most of it indirect but in sum total convincing, that regolith on slopes, however gentle, is slowly moving downward under the constant pull of gravity. The *imperceptibly slow downslope movement of regolith is soil-creep*. Its effects are evident in the consistent leaning of old fences, poles, and gravestones, in the derangement of road grades, and in tree trunks with a convex bend downslope, the result of tilting by creep combined with the constant urge to grow vertically (Fig. 8–11, A). Cuts made into bedrock show that steeply inclined layers curve strongly downslope in the zone of weathering, and blocks from distinctive layers have drifted downhill to considerable distances (Fig. 8–11, A, B).

A close cover of grass or other vegetation on sloping ground serves as a protective armor against the formation of gullies, and the casual observer may not suspect that ground so protected loses anything to

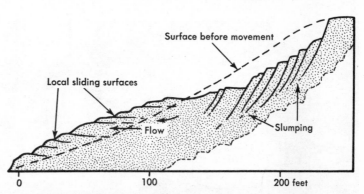

Fig. 8–10. Profile and section through a mass of moving regolith. The movement combines slumping, flowage, and sliding. This diagram represents movement wholly within a thick body of regolith. Locally some masses of debris slide on underlying bedrock.

143

A

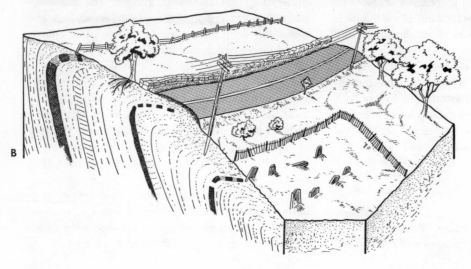

B

Fig. 8—11. A. Regolith above nearly vertical layers of shale and sandstone, exposed in a road cut, Santa Monica Mountains, California. Drag by the creeping regolith has bent all layers strongly downslope. The component c of gravity g is the responsible force. (H. B. Page.) B. Effects of creep on surface features and on bedrock. (Modified from C. F. S. Sharpe, Landslides and Related Phenomena.)

Camera case

Fig. 8—12. Blocks of granite softened by chemical decay and flattened by creep of the regolith. In lower part of the exposure, which is the wall of an artificial cut, the blocks have their original form. Nearer the original surface of the ground, the section of each deformed block appears as a long, thin, white lens. (S. R. Capps, U. S. Geol. Survey.)

erosion except for a little mineral matter dissolved by percolating water. But a little scientific sleuthing shows clearly that the entire regolith is creeping downslope, carrying the vegetation with it. Boulders of granite in some soils have been softened by weathering and drawn out by movement of the inclosing material into long thin sheets (Fig. 8–12).

Many factors contribute to the effectiveness of creep. In regions that have cold winters water in the pore spaces of the mantle freezes and increases in volume. Moreover, considerable water becomes segregated and frozen into layers of clear ice that separate layers of soil or clay (Fig. 8–13, **A**). This ice represents an increase in volume, and so there is uplift of the surface equal to the total thickness of ice layers plus the volume increase in pore spaces. This *lifting of rock waste by expansion in freezing of contained water is **frost heaving**.* On a hillside the surface of the ground is lifted essentially at right angles to the slope; but, when thawing occurs, each point tends to drop vertically and so moves downhill (Fig. 8–13, **B**). Other persistent activities produce effects that are combined to increase displacement of particles in regolith downslope. Animals burrowing into a slope pile most of the material they dig out on the downhill side, and later the burrows are filled by material creeping from upslope. The trampling of animals, wild and domestic, has an appreciable effect in forcing loose material to lower levels. Growing plant roots wedge material chiefly downslope, and cavities formed when roots decay are filled mainly by soil from upslope. Uprooted trees on hillsides tend to move downslope, urging soil and loose stones with them. As blocks of rock on a slope are broken up, most of the pieces fall or roll farther downhill. Removal of mineral matter in solution makes voids that are filled in large part by material urged downslope. These effects through countless repetitions add up to a large total; probably all the mass-wasting accomplished visibly by sliding and flowage is but a small fraction of that accomplished by imperceptible creep.

A special form of creep is common in Arctic regions and high mountains. Ground freezes to great depth, and when weather warms enough to thaw the upper part of the regolith the deeper part stays solidly frozen. Surplus water then can not drain downward, and the thawed layer, from a few inches to

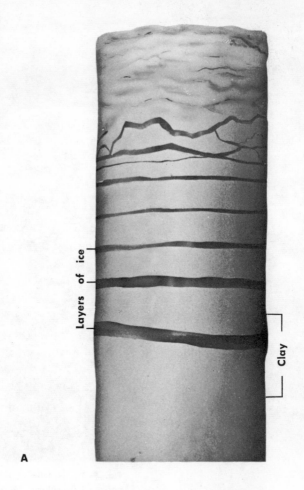

A

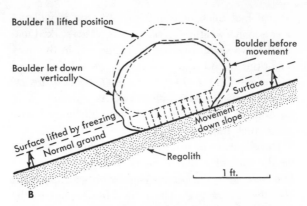

B

Fig. 8–13. A. Test cylinder of clay, after freezing in a laboratory apparatus to which water was admitted. Dark bands are ice, from water drawn in during the freezing. (Stephen Taber.) **B.** A block of rock is moved downslope by alternate freezing and thawing. The diagram explains the mechanism of one step in the movement.

145

Fig. 8–14. A lobe of solifluction debris on the east slope of Hesteskoen, Mesters Vig, in northeast Greenland. (A. L. Washburn.)

several feet thick, becomes so saturated it will not bear a man's weight. On slopes this water-soaked material flows sluggishly, like a stiff liquid; in this way quantities of soil and rock debris are slowly moved downslope (Fig. 8–14). This *slow flowage of water-saturated regolith is solifluction.* As a result of it, the soils in arctic regions are generally mixed with coarse rock fragments.

Development of a talus. Rock fragments loosened on the face of a cliff commonly accumulate into a *talus, a heap of rock waste sloping outward from the cliff that supplies it.* The term *talus* applies to the inclined sheet of fragments as a unit; the *material composing a talus is sliderock* (Figs. 8–15, 7–3). Pieces of bedrock, ranging in size from tiny chips to sizable blocks, are wedged off the cliff by frost ac-

tion or lose support by chemical weathering. They fall on the steep upper part of the talus and by rolling and sliding reach positions of rest on the slope. Characteristically, the profile of a talus is concave upward, steepening in the upper part to the largest angle at which the coarsest fragments will lie; for large angular blocks this is considerably above 30°. In the upper part of an actively growing talus equilibrium is so delicate that the fall of a large block may precipitate violent sliding. Many a climber learns to his sorrow that his weight has the same effect.

Exceptional blocks that fall in a position for rolling gain momentum and continue on to the gentler slope below; but generally the freshest blocks lie in the upper part of the talus. As blocks are weakened by weathering, they give way and thereby start repeated sliding for readjustment. In a moist region weathered materials are washed downslope, and the lower part, or *toe*, of a typical talus merges into a soil-covered slope set with grass or other vegetation (Fig. 8–15). This makes a sort of soil profile that extends laterally, in contrast to the vertical attitude of a normal soil profile.

Recession of high cliffs. Along the Colorado River, in southern Utah, gigantic blocks are sliding down from the steep valley walls and are migrating slowly toward the stream course, thousands of feet away (Fig. 8–16). The Wingate Sandstone, nearly horizontal and hundreds of feet thick, makes sheer cliffs above gentler slopes on weak rocks, largely shale. Vertical fractures cross the sandstone, some of them through its entire thickness, dividing the rock into blocks and columns. Many blocks of the smaller sizes topple from the cliff face and are broken as they hurtle down the steep slope beneath. Larger blocks,

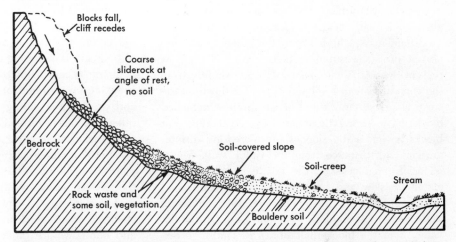

Fig. 8–15. A talus in characteristic relation to bedrock and to a lower soil-covered slope. The creeping regolith is slowly carried away as it reaches the stream. (Modified from C. F. S. Sharpe, Landslides and Related Phenomena.)

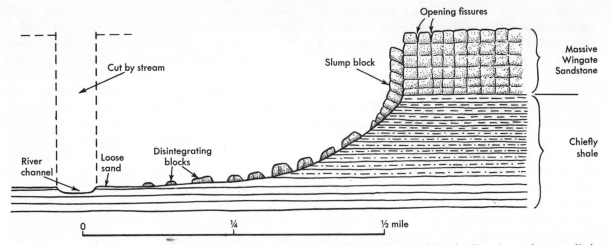

Fig. 8–16. Section across south side of valley of Colorado River in southeastern Utah, showing slumping of blocks and slow movement of debris toward the stream. This action becomes slower as the valley widens.

hundreds of feet in each dimension, sink slowly as the weak shale beneath them gives way under their weight, and rotate backward as they move down on a curved surface of fracture that is concave upward. This form results because the easiest relief is toward the valley. With progressive rotation, the layers in a moving block dip more steeply, and in blocks far out on the valley floor the layers are nearly vertical.

The history of these great blocks, as outlined above, is worked out by study of numerous units in various stages of their slow journey. This is a good example of "geologic detective work." No visible movement of any block has been reported. Conceivably, in the early stages of descent, with the heavy sandstone masses high above the valley, there are abrupt drops measured in feet or tens of feet. At present, we find some masses dropped slightly from the general plateau level and others far down on the steep slope, strongly tilted. These highest detached blocks have been little affected by weathering; but blocks lower on the slope show increasing disintegration with distance from the valley wall. Movement of the blocks on the gentle slopes must be extremely slow and halting; perhaps it consists of imperceptibly slow creep whenever the underlying shale becomes thoroughly wet from rain. On the flat valley floor the blocks halt until the sandstone disintegrates entirely, and the particles are then carried to the stream by soil-creep and running water.

An important kind of mass-wasting seen in these moving blocks is known as *slump, the downward slipping of rock or regolith in a unit mass, usually with backward rotation about a horizontal axis parallel to the parent cliff or slope.* In the example described above the material affected is bedrock. Some slumping is involved also in masses of regolith affected by sliding and earthflow (Figs. 8–9, 8–10).

The moving blocks along the Colorado River bring into focus the importance of mass-wasting in the development of a wide stream valley. As explained in Chapter 10, the stream itself does considerable lateral cutting as it abrades its channel. It is clear, however, that as a stream cuts down it receives a large supply of sediment by mass-wasting on the valley sides. Under a moist climate, the effects of weathering obscure some effects that are clearly displayed in parts of the Colorado Plateau. In Figure 8–16 the part of the val-

ley excavated directly by the stream in vertical down-cutting is suggested diagrammatically. Although the lateral component of abrasion in the main stream and contributions by tributary streams are ignored, proper emphasis is given to the importance of mass-wasting in the widening of a valley.

The role of mass-wasting in erosion

The several agents of erosion work together and react on each other in an intricate way. This interaction will become clearer as other aspects of erosion are discussed in later chapters; but a brief summary statement here will help tie the parts together.

Relation to weathering. A large part of the material moved in mass-wasting has come from the weathering of bedrock. Weathering continues while the material is in transit and helps the mechanism of movement. Breaking up of fragments in a talus removes support and precipitates sliding; the decay of feldspar and other minerals to form clay makes the rock waste flow more easily; solution by water not only aids creep but also weakens bedrock under some slopes and promotes landsliding. Mass-wasting, in turn, increases the effectiveness of weathering. Movement of mantle on hillsides exposes new bedrock to mechanical and chemical attack. Rock fragments moved in landslides and mudflows are broken by impact and grinding, and in this way fresh surfaces are exposed. When great masses of bedrock are smashed into widespread rubble, as by the Frank, Elm, and similar slides, enormous quantities of fresh material are exposed to the attack of weather.

Relation to running water. When a deep gully is cut into loose regolith, the steep banks start slumping and creep begins from both sides toward the new stream channel. On a much larger scale, the deep valleys cut by streams into highlands have set the stage for mass-wasting; the most active movements by sliding, flowage, and creep take place on the steep sides of valleys in mountains and plateaus. Running water and the many forms of mass-wasting are closely geared in the scheme of erosion. Most of the rock waste that moves from the continents to the sea floors is delivered by streams; but the greater part of this material is brought within reach of streams by mass-wasting. This point is well illustrated by the Colorado River valley in Utah (Fig. 8–16). In many mountain

Fig. 8–17. A stage in landsliding at Point Firmin, California. In the expensive development of homesites at this location the lurking danger underground was not suspected. (Spence Air Photos.)

Slump fractures

Break in highway

valleys, such as the Gros Ventre (Fig. 8–2), landslides deliver material faster than the streams can move it immediately. A stream that cuts down rapidly maintains steep valley sides on which mass-wasting operates vigorously, and the supply often exceeds the stream's capacity. In lower country the transfer from slopes to stream is mainly by slow creep, the stream carries away the load as it is delivered, and the whole mechanism is essentially in equilibrium.

Relation to wave erosion. Along many coasts bordered by steep cliffs landslides occur without any regard for man's property rights (Fig. 8–17). Flowage and creep of the regolith also feed material directly to the sea, supplementing the greater loads brought by streams (Chap. 16).

Submarine slides. Erosion does not stop at the seashore. In 1929 a severe earthquake started a great slide of loose material well below sea level south of Newfoundland, breaking and burying several transatlantic cables (Chap. 15). Cables have been broken in other places, probably by movements of this kind.

At the edge of the continental shelf loose sediments lying at the angle of repose can be caused to slide by slight disturbances, and great slides in that location may be much more common than on land. Gravity strives to level not merely the land surfaces but the whole Earth.

Practical considerations

Farming problems. Soil conservationists find it much simpler to check the loss of soil caused by sheet erosion and gullying than to control the large masses moved in creep and slumping. In semiarid parts of several western states overgrazing of range lands has caused increased destruction by rapid mass-wasting, which not only removes the topsoil from large areas but, after mixing this soil with clay and gravel, buries the rich soil of lower areas under the infertile mixture. The only remedy is to restore the protective sod, which requires a program of conservation to prevent the recurrence of overgrazing. Slumping of farm land along deep gullies can be checked by measures, now

149

Fig. 8–18. Slumping of loose regolith in the bank of a stream near Spartanburg, South Carolina. Unless protective measures are taken, this kind of mass-wasting can result in serious loss of soil. (C. F. S. Sharpe, U.S. Soil Conservation Service.)

extensively practiced, that lead to gradual filling of old gullies and prevent new ones from starting. Wasting of rich soil adjacent to streams can be checked by protecting stream banks from erosion during exceptional floods (Fig. 8–18).

Problems for engineers. Some knowledge of the principles of mass-wasting is essential in selecting successful locations for large buildings, bridges, dams, highways, and other engineering works. The St. Francis dam in southern California, which failed with appalling loss of life and property (1927), had one of its abutments in weak bedrock which had been further weakened by sliding movements. This would have been recognized if a competent geologist or an engineer with some knowledge of geology had been consulted. Some engineering works have to be constructed in spite of difficulties from mass-wasting. When

work was begun on the deep excavation known as the Culebra Cut in the Panama Canal, earth-flowage, sliding, and slumping occurred on such a scale that for a time the project appeared to face defeat. It was necessary to reduce the slopes by removing an enormous volume of material beyond the original estimate. Some landslide masses have been stabilized by building drainage tunnels to carry away water that played an important part in the movement. During construction of the Grand Coulee Dam on the Columbia River, a slowly flowing mass of saturated sand and silt gave serious trouble at a critical location until engineers hit on the ingenious plan of running pipes through the wet mass and circulating a freezing mixture; the frozen ground remained stable until the necessary construction was finished.

Private companies and government departments

are put to enormous yearly expense in repairing and rebuilding railroads, highways, aqueducts, and other major structures that are damaged by slides and other movements in rugged country. Some of this cost might be avoided by informed planning; the rest is part of the price we pay for civilized living on an unstable Earth.

SUMMARY

1. Rock materials move downslope in response to the leveling tendency of gravity.

2. Landslides involve masses of detached bedrock and large quantities of regolith. Rockfall, the dropping of rock masses almost vertically in an area of rugged relief, may continue as a landslide.

3. Movements in large bodies of water-soaked regolith are complex. Sliding movement on a steep slope commonly ends in sluggish flow on flat land at the base.

4. Regolith containing abundant fine material and saturated with water moves freely in a mudflow.

Large mudflows move massive blocks of rock and often destroy the works of man.

5. Soil and other regolith that is moderately saturated or lies on a low gradient moves sluggishly as earthflow.

6. Soil-creep operates imperceptibly wherever fine regolith lies on a sloping surface. Freezing and thawing, activities of animals and plants, solution, and other agencies are responsible for soil-creep.

7. Solifluction commonly operates when thawing occurs in the upper part of deeply frozen ground.

8. Taluses, made of sliderock below cliffs, commonly grade into soil-covered slopes.

9. An important part of widening a stream valley is performed by mass-wasting from the sides toward the stream which carries away the rock waste as it arrives.

10. Mass-wasting is intimately related to weathering and to erosion by running water and waves.

11. Many problems in agriculture and engineering result from the mass movement of rock materials.

REFERENCES

Eckel, E. B., editor, 1958, Landslides in engineering practice: Highway Research Board, Special Report 29, National Research Council.

Howe, Ernest, 1909, Landslides in the San Juan Mountains, Colorado, including a consideration of their causes and their classification: U. S. Geol. Survey Prof. Paper 67.

Sharpe, C. F. S., 1938, Landslides and related phenomena: New York, Columbia Univ. Press.

Terzaghi, Karl, 1950, Mechanism of landslides: Geol. Soc. America, Berkey Volume, p. 83–123.

CHAPTER 9. RUNNING WATER

Geologic importance   Stream flow and stream energy   Economy of a stream   Geologic activities of streams   Steep rocky channels   Broad valley floors   Braided streams, fans, deltas   Stability principle

Yellowstone River, Yellowstone National Park.

ANDREAS FEININGER

Geologic importance of streams

Stream activities. If you look at a small stream that has a moderately rapid current, you can, as a rule, see that the water is flowing at different rates at various points. Out in midstream the flow is more rapid than near the banks, where eddies are usually in sight. If the stream is clear and the bed consists of sand or gravel, you can see pebbles and sand grains moving downstream. Pebbles are likely to be rolling or sliding intermittently along the stream bed, whereas sand grains seem to hop downstream in long jumps, with rests of varied length between jumps.

A walk up or down the stream probably will show that the channel winds from side to side in a rather smooth system of curves. Perhaps the stream bank, undercut by the current at the outer side of a curve, is slumping into the stream, and, if the bank is of sand, the current can be seen distributing the sand grains along the bed.

Look again, during or after a heavy rain. The stream may appear swollen, and turbid with more silt than was being carried at the earlier time.

It will probably occur to you that all of these activities are related and that all are responses to a coordinated group of physical principles. Observation and experiment by geologists and engineers indicate that this is indeed the case and that stream activities are related to each other in a very complex way. These relationships are fundamental to an understanding of geology because the stream you have been watching is one of the millions of drainage ways by which water from rain and snow runs down over the land toward the sea (Fig. 9–1). Running water is a prime sculptor of the land, and the sediments it deposits form an important part of the rocks of the Earth's crust.

Streams as part of the hydrologic cycle. We noted in Figure 2–10, **B**, that a layer of water 30 inches thick is dropped onto the United States annually. Of this layer, 21 inches evaporates and 9 inches forms

runoff. We define **runoff** as *the part of the precipitation that appears in surface streams.* Runoff consists of two parts: **surface runoff** is *the part of the runoff that has flowed over the surface to the nearest stream;* **ground-water runoff** is *the part of the runoff that has traveled underground before reaching a stream.*

As the average altitude in the United States is about 2,500 feet, our 9-inch layer of water falls through that vertical distance as gravity pulls it down to sea level. The potential energy of the falling layer of water, equal to the weight of the water times the height of the land, is tremendous. This potential energy is converted into the kinetic energy of stream flow, most of which is consumed—that is, converted into heat energy—by friction. The small proportion of the kinetic energy not so consumed is spent in geologic work—in picking up and carrying rock particles.

Streams as geologic agents. Even though the proportion of kinetic energy spent in geologic work is small, its total value is greater than that of any other single rock-moving process. We can appreciate this when we observe that most of the world's landscapes consist of stream valleys with intervening hills. Running water (combined with mass-wasting processes) is, then, the greatest agency by which the land is

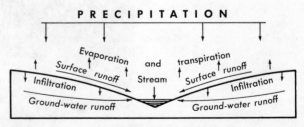

Fig. 9–1. Precipitation is disposed of by evaporation and transpiration, surface runoff into the nearest stream, and infiltration into the ground, followed by percolation through the ground (as ground water, Chap. 11), followed by emergence in a valley. The path shown for the last is only one of many possible paths.

eroded and the chief means of transport of the sediment resulting from such erosion.

Some of the sediment is deposited by streams on the land, at least temporarily. *Alluvium,* the general name for all *sediment deposited in land environments by streams*, exists in great quantity, and still larger quantities of it have been converted into sedimentary rocks. Much of the sediment, however, is carried into the sea and deposited there. The continental shelves consist partly of rocks made from such sediment. Indeed, streams are among the chief agencies by which the sedimentary rocks of the Earth's crust were accumulated.

In summary, streams are important in geology because (1) in combination with mass-wasting they are the principal sculptors of the land and (2) they are one of the chief agencies by which sediment is deposited, afterward to become sedimentary rocks. Economically, streams are important also because (1) they are a significant and increasing source of water supply, (2) they are a relatively small but essential source of water power, and (3) alluvium is a common underground storage reservoir. Other economic aspects of streams are (1) when in flood, streams can cause damage that requires measures for stream control and (2) rainwater running off over pastures and cultivated fields is probably the chief cause of loss of valuable soil by erosion.

Stream flow and stream energy

To begin with, a *stream* can be defined as *a body of water carrying rock particles and flowing down a slope along a definite path*. The path is the stream's channel, and the rock particles are an essential part of the stream itself.

Gradient and velocity. In any given part of its course a stream, then, is a quantity of water flowing down a slope at a certain average velocity. *A slope measured along a stream* is usually referred to as the stream's *gradient.* The gradients of some mountain streams exceed 300 or even 400 feet per mile, whereas downstream parts of the Mississippi River have gradients of less than 0.5 foot per mile. Gradients in many streams range between 10 and 20 feet per mile.

Average velocity is usually expressed in terms of feet per second or miles per hour. Velocities greater than 20 mph are unusual; on the other hand, veloci-

ties in some streams are less than 0.5 mph. In the majority of streams velocities lie between these values, most of them probably nearer the lower value than the higher.

Stream flow: turbulence. It has been demonstrated in the laboratory, by means of colored tracer dyes, that in a body of fluid moving very slowly the water particles travel in parallel paths. This kind of flow is *streamline* (or laminar) *flow,* defined as *flow without turbulence*. As we shall see later, the movement of ground water (Fig. 11–3) and also that of glaciers (Fig. 13–6) is generally streamline. However, the water in almost all natural streams flows so rapidly that the streamlines bend, become thoroughly confused, and form eddies, or turbulence. We can define *turbulent flow* simply as *flow characterized by eddies* (Figs. 9–2, 9–3).

Turbulence, however, is not uniformly intense from side to side of a stream nor from stream surface to stream bed. It is commonly greatest in two places (Fig. 9–4): the top center of the cross section, where forward velocity is greatest, and near the stream bed, where contact between water and bed sets up eddying.

Utilization of stream energy. Most of the turbulence shown in the top center of Figure 9–4 uses up energy by internal friction—that is, friction between particles of water. But part of the turbulence near the sides and bottom of the channel uses up energy by external friction against the channel itself and against loose particles of rock. Some of this activity moves rock particles and erodes the channel. This is geologic work.

Let us see how much of a stream's energy actually performs geologic work. Total energy, measured between any two points on the stream's course, is proportional to the mass of the water multiplied by the difference of altitude between the points. Most of it is used up (that is, converted into heat energy) in friction. As the velocity of flowing water increases with increasing gradient, turbulence increases and therefore friction increases, until the rate of consumption of energy equals the energy available. In this way the flow of a stream is self-regulating; in effect, turbulence acts as a brake on the velocity of the stream.

Most of the energy of a stream is dissipated in brak-

155

Fig. 9–2. Turbulent flow in the Potomac River at Great Falls, upstream from Washington, D. C. (The New York Times.)

ing by turbulence. This braking, by internal friction, acts to reduce substantially the energy available to erode the channel and carry away particles of rock. Yet, despite the fact that the proportion is small, the geologic work done by streams over long period of time is very great, as is evident in the large dimensions of some valleys and the great volumes of alluvium on the land.

Economy of a stream

A stream such as an irrigation canal, flowing in a concrete channel, can be studied independently of the channel because the channel is altered hardly at all by the stream. Most natural streams, however, flow through channels consisting partly or wholly of alluvium or other loose material, which they move from place to place, and so the channels are continually being altered. Because stream and channel are closely related and are ever-changing, they have to be considered together as an interrelated system. We can think of the *economy* of the stream and its channel as *the input and consumption of energy within the system and the changes that result.*

Factors in the economy. The economy of the sys-

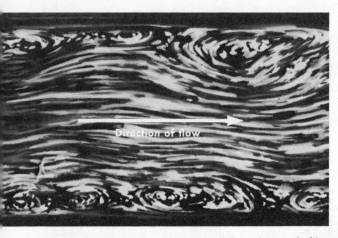

Fig. 9–3. Turbulent flow in an open channel, seen looking down onto surface of stream. Turbulence at the surface is greatest near the channel sides, owing to frictional drag, but is much greater at depth, as shown in Figure 9–4. (Drawn from a photograph in Prandtl and Tietjens, Applied Hydro- and Aeromechanics; courtesy Engineering Societies Monographs Committee.)

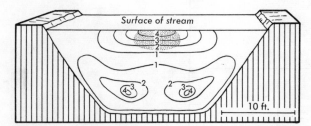

Fig. 9–4. Schematic cross section of a stream flowing toward the observer. Shading indicates area of maximum forward ve- locity. Numbered contours indicate intensity of turbulence, in- creasing from 1 to 4. (Simplified from John Leighly, Univ. Calif. Publs. in Geog., vol. 6, 1932, p. 7.)

tem depends on a continual interplay among four factors:

1. **Discharge** (*the quantity of water passing a given point in a unit of time*). Discharge is usually ex- pressed in cubic feet per second.

2. *Channel size and shape.*

3. **Load** (*the quantity of material the stream car- ries*). The load consists of rock particles of various sizes plus matter in solution.

4. *Velocity.*

These four factors in the stream's economy are meas- ured systematically at selected points along large and small streams for purposes of flood control, irrigation, water supply, and the like. The U. S. Geological Sur- vey, for example, maintains nearly 6,500 measure- ment points in various parts of the United States.

Relation of stream to channel. In order to see how the four factors are related to each other and how the channel reacts to changes in the stream, we can stand on the bank of a small stream and watch. With a sud- den downpour of rain upstream, we can see the water beginning to rise. In our small stream the change is apparent from hour to hour or even within a shorter time. Evidently discharge is increasing; so is velocity, as we can guess from the rate at which driftwood floats by. The energy in the system is increasing. Also the water is getting muddy: the load is increasing. The explanation of at least some of the mud becomes evident when we see a chunk of earth from the op- posite bank suddenly cave in and disappear beneath the water. The stream is eroding its channel. Through the muddy water we can not see the bottom, but soundings would probably show that the stream had become deeper while at the same time its surface was rising. It is flowing faster, enlarging and reshaping its channel by erosion, and carrying an increased load, all as a result of the increased discharge.

The general impression we have gained by watch- ing a stream rise in flood is supported by detailed measurements. These show clearly that, as discharge changes, velocity, channel, and load must follow suit. The relationship is definite; it can be expressed in the formula

Discharge equals *width* times *depth* of channel times *velocity.*

When discharge changes (as it does continually), the product of the other three terms must change ac- cordingly. Although load is not included in the for- mula, obviously it changes too. The way in which the fine-grained load increases with increasing discharge in a typical stream is shown in Figure 9–5.

The reason why velocity increases when discharge increases is mainly because of the geometry of the channel. The cross sections of many natural channels are more nearly rectangular than semicircular. An example is given in Figure 9–6. The cross-sectional area of a stream in a rectangular channel increases as the product of width and depth, whereas the perim- eter of the channel increases only as the sum of the

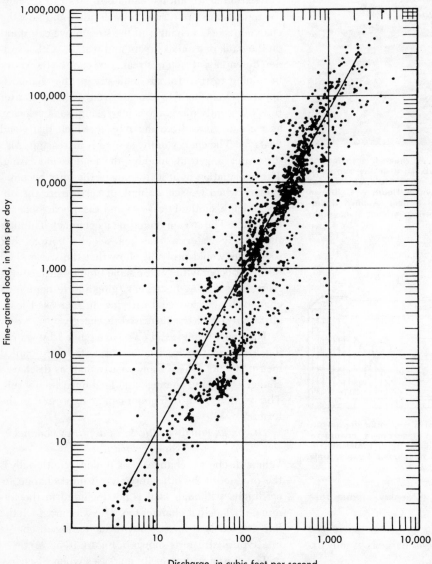

Fig. 9–5. Relation of fine-grained load to discharge (in cubic feet per second). Powder River at Arvada, Wyoming. (Leopold and Maddock, U. S. Geol. Survey Prof. Paper 252, 1953, p. 20.) Each point represents the mean discharge during one day and the mean suspended load during the same day at the gaging station. Both values are calculated from several measurements made at various depths and distances from the stream bank. Part of the increased load is picked up by the stream from its bed, but probably most of it was brought into the stream by small tributaries during rainstorms that caused the increased discharge.

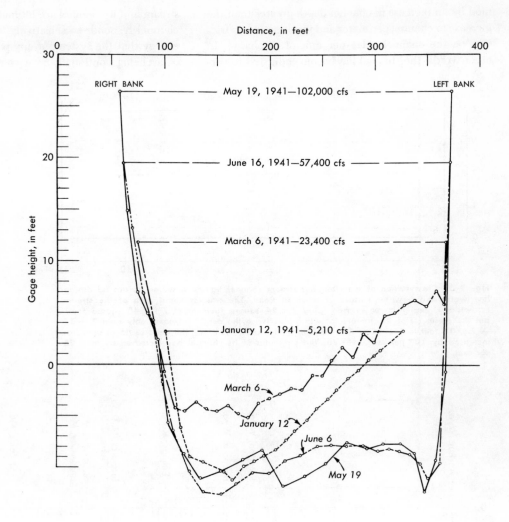

Fig. 9–6. Cross section showing changes in surface and bed of Colorado River at a point in the Grand Canyon, Arizona, during progress of a flood. Discharge (cfs = cubic feet per second) from January to May increased almost 20 times. With the exception of the March 6 values, the increase in discharge was accompanied by erosion that deepened the channel. Vertical scale is 10 times horizontal scale. (Leopold and Maddock, U. S. Geol. Survey Prof. Paper 252, 1953, p. 34.)

159

width and twice the depth (Fig. 9–7). Measurements (Fig.9–6) show that flood discharges are accompanied by an increase in channel depth greater than the increase in channel perimeter and resulting in less friction on the channel sides per unit of discharge. In other words, the channel has become adjusted to carrying both increased water and increased load.

This discussion adds up to the conclusion that a stream and its channel are intimately related, that the channel responds so sensitively to changes in stream energy that the system, at any point, can be thought of as being continually in a condition of near-equi-

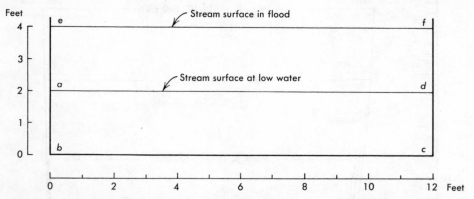

Fig. 9–7. Cross section of a rectangular stream channel having a water surface *ad* during low water and a water surface *ef* when in flood. The cross-sectional area of the stream (= width × depth) increases from *abcd* (= 24 square feet) to *ebcf* (= 48 square feet), but the perimeter of its channel (= width plus twice the depth) increases only from 2 + 12 + 2 = 16 feet to 4 + 12 + 4 = 20 feet. In this case, therefore, the cross-sectional area has increased by 100 per cent, whereas the perimeter of its channel has increased by only 25 per cent.

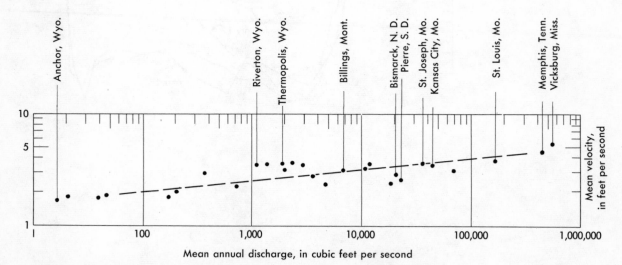

Fig. 9–8. Data from the Yellowstone-Missouri-Mississippi River drainage, demonstrating that average velocity increases downstream with increasing discharge. Dots represent measurement points. Velocities increase from around 3 feet per second in the headwaters to around 5 feet per second toward the mouth of the drainage system. Yet the slope decreases from around 10 feet per mile at some of the upstream stations to less than 0.5 foot per mile at the downstream stations. (L. B. Leopold, Am. J. Sci., vol. 251, 1953, p. 613.)

librium. When the stream's energy increases with increasing volume of water, the stream erodes and enlarges its channel and carries away the increased load until the increased discharge can be accommodated. When energy decreases, some of the load is dropped and the channel becomes less deep, and it once more comes close to equilibrium with the amount of water going through it.

Changes downstream. By watching events at a single point only, we have seen that a stream adjusts its channel so as to approach a stable condition at all times. We can now look at the whole length of the stream from head to mouth to see what changes take place. As we follow down the stream, we find that discharge increases as entering tributaries contribute additional water. With the increased discharge come (1) larger channel size, (2) increased velocity (Fig. 9–8), and (3) increased load, but with decrease in size of the individual rock particles that constitute the load. These changes take place in an orderly way (Fig. 9–9).

Long profile of a stream. The planning of dams, canals, and other hydraulic works along a stream demands not only discharge and channel data but also an accurate representation of the long profile of the stream. The *long profile is a line connecting accurately located points on the stream surface*; it is obtained by surveying. Figure 9–10 represents the long profile of the Platte-South Platte River in Colorado and Nebraska drawn to scale. This stream has its source in the Rocky Mountains, emerges on the Great

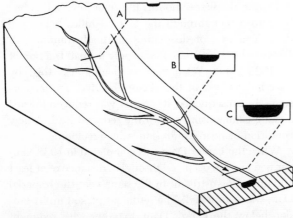

Fig. 9–9. Diagram illustrating ideal stream system. Discharge (indicated by entrance of successive tributaries) increases downstream. Width and depth channel (shown in cross sections A, B, and C) and velocity (shown by relative lengths of three arrows) likewise increase downstream. (After Leopold and Maddock.)

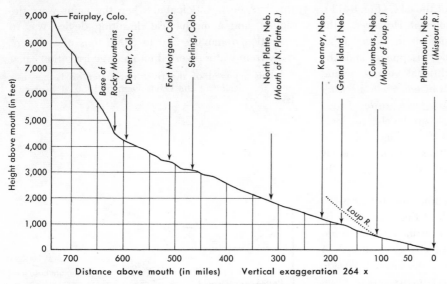

Fig. 9–10. Long profile of the Platte-South Platte River in Colorado and Nebraska, illustrating the common concave-up form of the curve. Profile of Loup River, a tributary (dotted line), shows a typical smooth accordant junction with the main stream. In drawing such profiles, vertical exaggeration is customary; with no exaggeration and on this horizontal scale the upstream end of the curve would not be visible above the base line 0-0. (Modified after Henry Gannett, U. S. Geol. Survey Water Supply Paper 44, 1901, pl. 8.)

161

Plains near Denver, and, flowing eastward, empties into the Missouri River near Omaha. The profile shows a more or less gradual decrease of slope from headwaters to mouth; in other words, it is concave-up. This is not exceptional; if minor irregularities are neglected, the long profiles of most large streams have this general form regardless of the stream's length, discharge, or kind of bed material.

The concave-up profile therefore must have a general cause. The cause lies in the maintenance of near-equilibrium, or stability, *at each point* along the stream. Not only velocity and channel dimensions but also gradient adjust themselves to accommodate the discharge that increases toward the stream's mouth. The adjustment at each point demands a continually reduced gradient in the downstream direction—in other words, a concave-up profile.

Base level. The vertical position of the mouth of a stream is determined by its *base level.* This is *the limiting level below which a stream can not erode* (Fig. 9–11). The **ultimate base level,** for streams in general, is *sea level, projected inland as an imaginary surface underneath the stream.* When a stream cuts down to that surface, its energy quickly reaches zero. However, some streams end in lakes. For such a stream, base level is the level of the lake (Fig. 9–11), for the stream can not erode below it. However, if the lake were destroyed by erosion at its outlet (Fig. 12–2), that base level would disappear, and the stream, having acquired additional energy, would deepen its channel. *The levels of lakes and all other base levels that stand above sea level* are **local base levels.** A common kind of local base level is the level of a belt of particularly hard rock lying across the stream's path. Even sea level itself changes slowly over long periods (p. 283) and this too affects the long profiles of streams.

Lower Colorado River. The adjustments that occur at each point along the length of the stream can be seen clearly when the stream is artificially interfered with and the distribution of its energy is altered. A good example is the response of the lower Colorado River to dams built across parts of its course (Fig. 9–12). The Colorado habitually carried a large suspended load and probably a large bed load also. When the Hoover Dam was completed in 1935, this load was trapped in the newly created reservoir be-

hind the dam; hence the water passing the dam was clear. With its slope and discharge unchanged, and having no load to carry, the stream below the dam applied the energy it had formerly used in transporting its load to increased velocity of flow and to picking up a new load from the materials of its channel. In the process the channel was deepened.

During the first 6 months the river lowered its bed by 2 to 6 feet through the first 13 miles below the dam. The rate of deepening gradually diminished; 10 years later, in 1945, it was only a small fraction of its 1935 value. What was happening was this: by lowering its bed in this sector the river reduced its slope. In consequence, its energy was reduced toward a value commensurate with the reduced load. A new condition of near-equilibrium was developing.[1]

When the Parker Dam was completed in 1938, similar bed erosion occurred through a distance of at least 100 miles downstream. In the same year the Imperial Dam was completed. The sediment picked up by erosion below the Parker Dam, together with sediment washed in from the sides of the valley, was trapped in the reservoir behind the Imperial Dam. By 1950, 12 years after it had been created, this reservoir was almost completely filled with the sediment. Of course, this had been anticipated when the dams were designed, and a mechanical de-silting device was in operation, removing 500 to 5,000 tons of sediment daily from water diverted into a large irrigation canal

[1] This segment of the river no longer exists because, with the closing of the Davis Dam in 1950, it became a lake.

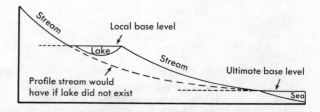

Fig. 9–11. Relation between ultimate base level (the sea) and local base levels such as lakes. Other local base levels are shown in Figure 9–12.

that leads away from the reservoir.

Sedimentation is occurring in the Parker reservoir also. In each of the segments between two dams, therefore, the Colorado River is adjusting itself to the new conditions imposed on it by deepening its bed below each dam and by depositing the resulting load farther downstream, where the horizontal water surface of a reservoir had been substituted for a continuous slope. The deposits in the reservoir are essentially deltas (Fig. 12–1).

The behavior of the Colorado illustrates the general tendency toward maintenance of a condition of stability. When one of the factors in the stream's economy is altered, the others must adjust themselves so as to approach stability under the altered conditions. Since the tendency toward stability exists at each point along the stream's course, the various factors continually interact to maintain a channel that, with increasing distance downstream, can carry an ever-increasing discharge and load.

Geologic activities of streams

Up to this point we have examined streams in order to try to understand their flow and their economy. Now we are ready to examine their geologic activities. These activities are as follows:

Erosion ⎡ hydraulic action
          abrasion
          solution
          transport

Deposition

Occurring in the channel, they are intimately related to each other, and all are in progress at each moment.

Erosion. Erosion by a stream involves hydraulic action, abrasion, solution, and transport. *Hydraulic action* is *the lifting and moving of loose particles by the force inherent in the flow of water*. It is illustrated by the impact of water from a garden hose playing upon loose soil; the soil is churned up and washed away.

Abrasion is *the mechanical wear of rock on rock*. In streams it is caused by friction and impact between rock particles moving with the stream at different rates and between moving particles and firm rock in the channel. Rubbing, scraping, bumping, and crushing are involved. Abrasion depends on the presence of rock particles in the stream, whereas hydraulic action can occur in a stream that has no sediment load. In most streams bed material and load decrease in average diameter from head to mouth of the stream. This results partly from abrasion and partly from gradual sorting out and deposition of the coarser particles as gradient, channel, and other factors gradually change from point to point along the stream.

Solution occurs as the water of the stream dissolves matter from minerals that constitute the bedrock in the channel and the rock particles in transport. However, only a small proportion of the matter in solution in stream water was dissolved by the streams themselves. Most of it was dissolved by ground water beneath the slopes tributary to the streams and was contributed to the streams later as the water percolated into them (p. 207, Fig. 9–1).

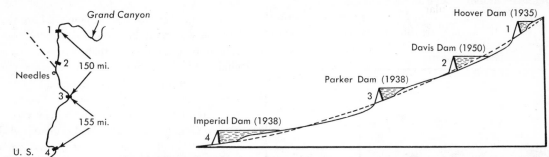

Fig. 9–12. Profile and plan of Colorado River from Hoover Dam to Imperial Dam. Profile shows changes in stream bed before Davis Dam was completed in 1950. It is diagrammatic only and is not drawn to scale. The vertical dimension is enormously exaggerated. Broken-line profile shows the stream bed before construction of the dams; continuous-line profile after completion of three dams. Channel cross section, not shown, probably changed correspondingly. (Data from J. W. Stanley.)

163

Transport. The load transported by a stream can be subdivided as follows:

Load
- Carried in solution — *Dissolved load*
- Carried mechanically as sediment
  - *Suspended load* (*sediment carried in suspension*)
  - *Bed load* (*sediment carried along the bed*)

For the particles moved mechanically the special definitions of familiar terms, shown in Table 3–2, are used. Although Table 3–2 is based only on diameters, both the shape and the specific gravity of a particle also influence the height to which it is lifted. Specific gravity is an important factor in the transport and deposition of particles of very heavy metallic substances such as gold, and shape is important in flaky minerals such as the micas, but with most particles commonly carried by streams diameter is the chief factor because the specific gravity of most of the particles carried by streams is between 2.6 and 2.7 and is therefore nearly constant.

The suspended load usually consists of clay or silt or both. Its quantity is measurable (Fig. 9–5), and a good deal of information about it is therefore available.

The length of time a particle remains in suspension depends on two opposing forces: (1) the velocity of fall the particle would have in still water, as determined by pull of gravity opposed by resistance of the fluid, and (2) the intensity of turbulence. As long as the upward lift of turbulence is greater than the tendency of the particle to fall, the particle will remain in motion above the stream bed.

The bed load commonly consists of sand or gravel or both. Its quantity is difficult to measure because

any sampling device lowered to the stream bed sets up eddies that immediately change the distribution of energy and rock particles in the vicinity of the sample. Hence we have little information about the proportion of bed load to suspended load, but the little we have suggests that in some streams bed load is about equal to or less than suspended load.

The movements shown in Figure 9–13 are simplified from actual conditions. Pebbles and larger rock particles slide or roll along the bed; sand grains are lifted above the bed by eddies and jump to new positions of rest. The smaller the particle, the higher the lift and the longer the jump, but sand grains rarely jump higher than about half an inch. *The jumping movement of rock particles in a stream of water or air* is referred to as *saltation.* Sliding, rolling, and saltation are transitional into the movement of the suspended particles; in fact, the various kinds of movement intermingle.

Furthermore, particles of a given size move in different ways at different times, as the energy within the stream varies with varying discharge. For example, during floods fine sand grains might constitute part of the suspended load, whereas at times of low water they might be moved only along the stream bed.

Deposition. Particles in the load are continually being *deposited* on the stream bed. In a long stream each particle in transport comes to rest many times, and during its journey downstream it is likely to spend much more aggregate time at rest than in actual motion. Each particle, therefore, moves in a series of jumps, short or long according to its size, and only a small part of the potential load is in motion at any time.

Geologic activity during floods. Many streams rise in flood seasonally because of the distribution of rainfall in time over the stream system. When its discharge increases during floods, a stream is able to transport an increased aggregate load. With a tenfold increase in discharge (a common flood-time occurrence in many streams) in the stream represented in Figure 9–5, the suspended load is increased about 100 times. Although velocity is not plotted, undoubtedly it too would increase with discharge.

An increase of velocity results in an increase not only of total load but also of maximum diameter of the rock particles a stream can carry. In the bed load

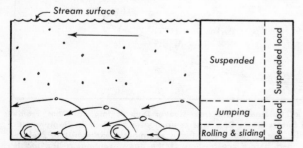

Fig. 9–13. Kinds of movement of rock particles carried in a stream; vertical distribution of bed load and suspended load.

Fig. 9–14. Flood of Quinebaug River at Putnam, Connecticut, in August 1955, the result of extraordinary rainfall. View looking north, upstream. River channel is at left, just out of view; its edge is seen as darker water in lower left corner of picture. Stream shown is water that overflowed from main channel. Although short lived, the overflow eroded a large area of a bank of sand and gravel about 25 feet thick (remnants are near flooded railroad tracks) and deposited the resulting load as a series of bars and islands, seen in foreground. Overflow rejoined main channel at lower left. (Providence Journal-Bulletin.)

diameter increase results mainly from increased force applied directly to rock particles on the bed. In the suspended load it results mainly from increased turbulence in which part of the force is directed upward. Experimental study shows that doubled velocity is accompanied by a large increase in the maximum diameter of rock particles that can be moved. An extreme example resulted from the sudden failure of the massive St. Francis Dam near Los Angeles in March 1928. As the dam gave way, the water behind it rushed down the valley below, moving 10,000-ton blocks of concrete over distances of more than 2,500 feet.

Part of the increased load that usually accompanies augmented discharge and velocity in a stream is sup-

plied by tributaries. Another part of it is picked up by the stream from its own channel, as is shown by gaging-station data. In Figure 9–6 increased discharge in the Colorado River during a flood in 1941 is seen to be accompanied (with one exception) by lowering of the bed as well as by rise of the stream surface. Sampling during that particular flood showed that the suspended load varied with variations in discharge.

More of a stream's geologic work, therefore, is accomplished during regular seasonal floods than during intervals of low water. In addition to seasonal floods, there are rare, exceptional floods (Fig. 9–14) outside the stream's normal economy and occurring perhaps only once in several decades or centuries. In these the geologic work done may be prodigious, but such events occur so rarely that their effects are less than the aggregate effect of normal activity throughout the very long periods intervening between them. As in the fable, this race, too, is won by the tortoise rather than by the hare.

Geologic features of steep rocky channels

Hydraulic plucking and abrasion of bedrock. Some streams, particularly in mountainous headwater areas, have steep slopes and channels consisting of bedrock. Turbulence resulting from the steep downstream slope sets up frictional forces capable of moving rock particles of very large diameter. The stream erodes its bed by *hydraulic plucking* (Fig. 9–15, **A**), *the lifting-out, by turbulent water, of blocks of bedrock* bounded by joints and other surfaces of weakness. The lift is accomplished by suction in strong eddies spiraling up around vertical axes. In some places lifts of boulder-size blocks through nearly 100 feet vertically have occurred.

Highly turbulent streams in rocky channels also make *potholes.* These are *cylindrical holes drilled in bedrock by abrasion*, where an eddy swirls pebbles and sand grains in spiral paths (Figs. 9–15, **B**; 9–16). Potholes more than 25 feet deep are made by this drilling process. In such streams abrasion between particles in the load and the rocky bed takes place quite generally, smoothing the rock surfaces laid bare by hydraulic plucking (Fig. 9–17).

Erosion at falls. Under the special conditions in which a stream falls over a rock ledge or cliff, as at Niagara Falls (Fig. 9–18), the increased velocity of the falling water sets up strong turbulence at the base of the falls, where both hydraulic plucking and abrasion deepen the stream bed exceptionally. The cliff is gradually undermined and the falls retreats upstream. The retreat of the Canadian Falls at Niagara Falls has been rapid. Measurements by survey show that between 1850 and 1950 the rate of retreat averaged around 4 feet per year. This rapid rate is favored by the fact that the lip of the falls consists of strong, resistant dolostone beneath which is weak, easily eroded shale. As the shale cliff is eroded back,

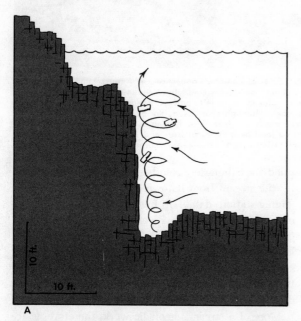
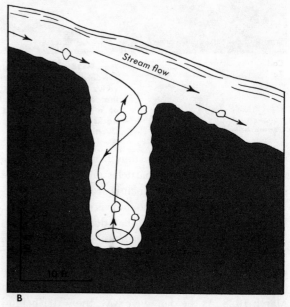

Fig. 9–15. Erosion of rocky stream beds by vertical eddies, at a locality near the one shown in Figure 9–2. A. Hydraulic plucking of jointed bedrock by upward-moving eddy. Note blocks of rock being lifted. The stream is flowing at right angles to the plane of the diagram. (After Gerard Matthes, Am. Geophys. Union Trans., vol. 28, 1947, p. 259.) B. A deep pothole being drilled by a downward-moving eddy. The spiral paths of the eddy-transported pebbles are inferred from observation of model streams in the laboratory. (After Olof Ängeby, Lund Studies in Geog., ser. A, no. 2, 1951, p. 24.)

Fig. 9–16. Potholes drilled into metamorphic rock by Kent Falls Brook, Kent, Connecticut. (Mary Eleanor Browning, Photo Researchers, Inc.)

Fig. 9–17. Granite bedrock and large boulders exposed in the bed of a channel (temporarily dry) of the Columbia River at Long Rapids, Washington. Results of both hydraulic plucking and abrasion are evident; in right foreground is a segment of a pothole. (M. B. Canning.)

the dolostone lip is undermined and caves in piecemeal (Fig. 9–19). The long, deep gorge downstream from the falls was created by retreat of the falls, through successive positions, over periods of many thousands of years. A joint Canadian-American engineering project was begun in 1954 in order to distribute the water more evenly over the entire width of the river, thus reducing the rapid rate of retreat at the most vulnerable places.

Geologic features of broad valley floors

In contrast with those that flow through steep rocky channels, streams that have broad valley floors show a quite different set of characteristic features. Not all the features occur in any one valley, but as most of them are found in the valley of the Mississippi River we can take that valley as a convenient example.

Meanders and point bars. From Cairo, Illinois, at the mouth of the Ohio River, to the mouths of the Mississippi, the straight-line distance is about 600 miles, but between the same points the river has a length of about 1,050 miles. The difference results from the meanders of the stream's channel. *Meanders are looplike bends in a stream channel;* they occur in very small streams as well as in large rivers (Fig. 9–20).

The meanders of the Mississippi and other large streams have been studied with care by engineers and geologists concerned with the control of floods. It has been learned that the sizes of meanders are proportional to width of channel and that meanders can form in a stream whether or not the stream is carrying a load. A meandering pattern appears to represent a condition of stability or near-equilibrium, but the mechanism by which a stream develops this pattern is still unknown.

As we have said, a load is not necessary for meander development. However, many meandering streams, among them the Mississippi River, carry abundant loads and deposit sediment according to a definite pattern. The pattern consists of *crescent-shaped bars built out from each convex* ("inside") *bank of the channel*. These are known as *point bars.*

The growth of point bars can be seen in experiments with model streams like the one shown in Figure 9–21. The cross sections in that figure show that the line of greatest velocity (V) and the location of greatest turbulence (T) are situated along the concave bank. (Compare Fig. 9–4). Sand eroded from that bank is deposited as a point bar along the convex bank next downstream, where velocity and turbulence are least. Although the growth of point

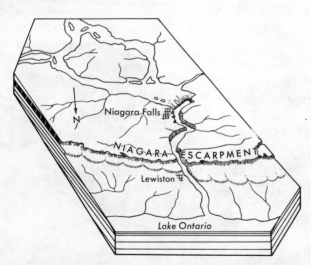

Fig. 9–18. Bird's-eye view of Niagara Falls, looking south, showing bedrock structure and Niagara Escarpment, at which the falls originated. By erosion the falls has retreated through an aggregate distance of about 7 miles. Greatest length of block = 35 miles. Vertical exaggeration, 2 ✕.

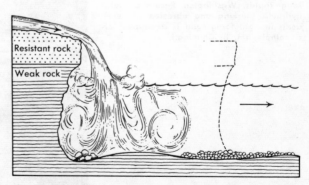

Fig. 9–19. A falls similar to Niagara Falls. The stream bed downstream from the falls was created by successive positions of the retreating cliffs; one former position is shown by the dotted line. Turbulence at base of falls keeps bedrock scoured nearly clean of sediment, but in less turbulent water downstream coarse gravel is deposited.

Fig. 9–20. Meanders of Pecos River near Roswell, New Mexico. View looking downstream. The areas covered with rows of bushes are point bars. At right of center is an oxbow lake. (Spence Air Photos.)

bars is not necessary to the development of meanders, possibly it speeds the growth of the stable meandering pattern. Figure 9–22 shows point bars whose rate of growth has been measured. They form the cores of two successive meanders of the Mississippi River channel. Such bars are conspicuous features of many broad valley floors.

Whether it meanders or not, a stream in a valley floored with alluvium accomplishes much erosion by bank caving.

Migration of meanders: cutoffs. Because of the slope in the down-valley direction, caving is a little more rapid on concave banks that face up-valley than on other banks. Therefore, meanders tend to

migrate slowly down the valley—subtracting from and adding to various pieces of real estate along the banks, according to location, and causing legal disputes over property lines and even over the boundaries between counties and states.

The behavior of model streams shows that if bank material is uniform the meanders are symmetrical and migrate down-valley at the same rate. But, since the bank material in a natural stream is not uniform, migration of the downstream limb of a meander can be slowed up by resistant bank material while the upstream limb, migrating more rapidly, intersects it at the "neck" of the meander. This causes a ***neck cutoff***, defined as the *intersection of a meander bend*

169

by the bend next upstream, causing the stream to bypass the loop between the bends (Figs. 9–22, 9–23, **B**). In the foreground of Figure 9–20 a neck cutoff is about to occur.

The usual result of a neck cutoff is an *oxbow lake, a curved lake occupying a cut-off meander loop* (Figs. 9–20, 9–23, **B**), as the cut-off part of the channel becomes blocked with alluvium at both ends. Oxbow lakes gradually fill up with clay and silt. The meander pattern in Figure 9–23, **A** is irregular chiefly because the resistant clay fillings of old oxbow lakes are encountered by migrating meanders.

Another kind of cutoff is a *chute cutoff.* This is *the abandonment of part of a meander by the cutting of a new channel across a point bar.* It occurs during floods, when rising water overtops the channel. Instead of following the gentle slope around the meander, the water flows down the steeper slope directly across the point bar and makes a new channel. If the flow continues for long, the new channel replaces

(cuts off) the meander, which then fills up with fine sediment. In a large river like the Mississippi the shift is gradual, often requiring many floods over a long period of years to make it complete (Fig. 9–23, **C**).

Since 1776 the aggregate length of channel abandoned by the Mississippi through cutoffs has amounted to more than 230 miles; yet the river has not been shortened appreciably because the lost mileage has been balanced by the enlargement of other meanders.

Floodplain: natural levees. The Mississippi River habitually floods during the spring season. Before the river began to be restrained by artificial flood-control measures, it frequently overtopped its banks and inundated the lower parts of the valley floor. *That part of any stream valley which is inundated during floods* is a *floodplain;* the natural floodplain of the Mississippi from Cairo to the delta has an area of 30,000 square miles, but more than half of this area is now protected against floods by dikes and other structures.

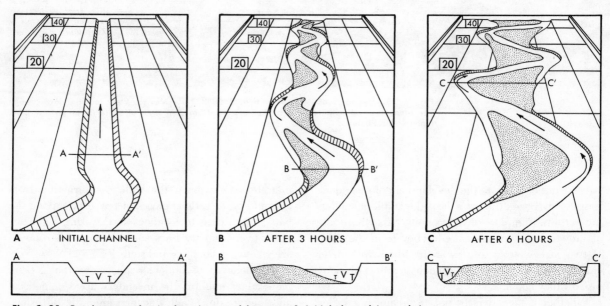

Fig. 9–21. Development of point bars in a model stream. **A** *Initial channel* in sand, in a wide sloping trough 50 feet long (numbers are distances, in feet, from the observer). The channel was made with an initial irregularity (in foreground). Water introduced into channel head flows downslope in direction of arrow. Cross section of channel at A-A′ is shown below. Sizes of *T* and *V* suggest relative intensity of turbulence and velocity. Stream starts to meander. **B** *After 3 hours* outside, concave banks are eroded and sand is deposited as point bars along the inside, convex banks next downstream. Cross section B-B′ shows unsymmetrical channel and point bar (exposed at low water). **C** *After 6 hours* meanders have enlarged and with them the point bars. Bars indicate that caving supplies a greater load than stream can carry away. (Modified after J. F. Friedkin, U. S. Waterways Experiment Station.)

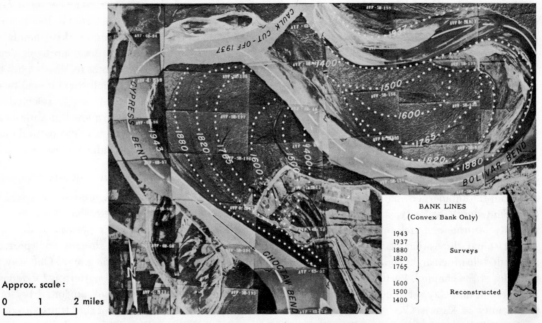

BANK LINES
(Convex Bank Only)

1943	
1937	
1880	Surveys
1820	
1765	
1600	
1500	Reconstructed
1400	

Approx. scale:

0   1   2 miles

Fig. 9–22. Point bars forming the cores of two meanders of the Mississippi River near Greenville, Mississippi, in 1943. Dotted lines show successive positions of convex banks of channel 1765 to 1943 (by surveys) and 1400 to 1600 (by reconstruction from archeologic and other data). The dates show that at Cypress Bend the channel has been shifting at a rate of nearly 60 feet per year. The Caulk cutoff, which occurred in 1937, resulted in gradual abandonment of Bolivar Bend. By 1952 the bend had become an oxbow lake. (H. N. Fisk, Mississippi River Commission.)

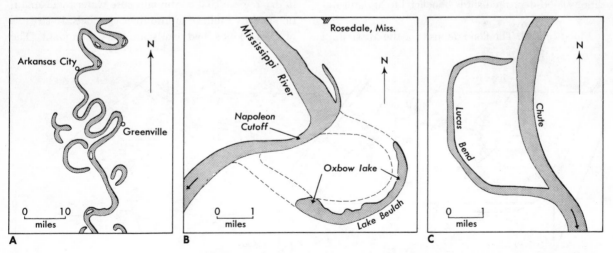

Fig. 9–23. Meanders and cutoffs on lower Mississippi River. **A.** River segment in Arkansas and Mississippi, showing meandering channel and cut-off bend. **B.** Napoleon Cutoff is a neck cutoff made in 1863. Before that year, main channel followed meander at lower right. Cut-off ends of the meander were gradually filled with sand, creating an oxbow lake. **C.** Chute cutoff 15 miles south of Cairo, Illinois. Originally, river followed Lucas Bend meander, but in 1880 flood overflow started the chute. By 1932 almost all the flow was going through the chute, and by 1945 Lucas Bend was abandoned and its upstream end had filled with sand. When its lower end is blocked it will have become an oxbow lake. (After Mississippi River Commission.)

The channels of the lower Mississippi and many other meandering streams are bordered by *natural levees.* These are *broad, low ridges of fine alluvium along both sides of a stream channel* (Fig. 9–24). Along the lower Mississippi natural levees are 15 to 25 feet high. The fine alluvium of which they are chiefly built becomes still finer away from the river and grades into a thin cover of silt and clay over the rest of the floodplain. Natural levees were built and are added to only during floods so high that the floodplain is converted essentially into a lake deep enough to submerge the levees. In the water that flows laterally from the submerged channel over the submerged floodplain depth, velocity, and turbulence decrease abruptly at the channel margins. This results in abrupt, rapid deposition of the coarser part of the suspended load (usually fine sand and silt) along the sides of the channel. Farther away from the channel finer silt and clay settle out in the quiet water. In the vicinity of Kansas City, Missouri, during an exceptional flood in 1952, Missouri River water deposited a layer of silt as much as 6 inches thick over wide areas of floodplain. In some places fences and other obstacles caused silt and fine sand to accumulate to thicknesses of as much as 5 feet. Under ordinary conditions flood-deposited silt is beneficial to agricultural lands.

Flood control. The flood deposits of the Mississippi River, including the natural levees, were built up over a long period, but the process has been interfered with by the engineering works (mainly dikes built of earth and concrete) designed to prevent the river from generally inundating its floodplain. The natural levees have been artificially heightened by earth dikes to hold in ordinary floods, and at selected points spillways have been built to allow the water of the highest floods to escape harmlessly into natural channels that parallel the channel of the Mississippi.

Braided streams, fans, deltas

Braided streams. A *braided stream* is *a stream that flows in two or more interconnected channels around islands of alluvium.* Its pattern is distinctive (Fig. 9–14). Most of these streams transport coarse bed material such as sand or gravel. One way in which a stream forms a braided pattern is by depositing, near the center of its channel, an initial bar of coarse alluvium, which can not be transported under the prevailing conditions. The bar becomes an island with a channel on each side, and other islands develop in a similar manner.

Another type of braiding is characteristic of streams that have their sources in glaciers (Fig. 13–20) and in dry regions that continually lose water by evaporation and by infiltration into their channels. In streams of these kinds bed loads are very abundant. The

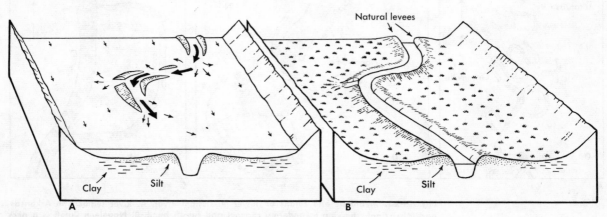

Fig. 9–24. Floodplain with natural levees. **A.** During a big flood much of the valley floor resembles a lake. Water with high velocity (long arrows) flows through the channel, and part of the water flows with diminishing velocity (shorter arrows) into the broad shallow areas adjacent, depositing sediment that builds natural levees. Highest parts of levees, added to only during still higher floods, form islands. **B.** At times of low water levees stand as low ridges along sides of channel; beyond them are swamp lands. Vertical scale much exaggerated.

stream deposits its bed load by filling up its channel, which becomes so shallow that the stream can not be contained in it and so spills out over one side. The overflowing water, having little or no bed load, is able to erode a new channel, which also soon fills up with deposited bed load. The stream spills over, and the process is repeated again and again, with several channels operating at once. The result is a braided channel pattern and a body of alluvium consisting of a distinctive series of channel fills that intersect each other in a complex way (Fig. 13–21).

Fans. When a stream flows down through a steep highland valley and comes out suddenly onto a wide and nearly level valley floor or plain, the abrupt decrease of slope reduces the stream's energy and, therefore, its ability to transport a load. The resulting deposit of alluvium is concentrated at the foot of the steep slope in the form of a *fan,* defined as a *fan-shaped body of alluvium built at the base of a steep slope* (Figs. 14–3, 18–19, B, 18–21). The surface of the fan slopes outward through a wide arc from an apex at the mouth of the steep valley. The profile of the fan, from apex to base in any direction, has the concave-up form characteristic of stream profiles.[1]

On most fans the stream-channel pattern is braided, and upbuilding is accomplished by the process of channel filling and cutting described in the preceding section. When one radius of a fan has been built up in this way, the stream shifts to an adjacent radius and builds that one up. Thus a wide area becomes covered with alluvium, creating a deposit having remarkably symmetrical form (Fig. 14–3) and stratification (Fig. 17–21, **E**).

Upbuilding of the fan steepens the slope of the stream at the fan itself, but upstream from the fan erosion is in progress, reducing the slope there. By the combination of erosion upstream and deposition on the fan, together with changes in channel cross section, the stream and channel become adjusted to a continuous profile, concave-up (Fig. 9–25). The form of the profile depends chiefly on discharge and the diameters of particles in the bed load; hence no two fans are exactly alike. A small stream with a coarse

load builds a shorter, steeper fan than a larger stream with a finer load.

Although a fan is localized originally by decrease of slope, as soon as its long profile has become smooth, the chief cause of further deposition on it is the spreading of water through braided channels, with consequent loss of discharge and velocity.

Unless special circumstances preserve it, the fan will be destroyed piecemeal by continuing erosion downward below the profile **CC'X** (Fig. 9–25). A fan, therefore, is likely to be a temporary deposit, representing a stream's quick achievement of near-equilibrium at a place where equilibrium on the original slopes is impossible.

Deltas. A *delta* is *a body of sediment deposited by a stream flowing into standing water*. The flow of the stream is checked by friction as the stream water diffuses into the standing water of sea or lake. The stream loses energy and deposits its load as a delta. There are several kinds of deltas. The kind that is easiest to recognize, and probably most common, is shown in Figure 9–26. It differs from a fan because of two facts: (1) loss of stream energy is gradual rather than abrupt; therefore, the sediments are deposited more slowly and in a more orderly arrangement; (2) the level surface of sea or lake sets an approximate limit to upbuilding of the deposit, the top of which is flatter than the profile of a fan.

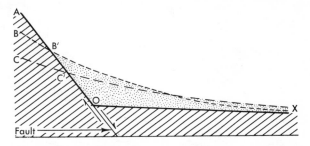

Fig. 9–25. Vertical section showing growth of a fan. Bedrock is shaded; alluvium is stippled *AOX* = profile of surface before deposition of fan. *BB'X* = long profile of stream at an early stage of fan building. *CC'X* = long profile at a later stage, after stream has cut away apex of fan *BB'X* and increased fan radius, while establishing a continuous, concave profile.

---

[1] In an extremely dry region, however, a stream that disappears on a fan, by a combination of evaporating and sinking into its bed, must deposit its entire load. Since no load is carried beyond it, the fan is convex-up.

The particles in the bed load are deposited first, in order of decreasing weight; beyond, the suspended sediments drop out. A layer deposited at any one time (as during a single flood) is sorted, grading from coarse at the stream mouth to fine offshore. The deposition of many successive layers creates an embankment that grows outward like a highway fill made by dumping. *The coarse, thick, steeply sloping part of each layer in a delta* is a *foreset bed.*[1] Traced seaward, the same layer becomes rapidly thinner and finer, covering the bottom over a wide area. This *gently sloping, fine, thin part of each layer in a delta* is a *bottomset bed.*

As successive layers are deposited, the coarse foreset beds one by one overlap the bottomset beds, producing the arrangement seen in Figure 9–26. The stream gradually extends seaward over the growing delta, erodes the tops of the foreset beds during floods, and at other times deposits part of its bed load in its channel. The channel deposits form the *topset beds* of the delta. We can define these deposits as *the stream-channel sediments that overlie the foreset beds in a delta.*

During floods the stream spills out of its channel and forms distributary channels, through which the

[1] Foreset, bottomset, and topset beds should properly be called layers rather than beds because many are thinner than beds in the strict sense (p. 328). However, because of its wide use, we retain the familiar term bed for the present.

water enters the sea independently, multiplying the topset deposits. Radiating distributary channels give the delta a crudely triangular shape resembling the Greek letter $\triangle$, from which the deposit derives its name.

It may seem surprising that the suspended load, much of which has been carried hundreds of miles through the channel of a large river without being deposited, should drop out so abruptly to form part of a localized delta instead of remaining in suspension long enough to be carried far from land. But the salts dissolved in sea water act to coagulate, or flocculate, the suspended fine particles into aggregates so large that they settle to the bottom promptly.

Some of the world's greatest rivers, among them the Nile, the Hwang Ho, the Mackenzie, the Colorado, and the Mississippi, have built massive deltas at their mouths. Each delta has its own peculiarities, and none is so simple as the small delta shown in Fig. 9–26. The Mississippi delta, with 12,000 square miles of land area (not counting the submarine part), is in reality a complex of several coalescing subdeltas built successively during the last several thousand years. Each subdelta was begun by a flood that created a new distributary. Figure 9–27 shows the sequence of distributaries and resulting subdeltas identified mainly from abandoned channels flanked by natural levees. In this, as in some other big deltas, there is no clear distinction between topset, foreset,

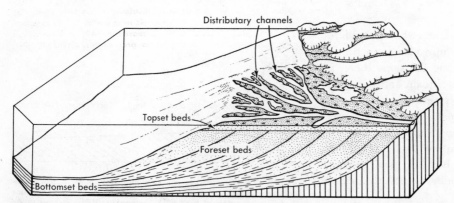

Fig. 9–26. Ideal small delta. Foreset beds consist of sand, which grades outward into silt and clay in the bottomset beds. The slope made by the uppermost foreset bed is shown in phantom view through the water. The area of such a delta might be one square mile or less. The less deep the water offshore, the less distinct this stratification.

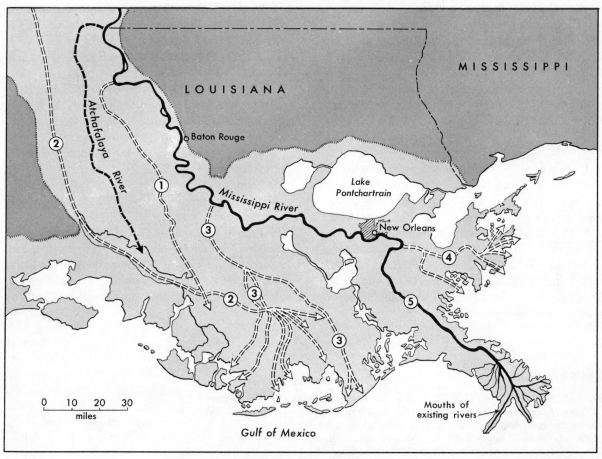

Fig. 9–27. The Mississippi River delta has grown to its present size by occupying successive distributary channels. Study of abandoned channels and deposits has revealed the order in which distributary routes were followed by the main river (① to ⑤ on the map). Estimated ages (in years) of the distributaries: ① 3,000; ② 1,500; ③ 1,000; ④ 700; ⑤ 400. The Mississippi is now gradually shifting to the Atchafalaya distributary (dashed line). By 1958 28 per cent of the Mississippi's discharge was following this new route. It is estimated that between 1965 and 1975 the percentage would have increased to 40, if preventive measures had not been undertaken. Construction of a barrier to prevent the diversion was begun in 1955. (After H. N. Fisk.)

and bottomset beds, owing to a number of complicating factors.

Stability principle in streams

We have seen that the characteristics of a stream and its channel are determined by the interplay of several factors at each point along the stream. The factors continually adjust themselves to each other, and the sum of the adjustments tends toward approximate stability at each point. The conditions at each point, added together, combine to determine the concave-up curve that is the stream's long profile.

Whether the stream's course is steep, narrow, and rocky or wider and more gently sloping, the tendency toward stability is in operation. Anything that disturbs stability sets up a response by the stream that tends to restore the stable condition. For instance, if the stream is checked by the sea or a lake, it responds by building a delta and thereby smoothing the profile at its mouth. If it is interrupted by a cliff, the stream responds by building a fan at the base of the cliff and thereby gradually restores its smooth profile. Meanders and braided patterns, likewise, are evidently approaches to stability in response to special conditions.

In Chapter 10 we shall see how this tendency toward stability in streams is reflected in the sculpture of the lands.

SUMMARY

1. As part of the hydrologic cycle, streams are the chief means of returning water from land to sea. As geologic agents, stream erosion and mass-wasting are foremost of the processes that erode the land.

2. Discharge equals width times depth of channel times velocity. Hence stream and channel are intimately related and constantly adjust to each other.

3. Long profiles of streams are concave-up curves. They become gentler with time but are limited downward by base level.

4. The geologic activities of a stream consist of erosion (hydraulic action, abrasion, solution, transport of load) and deposition of load.

5. A stream's load consists of bed load, suspended load, and dissolved load.

6. During floods, increased discharge and velocity increases total load and also diameters of the largest particles a stream can carry. Most of a stream's geologic work is done during seasonal floods.

7. Streams erode bedrock by hydraulic plucking and by abrasion.

8. Features of streams in alluvial valleys include meanders, oxbow lakes, point bars, natural levees, and floodplains.

9. Fans are built at the toes of steep slopes; deltas are built at the mouths of streams. A common kind of delta consists of foreset, bottomset, and topset beds.

10. Streams tend toward a condition of stability. If stability is interrupted, the stream will return to it.

REFERENCES

Fisk, H. N., 1952, Mississippi River valley geology in relation to river regime: *Am. Soc. Civil Engrs.* Trans., vol. 117, p. 667–682. Explanatory description of alluvium, meanders, natural levees, distributaries, and related features.

Hoyt, W. G., and Langbein, W. B., 1955, Floods: Princeton Univ. Press.

Leopold, L. B., and Maddock, T., Jr., 1953, The hydraulic geometry of stream channels and some physiographic implications: U. S. Geol. Survey Prof. Paper 252. Interrelations of the hydraulic factors in stream channels; illustrations are mostly graphs.

Leopold, L. B., and Wolman, M. G., 1957, River channel patterns: braided, meandering and straight: U. S. Geol. Survey Prof. Paper 282, p. 39–85.

CHAPTER 10. SCULPTURE OF THE LAND BY STREAMS AND MASS-WASTING

Relation of valleys to streams   Development of valleys   Sculptural evolution of a land mass   Interruptions in sculptural evolution   Effects of unequal resistance of rocks   Classification and history of streams

Badlands, South Dakota. (Josef Muench.)

Relation of valleys to streams

The preceding chapter is concerned with the flow of streams in their channels, the present chapter with the valleys through which streams flow. Valleys and valley systems are the most common features of the lands; throughout wide regions the face of the land is little more than a complex of valleys, created by erosion and separated by higher areas that erosion has not yet consumed. Valleys exist in such great numbers that they have never been counted except in sample areas. The enormous number of valleys is commensurate with the huge volume of water runoff over the land.

Can we prove the assertion that valleys are cut by streams? Before the middle of the eighteenth century no one seems to have analyzed the matter. Valleys were then generally accepted as the result of catastrophes that somehow broke the Earth's crust and pulled it apart, creating paths for running water to follow. As far as we know, the opposite idea, that streams came first and gradually made their own valleys, was first stated by Leonardo da Vinci. This idea was developed, about 1770, by Nicolas Desmarest (p. 98) during a study of basalt lavas in central France. Not only did he show that basalt is a volcanic rock (contrary to the view, then popular, that it was sedimentary), but he found three groups of basalt flows. One group was fresh and untouched by erosion, a second was cut through by valleys, and a third had been entirely destroyed by erosion except for a few remnants at the tops of hills. Desmarest perceived that these differences in extent of erosion were systematically related to the relative ages of the lava flows. He drew the inference that the valleys

were made by groups of streams, each of which had begun to flow after some group of lavas had solidified. He implied that the making of successive sets of valleys by some agency other than the streams themselves is very improbable.

In 1802 the Scottish naturalist John Playfair carried the argument further. He pointed out the general existence of two important relationships in valleys: (1) the size of a valley is proportional to the size of the stream that flows in it; (2) a stream's tributaries enter it generally at its own water level (as the Loup River enters the Platte; see Figure 9–10). Playfair reasoned that if streams merely occupy valleys ready-made for them by some other agency these two relationships would be, as he put it, "infinitely improbable." Hence, he concluded, valleys are made by streams.

To clinch the argument, we can add that streams are actually observed to make and enlarge valleys; capacious ones have been cut within the last 100 years (Fig. 10–10), and some are reported to be lengthening at rates as great as one mile per year. Furthermore, artificial rain creates runoff on model land surfaces set up in laboratories, and the runoff cuts miniature valleys analogous to the natural ones. The origin of valleys is therefore well established.

This does not mean that every depression through which a stream flows was created entirely by the stream. In some places running water does follow depressions already begun by other agencies, such as bending and fracturing of the Earth's crust (Chap. 18). In other places a tributary joins a main stream by cascading over a cliff (p. 236). But the geology of such places reveals special circumstances that explain these exceptions, and the general conclusion still holds true.

Development of valleys

Sheet runoff and sheet erosion. Water from long-continued rains runs off over smooth, sloping land surfaces in thin sheets and in networks of tiny rills. In the sheets flow is streamline or weakly turbulent; in the rills (essentially tiny streams) it is strongly turbulent. *Sheet runoff* is the term we use for *the water that runs off in sheets and rills.*

The erosion performed by sheet runoff is **sheet erosion;** its amount is surprising. Raindrops spatter up loose particles of small size, and the flowing water (mostly as rills) picks up more, chiefly by hydraulic action. As no obvious valleys are created by this process, the soil loss it causes was not fully realized until accurate measurements were devised. Figure 10–1 shows one of many experiment stations maintained by the U. S. Department of Agriculture, and the results of typical measurements are assembled in Figure 10–2. To farmers these results are of far more than academic interest, for they show that sheet ero-

Fine sediment settles out

Coarse sediment settles out; water continues

Runoff water and sediment are collected and sent through flume

Runoff plot

Fig. 10–1. Apparatus for measuring sheet erosion, Marlboro, New Jersey. Sheet runoff, carrying soil particles, flows down a slope of 3 feet per 100 feet; sediment is trapped in containers and measured by weight. Each plot has a different kind of plant cover. Results are shown in Figure 10–2. (U. S. Soil Conservation Service.)

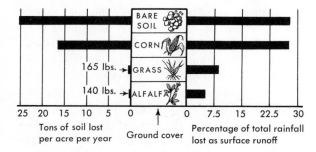

BARE SOIL

CORN

GRASS ← 165 lbs.

ALFALFA ← 140 lbs.

25 20 15 10 5 0   0 7.5 15 22.5 30

Tons of soil lost per acre per year   Ground cover   Percentage of total rainfall lost as surface runoff

Fig. 10–2. Effect of plant cover on rate of sheet erosion. Results of measurements over 4 years at a station like that shown in Figure 10–1, at Bethany, Missouri, on silty soil with a slope of 8 feet per 100 feet, and receiving annual rainfall of 40 inches. The chart shows that cover such as grass and alfalfa, which form a continuous network of roots and stems, is nearly 300 times as effective as "row crops", such as corn, in holding the soil in place. The erosional loss from bare soil shown here is at the rate of about 1.5 feet per 100 years.

179

Soil stripped away by sheet runoff

Bedrock exposed

Smooth, mass-wasted slope

Valleys

Fig. 10–3. Too many cattle were grazed on one of these two pastures in northern Kentucky, weakening the grass cover. Erosion did the rest. (U. S. Soil Conservation Service.)

sion is a menace to soil left unprotected on a slope. In recognition of this fact, good farming practice reduces areas of bare soil to a minimum and keeps the grass cover on pastures from being weakened by overgrazing. Figure 10–3 shows how sheet runoff and erosion are increased by weakening the protective plant cover. When crops such as corn, tobacco, and cotton must be planted on a slope, strips of such crops are often alternated with strips of grass or similar plants (Fig. 7–14) that resist sheet erosion.

How a valley starts. Although the aggregate area drained by sheet runoff is large, every natural surface is irregular. Therefore, no single sheet of water flows far downslope before it meets converging slopes and becomes concentrated into distinct streams. Concentration results in deeper water, increased turbulence, and increased erosion. Converging sheets and rills have become a stream, and the cutting of a valley has begun.

Valleys and mass-wasting. Although streams cut and deepen their valleys and transport the resulting loads of rock particles, the shaping of most of the land surface, including the sides of the valleys themselves, is the work not of streams but of sheet erosion and mass-wasting of weathered rock material (Fig. 10–4). To be sure, the downslope movement of regolith is promoted by stream erosion, which, by deepening a valley, increases local differences of height and slope. Therefore, the rate of mass-wasting is regulated not only by the rate of weathering but also by the rate of stream erosion at each point on the long profile of the stream. Conversely, the load fed to the stream by mass-wasting consumes stream energy that could otherwise be used in deepening the channel and slows the rate of deepening. Because of these relationships the rate of mass-wasting on a slope must approach a condition of stability in equilibrium with the rate of erosion of the stream channel at the foot of the slope; any change in one affects the other. The channel is essentially a local base level for the mass-wasting processes on the slope. Figure 7–14 shows slopes whose smooth profiles from base to top indicate

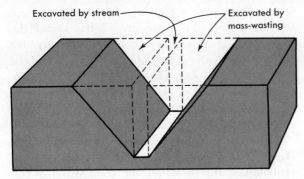

Excavated by stream

Excavated by mass-wasting

Fig. 10—4. In this segment of an ideal valley the volume of rock excavated by the stream is compared with the much greater volume excavated by sheet runoff and mass-wasting.

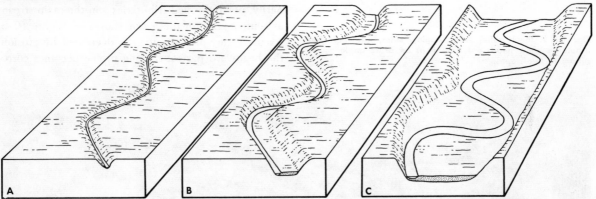

Fig. 10—5. Systematic changes, with time, commonly observed in a valley. The stream creates a valley floor, widens it, and develops meanders.

stability, with a slow rate of downcutting by the main stream to which they are tributary. Geologists call these smooth, stable profiles *graded* profiles. We can define a **graded profile** as *the profile of a stream or surface that is in near equilibrium with the processes that are shaping it.*

Evolution of a valley. Even casual observation shows that valleys range from small to large, from narrow to wide, and from very irregular to smoothly sinuous in pattern, and that usually a single valley changes in these respects from head to mouth. If maps or photographs of a hundred valleys are brought together and compared, the changes are seen to be systematic; they follow a progressive pattern. On this basis the future change in any valley can be predicted, at least in a general way.

The nature of the observed systematic change is illustrated in Figure 10–5, **A, B, C.** Early in the development of a valley its bottom or floor is hardly wider than the stream channel itself, **A.** At this stage the drainage area is small; therefore, the load contributed

from upstream is small; therefore, surplus energy is available for erosion of the bed; therefore, the valley deepens. At the same time, irregularities (present in all valleys; compare Fig. 10–7) deflect the current from side to side of the channel and cause erosion of the sides as well as the bottom.

As the drainage area enlarges, the loads of sediment poured by tributaries into the main streams increase. Moving these loads consumes more stream energy and leaves less for valley deepening; but the irregularities in plan continue to deflect the stream and thus promote side cutting.

The deflected stream deposits bed-load particles at the inner sides of bends where the water is slack (Fig. 9–22), and the channel shifts outward on the opposite sides, where turbulence and erosion are most effective. As a result, a flat valley floor covered with alluvium begins to develop, **B.**

When the stream has widened its valley floor to many times the channel width, a set of meanders has come into existence, **C.** The valley now has a wide

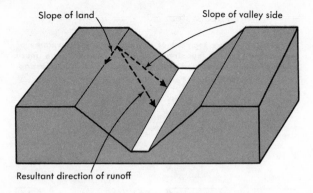

Slope of land — Slope of valley side

Resultant direction of runoff

Fig. 10–6. Ideal valley with sloping sides, showing that tributaries grow headward from it at an acute angle as resultant of two slopes.

floor covered with a thin layer of relatively coarse alluvium deposited from the stream's bed load. If the stream overflows its channel, it deposits very fine alluvium over parts of the valley floor, converting the floor into a floodplain (Fig. 9–24).

The broad floors of many valleys are underlain by alluvium that is abnormally thick, implying a more complicated history (p. 189).

Growth of tributaries. Sheet runoff down the side slopes of a valley concentrates into side streams (tributaries) that flow into the main stream. Ordinarily, newly formed tributaries join the main stream at acute angles for the reason shown in Figure 10–6. As the valley of a tributary is deepened by erosion, the headward part of its long profile becomes corre-

Fig. 10–7. This group of tributary valleys is growing headward, from their mouths in a main valley (*left*), up a broad sloping surface. An early phase of development of a drainage system. Horse Heaven Hills north of Pendleton, Oregon. (Brubaker Aerial Surveys.)

spondingly steeper. On the steepened slope the rate of erosion is increased, and as a result the head of the valley migrates up the slope. In other words, the valley lengthens in the upstream or headward direction. Rapid headward, upslope lengthening of a family of valleys is characteristic of new developing drainage.

Drainage systems. *A main stream with its family of tributaries is a* **drainage system.** An outstanding example is the Mississippi River system, whose basin extends from the Rocky Mountains at the heads of the Missouri, Platte, and Arkansas rivers, to the Appalachian Mountains at the heads of tributaries to the Ohio and Tennessee rivers, and includes about 40 per cent of the area of continental United States. The pattern of a drainage system resembles a branching tree (Fig. 10–7), and the spacing of the streams in it depends largely on amount of runoff, for tributaries develop only to the number necessary to carry the runoff away. Opposing systems like the two shown in Figure 10–8 grow headward up the regional slopes until each has accommodated to its neighbors, by mutual give-and-take, to dispose of the runoff in the most efficient possible way. The two drainage systems shown in the figure have left no part of their area undrained and have quite thoroughly *dissected* (cut up) the ridge into minor valleys and hills.

Not only are the streams of a drainage system nicely spaced to carry away the runoff, but long profiles of the tributaries are nicely adjusted to the main

Fig. 10–8. Headward parts of two stream systems draining a ridge that trends from upper right to lower left. Inyo County, California. (Spence Air Photos.)

streams into which they flow (Fig. 9–10). For each tributary the main stream acts essentially as a base level of a very temporary kind. The tributary can not erode below the level of the main stream at the mouth of the tributary, but, since the main stream itself is slowly lowering its long profile, the tributary can do so at a comparable rate; the whole drainage system, paced by the main stream, cuts downward in a co-ordinated way (Fig. 10–9).

Sculptural evolution of a land mass

Because streams make valleys and enlarge them by erosion and because streams move rock particles to the sea, running water must be removing the substance of the land and transferring it to the sea. Therefore, given enough time and freedom from interruption, streams and other processes should together be able to destroy the land. The surface rocks are attacked and weakened by weathering; the loosened and decayed rock particles are moved by mass-wasting and sheet erosion down the slopes to the streams, which carry them downward and away as at the same time they deepen and widen their valleys and dissect the land.

The whole complex is a grand destructive process, in which the forces of erosion are pitted against the resisting forces of cohesion within the bedrock, the regolith, and the plant cover on the lands. The erosional forces are limited downward by base level, below which they can not work. The raising of any land above base level creates potential energy, which is converted into kinetic energy in the streams that flow seaward across the land. Raising of the land also creates disequilibrium between two parts of the Earth's crust, but transfer of rock particles from the upraised land to the sea works to restore equilibrium. In the process the land is *sculptured* into a series of valleys and hills. The sculptured surface, slowly and continuously changing, is the expression resulting from (1) uplift of the crust modified by (2) destructive erosion of the uplifted area.

Rate of erosion. The cutting of valleys and the resulting loads of rock particles in streams are known through actual observation. The rate of erosion of the land is known also, more broadly than can be inferred from soil-erosion values like those in Figure 10–2. The rate is computed from measurements of suspended and dissolved loads in streams over a wide region.

From such computation it is calculated that the surface of the United States is being stripped away at an average rate of one inch every 760 years. This value has a margin of error of about 20 per cent because nonmeasurable bed loads are not included and because by no means every stream has gaging stations. Erosion of one inch in the lifetime of twenty-five human generations may seem a slow rate, but it involves the yearly removal to the sea of nearly 800 million tons of rock substance from the area of the United States alone. If concentrated on the Isthmus of Panama, this rate of removal could have excavated the Panama Canal in 73 days, and if concentrated on Manhattan Island it could reduce the island (not counting man-made skyscrapers) to sea level in a little more than 3 years. Since prehistoric, stone-age man hunted big game in the United States 10,000 years ago, an average of about a foot of material must have been stripped from the land surface.

Sequence of sculptured forms: cycle of erosion. Although the general character and rate of erosion are known by direct observation, the sequence of sculptured forms developed during long-continued erosion of a single land mass can not be observed because the changes take place much too slowly. However, when we compare a number of land surfaces, each in a different state of dissection, we perceive that their relation to each other is orderly. They can be arranged in a continuous series, each differing only slightly from the one preceding it. It seems probable, therefore, that a single land mass subjected to erosion will progress, in the course of time, through all these states. If so, we can predict in a general way the sculptural evolution that will take place. This concept is supported by the changes observed on a small scale during short periods; for example, the

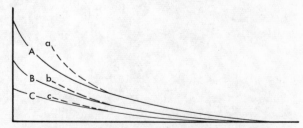

Fig. 10–9. Diagram illustrating successive long profiles of a main stream (*A, B, C*) and one of its tributaries (*a, b, c*) with the passage of time. Gradients progressively decrease, but at all times the tributaries are nicely adjusted to the main stream, which in turn is adjusted to its base level.

Fig. 10–10. This valley in Stewart County, Georgia, is growing headward, swallowing up farm land and threatening a road. Now more than 75 feet deep, it started more than 100 years ago. Valleys like this one often start in a rutted dirt road or in a field with furrows running downslope. (U. S. Soil Conservation Service.)

growth of small valleys in farm land (Fig. 10–10), spoil heaps, stockpiles, and laboratory models.

The sequence of forms, essentially valleys and hills, *through which a land mass is thought to evolve from the time it begins to be eroded until it reaches base level,* is widely known as the **cycle of erosion.** The cycle is theoretical, a concept, and can be described only in a generalized way because variations in precipitation, slopes, and kinds of rock from place to place create variations in the forms developed by erosional sculpture.

The evolution visualized in the cycle concept is shown diagrammatically in Figure 10–11 and is based on the assumption of homogeneous rocks, average precipitation (about 30 inches annually) and average runoff (about 9 inches). The sequence of changes can be summed up in this way: in the first part of the evolution (A, B, C) the surface is generally unstable in that stream gradients are steep [Fig. 10–9 (A, a)] and erosion is rapid, so that valleys are being actively deepened and make sharp cuts into the land. Because of the vigorous growth of valleys, a land surface in this condition is described as in *youth,* or *youthful.*

In the later part of the evolution (Fig. 10–11, **D, E, F**) the surface has become more stable. Valleys have dissected the entire surface, but stream gradients

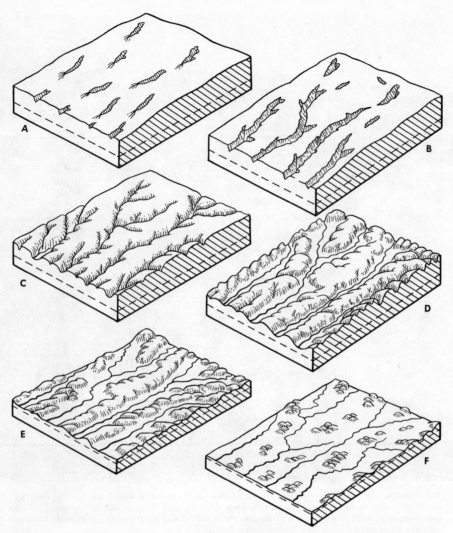

Fig. 10–11. Sculptural evolution of a land mass with time in a region of abundant runoff, illustrating the cycle of erosion in an ideal, generalized manner. **A, B,** and **C** represent early, generally unstable conditions, with drainage systems rapidly expanding and cutting sharply into the land, and correspondingly rapid changes in slope. **D, E,** and **F** represent later, generally stable conditions with streams and hillslopes more nearly in equilibrium. **F** represents a peneplane, a condition not observed in any extensive land area at present; it is deduced by projecting the foregoing conditions. Dashed line is base level, the lower limit of stream erosion.

have become gentler [Fig. 10–9 (B, b, C, c)] and streams are eroding more slowly. Slopes being eroded by soil creep have developed smoothly curved forms. A land surface in this condition is described as *mature*. As there is only a gradual transition, however, no sharp line can be drawn between youthful and mature surfaces.

The stable, or mature, surface is lowered toward base level very slowly, with the rate of erosion becoming increasingly slow as stream gradients become ever

more gentle. A surface in a late phase of erosion, lying close to base level, is described as in *old age*.

Peneplanes. A land surface in a very late phase of old age is a *peneplane* ("almost a plane"; Figs. 10–11, **F**, 10–12). We can define a **peneplane** as *a land surface worn down by streams and mass-wasting to very low relief*. With ever-decreasing energy, erosion of a mature surface becomes so slow that probably many millions of years are necessary for the creation of a peneplane. Despite its generally low relief, high

Fig. 10–12. Result of accelerated erosion. The smooth surfaces of the interstream areas are remnants of a formerly continuous stable surface, essentially a peneplane. Following a sudden and considerable increase in stream energy, streams are deepening their valleys and are extending them headward; the surface is being rejuvenated. It is believed that the energy increase resulted from faulting, which lowered the extreme foreground relative to the land next behind, thereby increasing the fall from stream heads to stream mouths. View west across south end of Inyo Range to Sierra Nevada, California. (John H. Maxson.)

steep hills may be present on it in places. *Conspicuous residual hills on a peneplane* are termed **monadnocks** and, as might be expected, are likely to be underlain by stronger, more resistant rocks than those beneath the area that surrounds them. The name was taken, in 1893, from Mt. Monadnock in New Hampshire, which at that time was believed to be a residual hill on an ancient peneplane. Current opinion as to that particular peneplane is divided, but the name continues in good standing.

Peneplanes are not observed today in an undisturbed state. A number of peneplanes have been submerged beneath the sea, deeply buried by thick layers of sediment, and later partly exposed by erosion of their covers of sedimentary rock so that we can see small parts of them. Others have been subjected to uplift and have been dissected so that again only small parts remain; an example is shown in Figure 10–12. No peneplane, therefore, is seen today lying unaltered in the position in which it was made. This fact implies considerable instability of the Earth's crust during at least the last few million years of geologic time, for, if the crust had remained quiescent, sculptural evolution of the lands should have been more advanced than it is.

In conclusion, the sculptural evolution of a land mass, as represented by the concept of the cycle of erosion, can not be described in quantitative terms. Nevertheless, it is a useful aid in visualizing the kind of changes to be expected during the slow reduction of a land mass toward base level.

Interruptions in sculptural evolution

Unstable systems: degradation and aggradation. The preceding section described an ideal land mass progressing through its sculptural evolution in an orderly way over a period of time measured in millions of years, uninterrupted by any outside influences. The whole system, consisting of streams, channels, valleys, and slopes undergoing mass-wasting, developed and maintained stability. However, close inspection of valleys shows us that very commonly the stable system has been interrupted. Since a land surface once stabilized does not become unstable unless altered by a disturbing force, we conclude that an interruption, in the form of a pronounced change in the energy of the system, has occurred. The interruptions fall into two groups, according to whether they have caused (1) conspicuously increased erosion or (2) greatly increased deposition.

Rejuvenation: stream terraces. Figure 10–12 illustrates a marked interruption in the sculptural evolution of an area in southeastern California. The interruption was apparently caused by faulting, which greatly increased stream energy upstream from the fault. The relations are like those shown in Figure 9–25. The increased stream energy is applied to erosion (downcutting) in the channels. This steepens the side slopes of the valleys, so that mass-wasting of them is also increased. The result is general instability. A land mass in this condition is said to be *rejuvenated* because, if in maturity or old age, it takes on anew the characteristics of youth. In Figure 10–10, which should be compared closely with Figure 10–12, rejuvenation is occurring on a small scale. Note that in Figures 10–12 and 9–25 the streams are already building fans at the base of the steepened slope. In so doing they are beginning to restore the stable condition that prevailed before the interruption occurred. *Rejuvenation,* then, is *the development of youthful topographic features in a land mass having stable features.*

Stream terraces are another example of interruption that caused increased erosion. **A *stream terrace* is *a bench along the side of a valley, the upper surface of which was formerly the alluvial floor of the valley.*** In a stream flowing on a broad valley floor cut from bedrock, like that in Figure 10–5, **C,** sudden increase in rate of erosion results in the cutting of a new valley within the older one. The floor of the older valley is

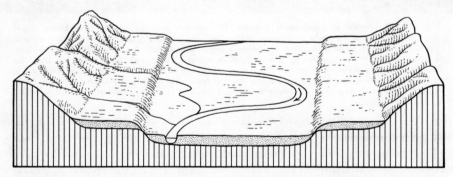

Fig. 10–13. Stream terraces (of alluvium-covered bedrock) result from a stream's cutting into its valley floor. Such terraces commonly occur in matched pairs (same height on both sides of valley). Although the terraces shown have been cut from bedrock thinly covered with alluvium, they can be cut from thick alluvial fill as well.

left as a pair of stream terraces (Fig. 10–13), which, of course, will in time be entirely destroyed by erosion.

Stream terraces of another kind common in valleys that have been filled with alluvium, and that do not occur in pairs, are shown in Figure 10–14.

Alluvial fills. The thickness of sediment deposited by a stable stream on its valley floor is slight; at most it can not exceed the depth of the stream when in flood. In small streams it may amount to no more than a few feet. Yet many valleys, even small ones, are filled or partly filled with alluvium scores or hundreds of feet thick. An *alluvial fill (a body of alluvium, occupying a stream valley, and conspicuously thicker than the depth of the stream)* indicates that some past event must have reduced stream energy below the level necessary to carry the load. As a result, the stream was forced to deposit part of its load, building up alluvium, until it had again reached a stable condition. But the new long profile was higher than the former one. Figures 10–14 and 10–15 are examples. Probably the kind of event responsible for most alluvial fills is variation in climate, through which the rate and character of weathering and mass-wasting and the rate of sheet runoff and stream discharge are altered. Other events include (1) reduction of the slope of a stream by movement of the crust, (2) creation of a natural dam across a stream, and (3) appearance of a glacier in a stream valley, creating outwash (p. 244).

Causes of interruptions. 1. *Movements of the crust.* Some interruptions in the stability of streams, valleys, and slopes can be traced directly to movements of the Earth's crust. If the upstream part of a drainage basin is lifted up in relation to the downstream part, energy increases because stream gradients increase and rejuvenation results. The streams flowing down the western slope of the Sierra Nevada in eastern California (Fig. 21–18) have been rejuvenated repeatedly by repeated elevation of the mountain range. Conversely, the western part of the same land mass in central California has been bent down and buried beneath accumulating sediments.

2. *Change of base level.* Rise and fall of sea level (p. 250) changes the base level of streams and can cause filling and erosion, respectively, in the seg-

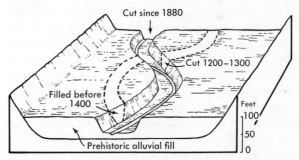

Fig. 10–15. Erosion and filling in a small valley in southwestern United States, dated as described in the text. Between 1400 and 1880 the stream changed its position, so that the older fill is transacted by the existing valley. (Modified after Sheldon Judson, Sci. American, vol. 187, 1952, p. 72.)

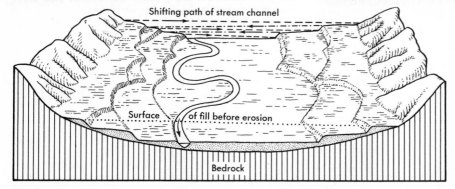

Fig. 10–14. Alluvial fill in a valley, later eroded to form stream terraces (of alluvium only). These events are recorded. 1. The stream excavated a broad valley in bedrock. 2. Reduction of energy in relation to load resulted in deposition of alluvium, half filling the valley. 3. Increase of energy in relation to load caused rejuvenation; meandering stream was deflected wherever it encountered bedrock beneath the alluvial fill, leaving terraces at various heights. Such terraces do not match up across the valley. Paired terraces, like those in Figure 10–13, can occur in fill as well as in bedrock.

189

ments of valleys that are near the sea. The creation of a dam across a valley, by a fan, a landslide, a glacier, a lava flow, or even a man-made dam, creates a local base level and can cause alluvial filling in the valley that is dammed. Erosion of the dam then can result in erosion of the fill.

3. *Glacial sediments.* A melting glacier commonly delivers so large a load of sediment to a stream that the stream can not carry it away and deposits it as a fill. The lower Mississippi Valley contains an alluvial fill more than 200 feet thick, believed to have resulted partly from the deposition of a heavy load of glacial sediment and partly from rise of sea level.

4. *Change of climate: erosion and filling in dry regions.* In the dry southwestern part of the United States deepening and headward extension of innumerable small valleys have been going on since about 1880. The valleys are bare, steep-walled canyons, cut into soft rock and loose sediment. Some of the canyons have grown headward as rapidly as one mile per year and have been eroded to depths as great as 75 feet. Yet Spanish settlers, before the accelerated erosion began, found the land surface stable and covered with vegetation.

Study of the ground and of weather records suggests that the cause lies mainly in very slight changes of climate. During long periods of drought, with few but heavy rainstorms, the grass cover deteriorates and lays the ground bare to erosion. During long periods with more frequent but lighter rains the grass cover improves and the valleys tend to fill with alluvium.

A period of few but heavy rains during the last half of the nineteenth century is believed to have caused the erosion now in progress, and overgrazing by cattle and sheep is thought to have accelerated the process. Some of the valleys contain clear evi-

dence of repeated erosion and refilling (Fig. 10–15). Fragments of ancient Indian pottery buried in the alluvium, coupled with records of ancient Indian migrations, give approximate dates of an earlier erosion and filling. A still earlier erosion is probably prehistoric, dating back to several thousand years ago.

Both rejuvenation and alluvial fills are so widely prevalent in drainage systems that land masses evidencing only one period of cutting and no filling are rather rare. From this we conclude that interruptions in the process of sculptural evolution are not the exception but the rule. If this is the case, then the concept shown in Figure 10–11 is clearly no more than an aid in visualizing a general trend that the common interruptions obscure or reverse.

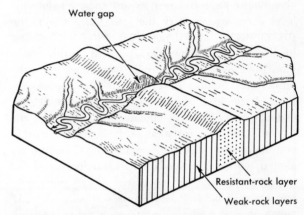

Fig. 10–17. Water gap formed where stream has cut through layer of resistant rock. In such rock valley is narrower and has steeper sides and gradient than in weak rock. Water gaps are common in the Appalachian region.

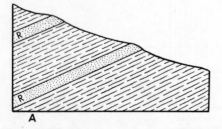
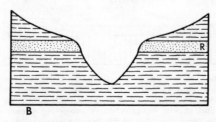

Fig. 10–16. Effect of outcrop of resistant strata R on the long profile of a stream A and on the cross profile of a valley B.

Effects of unequal resistance of rocks

Effects on profiles of streams and valleys. The extent to which rocks resist erosion by streams and mass-wasting affects streams and valleys in several ways. When a stream flows over a layer of resistant rock, its long profile is steepened (Fig. 10–16, **A**). An extreme example is shown in Figure 9–19. When a resistant stratum crops out along the sides of a valley, the cross profile of the valley takes on a steplike form (Fig. 10–16, **B**). A valley is likely to be narrower where it cuts resistant rocks than where it cuts weak ones. A *water gap (a pass in a ridge or mountain, through which a stream flows)* is a common feature at such a place (Fig. 10–17). The figure illustrates also that mass-wasting, sheet erosion, and stream erosion have lowered the surface underlain by weak rocks so effectively that the narrow belt of resistant rock has been left standing as a ridge above the general surface. The resistant rock is being eroded, but at a slower rate. When there are many such differences in rock resistance, a topography consisting of alternating ridges and lowlands develops.

Stream patterns. Not only the profiles of streams and valleys but also their patterns, as seen on a map, are affected by the kinds of rock on which they are developed. Stream patterns, however, are affected also by the history of the areas in which they occur. Three common kinds of stream patterns are shown in Figure 10–18.

The *dendritic* ("tree-like") *pattern is a stream pattern characterized by irregular branching in all direc-*

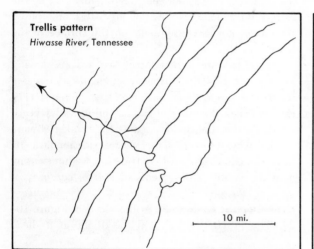

Trellis pattern
Hiwasse River, Tennessee

10 mi.

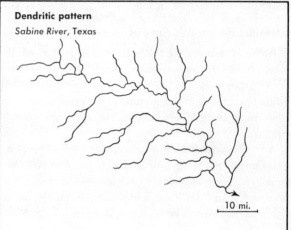

Dendritic pattern
Sabine River, Texas

10 mi.

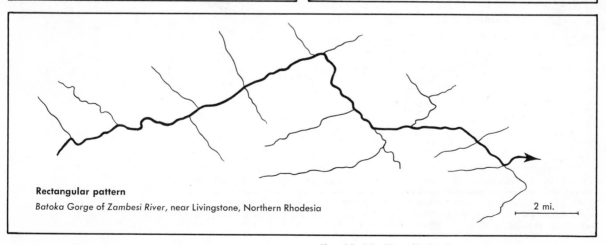

Rectangular pattern
Batoka Gorge of Zambesi River, near Livingstone, Northern Rhodesia

2 mi.

Fig. 10–18. Three kinds of stream patterns.

tions. This pattern is common in massive rocks and in flat-lying strata. In such situations differences in rock resistance have little or no control over the directions in which valleys grow headward.

The *rectangular pattern* is *a stream pattern characterized by right-angled bends in the streams*. Generally it results from the presence of joints (Fig. 18–17) and faults (Figs. 18–19, 18–21) in massive rocks or from foliation (p. 379) in metamorphic rocks; structures such as these, with their geometrical patterns, have guided the directions of headward growth of valleys.

The *trellis pattern* is *a rectangular stream pattern in which tributary streams are parallel and very long*, like vines or tree branches trained on a trellis. This pattern is common in areas like the Appalachian region, where folded sedimentary rocks, both weak and resistant, are exposed in long, nearly parallel belts.

Classification and history of streams

Kinds of streams. On the basis of their patterns and other characteristics, streams are classified into a number of groups, each of which implies something of the origin and history of the stream. These groups include consequent, subsequent, antecedent, and superposed streams.

A *consequent stream* is *a stream whose pattern is determined solely by the direction of slope of the land*. Therefore, consequent streams occur generally in massive and flat-lying rocks and commonly have dendritic patterns. The stream systems shown in Figures 10–7, 10–8, and 10–11 are consequent.

A *subsequent stream* is *a stream that occupies a belt of weak rock and whose pattern was determined by the weak rock*. When such belts are long and straight, subsequent streams constitute the long straight tributaries characteristic of trellis drainage patterns. Figure 10–19 illustrates the difference between consequent and subsequent streams.

An *antecedent stream* is *a stream that has maintained its course across a local uplift of the crust* that rose, by folding or faulting, in its path (Fig. 10–20). The name arises from the fact that the stream is antecedent to (older than) the uplift.

A *superposed stream* is *a stream that was let down, or superposed, from overlying strata onto a buried surface underneath them* (Fig. 10–21). The stream's path, therefore, was not controlled in any way by the surface on which it is now flowing. Most superposed streams began as consequents on the surface of the covering rocks.

Stream capture. When one of two streams, flowing in opposite directions from a single *divide (a line separating two drainage systems)*, has a much steeper gradient than the other, it can extend its valley headward, shifting the divide against the weaker stream. In this way it reverses the weaker stream little by little and can capture a long tributary by intersecting it at its mouth. This process of *stream capture* (or piracy), *the diversion of a stream by the headward growth of another stream*, is illustrated in Figure 10–22. The Provo River shifted the divide at its head

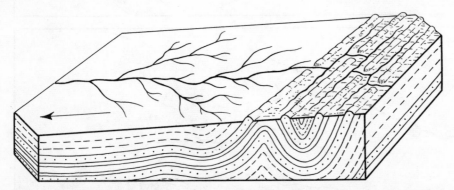

Fig. 10–19. Consequent streams contrasted with subsequent streams. In the area to the left the land surface is underlain by flat-lying strata. Drainage has developed under control of the slope of the land (shown by arrow) and is therefore consequent. To the right the same strata are folded. On them tributaries developed most readily along parallel belts of weak rock which determined stream locations. These tributaries are therefore subsequent streams. The main stream crosses ridges of resistant rock through water gaps.

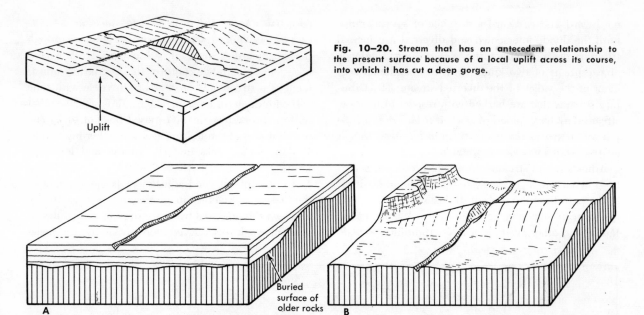

Fig. 10—20. Stream that has an **antecedent** relationship to the present surface because of a local uplift across its course, into which it has cut a deep gorge.

Fig. 10—21. Development of a superposed stream. **A.** Stream consequent on strata that bury a former land surface. **B.** After long-continued erosion the stream has become **superposed** and has cut a water gap through a hill that formed part of the older surface. Overlying strata have been removed by erosion, except for remnant in upper left. Compare Figure 10—20.

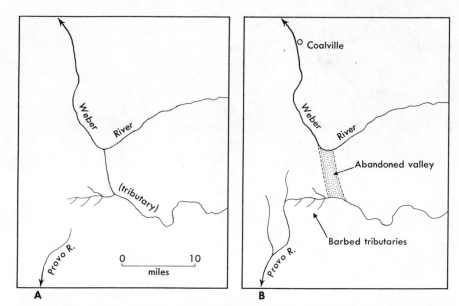

Fig. 10—22. Capture of tributary to Weber River by Provo River, upstream from Coalville, Utah. **A.** Reconstructed drainage pattern of an earlier time. **B.** Present drainage pattern. Provo River has extended its valley headward, capturing several small tributaries to Weber River and also the large tributary now part of Provo River. Abandoned segment of valley of former north-flowing stream is floored with stream gravel derived from the territory of the diverted stream. Small tributaries have barbed pattern showing former flow toward the east. Probable cause of capture: Provo River, shorter and with a steeper gradient than Weber River, had the greater erosion potential. (After G. E. Anderson, Am. Jour. Sci., vol. 40, 1915, p. 314.)

northward and eastward a distance of several miles until the divide intersected and diverted a principal tributary of its opponent, the Weber River. Evidence of capture is of two kinds: (1) an abandoned segment of the valley of the diverted stream; (2) tributary streams that are barbed with respect to the new stream they have joined. *A barbed tributary is a tributary that enters the new stream at an angle that is acute in the downstream direction.*

Adjustment of streams. In a long process of sculptural evolution, a stream system tends to adjust itself to the pattern of the rocks it drains, so that more and more stream segments occupy weak-rock belts, joints, faults, and other avenues of easy erodibility. A *well-adjusted stream system is a system a large proportion of which occupies weak-rock positions.* Through the headward growth of subsequent streams and occasionally through capture, the degree of adjustment of a stream system tends to increase with time and with depth of erosion. The result is a surface that reflects the pattern of the exposed belts of rock. The resistant rocks form hills, ridges, and other highlands, and the weak rocks underlie valleys and lowlands (Figs. 10–17, 10–19, 18–9, 21–19).

An example of good adjustment is the segment of the Delaware River drainage shown in Figure 10–23, in which the principal tributary streams coincide with areas of weak rocks. Even more strikingly, the Dela-

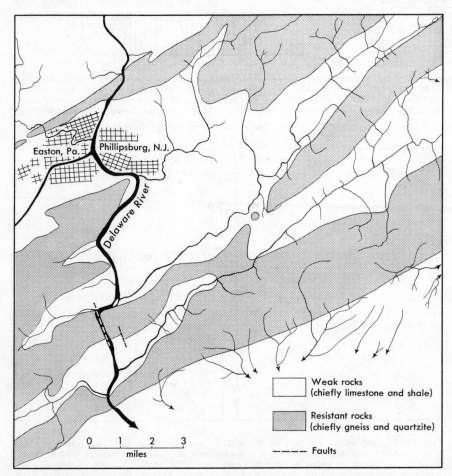

Fig. 10–23. Geologic sketch map of area around Easton, Pennsylvania, showing a stream pattern well adjusted to weak rocks. As the gneiss and quartzite resist not only stream erosion but mass-wasting as well, they are left as ridges about 500 feet higher than the weak-rock areas. (After W. S. Bayley, U. S. Geol. Survey Bull. 920, 1941, pl. 5.)

ware River, whose general course lies "across the grain" of the rocks, itself successfully avoids some of the belts of resistant rock and crosses others either at narrow places or at places where the rock is dislocated by faults.

How the tributaries became adjusted is fairly evident. Probably they are the successful competitors among many small streams whose valleys gradually grew headward from the Delaware at an earlier time in history. Those that started on resistant rocks developed very slowly; those on weak rocks lengthened more rapidly and secured most of the potential drainage area. "For he that hath, to him shall be given: and he that hath not, from him shall be taken. . . ." Out of context, this is an apt rule for the competition that occurs in a drainage system.

How the Delaware itself became adjusted is less easy to visualize, and we may never know in detail what led to its pattern. One hypothesis ascribes it to a similar competition between the young Delaware and other parallel streams, as all grew headward (northwestward) up the regional slope. The successful competitor was the one with the least amount of resistant rock to traverse and with a fault to help it at one place—in short, it was lucky. Whether this explanation is the true one is not known. Every area of complex rocks has its stream-location puzzles, to some of which there are solutions having a good degree of probability. But some of the puzzles may never be solved, simply for lack of enough surviving evidence, for the forces that develop sculptured forms also tend eventually to destroy them.

In contrast to streams such as the Delaware, antecedent streams (Fig. 10–20) and superposed streams (Fig. 10–21) are by definition not adjusted. Whatever their earlier degree of adjustment may have been, it was destroyed at the places where the antecedent or superposed relationship developed.

SUMMARY

1. Streams, aided by mass-wasting, cut their own valleys.

2. Mass-wasting accounts for the excavation of more rock than streams do. The main work of streams is to carry away the material fed to them by mass-wasting.

3. A land mass sculptured by streams and mass-wasting, if it were left uninterrupted, would go through a broadly predictable cycle of erosion, ending in a peneplane.

4. However, in most land masses this orderly development is interrupted. Among the interruptions are crustal movements and change of base level. These can cause rejuvenation or aggradation.

5. The pattern of rocks exposed at the surface induces adjustment of streams to the weak rocks and thereby strongly influences the stream pattern.

REFERENCES

Cotton, C. A., 1952, Geomorphology, An introduction to the study of landforms: 6th ed., New York, John Wiley and Sons.

Thornbury, W. D., 1954, Principles of geomorphology: New York, John Wiley & Sons.

CHAPTER 11. GROUND WATER

Geologic significance   Distribution and origin   Movement   Ordinary wells and springs

Artesian water   Economic aspects   Geologic work

A chamber in Luray Caverns, Virginia. Part of the cavern, formerly excavated by solution, has been refilled with dripstone, including stalactites, stalagmites, and columns.

Geologic significance

The results obtained from the digging and drilling of countless wells demonstrate that openings, both small and large, in bedrock and regolith generally contain water. This is *ground water,* defined simply as *the water beneath the Earth's solid surface.*[1] The geologic significance of ground water is fourfold: (1) it is an essential part of the hydrologic cycle (Fig. 2–10); (2) it performs geologic work by dissolving and depositing substances below ground; (3) it supplies plants and animals (including man) with a sizable fraction of their water requirements; and (4) by keeping the soil moist, it helps to prevent erosion of soil.

The questions we must try to answer are these. How is water distributed beneath the ground? How does it get into the ground? How does it move? What geologic work does it do? And last, but not least important, how do we locate and develop subsurface water for economic use and how does our ever-growing demand for water affect the supply?

Distribution and origin

One of the reasons why man has been able to establish permanent settlements, not only in well-watered country but also in desert lands, is that there are few areas in which holes, intelligently located and sunk far enough into the ground, do not find at least some water. In a moist country the depth of an adequate well may be only a few feet; in a desert it may have to be hundreds of feet. These facts have been learned by experience. There is water beneath the land nearly everywhere, but whether it constitutes

[1] This term is restricted by some geologists to the water beneath the water table, but the broader definition given here will simplify our discussion.

a usable supply depends on depth of occurrence, kinds of rocks present, kinds and amounts of substances dissolved in the water, and other factors. For this reason some places are much more favorable than others for obtaining ground water.

Origin of ground water. Hundreds of years before the birth of Christ it was recognized that rivers are fed, at least in part, by springs emerging from the ground and also that the discharge of rivers does not raise the surface of the sea appreciably. Although there was this vague concept of a hydrologic cycle, ancient Greeks thought that ground water was sea water driven into the rocks by the wind, and somehow desalted, or that it was created in some manner from rocks and air deep below the surface. The truth that ground water is derived mainly from rain and snow was recognized by Marcus Vitruvius, a Roman architect of the time of Christ, who wrote a treatise on aqueducts and water supply, a matter of great practical importance to the Romans.

Vitruvius' statement, although true, was qualitative only, and not until the seventeenth century was it established on a quantitative basis. Then Pierre Perrault, a French physicist, measured the mean annual precipitation on a part of the drainage basin of the River Seine in eastern France and also the mean annual runoff from it in terms of river discharge. Having estimated the land area involved, he calculated that runoff equaled only about 16 per cent of the water precipitated on the area as rain and snow. He concluded that the difference, 84 per cent, was more than enough to account for the amount of water in the ground. Even though we now know that much of that difference is lost by evaporation and transpiration (Fig. 2–10), Perrault's reasoning was sound. His work established precipitation as the source of ground water, except for a minute proportion that is juvenile, coming from substances within the Earth's interior.

The distribution of the radioactive element tritium (H³) supports the conclusion. Tritium, like radio-carbon (p. 58), is created only in the upper atmosphere; it enters into the compound H_2O and falls to the ground as rain and snow. It is present in ground water, which therefore must have been derived from the atmosphere.

Comparison of weather records with measurements of discharge of streams shows that over-all, despite the irregularity of rainfall, runoff is fairly steady. This is because much more moisture can be stored in the ground than can be stored in the atmosphere. A layer of regolith 1 to 2 feet thick can hold more water than the entire atmosphere, many miles thick, lying above it. So the ground—including not only the regolith but the rocks underlying it—acts as a storage reservoir that receives water irregularly but transmits it to streams at a more regular rate.

General distribution: water table. Much of our knowledge of ground-water occurrence has been learned the slow and hard way by the accumulated experience of many generations of men who have dug or drilled millions of wells. This experience (Fig. 11-1) tells us that a hole penetrating the ground ordinarily passes first through a *zone of aeration, the zone in which the open spaces in regolith or bedrock are normally filled mainly with air.*

The hole then enters the *zone of saturation, the subsurface zone in which all openings are filled with water. The upper surface of the zone of saturation is the water table.* Ordinarily the water table lies within a few feet or a few tens of feet of the surface, but it may be either more or less.

Has ground water a lower limit? Most of the water recovered through deep wells comes from depths of less than 2,000 feet. At greater depths the amount of water recovered decreases with depth. The deepest holes drilled for oil have revealed small amounts of water at depths exceeding 20,000 feet, but at such depths the openings in the rocks are so small that the water can not move through them. At depths of around 10 miles pressure from the weight of overlying rocks causes rock material to flow, closing all open spaces, and thereby excluding water. Recoverable ground water, therefore, is confined to a rather shallow zone with a lower limit that exceeds a depth of 2,000 feet only rarely.

Movement

We learned in Chapter 9 that the velocities of rivers are high enough to be commonly expressed in feet per second or miles per hour. Ground water, however, does not flow like a river; it is not turbulent. It moves so slowly that its velocities are expressed in feet per day and in some cases even in feet per year. To understand why this is so, we must understand the porosity and permeability of rocks.

Porosity. The amount of water that a rock can contain depends on the **porosity** of the rock; that is, *the proportion of total volume that consists of open spaces, or pores.* Generally the open spaces connect with each other. The porosity of some igneous rocks is less than one per cent, whereas the porosity of some sands and gravels is 25 to 45 per cent, if they are not tightly packed (Fig. 17-19). When a sediment is converted into a rock by deposition of cement between its grains, its porosity can be reduced by more than half (Fig. 17-20).

Permeability. The **permeability** of a sediment or rock is its *capacity for transmitting fluids.* When we drill a well, this property of rock becomes highly important because we want to tap a rock that will transmit the desired fluid (water, oil, or gas) into our well.

Although a rock may possess high porosity, it is not necessarily permeable. In determining permeability, an important part is played by the molecular attraction of rock surfaces for water particles. Molecular attraction is what makes a thin coating of water adhere to a rock surface, despite the pull of gravity; an

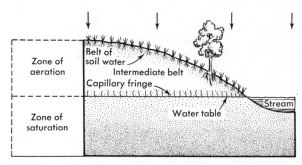

Fig. 11-1. Positions of zone of saturation, water table, and zone of aeration. (Adapted from W. C. Ackermann and others, U. S. Dept. of Agriculture.)

example is the wet film on a pebble that has been dipped in water.

Now, if a rock is made up of particles or grains that are extremely small, the open spaces between any two grains will be so small that the films of water adhering to the two grains will be in contact. In other words the force of molecular attraction will extend right across the opening, as shown on the left side of Figure 11–2. In this fine-grained rock, therefore, the water, at ordinary pressures, is held firmly in place and the rock is impermeable. This is what happens in clays and shales, whose component grains are less than 0.005 mm. in diameter (Tab. 3–2).

In contrast, in a rock whose grains are at least as large as sand grains (1/16 to 2 mm.) the open spaces are wider than the films of water adhering to the grains. As the force of molecular attraction does not extend across them effectively, water in the centers of the openings is free to move in response to gravity or other forces, as shown at the right in Figure 11–2. The rock is therefore permeable. As the diameters of the openings increase, permeability increases. With its very large openings, gravel is more permeable than sand and yields an especially large volume of water to wells.

Aquifers. *A body of permeable sediment or rock through which ground water moves* is called an *aquifer* (Lat. "water carrier"). Bodies of gravel and sand are usually good aquifers; clay is rarely an aquifer. Many sandstones, likewise, are aquifers, although the presence of cementing material between their grains reduces their effectiveness.

It might seem that shales, igneous rocks, and metamorphic rocks, all of which have extremely small spaces between their grains, should be impermeable and therefore not aquifers, but this is not necessarily true. Many such rocks are permeable because they have cracks, fissures, spaces between layers, and other openings that are too large to be controlled entirely by molecular attraction. Even so, as aquifers they are less effective than are coarse-grained sedimentary rocks.

Movement above water table. Let us return for a moment to Figure 11–1. Water from a rain shower infiltrates the soil, which usually contains clay resulting from weathering of the bedrock. Because of its fine-grained texture, the soil is generally less perme-

able than underlying materials. Part of the water, therefore, is held in place, literally suspended, by the forces of molecular attraction (Fig. 11–2). This is the belt of soil water in Figure 11–1. Some of it evaporates directly and much is taken up by plants.

The water in the soil that molecular attraction can not hold moves—actually it drips—downward through the intermediate belt shown in Figure 11–1 until it reaches the water table. In fine-grained rocks a fringe, immediately above the water table, is kept wet by capillarity wherever open spaces are so narrow that molecular forces can extend across them. Because of the presence of the fringe, the water table is not sharply defined but is slightly fuzzy. With every rainfall, the water is renewed from above, but, apart from the belt of soil water and the capillary fringe, the zone of aeration, as its name implies, is largely dry during the times between rains.

Movement below water table: percolation. We have said that the flow of ground water is not turbulent but streamline (p. 155), with the water particles moving along parallel paths. *Streamline flow through interconnecting spaces in saturated material* is called *percolation.*

In Figure 11–3 we can see that the water table is a surface consisting of slopes. In a region of abundant rainfall the water table is high under hills and low in valleys; indeed it is a subdued replica of the land surface above it. (In a dry region, however, it is different; see Figure 11–10.) Water is fed into the ground by infiltration from the land surface and is pulled down by gravity toward the level of the stream in the nearest valley. It emerges in the valley and

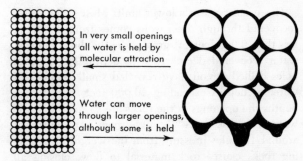

In very small openings all water is held by molecular attraction

Water can move through larger openings, although some is held

Fig. 11–2. Effect of molecular attraction in openings of different diameters. (Drawings are much larger than natural size.)

empties into the stream. The potential energy of the water (weight times vertical distance of fall) becomes kinetic energy of percolation. If there were no friction, the water would fall to the level of the nearest stream. But most of its kinetic energy is consumed in friction; the energy not so used is expressed in velocity of percolation.

The amount of energy lost in friction depends on the aggregate surface area of the rock particles between which the water percolates, and area in turn depends on particle diameters. In principle, a pail of buckshot has exactly the same aggregate amount of open space as the same pail filled with baseballs, but water percolates between the buckshot much more slowly because their aggregate surface area is much greater; hence loss of energy in friction is greater.

This is why percolation of ground water is slow. During the times between rains the water table slowly subsides. But, with each rain, renewed infiltration builds it up again; its hump-like form beneath each hill, then, is a direct result of the slow rate of percolation. This fluctuation of the water table with rainfall is still another proof that the source of ground water is mainly precipitation.

In Figure 11–3 the long curved arrows represent a few of the many paths (streamlines) followed by particles of percolating ground water. They curve downward at first and then bend upward toward the valley in which the water emerges. Their directions result from the tendency of the water to move both downward under the influence of gravity and laterally along the slope of the water table.

Percolation can be thought of in terms of three factors: permeability, slope of water table (h/l in Fig. 11–3), and velocity. These factors continually adjust to each other and so establish near-equilibrium, as do the factors in the flow of a surface stream (p. 161). Whenever rain adds water from above, the slope of the water table steepens, and, if permeability is constant, velocity must then increase.

Velocity and quantity of flow. We have already said that percolation of ground water is far slower than the flow of surface streams and that the low velocity of percolation is the result of friction. The most rapid percolation rate so far recorded within the United States is only 770 feet per day. This was measured in material whose permeability is exceptionally high and is a very unusual rate. Most measurements yield far lower values. They range between 5 feet per day and 5 feet per year.

Velocity of percolation is measured between pairs of wells. In one method two wells with metal casings are connected to form the electric circuit shown in Figure 11–4. Ammonium chloride, an efficient conductor, is poured into the upstream well and percolates downstream. On its arrival at the downstream well it creates a short circuit between well casing and electrode; this is recorded on an ammeter. Distance between wells divided by elapsed time gives the velocity.

Another means of measuring rate (and, of course, direction) of percolation is to put a strong dye, such as fluorescein, into a well and then time the appearance of dyed water in neighboring wells.

A major objective of the practical study of ground water is determination of the quantity of water in

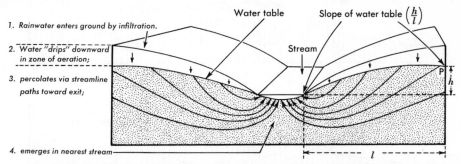

Fig. 11–3. Movement of ground water in uniformly permeable material. Long curved arrows represent only a few of many possible subparallel paths. Slope of water table at any point such as *P* is determined by height (*h*) above point of emergence in surface stream, divided by distance (*l*) to point of emergence. (After M. K. Hubbert, Jour. Geol., vol. 48, 1940, p. 930.)

motion at any place per unit of time because this determines the amount available for human use. Quantity is calculated from a formula derived from the work of Henry Darcy, engineer in charge of public works in the French city of Dijon in the middle of the nineteenth century. In a program of improvement of the city's water supply he experimented with percolation through sand used for filtering the water and found that with constant permeability velocity of percolation increases with slope of the water table.

A widely-used equation derived from Darcy's work is

$$Q = PiA,$$

in which Q is the quantity of water in motion per unit of time, P is a coefficient of permeability (essentially representing friction), i is the slope of the water table, and A is the cross-sectional area through which the water percolates.

Ordinary wells and springs

Ordinary wells. An ordinary well fills with water simply by intersecting the water table (Fig. 11–5). Lifting water from the well lowers the water level and so creates a *cone of depression, a conical depression in the water table immediately around a well.* In most small domestic wells the cone of depression is hardly appreciable. Wells pumped for irrigation and industrial uses, however, withdraw so much water that the depression may become very wide and steep and may lower the water table in all the wells of a district.

Figure 11–5 shows that a shallow well can become dry at times, whereas a deeper well in the vicinity may yield water throughout the year.

If rocks are not homogeneous, the yields of wells are likely to vary considerably within short distances. Massive igneous and metamorphic rocks, for example (Fig. 11–6, **A**), are not likely to be very permeable except where they are cut by fractures, so that a hole that does not intersect fractures is likely to be dry.

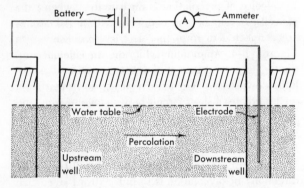

Fig. 11–4. Apparatus for measuring velocity of percolation.

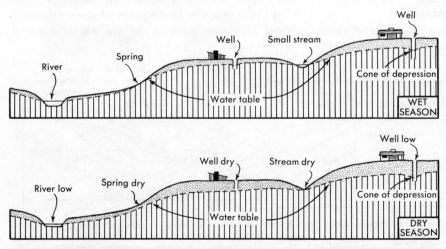

Fig. 11–5. Wells and a spring, showing cones of depression and effect of seasonal fluctuation of water table.

Since the fractures generally die out downward, the yield of water to a shallow well can be greater than to a deep one. Again, discontinuous bodies of permeable and impermeable material (Fig. 11–6, **B**) result in very different yields to wells. They also create *perched water bodies* (*water bodies that occupy basins in impermeable material, perched in positions higher than the main water table*). The impermeable layer catches and holds the water reaching it from above.

Gravity springs. A *spring* is *a flow of ground water emerging naturally onto the surface*. The simplest is an ordinary or *gravity spring*, whose flow results directly from the force of gravity. Three common kinds of gravity springs are illustrated in Figure 11–7.

Artesian water

Principle of artesian flow. In some regions an arrangement of inclined rock layers makes possible a special pattern of circulation of ground water. The essentials of the pattern are shown in Figure 11–8. In a series of inclined layers that includes a permeable layer, such as a sandstone, and an impermeable layer, such as shale or clay, overlying it, ground water can

percolate through the sandstone, which is then, by definition, an aquifer. In the shale, however, water is held immobile by molecular attraction in the tiny spaces between the grains that constitute the rock. In the area of water intake, where the sandstone is cut by the surface of the ground, rainwater enters the aquifer and percolates down its slope. Percolation is *confined* within the aquifer by the presence of the impermeable shale, which constitutes a roof, and by blocking of escape either laterally or downward. But the shale itself is saturated, and the whole system lies below the water table.

The aquifer is like a broad, flat, sand-filled pipe or conduit, holding its ground water confined, under the pressure of the column of water extending up to the water table at its upper end. Wells piercing the roof layer and penetrating the aquifer release the water, which rises in each well to the level of the intake, minus an amount determined by the loss of energy in friction of percolation. Hence the height to which the water will rise in any well depends on distance from intake, height of intake above the well head, and permeability of the aquifer. This is an *artesian well*, defined as *a well whose water rises*

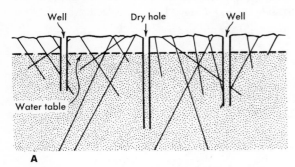

A

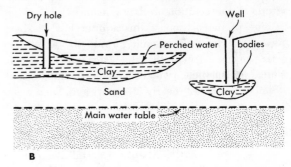

B

Fig. 11–6. Ordinary wells and adjacent dry holes in rocks that are not homogeneous. **A.** In fractured massive rocks such as granite. **B.** In discontinuous bodies of permeable sand and impermeable clay. Two perched water bodies are shown.

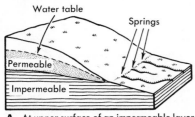

A. At upper surface of an impermeable layer

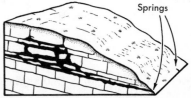

B. In fractured massive rock such as granite **C.** In cavernous rock such as limestone

Fig. 11–7. Three common locations of gravity springs.

above the aquifer. The name comes from the French province of Artois, in which, near Calais, the first well of this kind in Europe was bored. When the factors listed above are unusually favorable, pressure can be great enough to lift the water above ground to form fountains as high as 200 feet.

Deep wells bored into rock to intersect the water table are often called artesian wells, but this is an incorrect use of the term. Such wells are ordinary wells, like those in Figures 11–5 and 11–6.

Artesian system in New Jersey. Artesian-water circulation is of extreme practical importance to Atlantic City and other communities along and near the shore in southern New Jersey, for they draw their water supplies mainly from the aquifer shown in Figure 11–9. Altitude of the intake area is about 100 feet. Originally, the water rose to 25 feet above sea level in Atlantic City wells 40 to 50 miles southeast, the difference of 75 feet being accounted for by frictional loss. Now, however, so much water is being withdrawn that in some wells it rises no higher than 40 feet below sea level and therefore has to be pumped to the surface. This means that more water is being withdrawn from the aquifer than is entering it in the intake area. As the imbalance can not be allowed to continue, efforts at conservation are being made.

Rate of percolation in this aquifer has not been measured. However, assuming a rate of 500 feet per year, we can calculate that the water now being consumed in Atlantic City hotels entered the intake area, 48 miles northwest, nearly 500 years ago. Such water is, as it were, "aged in the rock."

Other artesian systems. Artesian water is obtained from systems essentially similar to that in New Jersey in many areas of the Atlantic Coastal Plain, from Brooklyn, New York, to Houston, Texas.

The largest artesian system in North America is based on the Dakota Sandstone. This very permeable sedimentary layer crops out and absorbs water along the eastern flanks of the Rocky Mountains, Big Horn Mountains, and Black Hills. Dipping generally eastward, the standstone layer underlies much of the Great Plains region from Saskatchewan to Kansas. The first well was drilled into this aquifer in 1882, since when more than 15,000 other wells have been drilled, to make the Dakota Sandstone the chief source of water for many parts of the region. Withdrawal of

water became so great that water levels in wells began to subside. Pressure in the system was gradually declining, as more water was being withdrawn from the aquifer than was entering it from rainfall. In some states this led to legislative action to reduce withdrawal to the point at which it would no more than balance supply.

Another large artesian system is the Illinois-Wisconsin system. Here there are two aquifers, the Potsdam Sandstone and the St. Peter Sandstone. Both crop out in Wisconsin and dip south, becoming less permeable in that direction owing to increase in their content of clay. Still another system is the Ocala Limestone system in Florida. The Ocala Limestone is an aquifer because it is full of caverns and smaller openings, intricately interconnected, created by solution. It crops out in the central and northwestern part of the peninsula and dips toward both coasts. Impermeable roofs are provided by layers of chert within the limestone. The system is the largest single source of water supply in Florida.

Artesian systems are not confined to wells. They operate also where the confined water has a natural outlet (usually through a fissure or along a fault) instead of through a well. The resulting outflows are *artesian springs* (Fig. 11–8).

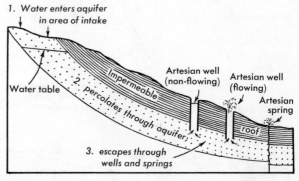

Fig. 11–8. Essential conditions for artesian wells: 1. An aquifer, 2, capped by an impermeable roof, 3, water pressure sufficient to make the water rise above the aquifer in any well.

Tapping an artesian system is a very ancient art. Four thousand years ago many artesian wells as much as 300 feet deep were in existence. In A.D. 1126 the well near Calais was brought in and is still flowing today. In that area, at any rate, withdrawal has not seriously exceeded supply.

Economic aspects

The economic importance of ground water is indicated by the fact that in the United States about one-fifth of all the water consumed in domestic, agricultural, and industrial use comes from beneath the ground. The rest comes from rivers, lakes, and artificial surface reservoirs all of which, like ground water, are supplied by rain and snow. The per capita consumption of ground water in urban households is about 120 gallons per day, but, when industrial and irrigation consumption are added, the per capita consumption rises to nearly 1,500 gallons. Among United States cities with populations exceeding 25,000, more than 30 per cent derive their water largely or entirely from below ground. These cities include Houston, Indianapolis, Memphis, and Spokane. With increase in population and industrialization, demand for water is growing very rapidly, and search for new sources of ground water is being intensified.

Water finding. Sites for farm and domestic wells are often located by persons who use forked twigs and other kinds of "divining rods" and who claim to possess supernatural powers. The search for water by this means, often called "dowsing," dates back at least to the time of Moses and is still widespread. Although there is no known scientific basis for this kind of claim, use of the divining rod persists, partly because in many areas shallow supplies of ground water are so widespread that successful results would be numerous even though sites were located at random. If the diviner were asked to indicate where water is *not* present below ground and if his predictions were then tested by boring holes, the statistical results would soon reveal the unsoundness of his claims. But, because little money is spent on holes in attempts to avoid water, this has never been done.

Recognizing the need for increasing the supply of ground water, government agencies in many countries have undertaken numerous studies of subsurface conditions in critical areas and have pointed the way to hidden sources of supply. This is one of the many direct ways in which geologic study aids the general economy. The location of a new aquifer or a successful well in a known aquifer is most reliably based on three activities: (1) detailed examination of geologic

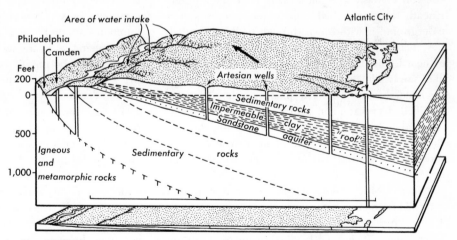

Fig. 11—9. Artesian system beneath the coastal plain in southern New Jersey. Surface is drawn from a map. Rock layers below surface are drawn from data obtained in drilling the 6 wells shown. Dashed lines show where knowledge is uncertain. The water table is so close to the surface that it is not shown separately. Vertical exaggeration is enormous—110 times. The lower block, showing the same area with a vertical exaggeration of only 2 times, illustrates why great exaggeration is essential for showing detail, even though it increases the apparent inclination of the rock layers. (Data from New Jersey Bureau of Geology and Topography.)

205

conditions at the surface, especially kinds and permeabilities of rocks, positions of rock layers, and character of fissures and other large openings; (2) exploration below the surface by seismic, electric, and other techniques used in petroleum exploration, and described in Chapter 22, to find possible buried aquifers; (3) study of the performance records of nearby wells or wells in analogous situations. Kinds of aquifers located by these methods include permeable sandstones, cavernous limestones, jointed and fissured crystalline rocks, lava flows, and coarse alluvium of various kinds.

Recharge. *The addition of water to the zone of saturation* is termed *recharge,* whether in a gravity system (Fig. 11–3) or in an artesian system (Fig. 11–8). In a dry region traversed by streams fed from mountains or other areas of substantial rainfall the water table is likely to be far below ground. In such a situation recharge can occur from the streams themselves (Fig. 11–10).

The intense demand for water in some areas has led to artificial recharging of the ground. One example is the practice of water spreading in dry parts of the west. A common way to spread water for recharge is to build a low dam across a valley. This holds back water in a surface stream that would otherwise run to waste and allows it to recharge aquifers beneath the stream bed. The water thereby stored underground is withdrawn through wells as needed.

A chemical-industrial plant in the Ohio River Valley near Louisville, Kentucky, was located on a valley fill of sandy alluvium more than 150 feet thick. Water was needed for cooling. The plant bought city water (purified river water) in winter when the water was cold and fed it into wells in the valley fill, thus recharging the sandy aquifer. In summer the cold water stored in the ground was pumped out for industrial use.

In some districts an aquifer is recharged with used water. This practice has increased with increased use of air conditioning, which requires a large volume of water. Some cities have laws requiring that certain water that has been used for air conditioning be returned to the ground, where it successfully builds up the water table. This illustrates the basic principle of ground-water conservation that withdrawal of water must, in the long run, be balanced by recharge; if it

is not, then either recharge must be increased or withdrawal curtailed.

Subsidence of ground. One of the consequences of continued excess of withdrawal over recharge is compaction of the aquifer. When the spaces between the grains of a sandstone or other sedimentary aquifer are no longer filled with water, pressure caused by the weight of the overlying rocks packs the grains together more closely, as shown in Figure 17–19. Not only does this permanently reduce the capacity of the aquifer; it may also cause serious subsidence of the ground above the aquifer. An example is the area of the city of Las Vegas, Nevada, which derives its water supply from pumped wells. Precise instrumental surveys show that during the period 1935–1949 the ground within an area 5 miles in diameter sank to form a conical depression that reflected the form of the cone of depression created in the water table underneath. Maximum subsidence was 14 inches. Pumping of ground water through 9,000 wells resulted in sinking of the area of Mexico City, between 1910 and 1952, by as much as 16 feet. During 1953 the rate of subsidence was 20 inches per year.

Pollution and sanitation. The most common source of contamination of water in wells and springs is sewage, and the infection most commonly communicated by polluted water is typhoid. Drainage from cesspools, broken sewers, privies, and barnyards contaminates ground water (Fig. 11–11). Although it might seem that in any well-populated district ground water would be unsafe as a source of domestic supply, such water can be of excellent quality. An example is a community of 70,000 people built as a unit in 1949–1950 in an area underlain by sand and gravel on western Long Island (Fig. 11–12). Each house has a septic tank for the disposal of sewage. The effluent drips downward 15 to 30 feet through the zone of aeration to the water table. The water supply for the entire community is drawn from eight ordinary wells, none of which is less than 100 feet from any septic tank. Despite the effluent contributed to the zone of aeration, the water supply would exceed legal purity requirements even if it were not treated chemically.

This rather startling fact is explained by passage of the water through sediment that possesses an enormous internal surface area with, in the aggregate, a large molecular force that attracts and holds much water while purification takes place. Purification is the combined result of (1) mechanical filtering-out of bacteria (water gets through but most of the bacteria do not), (2) destruction of bacteria by chemical oxidation, and (3) destruction of bacteria by other organisms. Purification goes on both in the zone of aeration and in the zone of saturation. In some communities river water polluted with sewage is pumped into the ground where it becomes a part of the local ground-water supply. In one city percolation through a horizontal distance of 500 feet removed all impurities from the sewage and made the water fit to drink.

Geologic work

Solution: chemical composition. The geologic work performed by ground water consists mainly of solution of minerals, transport of the solutes, and precipitation of the solutes as deposits in the rocks.

All ground water contains substances in solution. Its ability to dissolve and to oxidize results from its content of carbon dioxide and free oxygen as it enters the zone of aeration. Rainwater contains free oxygen and carbon dioxide acquired from the atmosphere, and as it passes through the soil it acquires much more carbon dioxide generated by soil bacteria. At the top of the zone of aeration, therefore, ground water is essentially a very dilute carbonic acid, a corrosive substance, and an efficient solvent.

This widespread acid attacks minerals and reacts with them to form salts, which go into solution in the ground water. The salts are mainly chlorides, sulfates, and bicarbonates of calcium, magnesium, sodium, potassium, and iron. Since some of these salts are alkaline, ground water gradually changes in character from mildly acid to mildly alkaline.

The composition of ground water varies from place to place according to the kind of rock in which it occurs. In much of central United States the water is "hard," that is, rich in calcium and magnesium bicarbonates, because the underlying rocks include abundant limestones and dolostones that consist of those carbonates. In some places within arid regions the concentration of dissolved substances, notably sulfates and chlorides, is so great that the ground water is unfit for human consumption. Furthermore, evaporation of water in the zone of aeration precipitates not only calcium carbonate but, in particularly dry regions, sodium sulfate, sodium carbonate, and sodium chloride. Soils containing these precipitates are loosely termed "alkali soils." They are unsuitable for agriculture because crops will not grow in them.

Some ground water is salty. Two of the various ways in which the water has become salty are these. Along some coasts, ground water has become contaminated by infiltration of sea water. In some deeplying sedimentary rocks, salty ground water is **connate water,** defined as *sea water, in sedimentary rocks,*

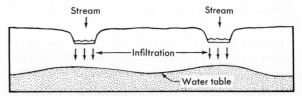

Fig. 11–10. Recharge of ground water in a dry region by infiltration from streams having their sources in mountains with abundant precipitation. The stream channels are actually leaking. Relation of water table to streams is the reverse of that shown in Figure 11–1, where leaking is impossible.

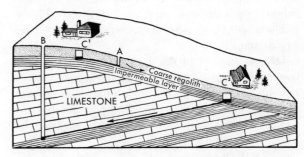

Fig. 11–11. Contamination of wells. The shallow dug well, A, was unwisely located downslope from a cesspool, C^1, and received contaminated drainage from it. The owner then drilled a deeper well, B. This well tapped layers of cavernous limestone inclined toward it from the lower cesspool C^2. The water flowed through openings in the limestone, and reached B unpurified by percolation. The well owner must relocate his cesspool or dig a shallow well upslope from C^1.

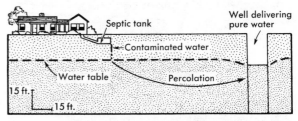

Fig. 11–12. Purification of contaminated ground water in sand and gravel during percolation through a short distance.

that was trapped at the time the rocks were deposited as a sediment. It has remained in them ever since.

The effect of solution on rocks constitutes part of the chemical alteration and resulting crumbling that are the chief element in weathering (p. 117). The solutes are carried by percolating ground water into streams, which transport them to the sea. There they form the source from which most marine animals secrete their shells and from which most of the limy sediments that later become limestones are made.

The quantity of mineral solids dissolved and exported by ground water has been measured in some districts. In an area in the Piedmont region of North Carolina, underlain by diorite, the discharge from streams and springs was measured and the quantity of mineral solids in solution in this water was determined. From these data it was calculated that in that area ground water is removing solids equivalent to a layer of rock one foot thick every 28,000 years. This, of course, is in addition to removal by mass-wasting and stream erosion. The rate is remarkable because diorite is composed mainly of minerals such as plagioclase, pyroxene, and amphibole, which are highly insoluble until they have been chemically altered by weathering.

Deposition. Part of the mineral matter, dissolved in ground water, that does not escape into streams is deposited in sediments and rocks below the surface. Perhaps the most obvious, though not the most abundant, deposits made in this way are in caverns, fissures, and other large openings. Those most commonly seen are deposits of dripstone, discussed below.

Less obvious but in the aggregate more bulky are deposits, from solution in *connate water* and other ground water, in the spaces between the grains of a sediment (Fig. 3–18, **B**). Such deposits, which in the course of time cement the grains firmly together, are the chief means by which sediments are converted into sedimentary rocks. Calcite, silica, and iron compounds, in that order, are the chief cementing substances. Most cementation takes place in the zone of saturation. Little is known about why the cementing substances are precipitated, but changes in pressure and temperature with consequent loss of carbon dioxide may be involved.

Replacement is *the process by which ground water dissolves matter already present and at the same time deposits from solution an equal volume of a different substance.* Evidently replacement takes place on a volume-for-volume basis because the new material preserves the most minute textures of the material replaced. Petrified wood (Fig. 4–5) is a common example. But replacement is not confined to wood and other organic matter; it occurs in mineral matter as well. Some ore bodies owe their origin to replacement (p. 456).

Another result of ground-water deposition consists of concretions (p. 336), common in some sedimentary rocks.

Caverns. Limestone (calcium carbonate), dolo-

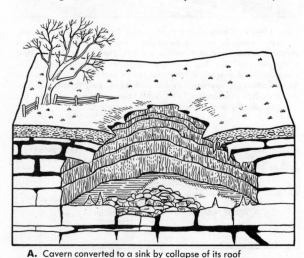

A. Cavern converted to a sink by collapse of its roof

Fig. 11–13. Common kinds of sinks.

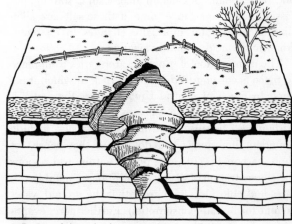

B. Funnel-shaped sink excavated at the surface

Fig. 11–14. Sink in limestone near Sunken Lake, Presque Isle County, Michigan. (I. D. Scott.)

stone (calcium-magnesium carbonate), and marble (a related metamorphic rock) constitute a group of carbonate rocks that underlie millions of square miles of the Earth's surface. These rocks are peculiarly susceptible to the attack of ground water which, as we have seen, is commonly a dilute solution of carbonic acid. Where ground water is abundant, carbonate rocks are riddled with cavities, ranging from tiny openings to very large ones. *A large, roofed-over cavity in any kind of rock* is a **cavern** (see illustration on p. 197).

Although most caverns are small, some are of exceptional size. Carlsbad Caverns in southeastern New Mexico include one chamber that is 4,000 feet long, 625 feet wide, and 350 feet high. Mammoth Cave, Kentucky, consists of a least 30 miles of interconnected caverns.

Some caverns have been partly filled with insoluble fine sediment, such as clay, that was present as an impurity in the limestone and was gradually released by solution. Others contain partial fillings of **drip-stone** (*calcite chemically precipitated from dripping water in an air-filled cavity*). Dripstone is deposited by loss of carbon dioxide from ground water as it drips from ceiling to floor. It takes on many curious forms, which are one of the chief attractions to cavern visitors. The most common shapes are **stalactites** (*icicle-like forms of dripstone, hanging from ceil-

ings*), **stalagmites** (*blunt "icicles" of dripstone projecting upward from floors*), *and* **columns** (*stalactites connected with stalagmites*) (p. 197).

Still other caverns, including most of those in the Black Hills, South Dakota, are partly or wholly lined with glittering crystals of calcite or quartz. As these crystals form only in water solutions of their substances, it is evident that the openings were in the zone of saturation at the time of crystallization and that since then the water table has subsided to expose them to view. In contrast, dripstone is deposited only in the zone of aeration. Neither crystalline linings nor dripstone, both of which are merely re-fillings, indicate which zone a cavern was in at the earlier time when it was being excavated. From the shapes of caverns it is believed that most were created in the zone of saturation but that some were made in the zone of aeration.

Sinks. In contrast to a cavern, a **sink** is *a large solution cavity open to the sky.* Some sinks are caverns whose roofs have collapsed (Fig. 11–13, **A**). Others are formed at the surface, where infiltrating water is freshly charged with carbon dioxide and is most effective as a solvent. Many sinks are located at the intersections of joints, where water can move downward most rapidly, and are likely to have a funnel-like shape (Fig. 11–13, **B**). A sink of the latter kind is shown in Figure 11–14. These illustrations portray

209

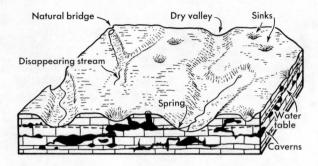

Fig. 11–15. Karst topography. The block has an area of 1 or 2 square miles.

sinks of small size. Some sinks, however, are very large. One, near Mammoth Cave, Kentucky, has an area of 5 square miles.

Karst topography. In some districts sinks and caverns are so numerous that they combine to form a peculiar topography characterized by many small basins. In this kind of topography the drainage pattern is irregular, with streams that abruptly disappear into the ground, leaving their valleys dry, and then reappear elsewhere as large springs. This has been termed *karst topography* (Fig. 11–15) because it is strikingly developed in the Karst region of Yugoslavia,

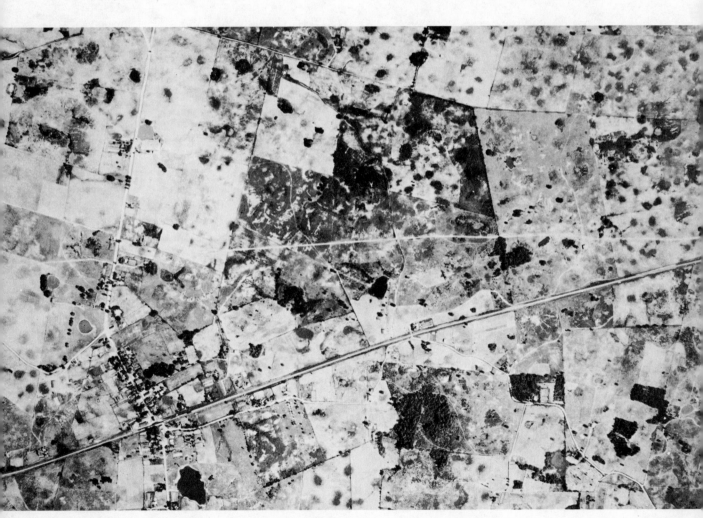

Fig. 11–16. Karst topography Mammoth Cave National Park, Kentucky. The dark-colored areas with white rims are lakes that occupy some of the sinks. The small gray spots with less definite boundaries are dry sinks. Surface streams are almost completely lacking. (Fairchild Aerial Surveys.)

inland from Trieste. It is defined as *an assemblage of topographic forms consisting primarily of closely spaced sinks.* Karst topography is developed in wide areas in Kentucky, Tennessee, southern Indiana, and northern Florida (Fig. 11–16).

Sinks and caverns record the destruction of a very large volume of carbonate rock. It is calculated from measured amounts of carbon dioxide in ground water and from the solubilities of limestones that the amount of precipitation falling on northern Kentucky is capable, as ground water, of dissolving a layer of limestone one foot thick every 2,000 years. This potential is far greater than the average erosional reduction of the United States by mass-wasting, sheet erosion, and streams (p. 184) or than the measured solution of diorite in North Carolina (p. 208). It depends on the presence of exceptionally soluble rocks.

SUMMARY

1. Ground water has its origin almost entirely in rain and snow.

2. Its distribution is nearly universal.

3. The water table marks the top of the zone of saturation.

4. In a moist region ground water percolates from beneath hills and emerges in valleys. In a dry region it is likely to move away from areas beneath surface streams.

5. Flow of ground water into most wells is by gravity, but in artesian wells it is by hydrostatic pressure.

6. A basic principle of conservation is that withdrawal of ground water must not exceed recharge.

7. Ground water dissolves mineral matter from rocks; much of the dissolved product eventually gets into the sea.

8. Ground water converts sediments into rocks by depositing substances as a cement between grains.

9. In carbonate rocks ground water creates sinks and caverns and deposits mineral matter in some caverns.

REFERENCES

Bretz, J H., 1956, Caves of Missouri: Missouri Geol. Survey, vol. 39.

Ellis, A. J., 1917, The divining rod, a history of water witching: U.S. Geol. Survey Water-Supply Paper 416.

Hubbert, M. K., 1940, The Theory of ground-water motion: Jour. Geology, vol. 48, p. 785–944.

Meinzer, O. E., 1923, The occurrence of ground water in the United States, with a discussion of principles: U. S. Geol. Survey Water-Supply Paper 489.

————, 1942, Occurrence, origin, and discharge of ground water, in Meinzer, O. E., and others: Hydrology, p. 385–477: New York, McGraw-Hill Book Co.

Tolman, C. F., 1937, Ground water: New York, McGraw-Hill Book Co.

U. S. Department of Agriculture, 1955, Water, The Yearbook of Agriculture: Washington, U.S. Govt. Printing Office.

CHAPTER 12. LAKES AND BASINS

Lake basins   Water economy of lakes   Lakes in dry regions   Lakes in moist regions
Swamps   Summary

Lakes, Annette Island, Alaska. (U.S. Navy.)

Lake basins

Creation and destruction of basins. Lake Mead occupies an artificial basin created in 1935 when Hoover Dam (Fig. 9–12) was built across the Colorado River. Water was allowed to fill the basin gradually; its greatest height was reached in 1941 (Fig. 12–1). The river began to deposit its load in the lake, and the accumulating body of sediment was closely watched. Accurate measurements of its surface form and its thickness were taken at intervals by echo sounding (p. 283) and of its internal character by core sampling (p. 291).

These observations showed that the sedimentary body is a typical delta (Fig. 9–26), with coarse-grained foreset and topset beds and very fine-grained bottomset beds. Its profile in each of the years 1937 to 1948 and 1959 is shown in Figure 12–1. From these profiles it can be predicted that sediment will eventually displace all the water in the lake and will fill the basin completely. But calculations based on the first 12 years of sedimentation showed that filling will not be complete until more than 400 years had

elapsed, so that, although the dam is expendable, it will have a long and useful life for water storage. However, the completion of a new dam 250 miles upstream from Lake Mead will intercept 75 per cent of the sediment that now enters the lake and will extend its life by many centuries.

What is happening in artificial Lake Mead is happening also in basins of natural origin. The general tendency of streams and mass-wasting is to create surfaces that slope continuously toward the sea. Against this tendency, many geologic processes create natural basins that in places interrupt the continuity of slopes. Streams themselves do so, as shown by the small basins in the original Colorado River profile in Figure 12–1, made partly by hydraulic plucking and partly by low dams of alluvium built by small, steep tributary streams.

Most basins are of the order of tens or hundreds of feet in diameter, but some are measured in hundreds of miles. A basin is an ephemeral thing, vulnerable to attack by agents of destruction, chiefly streams, that

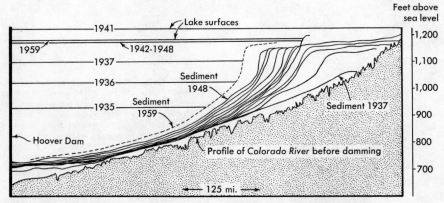

Fig. 12–1. Successive profiles of the body of sediment now gradually filling the basin of Lake Mead, Nevada-Arizona, determined by periodic surveys. (Modified after C. P. Vetter, Am. Geophys. Union Trans., vol. 34, 1953, p. 251.)

not only fill it with sediment but also breach its outlet by erosion (Fig. 12–2). The number of basins now existing in the land surface probably runs into the millions, and, as new basins are continually created and existing ones destroyed, the number fluctuates literally from day to day.

Basins, and the lakes that many of them contain, are of interest from at least three points of view: first, the economic value of the water and the mineral deposits they supply; second, the inferences relating to fluctuations of climate that can be drawn from abandoned shorelines of lakes and from the kinds of sediments deposited on lake floors; third, the information basins furnish for reconstructing geologic history.

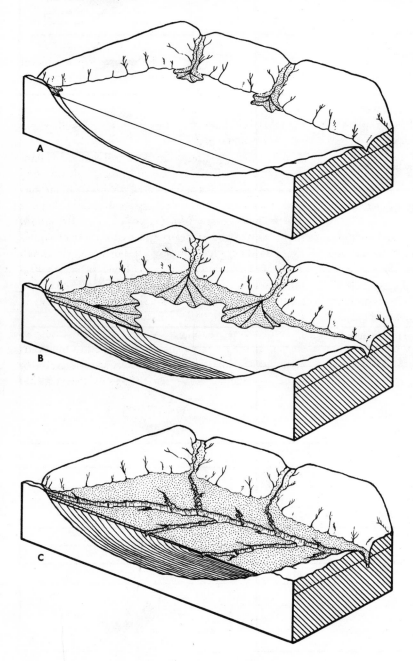

Fig. 12–2. Stages in the history of a lake. **A.** Stream system dammed by gentle upwarp across right-hand end of block, forming basin and lake with outlet across the upwarp. Streams build deltas; shoreline is eroded by waves. **B.** Deltas enlarge and merge, gradually filling basin. Outlet is deepened by erosion. **C.** Erosion outlet gradually drains lake; streams trench the lake sediments, creating broad terraces. The sediments in this basin are rock particles—sand, silt, and clay—brought in by streams. Compare the sediments in Figure 12–11, which consist of plant remains.

Table 12—1. Kinds of natural basins

Process	Basin	Example
Bending of crust *warping*	Valley blocked by local uplift	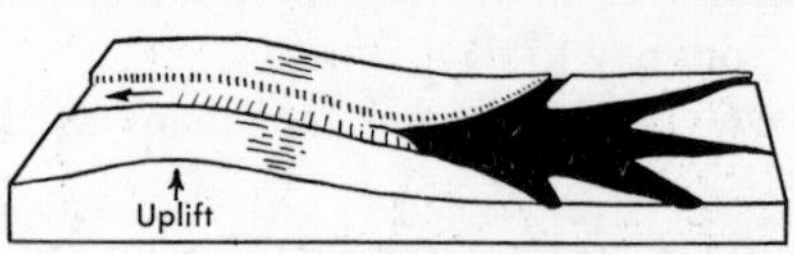 Uplift
Faulting	Fault basin	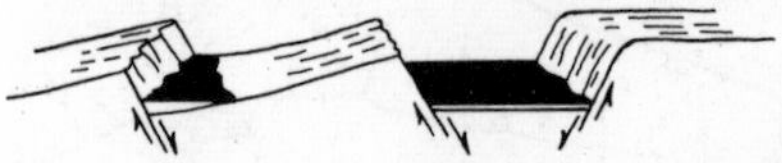
Volcanism	Crater	
	Valley blocked by lava flow	
Mass-wasting	Valley blocked by landslide	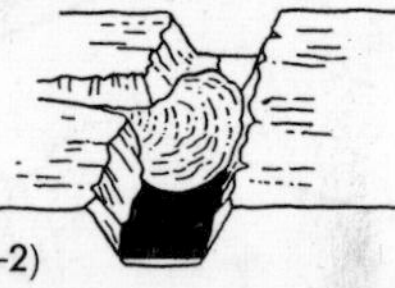 (Fig. 8—2)
	Basin in thawing frozen ground	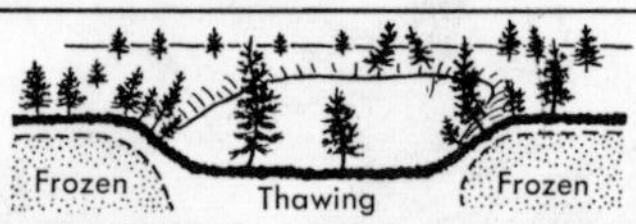 Frozen Thawing Frozen
Streams	Rock basin formed by hydraulic plucking	(Fig. 9—15, **A**)
	Cut-off meander	(Fig. 9—23, **B**)
	Valley blocked by fan	
Ground water	Sink	(Fig. 11—13)
Glaciers	Scoured rock basin	(Chapter 12 title page)
	Valley blocked by glacial drift or ice	(Not illustrated) *Fallen Leaf Lake*
	Basin in glacial drift *Kettle Lakes*	(Fig. 13—22)
Wind	Deflation basin	(Not illustrated)
	Interdune basin	(Fig. 14—25)
Sea	Basin in sea floor	(Not illustrated)
	Cut-off bay	 Sea

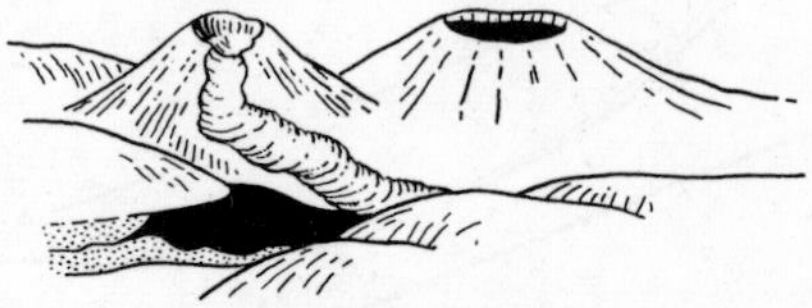

Former basins are recognized principally by remnants of the sediments deposited in them by streams and lakes; the existence of an ancient depression, therefore, can be recognized long after its topographic form has disappeared.

Kinds of basins. The number of ways in which natural basins are made is remarkably large. Nearly every geologic process creates basins of some kind. Table 12–1 by no means exhausts the list, but it includes the more common origins.

Water economy of lakes

Relation of water economy to climate. Some basins contain lakes, whereas others do not; this is a result of the water economy, or water balance sheet comparing gains and losses, in the basins (Fig. 12–3). The water economy of a lake is based primarily on climate. In a moist climate the level of water in a lake is controlled by the level of the outlet; any increase in the water received simply increases the discharge of the outlet stream. In a dry climate water level is controlled by the ratio of water received to water lost by evaporation and by leaking into the ground. Owing to fluctuations of climate, equilibrium is rarely maintained for long at one level; so lakes fluctuate with climate. This fact is clearly brought out by data from the Great Salt Lake, whose water economy is rather well known.

Great Salt Lake. Great Salt Lake (Fig. 12–4) is a shallow-water body occupying the deepest part of a large desert basin in western Utah. The basin was created mainly by faulting and is very deep. In fact, the lowest point in its rim stood, until recently, more than 1,000 feet higher than the lake, which is therefore a

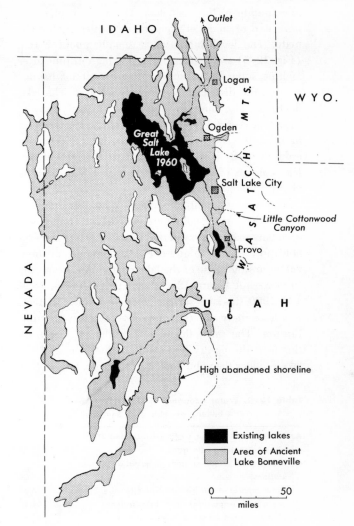

Fig. 12—4. Great Salt Lake and area covered by its predecessor, Ancient Lake Bonneville.

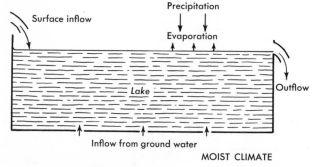

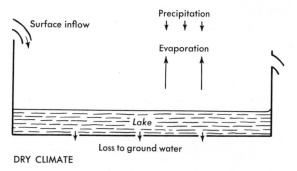

Fig. 12—3. Water economy of lakes in moist and dry climates.

mere puddle on the basin floor. The water level, being unrelated to an outlet, must be controlled by the climate. The level fluctuates seasonally about 2 feet (Fig. 12–5) and reaches its annual high in June after melting snow on the surrounding mountains has increased the discharge of tributary streams. The lake fluctuates also through intervals of many years, as shown in Figure 12–5. When at its historic maximum in 1873, the lake had an area of about 2,200 square miles. The dry lake floor that fringes the present-day lake consists of bare, dry silt and clay with patches of precipitated salts.

The water economy of Great Salt Lake is shown in Table 12–2. As the values are generalized from measurements made over a period of many years, they do not apply exactly to any one year. Changes in these values are the cause of the lake fluctuations from year to year. But Figure 12–5 shows that between 1850 and 1960 the lake surface fluctuated only 18 feet; therefore the water economy is very nearly in equilibrium. The small fluctuation results in part from this fact: during dry periods the reduced area of the lake reduces the volume of water evaporated, so that

the water level eventually becomes nearly constant, despite continued drought. During wet periods the greater area of the lake permits increased evaporation, and the water level again becomes nearly constant.

Near-equilibrium is reflected also by the chemistry of the lake water. Chemical analyses of the water of inflowing streams show that it contains only about 0.03 per cent dissolved solids, a percentage much too small to be detected by taste. Yet the water in the lake itself contains 14 to as much as 23 per cent dissolved solids, the percentage varying inversely with the curve in Figure 12–5. All this dissolved mineral matter, derived from the rocks of the surrounding region, chiefly through chemical weathering, is poured into the lake by streams and is concentrated by evaporation.

During years when the lake is low, its water becomes saturated with sodium chloride, which is precipitated. Sodium chloride is common salt (hence the name of the lake) and is the chief basis of an important local industry, in which salt is obtained by evaporation of the water. Sodium sulfate is present also in large amount. As the solubility of sodium sulfate varies with temperature, during cold winter weather it is precipitated and forms slushy, snow-like masses along the shores. In the summer season it is redissolved. Many other elements are present in the water in smaller amounts.

It is evident, therefore, that the chemical as well as the physical economy of the lake is in delicate balance, controlled principally by climate. Thousands of years ago the water economy of Great Salt Lake was very different from today, as is shown in the discussion that follows.

Table 12–2. Water economy of Great Salt Lake
(In billions of cubic feet annually)

A. Precipitation on lake surface (calculated from measurements on rain gages)	42.47
B. Inflow from major streams (measured at gaging stations)	95.09
C. Total measured addition of water (A plus B)	137.56
D. Measured evaporation from lake surface	161.17
E. Non-measured inflow (C minus D)	23.61
(E represents unmeasured surface inflow, inflow of ground water, and errors in measuring B and A.)	

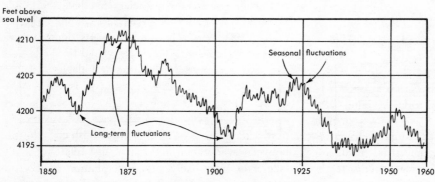

Fig. 12–5. Fluctuations of surface of Great Salt Lake 1850–1960.

Lakes in dry regions

Playa lakes and other saline lakes. In a dry region lakes are likely to be few in number, shallow, and saline; also, many are intermittent. They are scarce and shallow because precipitation is low and evaporation high. They are saline (that is, they contain an appreciable amount of dissolved mineral matter) because the solutes in the water are gradually concentrated by evaporation. Many of them are intermittent (present at times in winter, dry in summer) because of seasonal climate. The seasonal fluctuation of Great Salt Lake (Fig. 12–5) illustrates the seasonal influence of climate but the lake does not dry up completely.

In areas of higher temperature and smaller inflow, however, many lakes exist only a few days or a few weeks in each year, and in exceptionally dry years some of them never form at all. In the dry region of western United States *an ephemeral shallow lake in a desert basin* is called a *playa lake;* when dry (which is most of the time) the lake bed is a *playa* (Figs. 14–7, 14–8). Some playas are a dazzling white because of precipitated salts at their surfaces. More commonly, they are grayish because the salts are mixed with clay and other fine sediments that were suspended in the lake water. If the lake water can leak down through the basin floor before evaporation saturates the water with salts, no salts can be precipitated, and the playa sediments will consist mainly of clay.

We must not forget that the chain of events in the history of the salts is, in capsule form, solution of rocks by ground water → percolation → stream transport to lake → precipitation on lake floor. For this reason the chemical character of the water and the precipitates of a lake in a dry region depend on the kinds of rocks that underlie the drainage area of the lake. For example, in addition to salt lakes such as Great Salt Lake, there are alkali lakes rich in sodium and potassium carbonates, bitter lakes rich in sodium and other sulfates, and borax lakes rich in borax and related minerals. Potash, borax, soda, bromine, lithium, and many other substances are recovered from them. At Searles Dry Lake, in the Mojave Desert region in southeastern California, industrial plants are extracting such products from a surface layer of nearly pure salts with the extraordinary thickness of 80 feet.

The salts were precipitated during the evaporation of an ancient lake more than 700 feet deep. Today the floor of the lake basin is almost continuously dry.

Ancient Lake Bonneville. Let us return to Great Salt Lake and try to reconstruct its history. The physical evidence is very clear that in the recent geologic past the water economy of the lake was very different from its present economy. On the sides of the mountains that surround the basin are many abandoned shorelines in the form of wave-cut cliffs, beaches, and bars (Figs. 12–6, 16–7). At the mouths of stream valleys there are massive deltas. All these shorelines are now high and dry, at heights of hundreds of feet above the existing lake. The highest of all lies about 1,000 feet above the lake. At the northern end of the basin this high shoreline leads into a long stream-cut outlet (Fig. 12–4) that discharges into the Snake River. Clearly, the whole basin was once filled with water at least 1,000 feet deep in its deepest part. Then the basin was nearly emptied by evaporation, and this happened so recently that there has not been time for erosion to destroy the abandoned shorelines.

The huge lake that sculptured the highest shoreline has been named Ancient Lake Bonneville, after a U. S. Army captain who explored the region in 1833. It is calculated that Ancient Lake Bonneville had a volume comparable to that of Lake Michigan today. Unless some other factor was involved, we can infer that the climate then was both cooler and moister than now—enough to reduce evaporation and to increase precipitation so that the water surface could rise 1,000 feet and overflow the basin. Under such conditions the water would not have been salt but fresh.

Part of the east side of the lake basin is formed by the Wasatch Mountains. Canyons in these mountains contain deposits made by glaciers that developed high in the mountains during glacial ages. In one of them, Little Cottonwood Canyon, sediments deposited in Ancient Lake Bonneville are so related to the glacial deposits as to indicate that lake and glaciers existed contemporaneously. The relationship is expectable because temperatures low enough to create glaciers should also greatly reduce the rate of evaporation from a water surface and should establish equilibrium between evaporation and inflow at a relatively high lake level. Very likely, also, precipitation in this region was greater during glacial times than it is today.

Fig. 12—6. Two shorelines of Lake Bonneville along a spur of the Wasatch Range, between Salt Lake City and Provo, Utah. Vertical distance between the shorelines is about 350 feet. (J. S. Shelton.)

The sediment presently brought into the basin, as a result of erosion of the surrounding mountains, tends to fill it. Some of the sediment is deposited in Great Salt Lake, but by far the greater part of it is deposited in fans at the mouths of mountain canyons. Although many of the fans are very large, all their combined bulk has made only a beginning of filling the enormous basin. It is not hard to imagine that the sediments now filling the basin will some day be converted into rock and still later exposed, through erosion, to inspection by a future generation of geologists. The sediments will then appear as sandstones and conglomerates around the sides of the basin, with fine-grained lake-deposited sediment, including chemical precipitates, in the central part.

Other pluvial lakes. In the dry region west and south of the Rocky Mountains, extending from Ore-

gon to New Mexico, more than 100 other former lakes have been identified from sediments or shorelines (Fig. 12–7). Most of the basins are dry; a few contain shallow lakes. Although only one of these many former lakes, Searles Dry Lake in southeastern California, has been proved, by radiocarbon dating, to have existed during a glacial age, probably all of them were created by the cooler, moister climates of glacial times, which radically changed the water economy of the basins.

A former lake such as these (including Lake Bonneville) is known as a *pluvial lake.* No pluvial lakes exist today because, by definition, they are *lakes that existed under a former, different climate in areas that are now dry.* Although the name implies a pluvial, or rainy, climate, we realize that reduced evaporation caused by reduced temperature was a large factor in

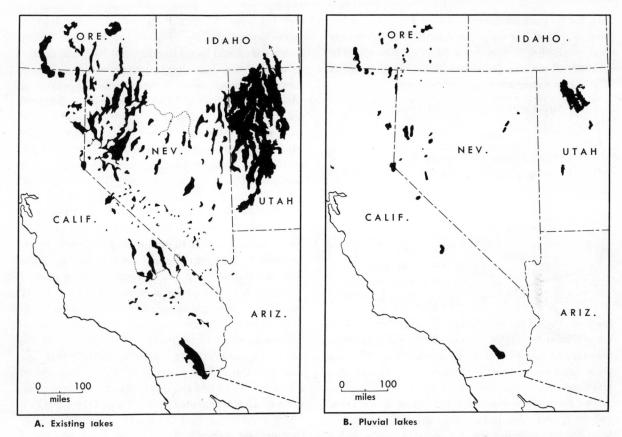

A. Existing lakes **B. Pluvial lakes**

Fig. 12–7. Existing lakes, A, and pluvial lakes, B, in the dry region of western United States. (R. F. Flint, 1957, Glacial and Pleistocene geology: New York, Wiley, p. 227; O. E. Meinzer, 1922, Geol. Soc. America Bull., vol. 33, p. 5.)

the changed water economy, but the name *pluvial* still sticks to the ancient lakes. It should not be supposed that because pluvial lakes were related in time to glacial ages they were fed by water derived from the melting of glaciers. Some of them were, but this was largely a matter of chance. Most of the lakes occupied basins to which glacial waters had no access.

Pluvial lakes were abundant also in other dry regions of the world. The desert area in the Andes of Bolivia, Chile, and Argentina contained many of them. Numerous pluvial lakes were present also in the Saharan region of North Africa and in western and central Asia. The largest in the world was an ancestor of today's Caspian Sea; another that is historically famous was an ancestor of today's Dead Sea. Despite their names, neither of these existing water bodies is part of the sea. Both are lakes.

Lakes in moist regions

Great Lakes. The Great Lakes system affords a fine example of water economy in a relatively cool, moist region, where annual precipitation ranges from 20 inches near the head of Lake Superior to as much as 46 inches near the lower end of Lake Ontario. Inflow exceeds evaporation, and the lakes overflow (Fig. 12–3).

A profile and section of the system are shown in Figure 12–8. The vertical dimension is exaggerated about 200 times. If shown to true scale, the section would appear no thicker than the line forming the base of the figure.

The system consists of a chain, or series, in which each lake discharges through a short river into the next lake. Actually, Michigan and Huron are a single

221

lake, for they are connected not by a flowing river but by a strait 150 feet deep. Final outflow of the system is through the St. Lawrence River to the sea. The quantity of outflow, Q (about 250,000 cubic feet per second), is determined by this formula:

$$Q = \left[\begin{array}{c} \text{direct rainfall on lakes } (D) \\ \\ plus \\ \\ \text{inflow from streams and} \\ \text{ground water } (I) \end{array} \right] minus \left[\begin{array}{c} \text{evaporation from lake} \\ \text{surfaces } (E) \\ \\ plus \\ \\ \text{net withdrawals for} \\ \text{water supplies } (W) \end{array} \right]$$

(D minus E) is only about 30 per cent of Q; and, since the value of W is small, Q must be supplied mainly from the factor I. Because the drainage area tributary to the lakes is nearly twice the area of the lakes themselves, this is a reasonable requirement. Unfortunately, actual figures are not available.

The enormous volume of water stored in the lakes (about 6,000 cubic miles) is so great that it could keep Niagara Falls flowing at its present discharge for nearly 100 years, even though no more rain were to fall. As a combined source of water supply, hydro-electric power, and water transportation, the Great Lakes are unequaled by any other lake system in the world.

Future of Great Lakes. It is interesting to speculate on what will happen to the Great Lakes in the normal course of geologic events, neglecting artificial control of the rate of erosion at Niagara Falls (p. 166). Evidently the lake basins will cease to exist, for the dual processes of erosion and filling with sediment are at work on them. At an average rate of recession of 4

feet per year, Niagara Falls should be cut back to Lake Erie at Buffalo (Fig. 9–18) in about 27,000 years and should begin to drain that lake in earnest—assuming, of course, that those responsible for water power and other values make no effort to prevent it. Meanwhile, the basin of Lake Erie is being filled with sediment discharged into it by streams and eroded from its shore by wave action. On the floor of Lake Michigan such sediment has actually been collected with a core sampler (p. 291) and measured, and is accumulating at a rate of roughly 3 inches per 100 years. On the assumption that the basin of Lake Erie is filling at the same rate, it would probably take nearly 100,000 years to fill it up. Destruction of the basin by drainage is therefore likely to precede destruction by filling up. In any case, the chain of basins will be converted into a continuous stream system.

The 27,000-year period mentioned above is a very thin slice of geologic time, and there is reason to believe, from a comparison of dates gained from radiocarbon measurements, that water began to fill the Lake Erie basin not very far from 15,000 years ago. Added to the 27,000 years for the future recession of Niagara Falls to Buffalo, this gives an estimated minimum of 42,000 years for the total life of the Lake Erie basin. Looking around the world, we find few lakes that can be shown to be old, and many records of lakes that have been destroyed. This is the basis of the statement at the beginning of this chapter that most basins are geologically short-lived.

History of Great Lakes. The basins of the Great Lakes are long and narrow (map, Pl. 1) and are localized along belts of weak rock, like the valleys of some headward-growing streams (Fig. 10–23). For these and other reasons the basins are believed to be parts of former stream valleys. Each basin lies within territory that has been glaciated, and features left by the former glaciers indicate that movement of the ice generally paralleled the elongate basins. Further-

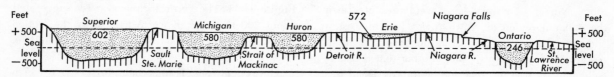

Fig. 12–8. Generalized profile and section through Great Lakes system. Depths shown are at deepest part of each lake; average depths are much less. Section is about 550 miles long.

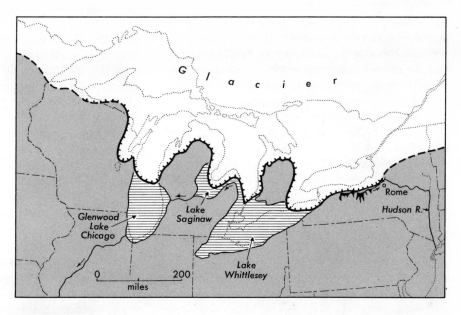

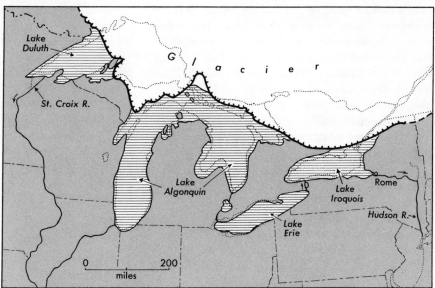

Fig. 12–9. Two of the many stages in the development of the glacial Great Lakes during the last 15,000 years. The glacier (white) gradually melted, increasing the sizes of the lakes. The lakes overflowed at various places at different times. Some of the lakes differ in name from existing lakes because they stood at higher levels, as we can see from old beaches. (R. F. Flint, 1957, Glacial and Pleistocene geology: New York, Wiley, p. 345.)

more, each basin has a bedrock rim entirely inclosing it, and all but that of Lake Erie are excavated to depths well below sea level. On this evidence it is thought probable that the basins are the product mainly of glacial erosion, which widened and deepened large river valleys, although other basin-making processes also played a part. The capacity of some of the basins was further increased by glacial deposits piled upon the southern rims.

The lakes themselves were created as the glacier ice melted away and poured its meltwater into the basins (Fig. 12–9). This origin of the lakes is inferred from three lines of evidence: (1) Lake sediments overlie glacial deposits; therefore the lakes postdate the glacier. (2) Old lake beaches, higher than the present shores, run around the southern ends of the lakes but end abruptly on the north. This implies that when the beaches were made the northern shores consisted of glacier ice. (3) Old abandoned lake outlets, higher than the existing lakes, drained toward the south, whereas the whole system today drains northeast. One of the old outlets leads through the city of Chicago southwest to the Mississippi River. Such outlets could have functioned only while the existing St. Lawrence River outlet was blocked; the most probable blockading mass was the former glacier itself.

Lakes Agassiz and Barlow-Ojibway. Late in the history of the Great Lakes two additional lakes created by the damming action of the ice sheet reached enormous size (Fig. 12–10). The larger was Lake Agassiz (A-ga-see), appropriately named for the nineteenth-century Swiss scientist who was the first to recognize a worldwide glacial age. When at its largest size, that lake (now extinct) was larger in area than all the modern Great Lakes combined. The other, Lake Barlow-Ojibway, was smaller, but still it was considerably larger than Lake Superior. Both former lakes are recognized by deposits of silt and clay

over their floors and by beaches and other shoreline features. This evidence tells us that the Great Lakes are the survivors of a formerly much larger group of lakes of glacial origin.

These two lakes differed from the pluvial lakes in two respects. First, the basins that contained them consisted partly of glacier ice; therefore, the basins existed only during the rather brief period when the glacier was present. Second, the water that filled them was derived mostly from melting of the glacier rather than primarily from rain and snow.

In the glaciated regions of the world many other former lakes, of similar origin, have been identified.

Swamps

Origin of swamps. *A swamp is an area of saturated ground.* Such ground is wet because runoff or infiltration of surface water is delayed or prevented. Many swamps occupy basins and represent a phase intermediate between lakes and dry land. Indeed, many basins vary seasonally in two or all three of the phases: dry land ⇆ swamp ⇌ lake.

Other swamps occupy nearly flat areas in which growth of vegetation alone prevents surface water from creating channels and forming streams. Roots and stems spread the water effectively, keep it dispersed, and force it to flow mainly by percolation.

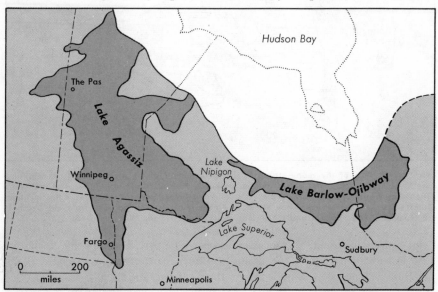

Fig. 12–10. Ancient Lake Agassiz and Lake Barlow-Ojibway, occupying basins blocked by the melting ice sheet along their northern shores, 7,000 to 8,000 years ago. Various outlets (not shown) were used. (Adapted from Glacial Map of Canada: Geol. Assoc. Canada, 1958; and Glacial Map of United States: Geol. Soc. America, 1959.)

Swamps are found most commonly in four kinds of situations: coastal areas, floodplains, glaciated areas, and areas of perennially frozen ground.

1. *Coastal swamps* are of two kinds. In one group are **tidal marshes,** *swamps that are alternately submerged and uncovered by the rise and fall of tides*. They occupy valleys at the mouths of streams and other inlets open to the sea. They contain channels through which the water moves in and out. The vegetation of tidal marshes consists of kinds of plants that can tolerate salt water.

In the other group are fresh-water swamps, cut off from the sea and occupying shallow basins on low, flat coastal plains. Many large swamps along the Atlantic and Gulf Coasts of the United States, including the Dismal Swamp in Virginia and North Carolina, the Okefenokee Swamp in Georgia and Florida, and the Everglades in southern Florida are in this group, as are the Pontine Marshes on the coast of Italy southwest of Rome.

2. *Swamps in alluvium.* Broad, flat alluvial areas, including floodplains and deltas, are the sites of many swamps. Abandoned channels and wide areas back of natural levees are common sites. In many alluvial areas the water is spread by growing vegetation, creating swamps without the necessity of a basin being present.

3. *Swamps in glaciated terrain.* Much of the country overrun by glaciers during the glacial ages contains basins both small and large; probably their number runs into the millions. Some were scoured out of bedrock by the moving ice; others are surrounded by irregular deposits of glacial sediments. A gradually forming swamp in a basin of this kind is shown in Figure 12–11.

4. *Swamps in areas of frozen ground.* In the wide belt of territory underlain by perennially frozen ground swamps are abundant. During the summer, when the frozen surface thaws, the water can not escape downward, and in flat country it can not run off easily. The resulting swamps, consisting of mosses and other low-growing plants adapted to the peculiar arctic conditions, remain frozen during the long winter.

Sediments of swamps. Sediments that accumulate in swamps contain a large proportion of organic matter such as *peat (partly decomposed plant matter formed in swamps)*. Figure 12–11 shows one way in which this material accumulates in a moist-temperate climate during conversion of a lake to a swamp. Aquatic vegetation, such as pond lilies, water weeds, and rushes, grows in shallow water close to shore. Dead plants are attacked and decomposed by bacteria beneath the water surface. The bacteria excrete waste products that are toxic to them; when the waste matter reaches a certain concentration in the water, the bacteria are killed, and the partly decomposed plant substance is preserved. When dry, peat is combustible. In some regions it is used as fuel, and indeed it is the first step in the making of coal. But in regions rich in coal, peat is little used because of its relatively low thermal efficiency. The enormous quantities of peat in swamp lands are, however, a potential source of fuel and with efficient handling can produce economically large amounts of energy.

Swamps also accumulate inorganic (mineral) sediments, mostly clay and silt. As most swamps are in rather flat country, running water can not transport coarse particles, and only fine-grained sediments are brought in. A complete gradation exists from mineral sediments to peat, depending on depth of water and rate of influx of sediments. This gradation is reflected in the occurrence of impure, clayey coal, representing deposits in ancient swamps into which streams were bringing mineral particles.

Drainage and reclamation of swamps. Many swamps, like lakes, are eventually destroyed by being drained by active streams (Fig. 9–11). The process has been greatly hastened by human agency, for the soil of some swamp land, because it is rich in humus, is potentially fertile. Large areas of such land (including much of the Everglades, Dismal Swamp, and Pontine Marshes) have been drained, mainly by cut-

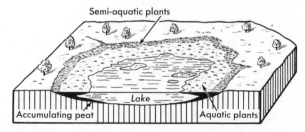

Fig. 12–11. Filling of a small lake with peat. (Compare Figure 12–2.) Growing vegetation gradually extends from shores toward center of lake. Some drops to bottom but a floating layer of living vegetation occupies the surface. Eventually the lake is completely replaced by peat. A lake is not essential for peat, which also accumulates in swamps not preceded by lakes.

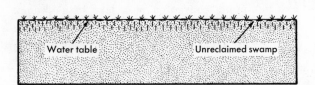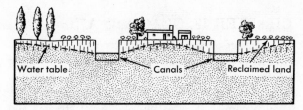

Fig. 12–12. This swamp land south of Rome, Italy, was drained by digging drainage canals and so was reclaimed for agriculture. Formerly useless, it is now very productive.

ting canals leading to the sea or to a near-by valley (Fig. 12–12) and thereby reclaimed for agriculture. Ground water percolates into the canals, increasing the slope of the water table. According to the formula stated on page 202, the quantity of water percolating must then increase, and this lowers the water table. The more closely spaced the canals, the lower the water table; in any reclamation project the canals are planned to produce the desired water table. Many small swamps are drained through pipes buried in the ground rather than through open canals.

On the other hand, the draining of swamps inland increases flood heights in streams because precipitation gets more rapidly into streams instead of being delayed by slow percolation through the ground. Each district has its special problems, which require thorough study before natural ground-water storage and runoff are interfered with.

SUMMARY

Significant points brought out in this chapter include these:

1. Natural basins are created in many ways, despite the general tendency of streams and mass-wasting to create smooth slopes free of basins.

2. Most basins tend to be destroyed by erosion and by filling up with sediment.

3. Whether a basin will contain a lake and whether a lake will fluctuate depend on the water economy of the basin. Great Salt Lake is an example of a water economy that has been measured.

4. Playa lakes and other saline lakes characterize basins in dry regions.

5. Hundreds of deep pluvial lakes existed during former glacial ages in basins that are now dry. One of the largest was Ancient Lake Bonneville, in the basin of Great Salt Lake.

6. The Great Lakes typify the fresh, overflowing lakes characteristic of moist regions. They originated in a glacial age and are the survivors of an even larger group of lakes.

7. Swamps occur most commonly along coasts and floodplains, in glaciated areas, and on perennially frozen ground.

8. A common sediment deposited in swamps is peat; peat represents an essential stage in the making of coal.

REFERENCES

Davis, W. M., 1933, The lakes of California: California Jour. Mines and Geology, vol. 29. p. 175–236.

Hough, J. L., 1958, Geology of the Great Lakes: Urbana, Univ. of Illinois Press.

Hutchinson, G. E., 1957, A treatise on limnology: New York, John Wiley and Sons.

Shaler, N. S., 1885, Seacoast swamps of the eastern United States: U. S. Geol. Survey, 6th Ann. Rept., p. 353–398.

CHAPTER 13. GLACIERS AND GLACIATION

Glaciers   Glaciation   Glacial erosion   Glacial transport   Glacial deposits   The glacial ages
Very ancient glaciations   Causes of glacial climates

The Jungfrau

Glaciers

Geologic significance of glaciers. Defined as simply as possible, a *glacier* is *a body of ice, consisting mainly of recrystallized snow, flowing on a land surface*. Unlike a stream, a glacier can not be seen to move; yet measurements show that it is flowing. They show also that long-term changes in its dimensions are closely related to variations of climate; so the study of glaciers has contributed much to what we know of the Earth's recent climatic history. The effects of erosion of bedrock by glaciers and deposits of the eroded material as glacial sediments are characteristic and easily recognizable. Their distribution shows us that in the recent past glaciers have been far more extensive than they are today. At the same time, this evidence has raised the problem of the cause of the "ice ages" when glaciers were widespread, a problem that is still only partly solved.

Kinds of glaciers: valley glaciers, piedmont glaciers, ice sheets. On the basis of their form, we can readily distinguish three kinds of glaciers. Most numerous and most familiar are *valley glaciers* (Figs. 13–1, 13–6, 13–10), the *glaciers that flow downward through valleys* like streams of water. Like streams, also, they vary in size from little things no more than a few acres in extent to mighty tonguelike forms many tens of miles long. In the Alps alone there are more than 1,200 valley glaciers. In the United States (excluding Alaska) there are about 1,000, most of them small.

A *piedmont glacier* (Fig. 13–2) is *a glacier on a plain at the base of a mountain, fed by one or more valley glaciers*. It is shaped like a covered frying pan whose narrow inclined handle represents a feeding valley glacier.

An *ice sheet* is *a broad glacier of irregular shape generally blanketing the terrain. A small ice sheet is an ice cap;* some ice caps, such as those in Figure 13–1, are very small. The best known ice sheet is the Greenland Ice Sheet. Its area is about 666,000 square miles, and its highest part is more than 10,000 feet above sea level. Seismic measurement (p. 404) of the approximate thickness of this glacier was made in 1951 at intervals along certain routes of travel. One of these routes is shown in Figure 13–3, together with a profile and cross section along it. From the cross section it can be seen that in places the base of the ice sheet is below sea level and that the ice is very thick; at one point its thickness exceeds 10,000 feet. Near its margins the ice sheet is held in by mountains, through which it flows along deep valleys to reach the sea. Icebergs floating in the sea are pieces broken off the ends of such glaciers.

The Antarctic Ice Sheet (Fig. 13–4) is far bigger. Its area is estimated at around 5,000,000 square miles, and seismic measurement has revealed a thickness, in one place, of about 14,000 feet. Although the average thickness of this huge glacier is probably not much more than half that amount, the volume of Antarctic ice is enormous.

Valley glaciers, piedmont glaciers, and ice sheets constitute a gradational sequence. Indeed, it is probable that a great ice sheet like that in Greenland began in coastal mountains with the growth of thousands of valley glaciers, which spread out in the interior as piedmont glaciers and gradually thickened to form a body of ice higher in places than the mountain peaks.

Distribution of glaciers: snowline. Two chief requirements for the existence of glaciers are low temperature and adequate snowfall. Therefore, glaciers

Fig. 13—1. Glaciers in St. Elias Range, Yukon Territory, Canada. Valley glaciers and ice caps are shown. The valley glacier in the center built a large moraine; its terminus retreated half way to its present position and built another, smaller moraine, since which time still further retreat has occurred. (Walter A. Wood.)

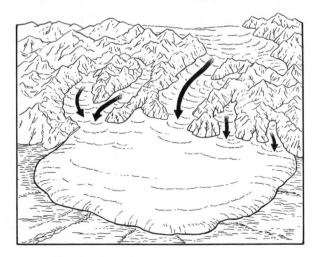

Fig. 13—2. Piedmont glacier on the Alaska coast, fed by valley glaciers. The glacier is many miles in diameter.

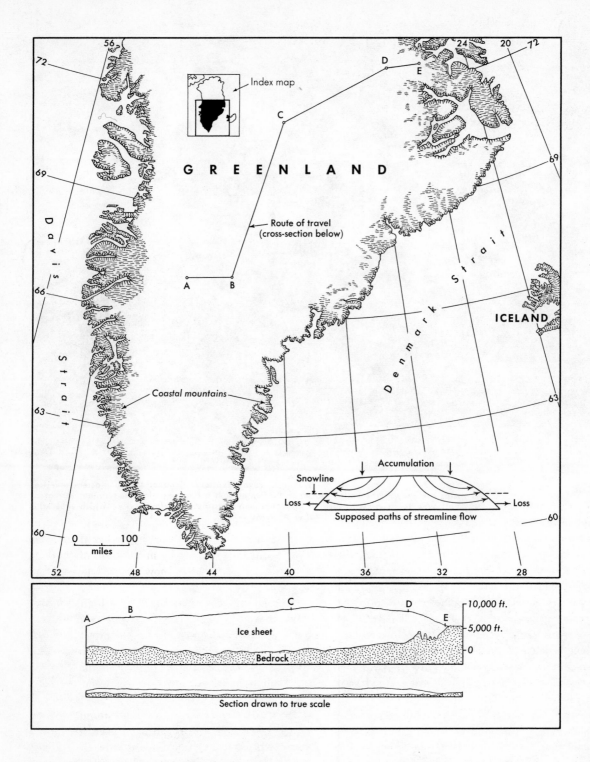

Fig. 13–3. Map of south half of Greenland, and cross section showing ice thickness. (Thickness data from A. Bauer, Expéditions polaires françaises.)

Fig. 13—4. Part of the Antarctic Ice Sheet, in Marie Byrd Land, with peaks of Edsel Ford Mountains projecting through its surface. In foreground are crevasses. (P. A. Siple, U. S. Antarctic Service.)

depend on climate. They are found in high latitudes and high altitudes and are larger and more numerous in wet coastal areas than in the dry interiors of continents. Glaciers are connected by the *snowline, the lower limit of perennial snow.* Above the snowline are *snowfields,* which are *banks and patches of snow,* usually in protected places, *that persist throughout the summer season* (Fig. 13–12, **B**). The snowline rises from near sea level in the polar regions to altitudes of as much as 20,000 feet in tropical mountains and also rises from coasts toward continental interiors. It passes across all glaciers and affords a convenient way of following their distribution.

More than 95 per cent of the total area of the world's glaciers is accounted for by the Antarctic and Greenland Ice Sheets. Although numbered by the thousands, the remaining glaciers together account for less than 5 per cent of the world total.

Conversion of snow into glacier ice. When temperatures fall below 0° C., some atmospheric moisture changes into the solid phase. Ice rather than water is then precipitated, usually in the form of the hexagonal ice crystals better known as snowflakes (Fig. 13–5, **A**).

Newly fallen dry snow has a very high porosity. This makes it light (its density may be no more than 0.05) and fluffy. Because of its high porosity and the star-like shapes of its flakes, a mass of snow has an internal surface area that is greater even than in ordinary sediments. Also, as the spaces between the flakes are large, snow is easily penetrated by air. Ice evaporates readily in the air and gives off water vapor more rapidly at the crystal points than at the crystal centers where surface area is less. Consequently, the individual particles gradually change from clusters of star-like crystals to nearly spherical grains ⅛ inch, or less,

231

A   B   └ 1 in. ┘   C   └ 1/4 in. ┘

Fig. 13–5. Conversion of snow into glacier ice. **A.** A snowflake consists of clusters of hexagonal crystals such as this one. (Many times natural size.) **B.** A pile of granular snow, about 8 months old, collected just below the surface of a glacier in Yukon Territory, Canada. Grain diameters are about $\frac{1}{16}$ inch. **C.** Ice from a glacier in the Swiss Alps. The sample has been sliced thin and is seen through a microscope. The broad irregular areas are individual grains; the small dark objects are bubbles of air that did not escape during compaction of the granular snow. (W. J. Bentley, courtesy, U. S. Weather Bureau; R. P. Sharp; M. F. Perutz, courtesy, Gerald Seligman.)

in diameter (Fig. 13–5, **B**). The whole mass, therefore, takes on the granular texture we find in old snowdrifts at winter's end. As the snow becomes granular, its porosity diminishes, its density therefore increases, and air is continually forced out from the diminishing spaces between the grains.

When the body of granular snow has reached a density of 0.8, it becomes impermeable to air and is then said to be *ice* (Fig. 13–5, **C**). Although this may seem strange, such ice is a rock, for it consists of crystalline grains of a mineral, just as some sandstones consist entirely of grains of the mineral quartz. Despite the changes in its crystalline grains, ice is essentially a sedimentary rock, precipitated (albeit not quite in its present form) in solid particles from the atmosphere. It is, of course, a rock with a far lower melting point than any other rock.

Ice is a very weak solid. If a body of ice is as much as 200 to 300 feet thick, its own weight is enough to overcome its slight rigidity and it begins to be deformed, flowing outward and downward somewhat as a very stiff fluid flows but remaining, nevertheless, a crystalline solid, as described more fully on p. 233. As soon as a body of ice becomes thick enough to flow in this way, it is a glacier. The process of flow deforms the individual ice crystals that compose the glacier, and the ice mass changes from a sedimentary

rock into a metamorphic rock. The density of glacier ice is around 0.9.

Glacier movement. The fact that glaciers move was established more than 100 years ago by year-to-year observation of change in position of conspicuous objects, such as boulders, on glacier surfaces. From these observations it was inferred that most glaciers move very slowly. Later, measurements of flow were put on a systematic basis by the use of surveying instruments. A marked stake or other target is driven into the surface of a valley glacier, and its position from day to day is accurately determined by instrumental surveying from positions on bedrock at the sides of the valley. Stakes placed at the center and sides of a valley glacier and surveyed in this way show that the central part of the glacier surface moves faster than the sides, as is true of a stream of water. Results of this kind of measurement give velocities ranging generally from a fraction of an inch per day to a few tens of feet per day, the values varying with slope, thickness, atmospheric temperature, and other factors. Glacier motion is therefore slow and can be compared with the rate of percolation of ground water.

At such velocities ice requires a long time to travel the length of a glacier. Although we have no means of measuring the time directly, probably hundreds or even thousands of years have elapsed since the ice now exposed at the downstream end of a long glacier fell as snow upon the upstream part.

These values pertain only to the upper surfaces of glaciers. It is not yet known how the directions and velocities of flow are distributed down within a glacier, but in an ice sheet or a piedmont glacier the streamlines of flow, like those in percolating ground water (Fig. 11–3), are usually thought of as represented in Figures 13–3 and 13–6.

Little is known, also, of the mechanics of flow of a glacier. The flow is mostly streamline. It deforms the crystalline grains to give the effect of foliation, much like the foliation in metamorphic rocks. This is the basis on which glacier ice is classed as a metamorphic rock. The energy of a glacier between any two points on its surface, like the energy of a stream, is measured by the mass of the glacier times the difference of altitude between the points. Most of this energy is expended in friction on its bed and in internal friction of flow. The energy needed to cause deformation of crystalline grains of H_2O is much greater than that needed to cause flow in water. As a result, the velocity of solid flow of ice is far less than the velocity of fluid flow of water at the Earth's surface. In mechanical terms, the process is very inefficient.

Many glaciers are cut by *crevasses* (Figs. 13–1, 13–4, 13–18), which we can define as *deep cracks in the upper surface of a glacier*. Because a glacier flows "under its own weight" (that is, flows because of the pull of gravity on its mass), its surface part, having little weight upon it, is brittle and nearly rigid. Brittleness of the surface part makes it crack as it is subjected to tension when the glacier flows over an abruptly steepened slope. Though they are fearsome obstacles to a geologist in the field, crevasses are less than 150 feet deep; there is reason to believe that at depths of 150 to 300 feet flow of the ice would prevent crevasses from forming. A glacier, therefore, like the Earth's crust itself (p. 370), can be said to possess an outer rigid shell (a zone of fracture) and an underlying mobile mass (a zone of flow).

Economy of a glacier. The economy of a glacier is closely related to climate and specifically to the snowline. Glaciers have their origin above the snowline, but by their movement they spread downward and outward below it. They maintain themselves in the zone below the snowline because their movement transfers ice from above it, faster than the ice can melt away. The length and volume of a glacier represent near-equilibrium among three factors: accumulation of snow, loss by melting and evaporation, and transfer by movement (Fig. 13–6), factors which change in response to slow gradual changes in the snowline. Glaciers therefore are a useful yardstick for measuring variations of climate. When the climate in any region becomes cooler and moister, glaciers expand; when it grows warmer and drier, they shrink. Nearly worldwide shrinkage of glaciers during the last few decades implies a general warming of climates (Fig. 13–7).

In the zone below the snowline a good deal of water is usually evident, at least in the summer season. This is *meltwater,* defined as *water resulting from the melting of glacier ice*. It is seen as small streams and pools on the surface of a glacier and in channels and tunnels within the glacier, right down to its base. Streams of meltwater often flow on the ground, directly along the lateral margins of a valley glacier. When it reaches the glacier terminus, all this meltwater either forms a lake (Figs. 12–9, 12–10) or combines into a stream flowing toward the sea, depending on whether the land slopes toward or away from the glacier.

Glaciation

The geologic work of glaciers is expressed in the process of **glaciation,** which is *the alteration of the land surface by glacier ice passing over it*. Glaciation includes erosion, transport, and deposition. As most

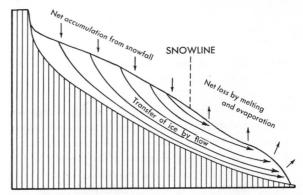

Fig. 13–6. Economy of a glacier. The streamlines of flow (suggested by long curved arrows) resemble those of percolating ground water (Fig. 11–3).

Fig. 13—7. Muir Glacier in a fiord, Glacier Bay, Alaska, August 9, 1950. The position of this shrinking glacier has been determined by instrument periodically since 1886. Until 1911 the glacier covered the point from which this photograph was taken; its end stood 2.5 miles to left of left edge of view. Later positions are shown by dotted lines. Distance between 1936 and 1958 positions is about 5.5 miles; hence glacier's terminus receded about 1,300 feet per year. Position in 1953 was about the same as in 1950. (William O. Field, American Geographical Society.)

glaciers at present are shrinking, we can see glacially eroded bedrock surfaces as they are uncovered from year to year by the melting ice and can actually watch the making of glacial deposits at the glacier margins. Similar things were observed early in the nineteenth century by various Europeans, who recognized such features as the work of glaciers. By examining glaciated districts from which glaciers have melted away, we can see that glacial erosion takes place mostly well back beneath the glacier and that deposition occurs mostly at or near the outer margin.

Glacial erosion

Glacial erosion, like stream erosion, includes abrasion and plucking and is generally accompanied by weathering in the form of frost wedging, just as stream erosion is accompanied by mass-wasting of various kinds.

Frost wedging. Although not strictly a process of glaciation, intense frost wedging accompanies glaciation because both occur in cold climates. When hills or mountains stand higher than the surface of a gla-

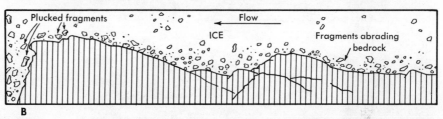

Fig. 13—8. A. Knobs of granitic rock abraded and striated on one side and plucked on the other. Unsymmetrical form shows former glacier was flowing southwest while erosion occurred. Lake Athabaska, Saskatchewan. B. Plucking and abrasion in progress. (F. J. Alcock, Geol. Survey of Canada.)

cier, wedged-out blocks of rock roll down onto the surface of the glacier, which carries them away. Intense frost wedging is responsible for much of the detail of the sharp, jagged peaks of glaciated mountains (Fig. 13–12).

Abrasion and plucking. It has been said that a glacier is at once a plow, a file, and a sled. As a plow it scrapes up regolith and lifts out blocks of bedrock; as a file it rasps away firm rock; as a sled it carries away the load of sediment acquired by plowing and filing, plus additional rock fragments fallen onto it from adjacent cliffs.

Glacial plucking is *the lifting out and removal of pieces of bedrock by a glacier*. It is broadly equivalent to hydraulic plucking by a stream of water. The bottom of the glacier breaks off blocks of bedrock and quarries them out, especially on surfaces unsupported on their downstream sides (Fig. 13–8). Near the edges of the glacier, at least, water aids plucking by freezing in cracks in the rock and prying out blocks.

Abrasion is the filing process. The under surface of the glacier is studded with rock particles of many

sizes, and with these as tools the ice makes long scratches (*glacial striations*) and grooves on bedrock (Fig. 13–9). Fine particles of sand and silt in the base of the glacier, acting like fine sandpaper, polish bedrock to a smooth finish. A striation or groove trending north-south does not as a rule show whether the glacier was flowing south or north. Direction of flow is determined by rock hills and small knobs that are unsymmetrical. Usually the upstream side of a rock hill is predominantly abraded, striated, and gently sloping, whereas the downstream side is predominantly plucked and therefore has a steeper slope (Fig. 13–8).

The great length and straightness of some grooves are made possible by the fact that the flow of ice is streamline. In contrast, rock surfaces abraded in the turbulent flow of water consist of a series of curves (Fig. 9–17).

Cirques. Among the characteristic features of glaciation in many mountain areas is the *cirque* (pronounced *sirk*). This is *a steep-walled niche, shaped like a half bowl, in a mountain side, excavated mainly*

Fig. 13–9. Glaciated surface of basalt bedrock, showing striations and grooves. Mechanical weathering of the surface is visible in the foreground. Near Coulee Dam, Washington. (K. S. Brown, U. S. Bureau of Reclamation.)

by frost action (Fig. 13–10). A cirque begins to form beneath a snowbank or snowfield just above the snow-line. It is at least partly the work of frost wedging. On summer days water from melting snow infiltrates openings in the rock beneath the snowbank. At night the temperature drops and the water freezes and expands, prying out rock fragments. The smaller rock particles are carried away downslope by meltwater during thaws. This activity creates a depression in the rock and enlarges it. If the snowbank grows into a glacier, plucking helps to enlarge the cirque still more, but frost wedging continues as water descends the rock wall of the cirque and freezes there. Many cirques have rock basins in their floors, usually containing small lakes. In summary, small cirques are made beneath snowbanks even where there is no true glacier; large cirques are mostly the work of glaciers that continue the excavation process.

Glaciated valleys differ in several ways from ordinary stream valleys. Their chief characteristics, not all found in every glaciated valley, are (Figs. 13–11,

13–9, 13–12) (1) cross profile is trough-like (U-shaped), and (2) floor lies below floors of tributaries, which therefore "hang" above the main valley. Both (1) and (2) result from erosion by the sides as well as by the base of the glacier, the thickness of which is far greater than the depth of an ordinary stream. (3) Long profile of the floor has step-like irregularities (Fig. 13–18) and shallow basins. Many of these are related to spacing of joints in the rock, which determine ease of plucking, a more effective process in glaciers than in streams. (4) Head of valley is likely to be a cirque or group of cirques.

Some valleys are glaciated from head to mouth. Others are glaciated only in their headward parts and downstream have only the form that is the work of streams and mass-wasting. This shows that the valleys were there before the glaciers formed and leads to the conclusion that glaciers, unlike streams, do not cut their own valleys. They occupy and remodel valleys already made.

Mountain sculpture. If we examine a mountain

Fig. 13–10. Small cirque in mountain side, interrupting the smooth slope created earlier by mass-wasting in a warmer climate. Note small patches of snow. Rocky Mountain National Park. Compare Figure 13–12, **D.** (Andreas Feininger.)

Fig. 13–11. Glaciated valley. Isterdalen, Norway. (Sawders from Cushing.)

area that has been glaciated by a large group of valley glaciers (Fig. 13–12), we find cirques, U-shaped troughs, hanging tributaries, and, in detail, striated and polished bedrock. In addition, the mountain crests have characteristic forms, mainly the result of frost wedging in a cold climate. The forms are combinations of three features, for which we use names given to them by Alpine mountaineers. An *aréte* is a *jagged, knife-edge ridge created by two groups of cirques that have eaten into the ridge from both sides. A col is a gap or pass in a mountain crest at a place where the headwalls of two cirques intersect each other. A horn is a bare, pyramid-shaped peak left standing where cirques have eaten into it from three or more sides.* The Matterhorn is a well-known example.

All these features are the work primarily of frost wedging. All are shown in Figure 13–12:

Fiords. The deep bay-like *fiords* (Fig. 13–7) along mountainous coasts like those of Norway, Alaska, and southern Chile are *glaciated troughs partly submerged.* The form and depths of many fiords imply depths of glacial erosion of 1,000 feet or more.[1] But some areas glaciated by ice sheets still preserve chemically weathered regolith beneath glaciated surfaces. Since such regolith is ordinarily thin, the thickness removed by glacier ice must have been small, possibly only a few feet. So the intensity of glacial erosion, like that of stream erosion, varies according to topog-

[1] The depths of fiord floors below sea level result in part from rise of sea level since the last glacial age (p. 250), in part (locally) from subsidence of the Earth's crust, and in part from glacial erosion below sea level. Sea level is not a base level for glaciers as it is for streams because glacier ice 1,000 feet thick, with density 0.9, can continue to erode its bed until it is submerged to a depth of 900 feet, whereupon it floats and bed erosion ends.

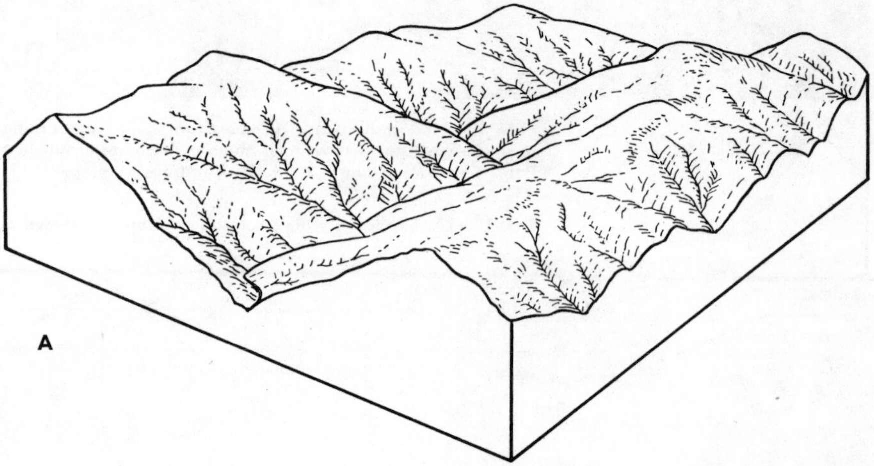

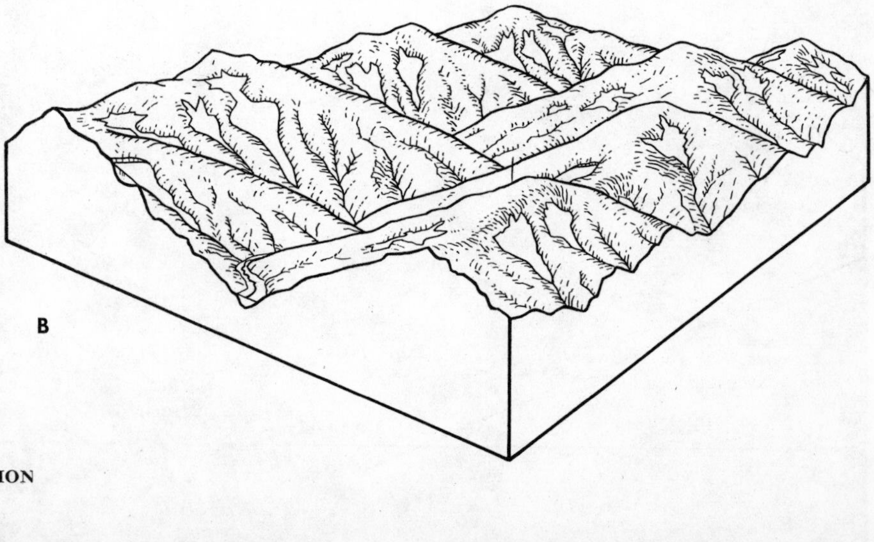

Fig. 13–12. Erosion of mountains by valley glaciers. **A.** Mountain region being eroded by streams. Main valley has many curves. **B.** As climate grows colder, snowfields form, and small cirques are excavated beneath them. Some snowfields become thick enough to form glaciers. **C.** Glaciers merge to form a large valley glacier with tributaries. Frost wedging begins to sharpen the mountain summits. **D.** After climate has warmed again and glaciers have disappeared, geologic work of glaciers is revealed. Valleys have been deepened, widened, and straightened, tributaries have been left hanging above main valley, and empty cirques, some with small lakes, indent the highest areas. Mountain crests have been frost-wedged to form knife-edge ridges with pyramid-shaped peaks.

raphy, kind of bedrock or regolith, and thickness and velocity of flow.

Glacial transport

A glacier differs from a stream in the way in which it carries its load of rock particles in two main respects: (1) its load can be carried in its sides and even on its top and (2) it can carry much larger pieces of rock and can transport large and small pieces side by side without segregating them into a bed load and a suspended load and without depositing them according to their individual weights. Because of this, deposits made directly from a glacier are not stratified.

The load in a glacier is concentrated in base and sides (Fig. 13–18) because these are the places where glacier and bedrock are in contact and where abrasion and plucking are effective. Most of the rock frag-

ments on the surface of a valley glacier got there by landsliding from clifflike valley sides.

Much of the load in the base of a glacier consists of very fine particles such as fine sand and silt. Most of these particles are fresh and unweathered. They also have angular, jagged surfaces and are clearly the product of crushing and grinding (Fig. 13–15). *Fine sand and silt produced by crushing and grinding in a glacier* is known as **rock flour,** a material that differs from the chemically weathered, more rounded particles found in the sediments of nonglaciated areas. Chemically fresh rock flour is evidently a product of rapid erosion of bedrock by glaciers, a mechanical process unaccompanied by chemical weathering.

Glacial deposits

Drift, till, and stratified drift. Deposition takes place mainly in the downstream parts of glaciers, where

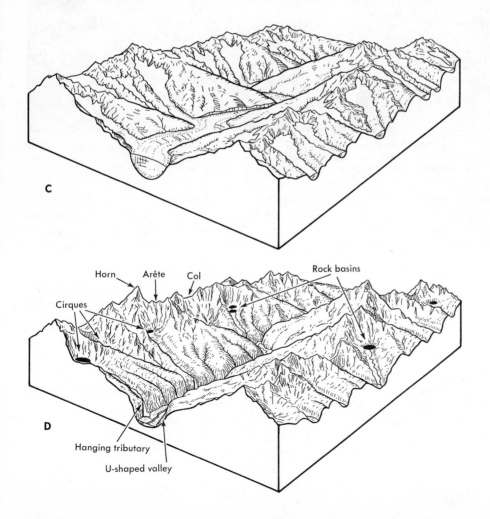

C

D

Horn Arête Col Rock basins

Cirques

Hanging tributary

U-shaped valley

Facets and polish on boulders

2 ft.

Fig. 13–13. Till exposed in a road cut near Bangor, Pennsylvania. Its nonsorted character is clearly evident. The fine sediment between the stones consists of rock flour. The two large boulders have faceted and polished surfaces. (Pennsylvania Geol. Survey.)

melting and evaporation release rock fragments from the ice. *The sediments deposited directly by glaciers, or indirectly in glacial streams, lakes, and the sea,* together constitute *glacial drift,* or simply *drift.* The name *drift* dates from the early nineteenth century when it was vaguely conjectured that all such deposits had been "drifted" to their resting places by the Flood of Noah or by some other ancient body of water.

Drift consists of two extreme types, *till* and *stratified drift.* Between them there is complete gradation. Drift whose constituent rock particles are not sorted according to size and weight but lie just as they were released from the ice (Fig. 13–13) is known as till, a name given it by Scottish farmers long before its origin was understood. Probably most till is plastered on the ground, bit by bit, from the base of the flowing

ice near the outer margins of glaciers. The pebbles and large fragments have facets (Fig. 13–14) joining along smoothed or rounded edges, and some also are striated. Facets are made because the pebbles turn from time to time in their matrix of ice as they scrape along the glacier bed. The sand and silt particles generally consist of rock flour (Fig. 13–15). We can define *till,* as *nonsorted drift.*

On the other hand, much drift is stratified, indicating that water from melting ice has moved and sorted rock particles carried in the ice and has deposited it in immediate contact with the ice or beyond the glacier itself. *Stratified drift,* then, is *drift that is sorted and stratified.*

Drumlins and other streamline forms. Stratified drift and till are sediments. They occur in various bodies, each having a rather distinctive topographic

Fig. 13—14. Pebbles collected from till, showing characteristic glaciated shapes, with facets. Chittenango Falls, New York. (R. F. Flint.)

Fig. 13—15. Rock flour, forming part of a body of till near Bethany, Connecticut. The particles (mostly quartz and feldspar) have very angular shapes as a result of crushing and abrasion. Enlarged about 10 times. (Microphoto by R. W. Powers.)

Fig. 13—16. Streamline hill molded from drift, near Madison, Wisconsin. Hills having this shape are known as *drumlins*. (Charles C. Bradley).

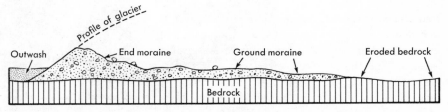

Fig. 13—17. Ideal sequence of deposits made during a single expansion and subsequent shrinkage of a glacier. Repeated glacial fluctuations pile up a complex sequence of deposits.

form. Some of the bodies are described in the following paragraphs.

In many areas the drift is molded by the streamline flow of the ice into nearly parallel smooth ridges and troughs that range up to many miles in individual length. These forms resemble the streamline bodies of airplanes and racing cars; they were molded to offer minimum frictional resistance to the ice flowing over them. The best-known variety of streamline form is the *drumlin, a streamline hill consisting of drift, generally till* (Figs. 13–16, 13–26). Not all such forms are built up, however. Some are chiseled out of rock or drift. They are closely related to striations and grooves, although they are formed on a much larger scale. Whether made by building up or cutting out or both, all these forms reflect streamline molding by flowing ice, and therefore their long axes are reliable indicators of the direction of flow of former glaciers.

Ground moraine and end moraines. *Widespread thin drift with a smooth surface consisting of gently sloping knolls and shallow basins* is *ground moraine* (Fig. 13–17). Probably its irregularities result from irregular distribution of rock particles in the base of the glacier.

A ridge-like accumulation of drift, deposited by a glacier along its margin, is an *end moraine* (Figs. 13–17, 13–18). It can be built by snowplow or bulldozing action, by dumping off the glacier margin, or by repeated plastering of sticky drift from basal ice onto the ground. End moraines range in height from a few feet to hundreds of feet. In a valley glacier the end moraine is built not only at the terminus but along the sides of the glacier as well for some distance upstream. The terminal part is a *terminal moraine;* the lateral part is a *lateral moraine;* but both are parts of a single feature (Figs. 13–1, 13–18, 13–26).

Erratics, boulder trains. Some of the boulders and smaller rock fragments in till are the same kind of rock as the bedrock on which the till was deposited, but many are different rocks, having been brought from greater distances. *A glacially deposited piece of rock that is different from the bedrock beneath it* is an *erratic* (Fig. 13–19). The word means simply "foreign," and the presence of foreign boulders was one of the earliest recognized proofs of former glaciation. Some erratics form part of a body of drift; others, such as the one shown in Figure 13–19, lie free on the ground.

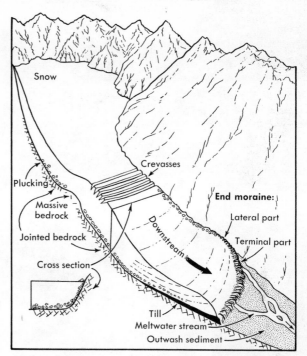

Fig. 13–18. Chief features of a valley glacier and its deposits. The glacier has been cut away along its center line; only the left half of it is shown. Compare Figure 13–1.

Fig. 13–19. Erratic boulder of granite, perched on top of a high ridge of dolerite, Mount Tom, near Northampton, Massachusetts. The nearest granite bedrock is many miles to the north. (C. R. Longwell.)

Fig. 13—20. Valley train being actively built up by meltwater coming from glaciers upstream. Near Berners Bay, Alaska. The stream has a braided pattern. The valley train has little vegetation on it because outwash sediments form a new layer over most of it every year. (U. S. Navy.)

In some areas that have been glaciated by ice sheets, erratics derived from some distinctive kind of bedrock are so numerous and easily identified that they can be readily plotted on a map. Generally, the plot shows a fan-like shape, spreading out from the area of outcrop of the parent bedrock and reflecting the spreading of the ice sheet. *A group of erratics spread out fanwise* is a **boulder train,** so named in the nineteenth century when rock particles of all sizes were called boulder trains. The boulder train shown in Figure 13–26 consists of quartzite, which is con-

spicuous in an area in which the bedrock consists of limestone and sandstone.

Outwash. On the downstream sides of most terminal moraines is *stratified drift deposited by streams of meltwater as they flow away from a glacier.* Sediments of this kind are **outwash** ("washed out" beyond the ice). *A body of outwash that forms a broad plain* beyond the moraine is an **outwash plain.** In contrast, a **valley train** (Fig. 13–20) is *a body of outwash that partly fills a valley.* Meltwater generally emerges from the ice as one or more swift streams, milky with a suspended load of rock flour and with a full bed load of pebbles, cobbles, and even boulders. The bed load is invisible, but it is there, as many a geologist trying to wade the current has discovered to his sorrow. The stream is generally braided; its deposits are very thick and have the kind of stratification shown in Figure 13–21. These characteristics are common in streams with full bed loads. The deposition of outwash is analogous to the building of a fan. The stream emerges from an ice-walled valley or tunnel onto a broad smooth surface; part of its load therefore becomes excess; it drops bed load, and its channel takes on a braided pattern. The entire thick deposit has a steep profile like that of a fan. As the coarse particles are dropped first, the average diameter of particles decreases downstream.

Although the bed load of a meltwater stream is invisible, the suspended load has been measured. The rock flour washed out of the Muir Glacier in coastal Alaska corresponds to a loss of one foot of bedrock, from the entire area beneath the glacier, every 16 years. That is 570 times faster than the one inch every 760 years estimated to be lost to the United States by weathering, mass-wasting, and stream erosion.

Ice-contact stratified drift. When rapid melting and evaporation reduce the thickness of the terminal part of a glacier to 300 feet or less, movement virtually ceases. Meltwater, flowing over or beside the nearly motionless stagnant ice, deposits stratified drift, which slumps and collapses as the supporting ice slowly melts away. *Stratified drift deposited in contact with supporting ice is **ice-contact stratified drift.*** It is recognized by abrupt changes of grain size, distorted, irregular stratification, and extremely uneven surface form (Fig. 13–22). Bodies of ice-contact stratified drift are classified according to their shape: *short, steep-sided knolls and hummocks* are **kames;** *terrace-like forms along the sides of a valley* are **kame terraces;** *long, narrow ridges, commonly sinuous,* are **eskers** (Fig. 13–23); and *basins in drift, created by melting out of knobs of underlying ice,* are **kettles** and in form are complementary to kames.

The glacial ages

History of the concept. As early as 1821 European scientists began to recognize features characteristic of glaciation in places at considerable dis-

Fig. 13–21. Outwash sediments, consisting of sand and pebbles, exposed in a valley train built during a glacial age, Wallingford, Connecticut. The currents moved generally from left to right. At the time this outwash was deposited the terminus of the glacier stood more than 25 miles north of the locality. (R. F. Flint.)

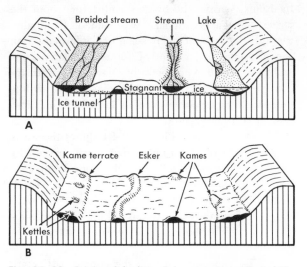

Fig. 13–22. Origin of bodies of ice-contact stratified drift. **A.** Nearly motionless, melting ice furnishes temporary retaining walls for bodies of sediment built chiefly by streams. **B.** As ice melts, bodies of sediment slump, creating characteristic knolls, ridges, terraces, and basins.

Fig. 13–23. This esker, overlying ground moraine in Morrison County, Minnesota, consists of gravel and sand deposited in a winding tunnel (Fig. 13–22) within an ice sheet but near its edge. When supporting ice melted away, the deposit was left as a winding ridge. (W. S. Cooper.)

tances from any existing glaciers. They drew the inference that glacier ice must once have covered wide regions that are now free of ice. Consciously or unconsciously, they were applying the principle of uniformity of process. The concept of a glacial age with widespread effects was first set forth in 1837 by Louis Agassiz, the Swiss scientist for whom the largest known glacial lake was named. Gradually, through the work of many scientists, information on the character and extent of former glaciation was added to the growing body of knowledge, until today we have a fairly comprehensive picture of former glacial times, although many important questions remain still unanswered.

Extent of glaciers. Figure 13–24 shows the areas in the Northern Hemisphere that were covered by glaciers during the glacial ages. In more detail, Figure 13–25 shows the extent of glaciation in eastern United States and part of Canada. These maps were compiled from the observations of hundreds of geologists on the distribution of features characteristic of glaciation.

In most mountain regions the characteristics are those shown in Figure 13–12, **D.** In most lowland regions, however, they consist generally of rolling ground moraine, end moraines, and other features (Fig. 13–26). The areas of former glaciation are now fairly well known. They add up to the impressive total of more than 18 million square miles, more than 30 per cent of the entire land area of the world. Today, for comparison, only about 10 per cent of the world's land area is covered with glacier ice, of which nearly 85 per cent (by area) is on the Antarctic Continent. If we neglect that continent and consider only the rest of the world, the glacier-covered area on non-Antarctic lands was more than 13 times larger during the glacial ages than it is on the same lands today.

Directions of flow. In most mountain regions the directions of flow of former glaciers were down the valleys (Fig. 13–12). In lowland regions, where the glaciers were ice sheets, the streamline forms and end moraines show that the flow was radial. The ice sheets spread out somewhat like batter on a griddle (Fig. 13–24). Flow directions are determined also by tracing erratics of conspicuous kinds to their places of origin in the bedrock. Native copper found as far south as Missouri has been traced to bedrock on the south shore of Lake Superior. In eastern Finland copper ore traced backward along the line of ice flow led to the discovery of a valuable copper deposit in the bedrock. Several large diamonds of good quality

Fig. 13–24. Areas (white) in the Northern Hemisphere that were glaciated during the glacial ages. Arrows show generalized directions of flow of glacier ice. Shorelines are shown as they were when sea level was 300 feet lower than it is today. The gray tone with irregular pattern represents floating ice in the Arctic Ocean, extending south into the Atlantic.

Fig. 13-25. Extent of glaciation in eastern half of United States and southeastern Canada. Inner line, during latest glacial age. Outer line during earlier glacial ages. (Adapted from Glacial Map of the United States East of the Rocky Mountains: Geol. Soc. America, 1959.)

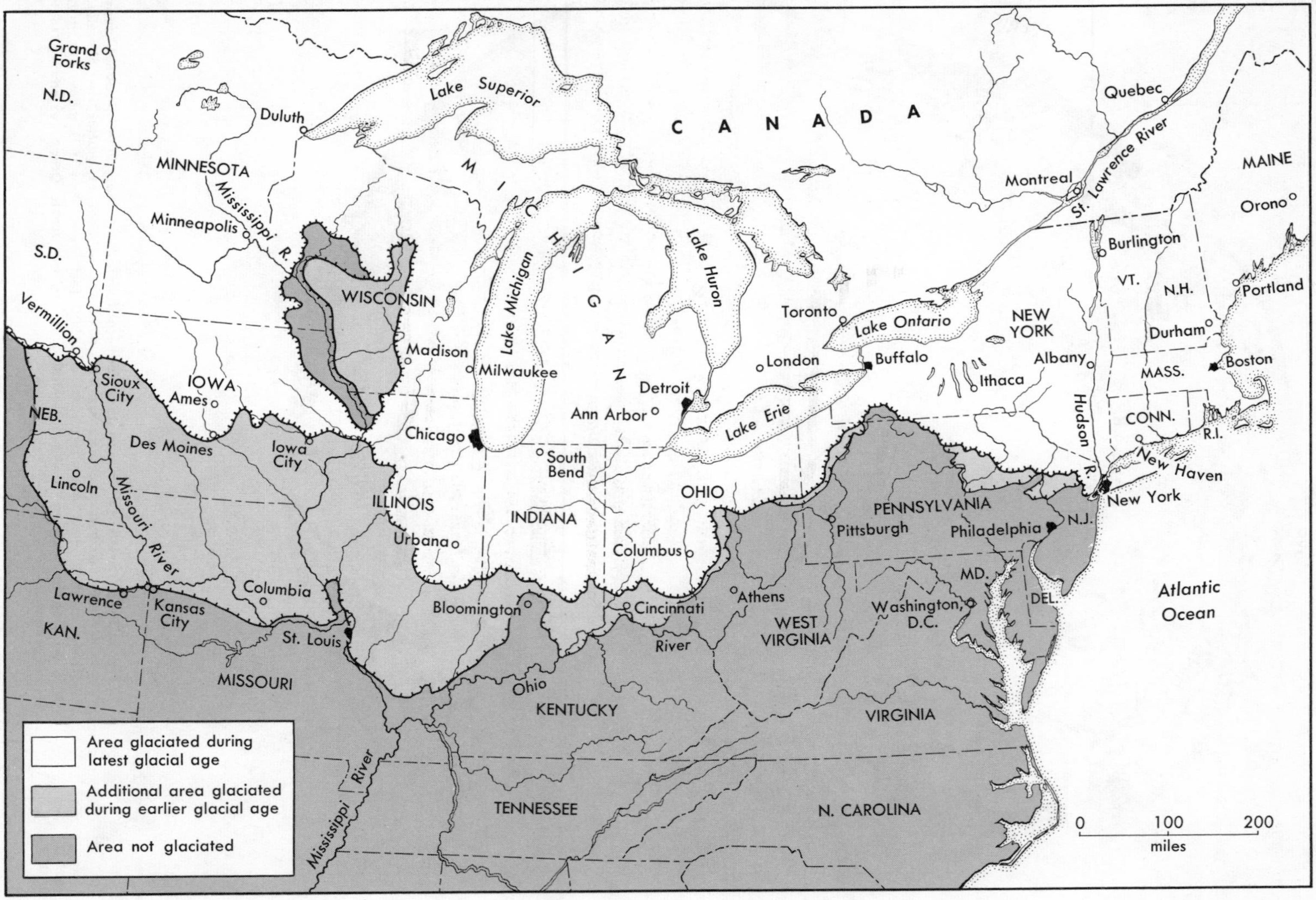

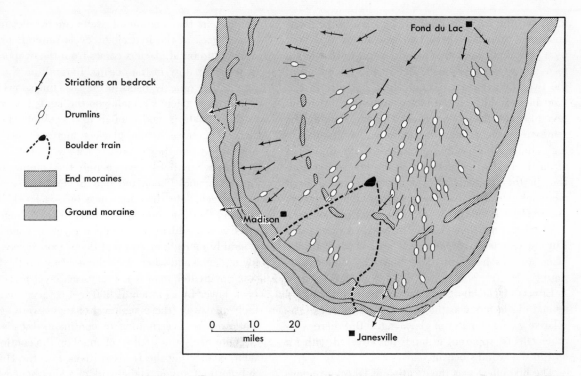

Fig. 13—26. Map of lobe-shaped layer of glacial drift in southeastern Wisconsin. Three successive end moraines (both terminal and lateral parts) mark successive positions of the glacier margin. Directions of drumlins, striations on bedrock, and a boulder train all show spreading of ice toward margin of glacier. (Adapted from Glacial Map of United States East of the Rocky Mountains: Geol. Soc. America, 1959.)

have been found in drift in Wisconsin, Michigan, Ohio, and Indiana. Their source, as yet unknown, is believed, from flow directions of former glaciers, to be in central Canada.

Amount of erosion. The great central parts of the former ice sheets in north-central Canada and northern Scandinavia and Finland removed much of the underlying regolith and some bedrock, together totaling perhaps 50 to 75 feet. Much of the load thus acquired by the ice sheets was deposited as drift beneath their broad outer parts. One such belt of drift reaches from Ohio to Montana; another extends from the British Isles to European Russia. In these belts the average thickness of the drift is believed to be as much as 40 feet. Most of the rest of the load went down the Mississippi River and down various rivers in Europe; some of it was picked up by the wind and blown away.

Where, as in New England and parts of Quebec, the bedrock is resistant and breaks into large chunks, the glacier ice spread boulders liberally over the surface, creating a soil very difficult for agriculture. Where, as in the southern Great Lakes region and on the Plains, the bedrock is weak and crumbles easily, the glaciers deposited a thick regolith supporting a rich soil. In this case, certainly, one man's meat is another man's poison.

Depression of the Earth's crust. We should note at this point the subsidence of the Earth's crust beneath the weight of the ice sheets. This effect is described on p. 234. Probably the surface of the crust beneath the central part of the Greenland Ice Sheet (Fig. 13–3, *section*) would stand as much as 2,000 or 3,000 feet higher if the ice sheet were not there.

Repeated glaciation. Since most of the drift is fresh and little weathered, it was realized very early that the glacial invasion was recent in terms of rate of weathering. But geologists began to find exposures showing a blanket of comparatively fresh drift overlying another layer of drift whose upper part is chemically weathered (Fig. 13–27). This led to the inference that there had been two glaciations separated by a period of time long enough to cause weathering to a depth of several feet. Before the beginning of the twentieth century, accumulated evidence of this kind had established the fact of not merely two but several great glaciations, each covering roughly the same areas, embracing the last million years of geologic time. This period, the Pleistocene Epoch, is often referred to collectively as the *glacial ages,* although the intervals of weathering included in it were not glacial at all. Those intervals, about as warm as the climate today, are known as *interglacial ages.*

The last time that glaciers in North America and Europe reached a great extent was around 18,000 years ago, as has been determined by radiocarbon dating.

Effects of glacial-age climates. The formation and spread of glaciers was the most obvious effect of the relatively cold climates of glacial ages. But there were other effects, apparent in lands not covered with ice and in the world's oceans.

The first effect was the creation of lakes in regions that are normally dry because of lower temperatures and more rainfall. These lakes were the pluvial lakes discussed in Chapter 12. It was stated there that some pluvial lakes were contemporaneous with glaciers that have since disappeared. Furthermore, radiocarbon dates have shown that one lake was contemporaneous with the most recent of the glacial ages. For these reasons it is thought likely that pluvial lakes as a class were contemporaneous with and a direct result of the glacial ages.

A second effect of glacial climates consisted of

Fig. 13–27. Evidence of repeated glaciation. A layer of "fresh" till, weathered only slightly at its surface, overlying an older till that had been deeply weathered before the overlying till was deposited.

changes in the amount of water in the oceans. A glance back at the hydrologic cycle reminds us that snowfall to build glaciers comes from the evaporation of water, mainly in the oceans. Rainfall on the land runs rather quickly back to the sea, but snowfall in the form of glaciers remains on the lands for as long as the climate is cold enough to perpetuate the glaciers. Therefore, when glaciers increase, sea level must fall; when they decrease, sea level must rise.

Since we do not know precisely the volumes of the Antarctic and Greenland Ice Sheets, we can not closely calculate their influence on sea level, but it is likely that the complete melting of those huge glaciers would add to the oceans a layer of water considerably more than 200 feet deep. Conversely, during a glacial age when the volume of ice on the lands was far greater than it is today, sea level must have been lower by as much as 300 feet or even more. In their own way, these sea level changes were as dramatic as the overrunning of continents by glaciers.

Quite likely the shallow channel on the continental shelf, connecting the Hudson River with the Hudson Submarine Canyon, is the work of a lengthened Hudson River during a glacial age with its lowered sea level (Fig. 15–15).

Measurements at harbor tide gages, and other data, suggest that since late in the nineteenth century sea level has been rising, relative to the land, at a rate possibly as great as 4 inches per 100 years. Much, if not all, of this rise results from recent rapid melting of glaciers.

A third effect was the spread of *permafrost,* the prevalent name for *ground that is frozen perennially.* Actually, it is the ground water that is frozen to form a firm cement in all openings within soil and rocks. Today the ground is frozen, and remains so from year to year, in a wide belt of Arctic country totaling in the Northern Hemisphere about 20 per cent of the land area of the hemisphere. Over this belt, average air temperatures are at or below freezing during most of the year, and loss of ground heat to the atmosphere is the cause of freezing of the ground water. During the short summer melting season only a thin surface zone, usually no more than two or three feet thick, thaws out. The thawed layer flows down slopes (solifluction), carrying with it the arctic vegetation that grows at its surface.

Drilling has shown that in places permafrost is 1,000 feet or more in thickness; a long period must have been required for freezing to so great a depth. During glacial ages the southern limit of permafrost stood much farther south than it does now. Today, under a climate that has been growing generally warmer, the area of permafrost is slowly shrinking, just as glaciers are shrinking. Although on the decline, as are glaciers and pluvial lakes, permafrost could be renewed if the climate once more became colder over a period of hundreds of years.

Very ancient glaciations

The glacial ages as a group are thought to represent only the last million years, or so, of geologic time. However, *tillite* (*till converted to solid rock*), with striated surfaces of still-older rock beneath it, occurs in strata that are hundreds of millions of years old (Fig. 17–9). This evidence, fragmentary but unmistakable, implies that glaciation has occurred at least several times in the remote past and is not peculiar to the last million years. The Earth's climates, evidently, have fluctuated slowly in a range great enough to cause large accumulations of ice on the lands from time to time.

Causes of glacial climates

As nearly as we can determine at present, the change from a nonglacial climate to a glacial climate requires a reduction of average temperature, in middle latitudes amounting to perhaps 6°C. Through the course of glacial and interglacial ages, therefore, world temperatures have fluctuated considerably. The cause of the fluctuations is still unknown. Many hypotheses have been suggested, but most have been put aside as improbable for one reason or another.

One hypothesis that seems more likely than some others holds that possibly certain portions of the radiant energy received by the Earth from the Sun varies in time. Although this variation has not yet been measured successfully, the pattern of circulation of the Earth's atmosphere, in middle latitudes, does vary with observed variations (a few years or a few tens of years long) in solar activity as represented by sunspots. Also, in two regions at least, the volumes of existing glaciers change with these short-period solar changes. Hence it is possible that variations in the Earth's climates reflect, at least in part, variations in output of energy by the Sun.

Such fluctuation of climate may have been going on throughout the Earth's entire history; yet the geologic record tells us that glaciation is a rather rare event, occurring only at infrequent intervals; that today, with 10 per cent of the land covered with ice, we are living in an extremely unusual and interesting part of geologic time. Something besides solar fluctuation therefore seems required to explain why glaciers have not been common throughout most or all of geologic time.

Comparison of (1) existing glaciers and (2) areas covered with ice during the Pleistocene Epoch with (3) topography shows that there is a close relationship between glaciers and high mountains and plateaus. Even the great ice sheets that spread out on low country appear to have taken form through the merging of many small glaciers that formed on highlands. This is reasonable because high mountains are likely to be snowy places. Now the structures (p. 236) in the rocks tell us that the Earth's surface has been marked by conspicuous mountains not only during the Pleistocene Epoch (those highlands are still with us) but also at other times, still more remote, when glaciers are known to have existed. In other words glacial times seem generally to have been times when mountains were conspicuously present.

Here, then, is a possible explanation of the causes of glaciation, based on (1) fluctuation of solar energy and (2) building of mountains. It is reasonable in that it seems to agree with the facts we now know, but it is still only a hypothesis. Further research will eventually confirm it or find a better explanation.

SUMMARY

1. On a basis of form, glaciers include valley glaciers, piedmont glaciers, and ice sheets.

2. Glaciers require low temperature and adequate snowfall. They are connected by the snowline, which rises from polar regions toward tropical regions.

3. Glaciers are accumulations of snow and flow under their own weight. Their surface parts are brittle; below these parts flow occurs.

4. A glacier erodes rock by plucking and abrasion,

transports the product, and deposits it as drift.

5. Valley glaciers convert stream valleys into U-shaped troughs with hanging tributary valleys. Cirques form beneath snowbanks and the heads of valley glaciers. Areas projecting above glaciers are reshaped by frost wedging into arêtes, cols, and horns.

6. The load of a glacier includes particles of all sizes, from large boulders to rock flour. It is carried chiefly in the base and sides of the glacier.

7. Till is deposited directly by the glacier. Stratified drift, deposited by meltwater, includes outwash deposited out beyond the ice, and kames, kame terraces, and eskers deposited upon or against the ice itself.

8. End moraines (both terminal and lateral) are built at the glacier margin. Ground moraine is built beneath the glacier.

9. During the glacial ages huge ice sheets repeatedly covered northern North America and Europe, eroding bedrock and spreading drift over marginal areas.

10. The accumulation of glaciers during the glacial ages lowered sea level. The cool, moist climates that prevailed in regions now dry created many pluvial lakes. Permafrost developed in areas free from glaciers but with below-freezing temperatures.

11. The cause of the glacial climates is not known. Possibly it is related to the existence of exceptionally high land plus variations of radiant energy emitted by the Sun.

REFERENCES

Charlesworth, J. K., 1957, The Quaternary Era: London, Edward Arnold.

Flint, R. F., 1957, Glacial and Pleistocene geology: New York, John Wiley and Sons.

Thwaites, F. T., 1946, Outline of glacial geology: Ann Arbor, Edwards Bros.

Zeuner, F. E., 1959, The Pleistocene Period: London, Hutchinson.

CHAPTER 14. DESERTS AND WIND ACTION

DESERTS: *Climate*   *World distribution*   *Geologic processes*   *Pediments*   *Cycle of erosion*

WIND ACTION: *Moving air and its load*   *Wind erosion*   *Wind deposits*   *Deposits of sand*

Deposits of silt   *Ancient wind-deposited sediments*   *Economic aspects: soil erosion*

Sand dunes between Yuma, Arizona and El Centro, California.
(Josef   Muench.)

DESERTS

Climate

Importance of climate in geology. If we look back over what has already been said about the geologic processes that operate at the Earth's surface, we can see that climate plays a fundamental part in determining process. We learned in Chapter 7 that the relative importance of chemical and mechanical weathering depends to a large extent on climate and noted in Chapters 9 and 10 that numerous streams, carrying away the products of weathering, characterize climates with abundant rainfall. In Chapter 13 we found that with sufficiently low temperatures and adequate snowfall glaciers become the dominant agents of erosion and transport. In a dry climate on the other hand, we find changes in the number and activities of streams and a great increase in the importance of the wind as a transporter of sediment. The present chapter deals with the geologic processes in arid lands and with the activity of the wind in particular, even though winds are effective also in some places that are not arid.

Desert climates. Although the word *desert* means literally a deserted, unoccupied, or uncultivated area, the modern development of artificial water supplies has changed the original meaning of the word by making many dry countries habitable. ***Desert*** has become a synonym for *arid land,* whether "deserted" or not.

A desert, obviously, must be defined in terms of climate. We think of a desert climate as having very little rainfall, but rainfall is only part of the picture. As we saw in connection with the former pluvial lakes (Chaps. 12, 13), evaporation also is important. The higher the temperature, the greater the evaporation, and consequently the more precipitation an area can have and still be arid. For if most of the precipitated water evaporates, little will be left for streams

and the growth of vegetation. In parts of southwestern United States evaporation of exposed water surfaces amounts to as much as 100 inches annually—up to 20 times more than annual precipitation. Again, if all the annual rainfall of a region came in a single month, its effects on streams and vegetation would soon be lost, and the region would be classed as arid. From these examples we can see that a desert or arid climate is defined by three factors: (1) temperature, (2) precipitation, and (3) seasonal distribution of precipitation. These factors can be shown by graphs, but in words they can be defined only in general terms. Broadly speaking, a *desert* is a land area characterized by low precipitation, high temperature, at least seasonally, and a rather high proportion of evaporation to precipitation. Comparing a map of the world's deserts (Fig. 14–1) with a map of the world's rainfall (Fig. 7–12), we can say that throughout much of the world desert areas coincide fairly closely with those areas that receive no more than 10 inches of precipitation.

Surrounding most desert areas are semiarid or *steppe* areas, in which annual precipitation ranges from about 10 to 20 inches or a little more. Desert grades outward through semiarid country into humid country, where most of the human population is concentrated.

The most intensely desert area in the United States is Death Valley in southeastern California. The highest temperature officially recorded there is 134° F (the world's record, at el Azizia, Libya, is 136.4°). Although rainfall averages between 1 and 2 inches annually, Death Valley has experienced years with no rain at all, and at stations in the Atacama Desert in northern Chile periods of more than 10 consecutive years without rain have been recorded.

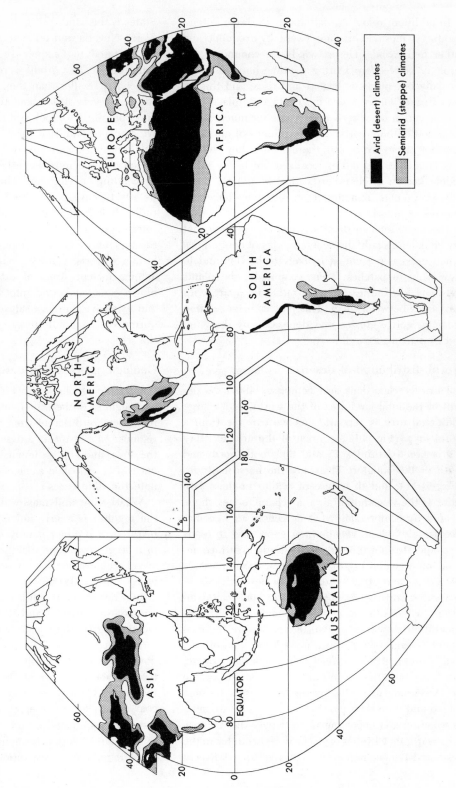

Fig. 14-1. Arid and semiarid climates of the world, plotted according to the Köppen–Geiger system.

Arid (desert) climates

Semiarid (steppe) climates

In addition to low rainfall and high daytime temperatures, most deserts are swept by frequent and rather high winds. Desert winds are commonly the result of convection. During daytime hours air over specially hot places is heated and rises, and this allows surface air to sweep in and take its place.

Convection likewise is responsible for much of the precipitation on deserts. As the columns of air rising over hot places are cooled, the moisture they contain may condense and fall as localized but heavy rains, widely known as cloudbursts. Sooner or later probably every part of a desert is visited by torrential showers of this kind.

The vegetation in deserts is a direct reflection of dry climate. Usually the vegetation is not continuous. When grass is present, it is likely to be thin and to grow only in patches. More commonly, the plants consist of low bushes, growing rather far apart, with bare areas between them. This pattern of vegetation promotes active erosion and deposition by the wind and by streams as well.

World distribution of deserts

Territory classed as arid comprises about 25 per cent of the total land area of the world; and a large additional area is semiarid. As we can see from a world map (Fig. 14–1), much of the arid territory lies between latitudes 15 and 35°, both north and south of the equator. These are the horse latitudes (Fig. 7–11), and the cause of aridity in these latitudes is the descending air that characterizes them. Heated by compression as it descends, air becomes increasingly able to retain water vapor and so tends to evaporate moisture from the Earth's surface instead of precipitating moisture on it. Examples are the Sahara and other deserts in northern Africa.

Another sort of desert is found in continental interiors, where heating in summer and dry cold continental air in winter prevail. Examples are the deserts of central Asia. A third, more local, kind of arid area is one that lies in the lee of a mountain range, which acts as a barrier to rainfall from moist oceanic air. Ascending over the barrier, air masses become chilled and drop their moisture on its windward side. Descending and becoming warmer over the territory to leeward, they keep it dry. The desert country in the Basin-and-Range region in Nevada and adjacent

States is this kind, being deprived of moisture by the Sierra Nevada and other mountains on the west.

As stated in Chapter 13, during former pluvial times deserts as a group were somewhat less dry and somewhat smaller than they are today, although we still know very little about their actual temperatures and rainfall. If we look still further back into history, we can speculate that for as long as the general circulation of the atmosphere has been about like that of today there must have been horse latitudes with descending, drying air. Therefore, we can expect deserts to have been rather persistent in those latitudes. It is likely, too, that there have been at least some deserts in the interiors of large continents throughout much of geologic history. Evidence of former deserts consists mainly of the occurrence among ancient strata of extensive bodies of wind-blown sand converted into sandstone (Fig. 14–32) and extensive layers of salt and gypsum precipitated during the evaporation of water in shallow arms of the sea.

Geologic processes in deserts

No major geologic process is entirely restricted to arid regions. Rather, the relative intensities of various processes are different from their intensities in moist regions. As a result, in a desert the forms of the land, the soils, and the sediments show distinctive differences. Let us look at some of the major processes and note the differences.

Weathering and mass-wasting. In a moist region the regolith is nearly universal, comparatively fine-textured, a product mainly of chemical weathering, in motion downslope mainly by soil creep, and covered by almost continuous vegetation. Because of soil creep, hill profiles as a rule are a series of curves.

In a desert the regolith is thinner, less continuous, and coarser textured and is a product of mechanical weathering (perhaps mainly as a result of hydration) to a greater degree. The slow motion of the regolith downslope develops slope angles that are adjusted to the average diameter of the fragments constituting the regolith; for it requires a steeper slope to move coarse particles by creep than to move fine ones. As the particles created by mechanical weathering tend to be coarse, slopes are generally steeper than in a moist region, and, as mentioned beyond, the base of a steep slope meets the flatter surface below it at a rather distinct angle instead of in a smooth curve.

Since mechanical weathering is controlled by joints in the bedrock much more closely than chemical weathering is, rock fragments tend to break off along joints, leaving steep, rugged cliffs. Hills cut by erosion from flat-lying rock layers with cliff-like slopes are the buttes and mesas (Fig. 7–13) common in dry regions. Likewise, as shown in Figures 21–17 and 14–2, the sides of valleys in dry country are less completely covered with regolith so that rock structure stands out more distinctly.

Fine-grained but somewhat permeable rock material exposed in a steep slope can become saturated with water following a cloudburst, lose its cohesion, and flow down through a valley as a mudflow. The liquid mud spreads out beyond the base of the slope, very commonly on an already existing fan, dries, and becomes part of the local deposits. In this way, the alluvium of some desert fans becomes interbedded with mudflow sediments, as can be seen where streams have cut into the fans, exposing their internal character (Fig. 8–6).

Rain pelting. Raindrops, and hailstones as well, are surprisingly effective in eroding bare regolith during cloudbursts. The pelting impacts splash small rock particles into the air and churn them around. On a slope the result is slow, ill-defined movement of particles down the slope.

Running water. One of the characteristics of deserts is that most of the streams that originate in them never reach the sea. They soon disappear by evaporation and by infiltration. *Drainage that does not persist to the sea* is **interior drainage.** Exceptions are long rivers, such as the Nile in Egypt and the Colorado in southwestern United States, which originate in mountain regions with abundant precipitation and have such large discharge that they can keep flowing to the ocean despite heavy losses where they cross a desert.

In a desert the regolith is generally loose and dry, and where it is bare it is easily eroded. As there is little obstruction to runoff by the roots of growing plants, the proportion of surface runoff during violent falls of rain is large. Streams are therefore subject to sudden "flash" floods that move heavy loads of sediment. The loads are deposited on fans at the bases of mountain slopes (Fig. 14–3) and as alluvium on the floors of wide valleys and basins. The deposits of some flash floods are spectacular (Fig. 14–4).

In many valleys streams in flood effectively undercut the side slopes of their valleys, causing the slopes to cave. Then, as the flood subsides, the load is deposited rapidly, creating a flat floor of alluvium. The result is a steep-sided, flat-bottomed "box canyon," characteristic of many dry regions (Fig. 14–5).

We have seen that on any land surface only that number of valleys develops which is required to dispose of the prevailing runoff. The small precipitation on a dry region therefore demands relatively few

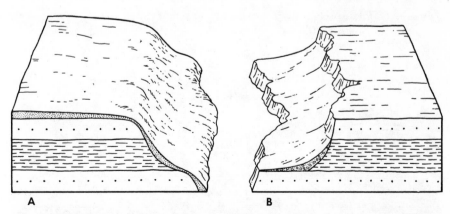

Fig. 14–2. Effect of climate on cross profiles of valleys. **A.** In a moist climate resistant strata are partly masked by creeping mantle of chemically weathered waste. **B.** In a dry climate resistant rocks stand out as broad platforms and steep cliffs, partly concealed by taluses.

Fig. 14–3. Fans being built out into Death Valley, California, from Black Mountains (left). View south from Furnace Creek Ranch (*right foreground*), showing Death Valley, a down-faulted basin with a white salt-incrusted playa. (Spence Air Photos.)

Fig. 14–4. This deposit of boulder gravel resulted from a single flash flood in a mountain valley. Los Angeles County, California. (U. S. Forest Service.)

Fig. 14–5. Small "box canyon" cut into silty alluvium. Cornfield Wash, Albuquerque district, New Mexico. (F. W. Kennon and H. V. Peterson, U. S. Geol. Survey.)

Fig. 14–6. Badlands. Death Valley California. (Josef Muench.)

Fig. 14–7. Braun's Playa, near Las Vegas, Nevada. The playa is nearly 5 miles in greatest diameter; the crest of the mountains is 15 miles distant. Playa lake on April 10, after an unusually large rainfall. The lake is no more than two or three feet deep. (C. E. Erdmann.)

valleys, and accordingly they are spaced far apart. There is an exception, however, in areas in which clay and silt are exposed in steep slopes, such as the side slopes of large valleys. Such material has little permeability so that there can be little infiltration of water. On the other hand, it is weak and yields readily to the attack of running water. Consequently, abundant runoff during violent rainstorms soon creates *a system of closely spaced narrow ravines with little or no vegetation.* Such intricately dissected terrain is known as *badlands* (Fig. 14–6), a name given to it by early travelers in western United States because it is almost impossible to cross.

The sudden precipitation of a large amount of water on a limited area can not create badlands if slopes are gentle to begin with. Yet the water must run off, for it generally comes down so suddenly that the open spaces in regolith or bedrock can not absorb much of it. Therefore, in such areas sheet runoff and small rills play a large part in disposing of the water and in eroding gently sloping surfaces.

Basins formed by faulting and other movements of the crust play a larger part in determining the general sculpture of the land in an arid region than in a moist one because there is rarely enough water to fill the basins, overflow them, and establish continuous drainage systems that will reach the sea. Streams flowing down out of a highland rarely last until they reach the center of the nearest basin, but after exceptional storms some of them discharge enough water to convert the basin floor into a very shallow lake that may last a few days or a few weeks (Figs. 14–7, 14–8). This is the playa lake described on p. 219. It occurs by the hundreds in major desert regions. Although not a playa lake, because it endures from year to year, Great Salt Lake has many of its characteristics.

Ground water. We noted in Chapter 11 that in a dry region the water table is likely to be far below ground, but in many places it is highest beneath streams (Fig. 11–10). Under such conditions there is little or none of the contribution from ground water to surface streams that occurs in a moist region. Now contributions from percolating ground water are the chief factor in the steady discharge of a stream. Therefore, in a desert the lack of such contributions, added to the cloudburst nature of the rainfall, produces the flash floods characteristic of desert climates.

Fig. 14—8. Dry playa two weeks later, after the lake has evaporated. The wind is blowing the fine-grained lake sediments (clay and crystals of salts) into dust clouds. Dark spots are desert bushes. (C. E. Erdmann.)

Wind. In dry country wind is an effective geologic agent. However, contrary to popular belief, deserts are not characterized mainly by sand dunes. Arabia, the sandiest of all dry regions, is only one-third covered with sand, and only one-ninth of the Sahara is sand-covered. Much of the nonsandy area of deserts is cut by systems of stream valleys, and in basins it is characterized by fans and broad alluvial plains. Therefore, even though the valleys are dry most of the time, running water leaves its mark upon a wider territory than does the wind. This can mean only that, except in restricted areas, streams, despite infrequent runoff, perform more geologic work than winds do.

The details of the way in which wind works in deserts and in other regions are set forth in a later section of this chapter.

Pediments

In deserts the land forms sculptured by erosion differ from those in country with more rainfall. When the terrain unit consists of a mountain range and an adjacent basin, two kinds of situations are common. One, shown in Figures 14–3 and 14–9, **A**, consists

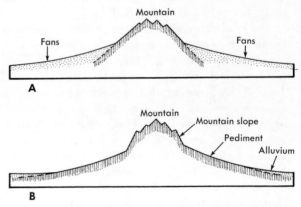

Fig. 14—9. Two common relationships at the bases of mountains in desert country. (**A.**) Fans built by streams at the foot of a mountain. (**B.**) Pediment eroded across bedrock at the foot of a mountain.

of a row of fans along the mountain base; the fans merge outward into a general fill of sediment in the basin. The other situation (Fig. 14–9, **B**), more remarkable and less easy to explain fully, consists of a sloping surface at the mountain base that closely resembles a merging row of fans. But the surface is not that of fans. Instead of being constructional, built of

GROWLER MTS.

AJO PEAKS

Pediment

Alluvium

Fig. 14–10. Pediment at south base of Little Ajo Mountains, Arizona. The black butte near center is about 1 mile long. Stripe-like rows of bushes are growing along faint, shallow channels. The view represents one-half of what is shown in the section (Fig. 14–11). (James Gilluly, U. S. Geol. Survey.)

alluvium, it is erosional, cut across bedrock. The bedrock, however, is not entirely bare. Scattered over it are rock fragments, some brought by running water from the adjacent mountains and some derived by weathering from the rock immediately beneath. Downslope, the rock fragments become more numerous until they form a continuous cover of alluvium. The rock surface, which may have a length of several miles, has passed beneath a basin fill.

The eroded bedrock surface is called a *pediment* because the surfaces adjacent to the two bases of a mountain mass, seen in profile, together resemble the triangular pediment, or gable, of a roof (Fig. 14–9, **B**). A *pediment*, then, is *a sloping surface, cut across bedrock, adjacent to the base of a highland in an arid climate.* The kinds of bedrock on which pediments are cut are those that yield easily to erosion in such a climate. Pediments (Fig. 14–10) have the concave-up profiles that we associate with the work of running water, and their surfaces are marked by channels, usually faint and shallow. For these reasons it seems probable that pediments are the work of running water flowing, according to local conditions, as definite streams, as sheet runoff, or as rills, and in any case flowing mainly during cloudbursts. In between the infrequent times of runoff weathering occurs. A pediment seems to be a near-equilibrium form, representing the most efficient means of disposing of the runoff that drains across it, under the conditions peculiar to the desert.

A remarkable thing about a pediment is that it meets the mountain slope not in a curve but at a distinct angle (Fig. 14–9, **B**). This seems to be the case regardless of the age of the pediment. Instead of becoming gentler with time, as in a wet region where chemical weathering and creep of the regolith are dominant, mountain slopes in the desert seem to adopt an angle determined by the resistance of the rock and to maintain it, gradually retreating under the attack of weathering and mass-wasting. Retreat of the mountain slope lengthens the pediment at its upslope edge. This growth of the pediment at the expense of the mountain should continue until the entire mountain has been consumed. During the whole time rock particles are being intermittently transferred downslope from mountain and pediment to the basin fill beyond.

This general outline of the way a pediment forms and develops, and its relation to the mountain slope, is not fully established and is partly a matter of opinion. Not until studies of many details have been completed can we expect to establish a complete picture.

Sculptural evolution: the cycle of erosion in deserts

In Chapter 10 it was shown that a theory of sculptural evolution of a land mass could be constructed. This was done by examining lands in several stages of development and arranging them in sequence to represent a continuous evolution. The example there illustrated (Fig. 10–11), constituting a cycle of erosion, was assembled from areas in which rainfall is abundant.

The concept of a cycle of erosion, an evolutionary sequence, applies equally well to desert regions. Here again, since no one district shows all the stages, several districts must be compared. Brought together, the stages appear to constitute a continuous series; hence it is believed that in the course of time a single land mass could evolve through all the stages. Figure 14–11 represents in a very generalized way three stages that can be seen today in parts of western United States.

The stage represented in *A* occurs commonly in northern Nevada. Mountains are being dissected actively. At the mouths of the mountain canyons the waste is spread out by streams in the form of fans,

grading outward toward the centers of basins into playas. Filling of the basins with waste from the mountains has begun. The wind picks up fine waste, sorts it, heaps the sand-size particles into dunes (Fig. 14–25), and lifts some of the finest particles out of the basin altogether. Meanwhile, the rocky spurs between the mouths of the mountain canyons are being worn back by weathering and mass-wasting.

In *B* (a stage occurring in southern New Mexico in the country north of El Paso, Texas) the mountain slopes have retreated, exposing a belt of bedrock at each mountain base to weathering and running water and thereby creating pediments. The steep mountain slopes, covered sparsely with coarse weathered frag-

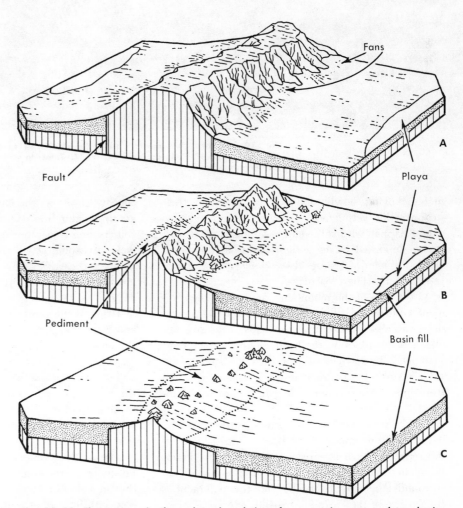

Fig. 14–11. Three stages in the sculptural evolution of a mountain range and two basins, originally created by faulting, in an arid climate.

Fig. 14–12. The "Dust Bowl" during the 1930's. A dust cloud approaching Springfield, Colorado, at 4.47 P.M. on May 21, 1937. Total darkness lasted 30 minutes. (U. S. Soil Conservation Service.)

ments moving slowly down them, maintain their steepness instead of becoming gentler with time, as would happen with soil creep in a moist region. The stream-deposited waste at their bases extends headward; the wind continues its work of sorting and of exporting the finest particles.

As the area of the mountains diminishes, the sediment contributed to the streams during rainstorms decreases also. This reduces the loads of the streams, which begin to erode the heads of the former fans, planing them down. In the process the streams cut sideways into the bedrock at and near the mountain front, planing it off and adding to the area of pediment.

In C, a stage seen in country northwest of Tucson, Arizona, the mountains have been reduced by gradual retreat of their steep slopes to a series of knobs projecting abruptly above the sloping pediment that surrounds them. Outward beyond the pediment is the surface of the basin fill, beneath which the pediment disappears without any break in the smooth,

concave slope. As the basin slopes become gradually gentler, water from the mountains reaches the basin centers more and more rarely, and increasingly the wind, sweeping across the basins, picks up fine sediments and carries them away. The stage shown in C is essentially the desert equivalent of a peneplane (Fig. 10–11).

Through the erosion of mountains and pediments and by the export of fine sediments from basins by the wind, the surface could continue to be smoothed and lowered. Theoretically, this could go on until the surface reached the water table, where moisture, and the resulting vegetation, would put an end to the picking up of fine sediment by the wind. That would take a very long time, and no example of this condition is known.

The whole cycle of erosion is slower than it would be under a wet climate. There is reason to believe that in southern Arizona the cycle has been in progress with little interruption for millions of years, and it still has a long way to go.

WIND ACTION

Moving air and its load[1]

Movement of air and rock particles. Wind is moving air, flowing like water. The most common cause of air movement differs from that of stream flow. Although in some places a thin layer of cold, heavy air flows downward over the surface from highlands to lowlands like a stream of water, the usual cause of movement is differences in air pressure created by differences in heating by the Sun. Heated air expands and rises; cooler air descends or flows in along the ground to take its place. Except for high mountain ranges, topographic irregularities have little effect on this flow.

Observers working in North African desert country have noticed, when strong winds are blowing, that there are two "layers" of rock particles in the air. The lower layer consists of sand grains and extends only a few inches to a very few feet above the ground. The upper layer consists of clouds of silt and clay particles; it extends much farther up, often to heights exceeding 2 miles. It is essentially a cloud of dust, like that shown in Figure 14–12. The difference between the two layers is fundamental, and the explanation of it lies in the relation between particle size and air turbulence. The streamline flow of air, like that of water, is rare in nature; at ordinary velocities the flow of air is not streamline but turbulent. As in water, the turbulent eddies include movements not only forward but in all other directions, including the upward direction. A tiny rock particle carried in an upward eddy is subject to two forces: (a) the velocity of the eddy and (b) the velocity of fall of the particle due to gravity. If (a) exceeds (b), the particle will tend to rise while it is being carried forward by the general movement of the air. If (b) exceeds (a), the particle will tend to fall.

Let us compare the ranges of values of (a) and (b) that are commonly found. For (a) observation and experiment show that a wind velocity of 11 miles per hour (about 5 meters per second) is about the minimum necessary to move sand grains lying on the

ground and that velocities of upward eddies in a wind are usually no more than one-fifth the average velocity of the wind as a whole. Hence, in a wind moving at 5 meters per second, upward eddies could reach a velocity of one-fifth this rate, or one meter per second. For (b) the data are given in Figure 14–13, in which velocity of fall is plotted against diameter (and therefore weight) of particle. The curve shows that at one meter per second, the velocity of one upward eddy, any particle with a diameter of less than about 0.2 millimeter should rise, whereas larger particles should fall out.

This theory is confirmed by observation. When we look at the deposits of sediment made by the wind, we find that the distinction between average sand particles and finer particles is maintained in the deposits as well as during transport in the moving air. In general, wind-blown sand of medium size falls out and is deposited in one group of places, whereas wind-blown finer particles (fine sand, silt, and clay) are deposited in others. When the diameters of the grains in a deposit of wind-blown sand are measured by putting a sample through a series of sieves of accurately controlled mesh, it is usually found that all or nearly all of the grains range between 0.3 and 0.15 millimeter. Particles finer than this were light enough to be lifted higher into the air, carried farther, and dropped in other places.

Movement of sand grains. We have noted that a strong desert wind has a thin layer of sand grains moving in its basal part and above that a far thicker layer

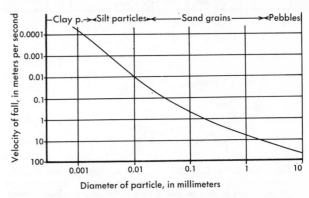

Fig. 14–13. Curve showing relationship between particle size and velocity of fall. (Adapted from R. A. Bagnold, The physics of blown sand and desert dunes: New York, William Morrow, 1942, p. 1.)

[1] Many of the data in this section are drawn from the fundamental treatise by R. A. Bagnold, listed among the references at the end of this chapter.

Fig. 14–14. Paths of sand grains being blown through a wind tunnel, photographed in a narrow beam of sunlight. Scale units are inches. (Agricultural Research Service, USDA, and Kansas Agricultural Experiment Station). Sand grains and small pebbles are visible on tunnel floor. Air current is moving from left to right. Traces of both splashing and bouncing impacts are visible (Fig. 14–15). (A. W. Zingg.)

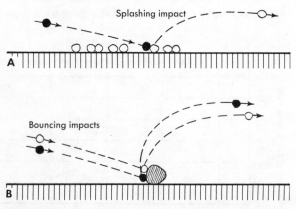

Fig. 14–15. In splashing impact, A, saltating sand grain strikes one or more other grains and splashes them into air at slow speeds and to low heights. Splashing happens most commonly when all grains are nearly the same size. In bouncing impacts, B, sand grains strike pebble or other wide surface and bounce up at high speed and to greater heights. Angle of rise depends on inclination of surface of impact.

of finer particles. Experiments with sand under controlled conditions in artificial wind tunnels have demonstrated how the sand grains move (Fig. 14–14). A sand grain has elastic properties. When it strikes a rock surface, a pebble, or another sand grain, it can bounce off it like a ping-pong ball. It rises into the air and follows a long curved path that brings it back to the ground again at a low angle. The technical word for the bouncing movement is saltation (p. 164), a term first used in experiments with rock particles in running water. But, although in both air and water, saltation refers to the movement of rock particles in long, flat jumps, there is a difference. Saltation in air involves a true elastic bounce, whereas in water, which is about 800 times heavier than air, saltation characteristically involves a hydraulic lift rather than a bounce.

A sand grain gets into the air only by bouncing or by being knocked into the air through the impact of another grain. When the wind becomes strong enough, a grain starts to roll along the surface under the pressure of a fast-moving forward eddy. It strikes another grain and knocks it into the air. When the second grain hits the ground, it either splashes up still other grains, making a tiny crater, or bounces in a new jump (Fig. 14–15). In a very short time the air close to the ground has become filled with jumping, saltating sand grains, which hop and bounce, moving with the wind, as long as wind velocity is great enough to keep them at it.

Note again that the jumping sand grains never get far off the ground. They are usually limited to a few inches, as in the experiment shown in Figure 14–14. In desert country they generally jump no higher than about 18 inches, as shown by telephone poles, which are sandblasted up to about that height but no higher. Even in the strongest desert winds the height of jump hardly ever exceeds 3 or 4 feet. This fundamental fact explains why wind-blown sand rarely moves far except on very smooth surfaces. Being always close to the ground, it is easily stopped by obstacles and heaped into dunes.

Movement of finer particles. The movement of clay and silt particles by the wind is different. These particles do not jump. Sprayed into the air by the impacts of sand grains, they are lifted by updrafts within the general turbulence and are carried in true suspension, like the suspended load in a stream of water. Since their rate of fall is very slow (Fig. 14–13), they remain in the air much longer than sand grains, and so, on the average, they are carried much farther.

It would seem that when a fine particle settles to the ground it could be lifted again very easily. However, this is not necessarily true. The moving air above a sandy surface is full of tiny eddies set up by the rough surface of the sand grains. But the surface of a deposit of silt and clay particles is so smooth that it does not set up eddies. As a result there is a layer of dead air just above it (Fig. 14–16), so that not even a strong wind can move the fine particles. The dead-air layer is a trap for more fine particles. These accumulate and their smooth upper surface remains stable.

An example is a dusty road in dry country on a windy day. The wind blowing across the road generates little or no dust. But a car driving over the road creates a choking cloud, which quickly settles after the car has passed. The car wheels have broken up the surface of powdery silt, which was too smooth to be disturbed by the wind. However, on a surface of mixed silt and sand, the sand grains project through the layer of dead air like islands in a shallow lake and soon begin to move. The saltating sand grains quickly splash silt particles into the air, just as the car wheels did. Probably this is what is occurring in Figure 14–8.

An additional factor in the relative stability of a surface of fine sediments is the tendency of the particles to cohere because of films of moisture adsorbed onto their surfaces. These films of moisture are what make a silty or clayey soil slightly sticky, whereas in a sandy soil the grains tend to be loose.

The result of this difference in behavior between sand grains and finer particles is that the wind continually sorts the sediments it carries, winnowing out the finer sizes and transporting them over long distances, whereas the sand grains, left behind, travel much less far.

Amount of load. Of course, a current of air can not hold in suspension nearly so much sediment as a current of water of similar velocity and cross-sectional area because air is far less dense than water. Nevertheless, it has been estimated that the theoretical sediment-transporting capacity of the winds blowing across the Mississippi River drainage basin is around 1000 times that of the Mississippi River if both were fully loaded. The apparent anomaly is explained by the frequently greater velocities and vastly greater cross-sectional area of the moving air. The amount of sediment actually moved by the atmosphere, year in and year out, is probably only a fraction of one per cent of capacity, for the air is rarely if ever fully loaded.

During the great wind storms in the dry years of the 1930's, however, loads became very heavy. In a particularly great storm on March 20, 1935, when the sky looked much as in Figure 14–12 (compare also Figures 15–13 and 6–7), the cloud of suspended sediment extended 12,000 feet above the ground, and the load in the Wichita, Kansas, area was estimated at 166,000 tons per cubic mile in the lowermost layer one mile thick. But only a little of this huge load was deposited in any one place, for a sample of sediment trapped on the roof of a laboratory building in Lincoln, Nebraska, indicated that during that day only about 800 tons of rock particles—around 5 per cent

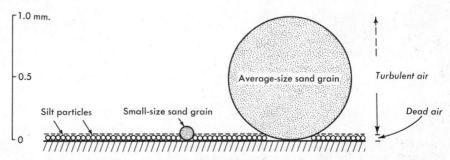

Fig. 14–16. Silt particles form a smooth surface that creates no turbulence and is therefore stable. Sand grains, even small ones, create turbulence and so are unstable.

of the load suspended in the lowermost one-mile layer—were deposited on each square mile. Enough sediment was carried eastward on March 21 to bring temporary twilight over New York and New England, 2,000 miles east of the principal source area in eastern Colorado. The distance and travel time imply wind velocities of about 50 mph.

March 20 was an exceptional day, a "black blizzard," but even if we allow for normal conditions, when no sediment is visible in the air, the total amount of rock material moved by the atmosphere in a single year must be enormous. This is shown by the radioactive dust carried to leeward from the localities of nuclear explosions and detected by sensitive instruments right around the Earth. The educated guess has been expressed that every square mile of the Earth's land area probably contains rock particles brought by the wind from each of the remaining square miles. Of course, this statement can not be proved, but probably it is nearer the truth than is generally realized.

Wind erosion

Deflation. The presence of sediment in the atmosphere implies wind erosion, which is of two kinds. The first kind, *picking up and removal of loose rock particles by wind*, provides most of the wind's load and is known as **deflation** (Lat. *deflare,* to blow away). The second kind, *abrasion* of rock by wind-driven rock particles, is analogous to abrasion by running water.

Deflation is conspicuous only in the absence of vegetation and only, of course, in material that is capable of being picked up by the wind (Fig. 14–8). The great areas of deflation are the deserts; others are the beaches of seas and large lakes and, of greatest economic significance, bare plowed fields in farming country during times of drought, when moisture to hold the soil particles together is lacking.

The effect of deflation on the form of the land is not great. In most areas the results are not easily visible, inasmuch as the whole surface is lowered irregularly. In places, however, measurement is possible. In the dry 1930's deflation in parts of western United States amounted to several feet within only a few years—a tremendous rate compared with our standard estimate of rate of general erosion. In Figure 14–17 the tuft-like yucca plants held the soil in place, but elsewhere it was deflated. In the few years before the photograph was taken, 4 feet of soil had been deflated. The silt and clay particles had been exported in suspension, sand grains had been sorted out and had remained behind, and had been added to by further sand moving in from the area upwind.

Probably the most conspicuous evidence of wind

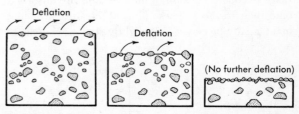

Fig. 14–18. Three stages in the development of a deflation armor.

Fig. 14–17. A direct record of 4 feet of deflation of overgrazed pasture. The plant roots at the level of the man's hand mark the position of the surface before deflation. Dalhart, Texas, 1948. (U. S. Soil Conservation Service.)

work of this kind consists of **deflation basins,** which are *depressions excavated by deflation.* These occur by the tens of thousands in semiarid regions, as in the Great Plains region from Canada to Texas. Most of them are less than a mile in length and are only a few feet deep. In wet years they are clothed with grass and some even contain shallow lakes; an observer seeing them at such times would hardly guess their origin. But in dry years soil moisture evaporates, the grass dies away in patches, and the wind deflates the bare soil. At the same time drifting sand accumulates to leeward, especially along fences and other obstructions.

When deflation is particularly easy, basins may reach depths of 150 feet, as in southern Wyoming, and even greater depths, as in the Qattara basin in the Libyan Desert in western Egypt, where the basin floor reaches 420 feet below sea level. Deflation there, as in any basin, is limited finally only by the water table, which moistens the surface, encourages vegetation, and inhibits wind erosion.

A natural preventive of deflation is a cover of rock particles too large to be removed by the wind. Deflation of a sediment such as alluvium, which consists of silt, sand, and pebbles, creates its own protective cover (Fig. 14–18). Sand and silt are blown away and in places are carried off by sheet erosion also, but the pebbles remain. When the surface has been low-ered just enough to create a continuous cover of pebbles, the ground has acquired a **deflation armor**—*a surface layer of pebbles concentrated chiefly by deflation* (Fig. 14–19). Deflation armors are also called *desert pavement* because long-continued removal of the fine particles makes the pebbles settle into such stable positions that they fit together almost like blocks in a cobblestone pavement.

A more widespread preventive of deflation is a continuous cover of vegetation. This is the principal reason why deflation is evident mainly in desert regions, which lack such cover. However, deflation is very evident, in semiarid country and in coastal areas, in sand dunes that have become covered with grass. During seasons of drought or as a result of trampling by animals the grass is killed off in patches and allows deflation to start, converting the bare patches into irregular, shallow basins known as *blowouts.* A **blowout** is merely *a deflation basin excavated in dune sand.*

Abrasion: ventifacts. In desert areas bedrock surfaces, pebbles, and boulders are abraded by wind-driven sand and silt, which can cut and polish them to a high degree. A **ventifact,** the name given to *a wind-cut rock fragment,* is recognized by polished, greasy-looking surfaces, which may be pitted or fluted, and by facets separated from each other by

Fig. 14–19. Deflation armor ("desert pavement") on the floor of Death Valley, California. Some of the stones have distinct wind-cut facets. Length of front of photograph is several feet. (Eliot Blackwelder.)

sharp edges (Fig. 14–20).

Laboratory experiments with pieces of plaster of Paris subjected to sand blasting show that the facets always face the wind (Fig. 14–21). A stone can be worn down flush with the ground by enlargement of a single facet. If the stone is undermined or otherwise rotated or if the wind direction varies from time to time, two or three facets can be cut on it (Fig. 14–20).

Far from being confined to deserts, ventifacts are found in large numbers at the upper surfaces of layers of glacial drift in northern United States and Europe. Evidently they were made during glacial ages, just beyond the margins of ice sheets, where surfaces temporarily bare of vegetation were subjected to strong winds.

Although locally striking, the effect of wind abrasion in the aggregate probably is not great. Rocks of various odd shapes in dry regions are often popularly ascribed to wind abrasion, but most of them result from weathering. Wind abrasion, then, is a minor process; the quantitative importance of wind erosion lies not in abrasion but in deflation.

Wind deposits

Much as in a stream of water, the saltating sand grains close above the ground move relatively slowly and are deposited early, whereas the suspended finer particles travel faster and farther before dropping to the ground. This is known from systematic sampling of wind deposits derived from a known source. Sampling shows a progressive decrease in the diameters of the rock particles with increasing distance from the source. Generally there is also a difference in topography between sand deposits, which occur in heaps and mounds near the source, and deposits consisting predominantly of silt and clay, which occur as a general blanket over the ground farther from the source.

Deposits of sand

Ripples. On any very small irregularity of the surface of sandy ground, jumping sand grains strike the windward side in greater numbers than they do the lee side (Fig. 14–22). In the little basin *ABC* more grains accumulate on the side *BC* facing the wind, than on the side *AB*. This increases the irregularity, heightens *C*, and develops a new slope *CD*, beyond which a second accumulation must occur, and so on. In this way, there is quickly formed a series of ripples trending at right angles to the wind direction. Their spacing (usually a few inches apart) depends on wind velocity and grain diameters, which determine the lengths of the jumps. The height of a series of ripples increases until they reach a level at which wind velocity, increasing upward, is great enough to blow as many grains off a ripple as are added to it.

Thus, for any velocity and grain size, ripples develop a uniform height and spacing, which are reworked and remade with each change in the wind. The common presence of ripples shows that on bare wind-blown sand flat surfaces are generally unstable.

Dunes. A *dune* is *a mound or ridge of sand depos-*

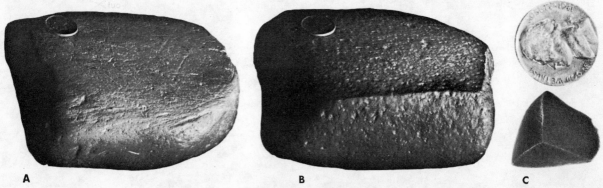

Fig. 14–20. Ventifacts. **A.** Two sides of a basalt cobble, showing a facet and striations made by glacial abrasion. New Haven, Connecticut. **B.** Two more sides of the same cobble, not visible in **A.** Two facets, smoothed and pitted by wind-driven sand, are visible. Because pits cut the glacial striations, cobble was glaciated first, then wind-cut as it lay on the ground in the lee of a body of outwash. **C.** Ventifact with two facets and a third surface whose curved form suggests it is remnant of original round pebble. From stream gravel on terrace of Big Horn River, Wyoming. (R. F. Flint.)

ited by the wind. Dunes occur in two principal environments: (1) deserts, where the dunes are bare and interplay between wind and sand is free, and (2) coasts, where vegetation, induced by moist climate, interferes with free interplay. Anyone who has looked thoughtfully at groups of dunes will realize that the variety of dune forms is complex. The complexity is caused by many factors, including topography of floor, variations of wind direction, amount of sand available, climate, and vegetation. The complexity has not yet been reduced to order, for there is much about dunes that we do not yet understand. However, we can state a few principles.

One of these is that many dunes are caused by obstacles. Some are obvious, like cliffs. Others are no more than slight irregularities in the ground. The energy of an air current within a few feet of the ground varies with even the slightest irregularity. As it sweeps around and over the obstacle, the air leaves a pocket of lower-energy air containing eddies both behind and just in front of the obstacle. In this pocket sand accumulates and forms a dune (Fig. 14–23) which, as it grows, can itself act as an obstacle and trap more wind-driven sand.

Slip-face of a dune. Saltating sand grains on the windward slope of a bare dune roll or bounce up the slope. At the summit they are swept onward into the pocket of quieter air and drop onto the lee side of the dune (Fig. 14–24). Most of them fall near the top, building up the lee slope and steepening it until it reaches the angle of repose (generally 30 to 34°) representing equilibrium between the pull of gravity and the force of friction among the grains. Any sand added thereafter causes small landslides (really sand slides), which act to keep the slope straight and very close to the angle of repose. Because of this sliding or slipping, *the straight leeward face of a dune* is called

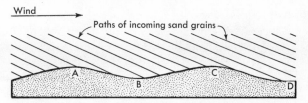
Fig. 14–22. Theory of wind-ripple development. (After Bagnold.)

Fig. 14–23. Wind blowing from left to right deflated the bare dry field, carried away the finer particles in suspension, and dropped sand along the obstacle created by a wire fence with weeds caught in it, to form a dune. Hereford, Texas. (A. Devaney, Inc.)

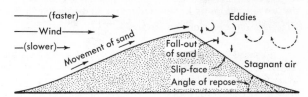
Fig. 14–24. Development of windward and lee slopes of an ideal bare dune.

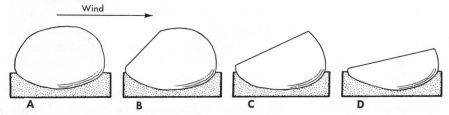
Fig. 14–21. Four stages in the cutting of a ventifact. The pebble becomes a ventifact between stage **A** and stage **B**.

Fig. 14–25. Bare dunes on the floor of Death Valley, California, a true desert. Slip-faces are to the right, showing that wind responsible for them was blowing from left to right. (Al Greene, Associates, Photo Researchers, Inc.)

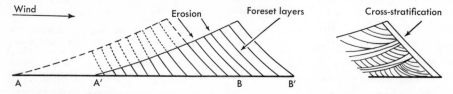

Fig. 14–26. Development of stratification in a migrating dune. Foreset beds (*left*) made by ideal wind, having uniform direction and velocity. Cross-stratification (*right*) caused by variations in direction and velocity. Compare Figure 14–32.

the *slip-face;* it meets the crest at a very sharp angle (Figs. 14–24, 14–25). The angle of slope of the windward side varies with wind velocity and grain size, but it is always less than that of the slip-face. Therefore, the asymmetry of a dune with a slip-face indicates the direction of the wind that shaped it.

Height and migration. Many dunes grow to heights of 100 to 300 feet, and some dunes in the Sudan reach the great height of 700 feet. Possibly the height to which any dune can grow is determined by upward increase in wind velocity, which at some level will become great enough to whip sand grains off the top of a dune as fast as they arrive there by climbing the windward slope.

Transfer of sand from the windward to the lee side of a bare dune can cause slow migration of the whole dune in the downwind direction (Fig. 14–26). Measurements on desert dunes of the type shown in Figure 14–27 show rates of movement around 50 feet per year. The migration of dunes, particularly along coasts just inland from sandy beaches, has been known to bury houses and threaten the existence of inhabited places. In such places sand encroachment is combatted most effectively by planting dunes with vegetation that can survive in very dry sandy soil. A good plant cover inhibits dune migration for the same reason that it inhibits deflation: if the wind can not move sand grains across it, a dune can not migrate.

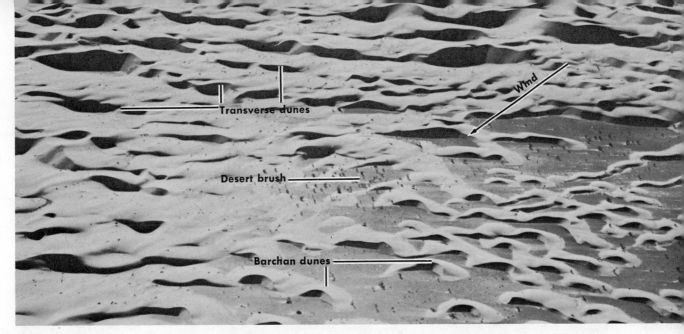

Fig. 14–27. Transverse dunes separating (*right*) into barchan dunes. Near Calexico, California. Foreground of view is about half a mile wide. (Spence Air Photos.)

Stratification of sand in dunes. The dropping of sand grains over the crest onto the slip-face of a dune produces foreset layers much like those in a delta (Fig. 9–26). Erosion of the windward slope continually erodes the foreset layers as new ones are added to the slip-face (Fig. 14–26). Because of variations in direction and velocity of the wind, no dune, however, shows so uniform an arrangement. As a result erosion alternates with deposition, and the foreset layers slope in various directions to produce *cross-stratification* (p. 330). If there is some vegetation on the windward slope of a dune, it traps sand and causes deposition there as well; this results in additional irregularity in stratification. Despite the irregularities, however, the general direction of dip of the steep foreset layers in wind-blown sand is the direction toward which the wind that built them was blowing. This is a useful relationship because it enables us to reconstruct ancient wind systems from measurement of layers of wind-blown sand in which the forms of the dunes themselves have been completely destroyed by erosion.

Kinds of dunes. We have discussed some general characteristics of dunes without much regard to dune form. Actually, dunes have many different shapes, and the factors that determine the shapes are only partly understood. Most shapes can be roughly classified into five groups:

1. *Beach dunes.* Along the coasts of seas and large lakes beaches afford a source of abundant sand that is continually renewed by the action of waves. Onshore winds deflate the beach sand and pile it into dunes, most of which are small things, heaped around minor obstacles and without slip-faces. On some coasts, however, the dunes form ridges parallel with the beach; when onshore winds are strong the ridges can become high. These ridges are one variety of transverse dune.

2. *Transverse dunes* are *dunes forming wave-like ridges transverse* (at right angles) *to wind direction.* They occur where sand supply is abundant and where vegetation does not interfere with the growth of dunes. They have well-marked slip-faces. Many transverse-dune ridges are seen in the left and upper parts of Figure 14–27 and in places grade into barchan dunes.

3. *Barchan dunes* are *crescent-shaped dunes, the horns of which point downwind.* They form chiefly in desert areas and seem to require a hard, flat floor, wind from a constant direction, and a rather limited supply of sand. They are always bare, migrate actively, and their lee sides are slip-faces. They seem to be

273

Fig. 14–28. U-shaped dunes near Eltopia, Washington. Centers of some of the U's are indicated by stars. Foreground is about one-third mile wide. (Washington National Guard.)

related to transverse dunes, which in some places separate into barchan dunes, as can be seen in Figure 14–27. Although many barchans are as much as 100 feet high, little ones are no more than 3 feet high and 20 feet in diameter from horn to horn.

4. *U-shaped dunes* are *dunes of U-shape with the open end of the U facing upwind* (Fig. 14–28). The relation of shape to wind direction is therefore exactly opposite to that in a barchan, and the steep slip-face, of course, is on the convex side. U-shaped dunes do not occur commonly in desert areas; usually they have patches of vegetation on them. Some U-shaped dunes seem to form during the growth of a blowout, by the piling-up of sand around the blowout's leeward and lateral margins.

5. *Longitudinal dunes* are *long, straight, ridge-shaped dunes parallel with the wind direction.* They develop in desert areas in which sand supply is very scanty and winds are strong (Fig. 14–29).

There are still other dune shapes, many of them dependent partly on the topography of the terrain on which they are built. For example, long ridges are built streaming downwind from steep narrow buttes, sheets of sand accumulate against cliffs facing the wind, and sand blown across a plateau may

drop over a cliff facing to leeward and build up a sloping pile.

Composition and shape of sand grains. Virtually all dunes are made of sand-size particles. Since quartz is the most common mineral in sand-size sediments, it is not surprising that most dunes consist of quartz sand. Where other minerals are abundant, however, dunes can be built from them. The island of Bermuda consists mainly of wind-blown particles of calcite, derived from the beach, which is underlain by limestone and which shifted with changes of sea level. The White Sands National Monument, an area of 500 square miles near Alamogordo, New Mexico, is covered with dunes built of snow-white gypsum grains deflated from beds of gypsum exposed at the surface. In many areas dunes are built of clay and silt, but these materials were picked up by the wind as aggregates, each the size of a sand grain and each consisting of many particles of clay or silt firmly cohering. The diameters of the aggregates, rather than the diameters of the particles in each determined the manner in which they were handled by the wind: they moved by saltation rather than in suspension.

Sand grains become rounded more rapidly in wind than in water because air, being less dense, cushions impacts less effectively. The impacts, therefore, wear away edges and corners to produce round shapes. Also, by making multitudes of tiny pits, the impacts create on quartz grains frosted surfaces that resemble ground glass.

Deposits of silt

Loess. Fine sediment, carried in suspension in the air, is present in much of the soil, mixed with other materials and not clearly distinguishable from them. Beneath wide areas sediment having this origin is so thick and so pure that it constitutes a distinctive deposit. It is known as *loess* (lûs) (Fig. 14–30), and is defined as *wind-deposited silt, usually accompanied by some clay and some fine sand*.

Although some loess is stratified, most of it is not, apparently because the range of grain size is too small to produce distinct layering and also perhaps because plant roots, worms, and other organisms turn over and churn up the sediment as it is deposited.

Loess is so widespread and uniform, especially in the region of Nebraska, South Dakota, Iowa, Missouri, and Illinois, that it was once believed to have been deposited by water. But when after wider study it was found to mantle hills and valleys alike over an altitude range of 1,500 feet the belief was abandoned.

Minerals composing loess are chiefly quartz, feldspar, micas, and calcite. The particles are generally fresh, showing little evidence of chemical weathering other than slight oxidation that has occurred since deposition and that gives a yellowish tinge to the deposit as a whole. The loess in many areas closely resembles the rock flour ground up mechanically by glaciers. The resemblance led geologists to suspect loess to be glacial drift picked up, sorted, and redeposited by the wind. The suspicion was confirmed by the distribution of loess, much of which occurs immediately to leeward of large areas of glacial out-

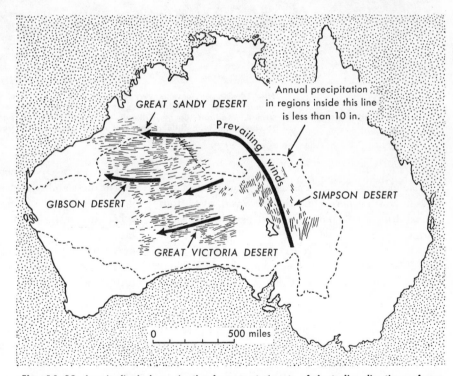

Fig. 14–29. Longitudinal dunes in the four great deserts of Australia, directions of prevailing winds, and region with less than 10 inches of precipitation. Ridges are 25 to as much as 100 feet high and as much as 100 miles long. Together they cover half a million square miles. Each line represents four ridges, plotted from aerial photographs. (Dunes after T. W. E. David, 1950, Geology of the Commonwealth of Australia: London, Edward Arnold, vol. 1, p. 634; winds after C. T. Madigan, 1936, Geographical Review, vol. 26, p. 205.)

Fig. 14–30. As loess is very cohesive and has vertical joints, it forms cliffs as jointed bedrock does. This cliff of loess, in a borrow pit in the east bluff of the Mississippi River Valley, Madison County, Illinois, shows the typical surface expression of bare loess. It will stand with little change for many years. (J. C. Frye.)

wash (Fig. 14–31).

Glacial loess. Today it is agreed that most of the loess in North America and Europe was derived from glacial drift, chiefly outwash. The loess was deposited during glacial ages when the areas just outside the margins of ice sheets were cold and windy and when glacial outwash—gravel, sand, and silt—was filling up river valleys so fast that plants could not gain a foothold on valley floors (Fig. 13–20). With a windy climate and no vegetation, deflation of valley floors was easy. Saltating sand grains splashed silt particles into the air to be carried away in suspension. The silt settled out, forming blankets 50 to 100 feet thick near the source valleys and thinning downwind to thicknesses of 2 to 5 feet over thousands of square miles.

Why was the silt not picked up again and again

and carried even farther by the wind? One reason lies in the stability of a silt surface, owing to its fine grain size (Fig. 14–16) and its cohesiveness. Another, and in the case of loess perhaps a more important reason, is that the loess settled out chiefly in grassland and to some extent even in forested areas. In such environments it would be in no danger of further deflation.

Desert loess. In some regions loess is found over enormous areas that lie to leeward of deserts, an obvious source of mechanically weathered sediments. The loess that covers much of western China, blown from the great desert basins of central Asia, reaches a thickness of more than 200 feet. Probably the immediate source of such loess is chiefly fine alluvium, washed down by cloudburst streams from the mountains onto desert floors.

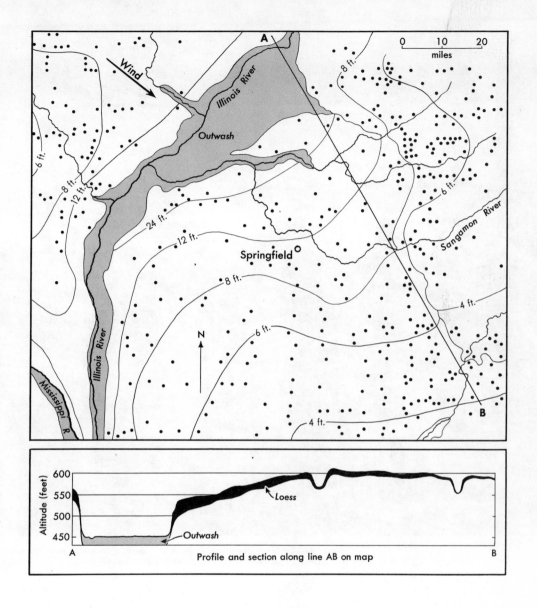

Fig. 14–31. Loess in central Illinois. Thicknesses were determined by borings at places shown by dots. Lines connect points of equal thickness. Profile and section were plotted from thickness lines. Thickness decreases away from body of outwash in both directions, but loess is thickest on southeast side, the leeward side for prevailing winds. Grain diameters also decrease in both directions away from outwash, and mineral content of loess and that of outwash are similar. Hence it is inferred that the loess resulted from deflation of the outwash. (Adapted from data in G. D. Smith, 1942, Univ. of Ill. Agric. Expt. Sta. Bull. 490.)

Fig. 14–32. Cross-stratification in dune sand of Jurassic age, consolidated to form hard sandstone. Zion National Park, Utah. (Andreas Feininger.)

Ancient wind-deposited sediments

Sediments deposited by the wind are useful indicators of events in Earth history. Dunes no longer active, because firmly fixed by a continuous cover of vegetation, indicate that when they were built conditions were generally drier than they are today. The grassed-over Sand Hills, covering an area of 20,000 square miles in western Nebraska, record a period or periods when aridity was greater than it is now.

From the shapes of dunes and from the directions of their steep foreset beds (always inclined downwind) the directions of former winds can be inferred.

Sheets of loess in the lee of outwash bodies record times when meltwater streams spread out sediments to be picked up and transported by the wind. They are therefore generally indicative of glacial ages.

In ancient layers of sedimentary rock, in which no traces of dune shape remain, the combination of cross-stratification (Fig. 14–32) and rounded, frosted sand grains records the deposition of wind-blown sand at times far back in the Earth's history.

Economic aspects: soil erosion

With climates that continually fluctuate, regions ordinarily suitable for agriculture have dry periods during which soil erosion by the wind reaches tremendous proportions. During the dry years of the 1930's an enormous volume of soil was blown away from parched, unprotected plowed fields in the "Dust Bowl" region of the Great Plains (Figs. 14–12, 14–17). The sand-size particles were piled up along fences and around farm buildings (Fig. 14–23), and finer particles were blown eastward to be deposited over wide areas; a good deal of such material was dropped into the Atlantic Ocean.

Why the "Dust Bowl"? As we saw earlier, air flowing at 11 mph will move sand grains on the ground. The "Dust Bowl" area very nearly coincides with the largest area in the United States in which the average wind velocity is more than 10 mph. All that was needed further was a long succession of dry years—the drought in the 1930's, clearly reflected also in the shrinking of Great Salt Lake (Fig. 12–5). We now realize that with only very slight changes in the Earth's climates deserts expand and contract and can be created or can disappear.

In the "Dust Bowl" area good practice includes the planting of windbreaks (Fig. 14–33), consisting of bushes and hardy trees set in strips at right angles to the strongest winds, at intervals of a mile or so. It also involves planting strips of grass alternating with strips of cultivated grain (Fig. 7–14), for the latter must lie bare and fallow during alternate years in order to accumulate moisture sufficient to grow grain. The strips of trees and grass retard wind ve-

Fig. 14–33. Windbreaks on dry sandy farm land in northern Texas. (U.S. Soil Conservation Service.)

locities at ground level enough to prevent serious deflation of the bare strips in their lee.

SUMMARY

1. Deserts are generally areas of slight rainfall, high temperature, great evaporation, relatively strong winds, sparse vegetation, and interior drainage. About a quarter of the world's land area is desert.

2. No major geologic process is confined to deserts, but mechanical weathering, rain pelting, flash floods, and winds are very effective. Badlands occur locally, and the water table is low.

3. Pediments are a conspicuous feature of many deserts. They seem to be shaped by streams, rills, sheet runoff, and weathering.

4. In the arid cycle of erosion pediments grow headward at the expense of mountain slopes, which appear to retreat without becoming gentler as they do in a moist region. Wind plays a part in the removal of rock waste.

5. Wind carries its load in two distinct layers: sand grains moving by saltation close to the ground and finer particles in suspension higher up. The result is sorting of the sediment.

6. The wind erodes by deflation and abrasion, chiefly in dry regions and on beaches. Resulting features are deflation basins, blowouts, deflation armor, and ventifacts.

7. Many dunes are localized by obstacles. Bare dunes have a windward slope and a slip-face and grow or migrate downwind. As a result, the dune has an unsymmetrical profile and cross-stratification.

8. Dunes can be classified by form into groups, some of which are beach dunes, transverse dunes, barchan dunes, U-shaped dunes, and longitudinal dunes.

9. With long-continued wind activity, sand grains become rounded and develop frosted surfaces.

10. Loess is formed chiefly in the lee of (1) glacial-outwash bodies and (2) deserts. Once deposited, it is stable and little affected by further wind action.

REFERENCES

Bagnold, R. A., 1942, The physics of blown sand and desert dunes: New York, William Morrow & Co.

Blackwelder, Eliot, 1954, Geomorphic processes in the desert: California Div. Mines Bull. 170, Chap. 5, p. 11–20.

Bryan, Kirk, 1923, Erosion and sedimentation in the Papago Country, Ariz., with a sketch of the geology: U. S. Geol. Survey Bull. 730, p. 19–90.

Cooper, W. S., 1958, Coastal sand dunes of Oregon and Washington: Geol. Soc. America Mem. 72.

Finkel, H. J., 1959, The barchans of southern Peru: Jour. Geology, vol. 67, p. 614–647.

Hume, W. F., 1925, Geology of Egypt, vol. 1: Cairo, Gov't Press.

Thorp, James, and others, 1952, [Map of] Pleistocene eolian deposits of the United States . . .: New York, Geol. Soc. America.

CHAPTER 15. THE SEA: SUBMARINE GEOLOGY

Dimensions, water economy, and composition of the sea   *Sea level*   *Topography of the sea floor*

Movements of sea water   *Sediments of the sea floor*   *Special features and problems*

A diving marine geologist examines a specimen from the sea floor.
(R. F. Dill, Navy Electronics Laboratory.)

Geographic research on the sea

We can define the *sea* as *the entire body of confluent salt water of the Earth*. The sea is the region in which oceanographers and geologists cooperate in research, and a wide region it is, for altogether it covers 71 per cent of the Earth's surface. Research at sea is difficult and expensive and requires the use of very specialized instruments and equipment, including specially constructed oceanographic research ships. Until recently, therefore, growth of knowledge of the topography and sediments of the sea floor lagged behind the parallel study of the lands. But, with the perfection of new devices for sounding the sea bottom and for sampling its sediments, teams of seagoing oceanographers, geologists, and geophysicists have begun to put submarine geology on a footing almost as solid as that already established on the land. Diving geologists have visited, photographed, and mapped sea-floor areas at depths as great as 150 feet. In January 1960 two observers descended in a *bathyscaph* to 35,800 feet, where they viewed the sea floor in the deep Marianas Trench in the western Pacific Ocean. This feat opens the way to obtaining geologic information by direct observation at depths equal to the average depth of the sea.

Before turning to the geology of its floor, we must look briefly at some data on the sea itself (that is, oceanographic data) that have a special significance for geology.

Dimensions, water economy, and composition

Dimensions. Since it covers 71 per cent of the Earth's surface, the sea is more than twice as extensive as the land. The greatest ocean depth yet measured, 35,800 feet, is in the Marianas Trench in the western Pacific. This point, then, is more than 6.5 miles below sea level, whereas the highest point on land, Mount Everest, is only about 5.5 miles above sea level. The average depth of the sea is a bit more than 2.6 miles, compared with only a little more than half a mile as the average height of the land. Hence if the matter that constitutes the land were removed and placed in the ocean, the result would be a universal sea with no land at all. Although erosion is indeed continually transferring material from land to sea, nevertheless a universal sea is improbable. This is shown in Chapter 20.

Water economy. The sea is the Earth's great reservoir of moisture. Knowing its area and its average depth, we can compute roughly its present volume at around 330,000,000 cubic miles. We say "present volume" because it is clear that volume fluctuates with the growth and melting of glaciers. The water economy of the sea, closely related to the hydrologic cycle, is that of a vast lake without an outlet. Its volume at any time, like that of the Great Salt Lake, is measured by income from direct precipitation and from inflowing streams and springs, minus outgo in the form of evaporation. If, as some measurements suggest, sea level as a whole is rising today, the sea's water economy is not in balance, for the sea is gaining slightly more, as glaciers melt and add more water to it, than it is losing by evaporation.

Composition. About 3.5 per cent average sea water, by weight, consists of dissolved mineral substances. As everyone knows, this is enough to make the water undrinkable. It is enough also, if precipitated, to form a layer of solid salts about 185 feet thick over the entire sea floor. When sea water is evaporated, more than 75 per cent of the dissolved matter is precipitated as common salt ($NaCl$). Among the many other substances precipitated are silica (SiO_2), calcium carbonate ($CaCO_3$), and calcium sulfate ($CaSO_4$).

Most of the dissolved matter is the product of chemical weathering on land and has been brought to the sea, via ground water and streams, at an estimated present rate of 2.5 billion tons per year. But some of it, especially some of the carbon dioxide (which is continuously abstracted in enormous amounts by animals that build their shells of calcium carbonate) and chlorine (a constituent of salt), may be coming from hot waters and gases that reach the Earth's surface from magmas cooling within the crust. It is even possible that sea water itself is being added to by volcanic steam.

The quantity of substances dissolved in sea water therefore consists of the large amount that has been contributed to the sea, minus the large amount removed by marine organisms in building shells and skeletons and minus also the small amount precipitated chemically in warm shallow water where evaporation is very rapid. Limestones and related sedimentary rocks represent an enormous volume of matter withdrawn from solution in sea water during wide transgressions of shallow seas over the lands throughout long periods of time. We do not know whether withdrawal balances supply—whether this great chemical system is in equilibrium or not—although it seems rather likely that it has not departed far from equilibrium during the last few hundred million years of geologic time.

Sea level

The familiar shape of an island or continent, by which we recognize the feature on a map, is determined by its shoreline and therefore by sea level. Because of this, the shape is essentially accidental. The same island or continent probably had a considerably different shoreline at some time in the geologic past because changes of one kind or another are continually in progress.

An important aspect of sea level is the way in which we have to measure it. We can not measure its distance from the center of the Earth. What we have to measure is its vertical position *relative to the land* along the coast. Sea level, therefore, is not a fixed or absolute level but a relative one. Hence,

when readings on harbor tide gages tell us that during the last several decades "sea level has been rising," we have to realize that perhaps the land where the gages are located has been sinking.

Change of sea level, then, can have more than one cause. Some of the possible causes are these:

1. Rise or fall of world sea level by net addition or subtraction of water, as glaciers decrease or increase with change of climate
2. Subsidence or uplift of the land along a coast (Chap. 18)
3. Subsidence or uplift of part of the sea floor; this would alter the form of an ocean basin, hence the level of the water in it

There are other possible causes, but these are enough to indicate that sea level is by no means fixed. Beaches many hundreds of feet above sea level on the coast of California are believed to be in large part the result of uplifts of the coast because they are not horizontal. On the other hand, a shoreline, now 20 to 25 feet above present sea level, extends over hundreds of miles along the south Atlantic coast of the United States. Since it maintains that vertical position throughout that distance, it is thought to record a fall of world sea level without movement of the coast.

Topography of the sea floor

Echo sounding. Contrary to the belief that was general a generation ago, the sea floor is by no means smooth. At first, most soundings were made laboriously by lowering weighted wires to the bottom. These soundings were so few and so widely spaced that they gave little idea of topographic details. The disastrous sinking of the liner *Titanic*, which struck an iceberg in the Atlantic in 1912, led to the development of a device for detecting icebergs by the use of sound-wave echoes: this was soon adapted for sounding the sea floor as well and has become the standard basis for mapping the topography of the sea floor. A transmitter in the ship's hull emits sound waves that reach the bottom and, reflected as an echo, are picked up by a microphone in the hull of the same ship (Fig. 15–1). The elapsed time between transmission and reception is measured accurately, and depth is computed as follows: $d = \frac{1}{2} t \times v$, where d = depth, t = round-trip travel time, and v = velocity of sound in sea water (about 4,800 feet per second, subject to corrections for variations in temperature and salinity).

If, at a particular place, $t = 6$ seconds by measurement, then $d = \%_2 \times 4,800 = 3 \times 4,800 = 14,400 =$ depth of sea in feet. This computation is performed automatically on the ship by an instrument that prints a continuous profile of the sea floor along the line of course of the ship (Fig. 15–2, **A**). The ship's geographic position, meanwhile, is continuously determined by the travel time of radio waves sent to the ship from shore stations at known points. Hence each point on the sea floor can be plotted accurately, and a series of crisscrossing profiles can be used to make a map of the bottom (Fig. 15–2, **B**).

Echo-sounding equipment is not confined to surveying ships but is widely used on commercial ships, not only to detect shallow water but also to determine their positions in thick weather. Parts of the sea floor are now mapped so accurately that a ship can take a profile such as that in Figure 15–2, fit it to a map of the sea floor, and thus determine her position.

Major features. Having seen the way in which submarine topography is determined, we can now examine the topographic features themselves. Not only is the sea floor as a whole by no means smooth, it is just about as diversified as the topography of the land. Long mountain chains, isolated hills and mountains, including volcanic cones, broad featureless plains, great escarpments, deep basins, and canyons mark the ocean floor just as they mark the land. Figure 15–3 is an artist's conception of a bit of the Pacific Ocean floor, minus the ocean. In Figure 15–4 we have a deep-sea basin and a continent shown in true profile and on the same scale. Comparing them, we can see that there is not much to choose between them as far as size and number of hills, valleys, and other topographic features are concerned. Figure 15–5 shows part of the Atlantic Ocean floor, the topography of which is relatively well known. It is worth comparing with Figure 15–4, which, however, represents a line farther south.

What are the individual topographic features of the sea floor? Here are some of the more important ones:

Continental shelf (Figs. 15–5, 15–6, 15–15). *The nearly flat submerged border of a continental mass.*

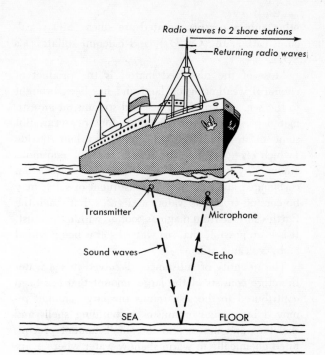

Fig. 15–1. Echo-sounding technique for measuring distance to sea floor.

Fig. 15–2. A. A strip of sea-floor profile, automatically made from continuous echo soundings and printed photographically aboard ship. Horizontal lines show depths in fathoms (1 fathom=6 feet) and are spaced at 100-fathom intervals; vertical lines separate 6-minute intervals of time. Pencil jotting shows most of profile was made between 10 and 11 A. M. (on a day in 1947 by the survey ship Pathfinder, cruising ESE at approximately 15 statute mph). Horizontal distance was calculated from ship's speed; the 5 nautical miles shown are equivalent to about 6 statute miles. The feature shown is a truncated cone, almost certainly volcanic. Its top is at Lat. 52° 34' N., Long. 151° 19' W., about 550 statute miles southwest of Seward, Alaska, and is 857 fathoms (5,142 feet) below sea level. The sea floor at its base (not shown) is at 14,700 feet, hence the cone is 9,600 feet high. B. Contour map of sea floor beneath part of Gulf of Alaska, made from echo-sounding profiles, showing conical mountains. Arrow points to truncated cone shown in profile in A. Depths shown are expressed in feet. (After H. W. Menard and R. S. Dietz, 1951: Geol. Soc. America Bull., vol. 62, p. 1264)

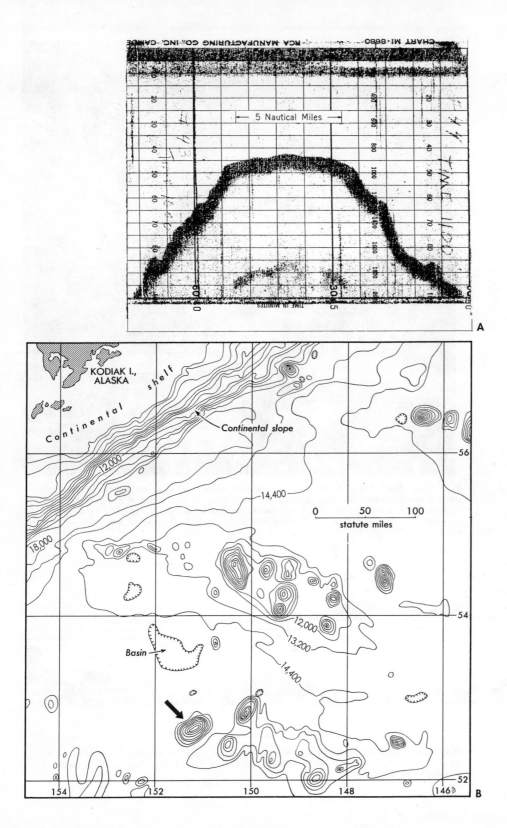

Fig. 15–3. Part of the ocean floor in the mid-Pacific, as it would appear if the water were drained away. The two flat-topped mountains in the distance are guyots. In the foreground is a valley cut into a seamount, the top of which is out of view behind the observer. (From a painting by Chesley Bonestell, in E. L. Hamilton, Geol. Soc. America Mem. 64. 1959, pl. 1.)

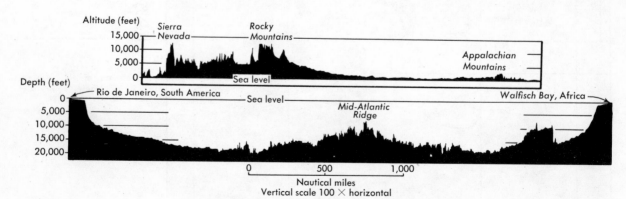

Fig. 15–4. Accurate profiles show that the topography of the Atlantic Ocean basin is fully as rugged as the surface of North America. (Modified from F. P. Shepard, 1948, Submarine geology: New York, Harper, p. 282.)

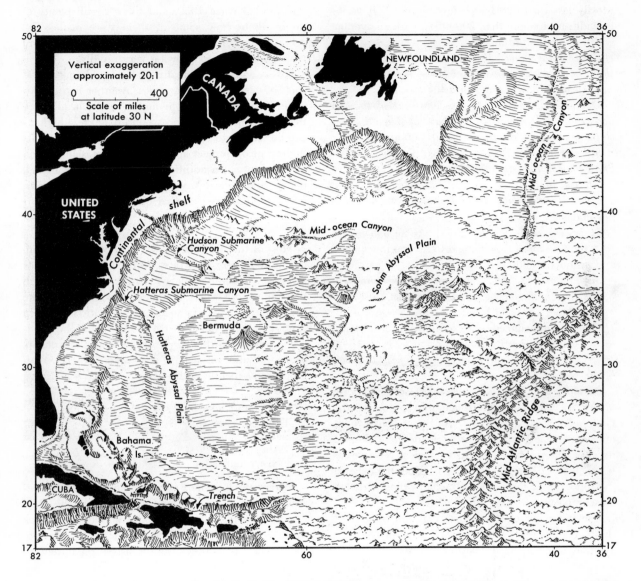

Fig. 15—5. Sketch diagram showing some of the topographic features of the western part of the North Atlantic Ocean basin. (Simplified from Heezen and others, 1959, The floors of the oceans, I: Geol. Soc. America Special Paper 65, pl. 1.)

Mostly less than 600 feet below sea level. It varies in width up to more than 200 miles, with an average width of around 40 miles.

Continental slope (Fig. 15–6). *The pronounced slope beyond the seaward margin of the continental shelf,* leading down into deep water.

Deep-sea floor (Fig. 15–5). *The part of the sea floor that lies seaward of the base of a continental slope.* Its average depth is around 14,000 feet.

Submarine canyon (Fig. 15–15). *A deep, canyon-like valley in a continental slope.*

Abyssal plain (Fig. 15–5). *A large flat area of the deep-sea floor having slopes less than about 5 feet per mile.*

Mid-ocean canyon (Fig. 15–5). *A long valley-like feature in an abyssal plain,* one to several miles wide and as much as 600 feet deep.

Seamount (Fig. 15–2). *An isolated hill, more than 3,000 feet high, on the deep-sea floor.* Most sea-mounts have a conical form.

Guyot (pronounced ghee-o; named for a nine-teenth-century scientist of Swiss origin) (Figs. 15–2, 15–3). *A seamount with a conspicuously flat top well below sea level.*

Sea-floor trench. A long, narrow, very deep basin in the sea floor. Although trenches are present in the Caribbean Sea (Fig. 15–5), the most conspicuous ones are in the Pacific Ocean, most of them close to its coasts. Some trenches are geologically active, as we shall see in Chapter 21. This list does not exhaust the topographic forms, but it includes those that are most important for our purpose.

Looking more closely at the diagram of part of the North Atlantic Ocean floor (Fig. 15–5), we can see how some of these features are related to each other. Many of the features have been discovered and plotted since 1950, and there is still plenty of doubt about how some of them were made. The ocean floor is a vast frontier of research, an area in which knowledge is growing very rapidly.

A very conspicuous feature is the broad continental shelf of eastern North America. Another is the Mid-Atlantic Ridge, a rocky mountain chain in all more than 7,000 miles long and around 6,000 feet high, as can be seen in the profile in Figure 15–4. Some of its highest peaks project above sea level as islands, such as the Azores. In addition, there are visible abyssal plains, mid-ocean canyons, and submarine canyons, which are discussed farther on.

Movements of sea water

Most of the water in the sea is in constant motion, generally at very slow rates, to be sure, yet in places at velocities comparable with swift rivers. Although the immediate causes of motion vary, basically the chief motive power is solar energy, with some help from the energy of the Earth's rotation and the gravitative pull of Earth, Moon, and Sun. Motion consists of several kinds of currents and waves, which we can group conveniently in this way:

Waves and longshore currents Tidal currents	geologically important chiefly along coasts
Surface ocean currents Density currents	

Waves and longshore currents. These are the movements most easily seen and are probably the chief agents by which the sea erodes and deposits rock material. So widespread and distinctive is their geologic work that they are discussed separately in Chapter 16.

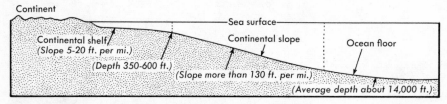

Fig. 15–6. Profile seaward from a continent, showing continental shelf, continental slope, and part of ocean floor.

Tidal currents. Tides are caused by the movement around the Earth, as it rotates, of two bulges, each a few feet in height, in the surface of the sea. One bulge faces the Moon; the other is on the opposite side of the Earth. The bulge facing the Moon (Fig. 15–7) is caused by piling-up of water by direct gravitational attraction of the Moon for masses in the Earth. The attraction is greatest at **A**, less at **E**, and still less at **B** (see Newton's law, p. 405). As **E** is attracted toward the Moon more than is **B**, pulling away from **B** and, as it were, leaving it behind, there is created at **B** a second bulge almost as great as the one at **A**. The two bulges represent high tide, and, as the Earth rotates once a day, each point on the sea surface normally experiences high tide twice a day.[1] When Earth, Moon, and Sun are in general alignment, tides have their maximum range (spring tides); when the Earth-Sun line is at right angles to the Earth-Moon line, the range from high tide to low is smallest (neap tides). Despite its tremendous mass, the Sun is so far distant from the Earth that its tide-raising force is less than half that of the small but nearby Moon.

Tidal currents—currents set up by the rise and fall of the tide—become important in moving sediment only in narrow bays and in straits between islands and mainlands, where narrowness results in unusual rates of flow. Velocities up to 14 mph have been measured in very narrow places, and, at the heads of long funnel-shaped bays, high-tide water piles up to more than 50 feet above low-tide level. Such currents erode the sea floor and transport sediment at depths as great as 1,200 feet.

So-called "tidal waves" are caused not by tides but

[1] Some odd local exceptions are caused apparently by the sizes and shapes of the ocean floors.

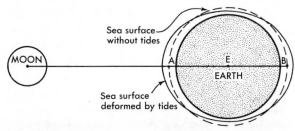

Fig. 15–7. Theory of tides, considering only the Moon's attraction and neglecting the Sun. Distance between Earth and Moon greatly shortened; thickness of sea much exaggerated.

by earthquakes. Their proper name is seismic sea waves (p. 403).

Surface ocean currents. Compared with tidal currents along coasts, *surface ocean currents* are *very broad, slow drifts of surface water.* They are set in motion by prevailing surface winds. The air flowing over a water surface drags the water slowly forward, creating a current as broad as the current of air but rarely more than 200 or 300 feet deep. The effect of winds on the ocean is evident when we compare a map of surface ocean currents (Fig. 15–8) with the positions of the belts of prevailing winds (Fig. 7–11). In low latitudes surface sea water moves westward with the trade winds; in higher latitudes it moves eastward with the westerlies. In each ocean this movement becomes a movement of rotation. Rotation is caused partly by deflection, where a current encounters a coast, and partly by the tendency of horizontally moving objects to be deflected to the right in the Northern Hemisphere and to the left in the Southern (p. 122).

In the northern Atlantic, then, the North Equatorial current flows west. Deflected water is represented by the Florida current, the Gulf Stream, and the North Atlantic current. Being warm, the water transfers heat to higher latitudes and therefore has a considerable effect on climates. Part of the North Atlantic current moves into the Arctic Ocean, taking heat with it, and part is deflected south along the European-African coast as the Canaries current. This water has by then lost so much heat that it is cooler than the surrounding tropical water. Approaching the equator, it has completed its circulation and once more begins to be dragged westward by the trade winds.

We can follow a similar pattern in the northern Pacific Ocean, where we have this sequence: North Equatorial current, Kuroshio current, North Pacific current, and the cool California current. The surface ocean waters, then, slowly shuttle between two belts of winds.

Although rates of movement are generally slow, in a narrow, confined area they are faster. In the strait between Florida and Cuba the rate approaches 3 mph.

Density currents and deep-sea circulation. While the great currents set up by the winds are moving

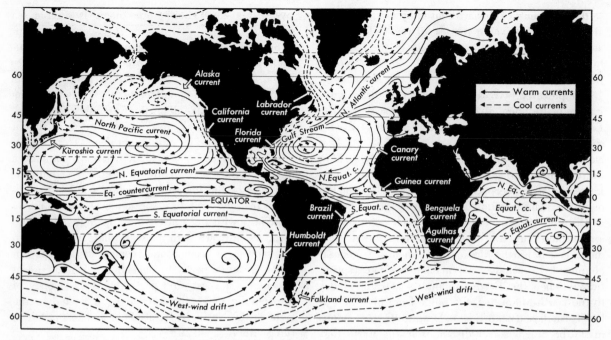

Fig. 15–8. The surface currents of the ocean form a distinctive pattern, curving to the right in the Northern Hemisphere and to the left in the Southern. (Modified from a map by U. S. Navy Hydrographic Office.)

slowly through a shallow surface zone, a deeper circulation of water is occurring, set up by differences in density. The density of sea water increases as the water gets colder and also as it becomes more saline. Dense water tends to sink, displacing less-dense water below.

The surface water in the polar seas becomes chilled while in contact with the atmosphere. As it grows denser, it tends to sink and slides slowly along the ocean floor into the tropics and even into the opposite hemisphere.

In contrast to polar water, which sinks mainly because it is cold, water in the Mediterranean Sea sinks mainly because it is very saline. The warm, nearly inclosed Mediterranean evaporates at such a rate that its surface water becomes saline and therefore denser; consequently, it tends to sink. The dense, saline water meets the less dense water of the Atlantic at the Strait of Gibraltar, where a rocky sill or threshold separates the two basins. Mediterranean water flows across the sill as a density current and down into the Atlantic, where it spreads out and

mixes with the water surrounding it. In the Strait of Gibraltar, above the west-flowing density current, less-dense Atlantic water flows eastward into the Mediterranean to compensate for the loss and to keep the levels of the two seas in equilibrium. So, because of differences in density between two great water bodies, the Strait of Gibraltar carries two currents, one above the other, flowing in opposite directions.

Turbidity currents. We can define a *turbidity current* as *a body of muddy water which, because of its high density, flows along the bottom of a body of standing water.* It is a special kind of density current that owes its condition to suspended mud rather than to low temperature or to high salinity. Despite the fact that no one has yet actually seen a turbidity current in the sea, we believe such currents occur. We believe also that they are and have been important in depositing sediments on the ocean floor and probably also as agents of submarine erosion. We can discuss them more profitably in a later section, after we have learned something about the nature and distribution of marine sediments. In summary, a *density* *current* is a localized current within a body of water; it consists of water denser than the water through which it moves.

Sediments on the sea floor

Sampling of sediments. Systematic study of the carpet of sediment that mantles the sea floor dates from 1872 to 1876, when the British scientific ship *Challenger*, on a history-making cruise, collected a vast number of samples at carefully chosen positions. So long and thorough was the resulting study, directed by Sir John Murray, that the published reports were not completed until 1894. Most of the samples were obtained by dredges dragged along the bottom or by small clamshell buckets that take a bite of sediment and then snap shut.

Since the classic cruise of the *Challenger*, other expeditions of various nationalities have added greatly to the take of samples. The most valuable modern improvement in sampling is the coring device, a long metal tube, let down on a cable, that can be forced into the sea floor by one of several mechanisms. The tube closes and brings up a core sample in which all except the topmost layers of sediment are undisturbed. Cores as much as 70 feet long have been obtained.

Kinds and distribution of sediment. Minute analyses of the samples have made it possible to sort out the various sources from which the sea-floor sediment is derived. There are four general sources, listed in Table 15–1—one on land, two in the sea, and one outside the Earth.

Note that Table 15–1 shows sources, not the sediments themselves. This is because study of great numbers of samples indicates clearly that all the sediments are mixtures; no one body of sediment comes entirely from a single source. Therefore, we have to classify the sediments according to their chief constituents, the predominant kind of material they contain. Four principal kinds are described in Table 15–2, but we must remember that these are mixtures and grade from one to another. Figure 15–11 is a map on which the distribution of the four kinds of sediment is shown. The scale of the map is so small that the sediment areas are greatly generalized. If we compare what it shows in the western North Atlantic with the more detailed topography in Figure 15–5,

Table 15–1. Origins of sediment on the sea floor

1. *Terrigenous sediment* (Lat. "derived from the lands"). Sea-floor sediment derived from sources on land. Contributed by (a) rivers, (b) erosion of coasts by waves, (c) wind (clay and silt, including volcanic ash), (d) floating ice.

2. *Pelagic sediment* (Gr. "belonging to the deep sea"). Sediment, on the deep-sea floor, consisting of material of marine organic origin. Shells and skeletons, mostly microscopic, of marine animals and plants.

3. Sediment derived from submarine volcanoes. Volcanic ash.

4. Extraterrestrial sediment (derived from outside the Earth). Meteorite particles, mostly microscopic.

Table 15–2. Classification of kinds of sediment on the sea floor

1. Terrigenous sediment
   Mainly on the continental shelves, continental slopes, and abyssal plains. Mud, sand, and gravel, varying greatly from place to place.

2. Red clay (also called pelagic clay) (Fig. 15–9, **A**)
   Confined to the deep-sea floor, mostly in high latitudes or at depths greater than 13,000 feet. Contains, by definition, less than 30 per cent calcium carbonate. Chief constituents are clay minerals, quartz, and micas. Since these are the sorts occurring in weathered soils, volcanic ash, and fine wind-blown material, they are thought to come from such sources. The clay is red or brown as a result of gradual oxidation during the very slow process of deposition.

3. Calcareous ooze (Fig. 15–9, **B**; 15–10)
   Contains, by definition, more than 30 per cent calcium carbonate, most of it consisting of shells and skeletons. Confined to regions in which surface waters are warm and surface organisms exist in myriads; the resulting shells, falling like snow, accumulate on the bottom more rapidly than the inorganic clay. Because it contains much carbon dioxide, deep-sea water dissolves calcium carbonate. As the shells drift slowly down, they are gradually dissolved, but only at depths of more than 16,000 feet are they completely consumed. Hence calcareous ooze rarely occurs at such depths.

4. Siliceous ooze
   Contains a large percentage of skeletons built of silica. Occurs where organisms with calcareous shells are few in the surface waters and in areas in which such shells are destroyed by solution before they reach the sea floor.

Fig. 15—9. Sediments from the deep-sea floor. **A.** Red clay from the floor of the Pacific Ocean, 900 miles west of Mexico. The sample came from 5.5 feet beneath the floor, at a depth of more than 14,000 feet. This electron-microscope photograph shows crystals and fragments of various minerals, mostly clay minerals, about 10,500 times natural size (compare Fig. 3—4) **B.** Calcareous ooze from a depth of 2,900 feet on the floor of the Caribbean Sea.

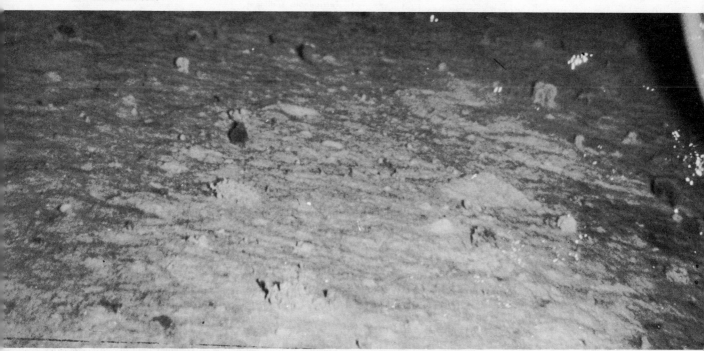

Fig. 15—10. Five square yards of sea floor at the equator, about 3,000 miles west of the Panama Canal, at a depth of nearly 15,000 feet. Calcareous ooze covers the floor, on which are various kinds of invertebrate animals. (C. J. Shipek, U. S. Navy Electronics Laboratory.)

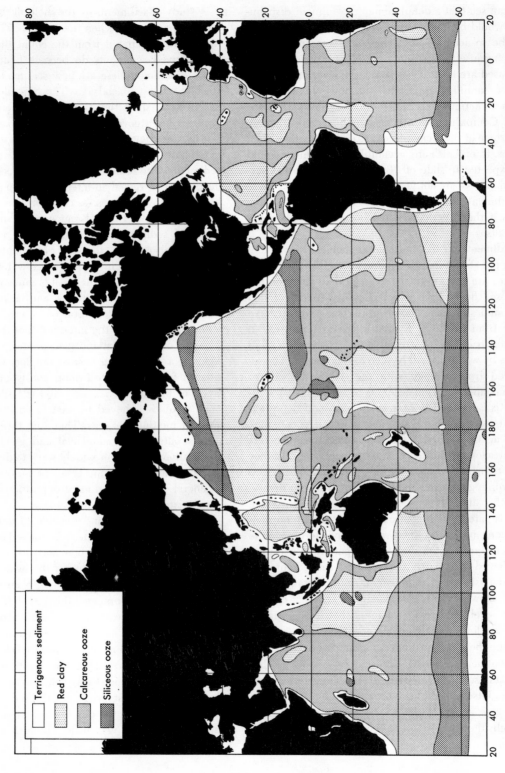

Fig. 15–11. Distribution of the four chief kinds of sediment on the sea floor. The map is much generalized and does not show detail. Note how the terrigenous sediment fringes the lands.

Terrigenous sediment

Red clay

Calcareous ooze

Siliceous ooze

293

we can see that a detailed map of sediment distribution would be much more complex. Even so, it could not be so accurate as a map of a comparable land area because the sediment samples on which it must be based are taken from points quite far apart.

The sampling apparatus put down by exploring ships sometimes hits not sediments but bare, hard rock. Comparison with echo-sounding records shows that some of the rocky places are cliffs and other steep slopes, from which any accumulating sediment would be expected to slide off. But still others are flat surfaces, and we are not yet sure why they have no cover of sediment. Some such surfaces might be recent lava flows. Others, perhaps, have been scoured bare by currents.

Sediments on the continental shelves. Much sampling has shown that the sediments on the continental shelves are coarser on the average than those on the deep-sea floor. This is because they include much sand and silt, and a large proportion of them have come from the land. Evidently the material was in part contributed by streams and in part worn from coasts by waves, as will be seen in Chapter 16. Theory derived from analogy with the sediment loads of streams and the wind leads us to suppose that sediment is carried offshore in suspension and deposited in water too deep for waves and shore currents to pick it up again. Theory suggests also that the diameters of particles should decrease with increasing distance from the shore.

Sampling on some shelf areas confirms the theory. On other areas, however, the distribution of particle sizes is patchy, with coarse sediments, which normally belong near shore, occurring far offshore near the seaward limits of the shelves. The patchy distribution is believed to be partly the work of localized currents that deposit coarse sediments at some distance from shore. However, it is also partly the result of change of sea level. When we remember that during glacial ages sea level was lowered repeatedly, we can see that the shoreline must have migrated seaward across the continental shelves, exposing new land. Patches of coarse sediment, deposited near shore or even on the land itself, could have been submerged as the sea level rose again. If the water over them was deep enough, the coarse material could not be picked up and moved.

A study of sediments on the shelf off the California coast indicates that when the "maverick" coarse sediments are eliminated from the count the remaining land-derived sediments do become finer in the offshore direction. These are new sediments, deposited since the latest glacial age. The time since that age has been so short that the new sediments have not yet completely covered the patches of coarse material, but in time they can be expected to do so.

Climate and chronology indicated by deep-sea sediments. The sediments recovered in cores from the deep-sea floor reveal an interesting record of changes in the Earth's climates. A common characteristic of many cores from tropical regions is an alternation of layers of sediment of two kinds. One is calcareous ooze, which contains the shells of minute organisms that today live only in warm surface water. The other is red clay, which contains fossil organisms that today live in higher, cooler latitudes, and lacks the warm-water kinds. The alternation of "warm" and "cool" sediments has led to the inference that the layers are a record of nonglacial and glacial ages, respectively. Again, cores taken right across the floor of the North Atlantic from Canada to Britain, consist of alternating layers of (1) calcareous ooze, and (2) silt, sand, and small pebbles believed to have been dumped from hosts of melting icebergs. Therefore these cores also suggest alternating nonglacial and glacial ages. So many other cores from widely separated parts of the sea floor have alternating layers of various kinds that a general control of sediment deposition by fluctuating climates seems very probable.

It has also been found possible to determine the dates of at least the higher, younger layers by the measurement of radiocarbon and other radioactive isotopes contained in them. In this way, the beginning of a chronologic record has been established. With further development, this research will enable us to determine the rates at which various kinds of deep-sea sediment have accumulated by measuring the thickness of sediment between two closely spaced points along a core. Thus the sea-floor sediments should become a remarkably valuable record of a late part of geologic history. As for the sedimentary layers that lie beneath the depth penetrated by the core samplers, we know very little. The little we do know comes mainly from the evidence of seismic waves that traverse the crust beneath the sea floor. Although this evidence has been interpreted in more than one way, one possible interpretation is that sediments comparable with those in the cores are thousands of feet thick and are being gradually compacted, as one stage in their conversion to sedimentary rock, under the weight of the overlying sediments.

Special features and problems

Some of the features of oceanic topography and sediments do not fit neatly into the foregoing discussion, partly because some of them involve *both* topography and sediments and partly because knowledge of some of them is very incomplete. So we discuss them here, pointing out again as we have done earlier, that we are only part way along the road to more complete understanding of the Earth.

Continental shelves. Among these special features, continental shelves have great importance in geology because they contain a record of what happens at the margins of continents. A good example is the shelf off the coast of the Carolinas because it has been more fully studied than most.

A section (Fig. 15–12) running southeast from Raleigh, North Carolina, to the toe of the continental slope passes close to three holes drilled for oil. The detailed records of the drill holes, supplemented by geophysical exploration, show the nature of the shelf, which in that latitude is rather narrow. The body of

the shelf consists of a wedge of sedimentary rocks, almost 2 miles thick near the continental slope and thinning landward, overlying a sloping floor of very old crystalline rocks. Examination of the kinds of sediments and fossils in the drill cuttings shows that this great wedge consists mainly of marine sediments, evidently deposited in the comparatively shallow water of the shelf. As the sediments now lie as much as several thousand feet below sea level, yet are of shallow-water origin, they must have sunk below their original positions. The sediments are in various stages of transformation into rock, some of which is more than 70 million years old. Sections like this one suggest that through long periods of time the margins of continents have been receiving sediment from the land and have been gradually subsiding.

Not all the shelves are like this example, but we can not hope to understand the differences until after a vast amount of additional study has been carried out.

Some of the sedimentary rocks beneath the shelves contain large amounts of oil and gas—the so-called offshore oil resources—which are now being exploited along the Gulf Coast of the United States.

Nature of turbidity currents. Among the fascinating problems of sea-floor geology are how relatively coarse sediments can be deposited at depths of 13,000 to 15,000 feet, how abyssal plains are created, and how continental slopes are eroded. The solution of

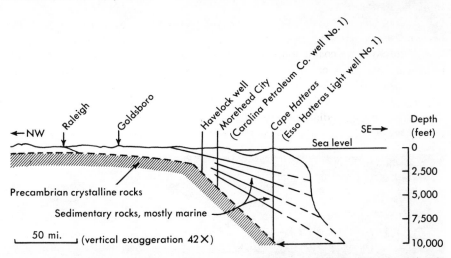

Fig. 15–12. Section through coastal North Carolina and continental shelf, showing subsurface conditions. (Adapted from W. F. Prouty, 1946, Amer. Assoc. Petrol. Geologists Bull., vol. 30, p. 1918; B. C. Heezen and others, 1959, Geol. Soc. America Special Paper 65, p. 47.)

these problems seems to lie, at least in part, in turbidity currents, which we defined in an earlier section. A closer look at these currents will be worth while.

In 1935, soon after Hoover Dam had been completed, engineers were surprised to find that the clear water discharging through the lowest outlet pipes (just below the 1935 water level of Lake Mead, Fig. 12–1) became muddy for short periods. At the same time researchers at California Institute of Technology were pouring into a water-filled tank streams of water containing either dissolved salts or suspended silt and clay to make it denser than ordinary water. They found that the dense water, with kinetic energy acquired by flowing down the front of a delta, possessed enough inertia to travel along the bottom, on an extremely small slope, past the clear water above (Fig. 15–13). Energy not expended in friction en route even enabled the current to climb part way up the face of a dam at the far end of the tank. The current had distinct boundaries, like a cloud of dust; in fact, someone described it as "a dust storm under water." Indeed, it is essentially the same thing, mechanically, as a dust storm and as a nuée ardente.

It was realized that such a current, climbing part way up Hoover Dam, could explain the muddy water discharging through pipes situated nearly 200 feet above the bottom of Lake Mead. Observations in this and other reservoirs confirmed that the suspended loads of rivers were the source of the currents of turbid, dense water, which were then named turbidity currents.

As a result of more laboratory experiments, it was learned that turbidity currents could perform a surprising amount of erosion. The densities of natural turbidity currents on gently inclined lake floors are rarely as great as 1.02, and their velocities are less than one foot per second. But greater densities and velocities have been produced in the laboratory, and a submarine turbidity current, flowing down a continental slope with an inclination of 200 feet per mile, should develop a velocity greater than that of the swiftest streams on the land. In theory, a current with a density of 1.5, moving at about one mile per hour, could move a rock particle 14,000 times the diameter of the largest particle that can be moved by clear water at the same velocity.

Turbidity current on a continental slope. Turbidity currents, then, have been observed in lakes, can be created in the laboratory, and, according to theory, have enormous potential for the transport of sediment. But do they occur in the sea? In 1952 re-examination of the record of an old earthquake suggested strongly that they do.

On November 18, 1929, a severe earthquake occurring on the continental slope off Nova Scotia broke 13 transatlantic cables in 28 places. At the time it was supposed that the breaks were the direct result of faulting of the sea floor, the usual cause of sub-

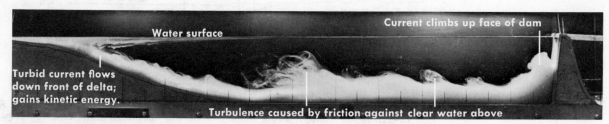

Fig. 15–13. Turbidity current seen through glass wall of water-filled laboratory tank. (U. S. Soil Conservation Service, California Institute of Technology.)

marine earthquakes. But there were two odd things about these breaks. Although all the cables on the continental slope and deep-sea floor were broken, not one of the many cables crossing the continental shelf was damaged. The breaks occurred in sequence, in order of increasing depth, over a period of 13 hours and a distance of 300 miles from the earthquake center. Repair ships found that each cable had been broken at two or three points more than 100 miles apart. The detached cable segments, between the breaks, had been carried part way down the continental slope or buried beneath sediment beyond the bottom of the slope.

The whole event was like a huge laboratory experiment with times and distances controlled by measurement. Each break was timed by the machines that automatically record cable messages transmitted and was accurately located after the quake by the electric resistance measurements always made to enable ships to locate breaks and repair damage.

The only hypothesis yet formulated to explain all of these facts is that the quake set off great submarine slides on the continental slope; these quickly became turbidity currents, which flowed down the continental slope, breaking each cable as they came to it. Eight cables on the slope were broken instantaneously at the moment the quake occurred, and five others were broken at times ranging from 59 minutes to 13 hours, 17 minutes after the instant of the quake (Fig. 15–

14). The area affected was about 200 miles wide and at least 400 miles long.

From the times of the breaks and the distances between them the velocities of the inferred turbidity currents could be calculated. Velocities ranged from 58 mph at the toe of the continental slope down to 14 mph at the latest and farthest break. Even at the latter point the velocity was four times and the slope 600 times that of the lower Mississippi River.

A velocity of 58 mph may seem high, but it is small compared with that of the nuée ardente from Mt. Pelée, likewise a turbidity current (of air), which flowed downslope at 350 mph.

Theoretical calculations suggest that near the earthquake area velocities may have approached 90 mph, and the thickness of the turbidity current may have reached 900 feet. As the currents lost energy, the sediment eroded from the continental slope was dropped onto the ocean floor, burying some of the long, broken pieces of cable beneath deposits of "sand and small pebbles," the bottom sediment reported by the repair ships. Two core samples collected from the sea floor, downslope from the cable breaks, show that the floor is blanketed with a layer of silt and muddy sand in the form of a graded bed (Fig. 17–8). In one core the layer is 28 inches thick; in the other it is 51 inches.

A graded bed is the result of rapid, continuous loss of energy in the transporting agent. This would

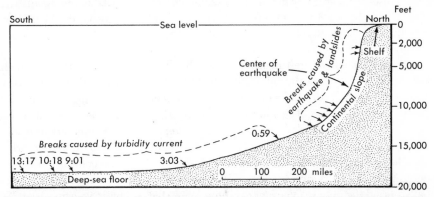

Fig. 15–14. Profile of sea floor off Nova Scotia, showing events of the earthquake of November 18, 1929. Short arrows show locations of breaks in transatlantic cables. Numbers show times of breaks in hours and minutes after earthquake. Vertical scale is exaggerated enormously. (After B. C. Heezen and M. Ewing, 1952, Am. Jour. Sci., vol. 250, p. 867.)

occur in a spent turbidity current, but it is not expectable in the other sorts of marine currents we have described.

So, although a turbidity current on the continental slope off Nova Scotia on November 18, 1929, is not proved, it is the only hypothesis that seems able to explain all the facts. The record shows that similar events have occurred at least twice at each of 40 localities around the world within the past 75 years. Some were related to earthquakes; others occurred off the mouths of large rivers, suggesting that the inferred turbidity currents were set off by stream floods. This evidence is impressive. It leads us to believe that turbidity currents are effective agents on continental slopes, despite the fact that no one has yet seen such a current in actual operation in the sea.

Origin of abyssal plains. If sediment is carried down a continental slope by turbidity currents, it should be deposited on the ocean floor beyond the slope. Several localized deposits of this kind have been found. They are fanlike in form and occur at the mouths of submarine canyons.

One, at a depth of 15,000 feet, beyond the mouth of Hudson Submarine Canyon southeast of New York City (Fig. 15–15), was cored in 1951. Fifteen cores, each 25 to 30 feet long, show that the deposit consists of layers of fine clay appropriate to the depth, alternating with layers of sand, silt, and broken shells arranged in graded beds and derived from the continental shelf above. This composition suggests strongly that the deposit was built up by repeated turbidity currents and that during long intervals between the turbid discharges ordinary fine-grained sediments settled out on the sea floor. Several similar fans, one of which has a radius of 200 miles, occur at the mouths of submarine canyons off the coast of California.

Far more extensive are the sediments of the abyssal plains. The Sohm Abyssal Plain, shown in Fig. 15–5, has been cored. Mud in graded beds has been identified in the cores. The mud is far coarser than are the oozes and red clay common at great depth. This, and the extremely gentle slope of the plain, have led to the hypothesis that abyssal plains are the deposits of spent turbidity currents, which have gradually buried the hilly sea-floor topography, somewhat as a river makes a valley fill by depositing alluvium. It has even been proposed that the mid-ocean can-

yons, such as the two shown in Figure 15–5, are likewise the work of turbidity currents, but so little is known about the canyons that their origin remains uncertain. We can note, however, that the mid-ocean canyon, part of which appears in the northeast corner of Figure 15–5, is at least 1,200 miles long.

Origin of submarine canyons. The enormous submarine canyons that indent the continental slopes of all continents are still among the great puzzles of geologic research. These huge valleys are cut into bedrock, which is blanketed in places by loose sediment. They have steep side slopes, lengths measured in tens of miles, narrow floors sloping seaward at as much as 400 feet per mile, depths of floor below rim of as much as one mile, and depths below sea level of as much as 2 miles. Some, such as the Hudson Submarine Canyon, appear to be seaward extensions of land rivers; others are not.

Some of these great canyons closely resemble big stream valleys and are thought to be the valleys of mountainous lands along coasts that subsequently subsided beneath the sea. Others differ from land valleys and occur off coasts where profound subsidence seems very improbable.

Many ideas have been advanced to explain these tremendous valleys. Among them are that the canyons were made (1) by rivers when sea level stood thousands of feet lower than today, (2) by tidal currents, seismic sea waves, or submarine artesian springs, and (3) by movements of the crust, such as faulting. All these ideas encounter difficulties, and again turbidity currents are urged by some geologists as the agents that cut the canyons. There is almost no doubt that such currents do repeatedly pass down the canyons as a stream flows through a land valley. What we do not know is whether a turbidity current can erode bedrock and, if so, how the erosion takes place. This is an unfinished story of research in progress. Some day, perhaps soon, the origin of the canyons will become clear.

Seamounts and guyots. Seamounts probably have several different origins, as do mountains on land. The conical form of many of them suggests that they are volcanic cones; indeed, they are identical in form with volcanic islands. Both seamounts and volcanic islands have been built up from the ocean floor, probably over a long period of time.

The seamounts called guyots, having the form of truncated cones, exist by the hundreds in the Pacific Ocean, and the flat tops of many lie 3,000 to 6,000 feet below sea level. One guyot which has been studied in detail has sediment on its flat top, thousands of feet below sea level. In the sediment are fossils of ancient shellfish of kinds that today live only in water less than 500 feet deep. This evidence suggests that the seamount once stood above sea level, that it was truncated by streams and by waves along its shores, and that later it subsided as part of a downward movement of the Earth's crust in this part of the Pacific. Guyots of this kind are among the oldest uneroded mountains known to geology. If they had stood on a continent, they would long ago have been reduced to base level.

Coral reefs. Related to the supposed history of guyots is that of many coral reefs, which abound in most of the world's equatorial seas. A *coral reef* is defined as *a ridge of limestone built by colonial marine organisms*. The name is an oversimplification because most reefs are built by many different organisms, of which coral polyps are only one kind. These animals and plants secrete calcium carbonate as limy skeletons outside their bodies. Each lives in its own tiny chamber like a cliff dweller in a city of stone. Living in colonies of millions of individuals, they combine to build a structure of great size. Because of temperature, light, and oxygen requirements of the organisms that inhabit them, reefs are built only

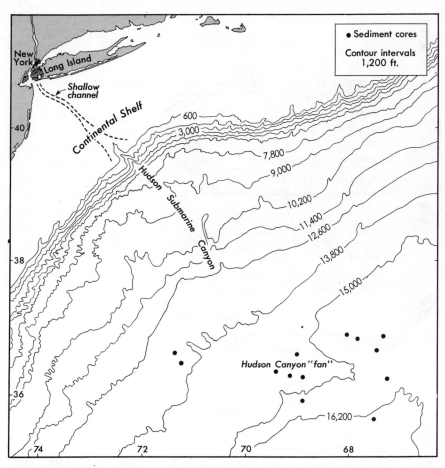

Fig. 15—15. Hudson Canyon, a typical submarine canyon, and Hudson Canyon "fan" represented by contour lines plotted from echo-sounding profiles. Circles indicate locations of core samples. The lateral extent of the "fan" is not known. (Modified from D. B. Ericson and others, 1952, Geol. Soc. America Bull., Vol. 62, p. 961.)

Fig. 15–16. Coral reef, at the end of an island, partly inclosing a lagoon. Waves are breaking on the reef. Tobago, British West Indies. (Henle from Monkmeyer.)

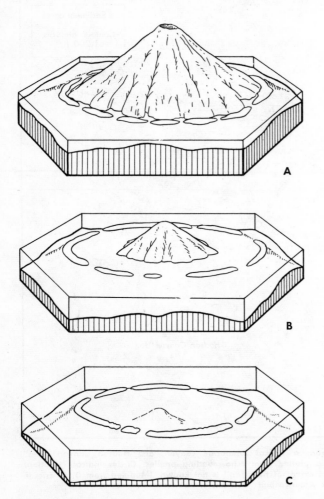

Fig. 15–17. Chief kinds of coral reefs. **A. Fringing reef.** A reef that is attached to the shore of a land mass. **B. Barrier reef.** A reef that lies offshore from a land mass. **C. Atoll.** A reef that forms a nearly closed figure within which there is no land mass.

at or close to sea level. Therefore, they occur along coasts, especially island coasts (Fig. 15–16) and can be classified into three kinds based on their relation to the land. The three kinds are defined in Figure 15–17.

From that figure it is not difficult to judge that if an island slowly subsided a fringing reef would grow upward, since the organisms can live only at or near sea level. In time this would produce a barrier reef inclosing a lagoon (p. 316). If subsidence exceeded the original height of the island, the island itself would disappear, leaving only the reef, now an atoll. This is believed to be the origin of many fringing reefs and atolls in the southwest Pacific, although rising sea level, related to glacial ages, may have played a part in some places. Like guyots, therefore, some reefs owe their origin to gradual subsidence of the Earth's crust.

SUMMARY

1. The economy of the sea is that of a lake without outlet. Its surface fluctuates inversely with the amount of glacier ice on the land. Sea level, relative to the land, changes also with movements of the Earth's crust.

2. Salts in the sea come almost wholly from the land and are a product of chemical weathering of rocks.

3. Topographic features of the sea floor include continental shelves and slopes, submarine and mid-ocean canyons, sea-floor trenches, abyssal plains, seamounts, and guyots.

4. Ocean waters are kept in motion, mostly very slow, by surface ocean currents driven by the winds, and by density currents.

5. Sea-floor sediments are derived from sources on land, in the sea, and outside the Earth.

6. The chief kinds of sea-floor sediments are terrigenous (relatively coarse), red clay, calcareous ooze, and siliceous ooze.

7. Both past climates and chronology can be reconstructed from core samples of sea-floor sediments.

8. At least some continental shelves consist of sediments derived from the adjacent lands.

9. Turbidity currents probably sweep down the continental slopes and deposit relatively coarse sediments at depth to form abyssal plains.

10. Some submarine canyons are probably sunken land valleys. Others were made beneath the sea, possibly by turbidity currents.

11. Most seamounts are probably volcanoes. Guyots and some coral reefs indicate subsidence of the crust beneath the sea floor.

REFERENCES

Emery, K. O., 1960, The sea off southern California. A modern habitat of petroleum: New York, John Wiley and Sons.

Hamilton, E. L., 1956, Sunken islands of the mid-Pacific mountains: Geol. Soc. America Mem. 64.

———, 1957, the last geographic frontier: the sea floor: Sci. Monthly, vol. 85, p. 294–314.

Heezen, B. C., and others, 1959, The floors of the oceans, I. The North Atlantic: Geol. Soc. America Special Paper 65.

Kuenen, Ph. H., 1950, Marine geology: New York, John Wiley and Sons.

Shepard, F. P., 1948, Submarine geology: New York, Harper & Brothers.

Sverdrup, H. V., Johnson, M. W., and Fleming, R. H., 1942, The oceans, their physics, chemistry, and general biology: New York, Prentice-Hall.

CHAPTER 16. WAVES, CURRENTS, AND THE SCULPTURE OF COASTS

Wave motion   Attack of waves on the shore   The shore profile   Beaches, bars, and other depositional shore features   Classification of coasts   Sculptural evolution of coasts

Hawaiian coast line. (Henle from Monkmeyer.)

Wave energy on the coast

No one who closely observes a stretch of shore for a few weeks and notes the changes that take place, particularly after storms, can fail to realize that erosion and deposition by the surf are continuous and are shaping the coast itself. The sculpture of coasts is mainly the work of waves and, in lesser degree, of shore currents. Most waves, in turn, are generated by winds. The water particles in a wave move in loop-like paths. But, as the wave approaches shore, the loop-like motion is transformed into forward movement of the whole mass of the wave as it dashes against cliff or beach, eroding rock and moving sediment. The successive transformations of the energy involved would look like this:

Solar energy → wind → loop-like wave motion →
     mass movement of water → erosion of shore

To be sure, this is a very inefficient application of the Sun's energy; yet the tiny fraction of the Earth's budget of solar energy that is applied in this way performs, over-all, a surprisingly large amount of work.

Wave motion

In shallow water, close to shore, a floating object is carried forward on the crests of breaking waves. This is what makes surfboard riding possible. But out at sea a floating object rises and falls with the passage of waves beneath it, yet moves forward only slightly. The difference is basic, for the water in a wave changes its motion when it nears the shore. The wave breaks; the water becomes turbulent[1] and is transformed into an active agent of erosion. It is

[1] This does not imply that in contrast the loop-like motion is streamline. It can not be streamline because it does not consist of *flow*.

worth while to look more closely at the two forms of wave motion.

Waves of oscillation in deep water. Figure 16–1 shows the significant features and dimensions of waves in deep water, where they are unaffected by the bottom. *The elapsed time between the arrivals of two successive crests at any point* is the **period** of the wave. Wave height, wave length, and period vary with wind velocity and with distance and time during which the wind blows. The many military landings on beaches during World War II necessitated detailed studies of waves, so that their height, length, and period as they approached a beach could be predicted. As an example, it can be calculated that a wind blowing at 30 miles per hour for 24 hours across an area of deep, open ocean 300 miles wide will create waves 15 feet high and 300 feet long, with a period of 7.5 seconds. As they move away from the storm area, the waves continually lose energy; this diminishes their height and increases their length and period. After traveling 2,000 miles, the approximate dimensions of the waves will be: height 2.5 feet; length 1,300 feet; period 16 seconds.

Velocity, which equals wave length divided by period, is easily computed, but it is not so significant as height in the study of the geologic work of waves. The nature of wave motion shows why this is so.

These waves, characteristic of deep water, are *waves of oscillation,* so called because they are *waves in which each particle of water oscillates over a short distance as the wave form itself moves forward.* The motion of the wave, therefore, is very different from the motion of the water particles within it. As the wind sweeps across a field of grain or tall grass, the individual stalks bend forward and then return to their positions (Fig. 16–2), producing a wave-

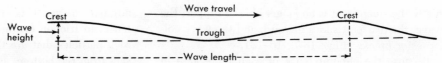

Fig. 16–1. Profile of waves in deep water.

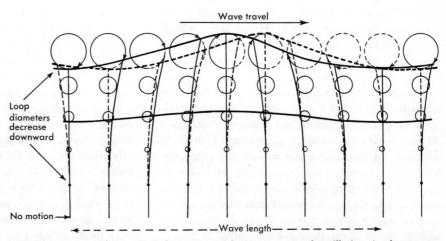

Fig. 16–2. Loop-like motion of water particles in a wave of oscillation, in deep water. To follow the successive positions of a water particle at the surface, follow the arrowheads in the largest loops from right to left. This is the same as watching the wave crest travel from left to right. Particles in smaller loops underneath have corresponding positions, marked by continuous, nearly vertical lines. Dashed lines represent wave form and particle positions one-eighth period later. Resemblance to grain stalks bending in the wind is now apparent. (After Ph. H. Kuenen, 1950, Marine geology: New York, John Wiley and Sons, p. 70.)

like effect. In water, similarly, the wave form moves continuously forward, but each water particle revolves in a loop, returning, as the wave passes, very nearly to its former position. This loop-like, or oscillating, motion of the water, first determined theoretically, was later proved by injecting droplets of colored water into waves in a glass tank and photographing their paths with a movie camera.

Because waves receive their energy from winds, they can receive it only at the water surface. Since the wave form is created by oscillating motion of water particles, the diameters of the loops at the water surface exactly equal wave height (Fig. 16–2). But there is progressive loss of energy (expressed in diminished diameters of the loops) downward from the water surface at which energy is received. The rate of energy decrease downward is very rapid; at a depth equal to only half the deep-water wave length, loop diameters are so small that motion is negligible.

Waves in shallow water. A depth equal to half the deep-water wave length is therefore the effective lower limit of wave motion. At that depth waves moving toward shore "feel bottom," and this slowly affects wave form. The loop-like paths of water particles gradually become elliptical, and velocities of the particles increase. As the wave moves into ever-shallower water, motion at the bottom becomes great enough to move fine rock particles back and forth. But the proportion of wave energy spent in this way is very small. As the wave moves forward, increasing interference of the bottom with its motion results in increased (often doubled) wave height and decreased wave length; in other words the wave becomes steeper. Since the front of the wave is in shallower water than the rear part, it is steeper than the rear. Eventually the steep front is no longer able to support the wave, the rear part slides forward, and the wave collapses or *breaks* (Figs. 16–3, 16–13).

Because the circumference of each large loop in Figure 16–2 is less than the wave length, the velocities of the water particles are less than the velocity of wave travel, as long as the waves are in deep water. But after wave motion has begun to "feel bottom," wave velocity gradually slows until it becomes less than water velocity in the loops. When this happens, the wave breaks because the greater velocity in the loops moves the surface water forward over the front of the wave.

Surf. As a wave breaks, its water suddenly becomes turbulent, and it ceases to be a wave of oscillation. It becomes a turbulent *wave of translation* because it has now become *a wave in which not only the wave form but the water as well is moving forward*. The "broken water," consisting of turbulent waves of translation, is called *surf*, defined as *wave activity between the line of breakers and the shore*.

In turbulent surf each wave finally dashes against rock or rushes up a sloping beach until its energy is expended. Then it flows back. Water piled against the shore returns seaward in an irregular and complex way, partly as a broad sheet along the bottom and partly in localized narrow channels. The returning water is mainly responsible for the currents known to surf bathers as "undertow."

When a wave breaks, it still possesses most of its original energy. This energy is consumed in turbulence, in friction on the bottom, and in moving the rock particles that are thrown violently into suspension from the bottom, as in a stream. Ceaselessly the sediment is shifted landward and seaward within the surf zone. Some of the finest particles are carried in suspension into deeper water, where they settle out on the bottom.

Most of the geologic work of waves, therefore, is accomplished by the surf, shoreward of the point where the waves break. How deep below sea level can the surf erode rocks and move sediment? Obviously this depends on the depth at which the waves are breaking at any time. According to their height and period, waves usually break at depths ranging roughly between wave height and 1.5 times wave height. Since waves approaching shore are rarely more than 20 feet high, the depth of vigorous erosion by surf should be limited theoretically to about 1.5×20 feet, or about 30 feet below mean sea level. The theoretical limit is confirmed by observation of breakwaters and other engineering structures, which are only rarely affected by surf at depths of more than 25 feet. The surf zone, the zone of turbulence, then, is the place where high-energy turbulent water cuts effectively into the land.

This does not mean that no geologic work at all is performed by waves of oscillation at greater depths. As we have noted, a small proportion of wave energy is available for shifting sediment on the bottom out-

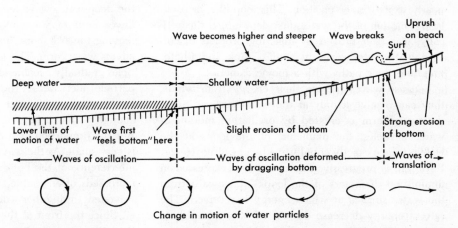

Change in motion of water particles

Fig. 16–3. Waves change form as they travel from deep water through shallow water to shore. Circles and ellipses are not drawn to scale with the waves shown above. (Compare Fig. 16–2).

Fig. 16–4. Bedrock forming coastal cliffs near San Francisco, California, is being eroded by hydraulic action along joints and to some extent by abrasion as well. (Henle from Monkmeyer.)

side the surf zone. Observation has shown that sediment is shifted by waves at much greater depths than 30 feet. Indeed, in the Pacific Ocean, waves as long as 2,000 feet are known. Since, as we have seen, waves begin to "feel bottom" at depths equal to half their lengths, these Pacific waves could begin to stir fine bottom sediment at a depth of 1,000 feet. Nevertheless, the lion's share of erosion is performed by the surf at depths of 30 feet or less.

Attack of waves on the shore

Hydraulic action. Even though energy transmitted by wind to waves is applied inefficiently to the shore, the results, in terms of erosion of the shore, are large. At Wick in northern Scotland, during a great storm, a solid mass of stone, iron, and concrete weighing 1,350 tons was ripped from the end of a breakwater and moved inshore. The damage was repaired with a block weighing 2,600 tons, but 5 years later storm waves broke off and moved that one too. The hydraulic pressure exerted by storm waves on the Wick breakwater, calculated from estimated wave heights and wave lengths, exceeded 3 tons per square foot. Actual pressures, measured by specially devised dynamometers, at places on the west coast of Scotland average ⅓ ton per square foot in summer and 1 ton in winter, with a maximum storm reading of 3 tons.

Such hydraulic pressures, applied directly, can and do break loose and move blocks of bedrock limited by joints and stratification surfaces much as a stream erodes its rocky channel by hydraulic plucking (Fig. 16–4). Hydraulic pressure also acts indirectly by

Fig. 16—5. These boulders and cobbles show the effect of abrasion in the surf. After having been torn from the bedrock, as in Figure 16—4, they have been tumbled and abraded. (Fujihira.)

violently compressing the air in rock fissures; the compressed air pushes out large blocks of rock. Finally, hydraulic pressure concentrated at one point, in a rock fragment or even a large piece of driftwood flung like a battering ram against a cliff, has been known to shatter firm rock.

The vertical distance through which water can be flung against the shore would surprise anyone whose experience of coasts is limited to periods of calm weather. During a winter storm in 1952, on the island of Hoy, 30 miles north of Wick, the bow half of a small steamship was thrown against a cliff and left there, wedged in a big crevice, 148 feet above sea level.

Abrasion. The wearing down of rock surfaces by wave-driven rock particles is erosion of another important kind. Wave abrasion is vigorous only when wave motion is felt strongly on the bottom, namely,

within the surf zone at depths of less than about 30 feet. There the waves actively move rock particles worn from the land by wave erosion as well as those contributed by streams. By continuous rubbing and grinding with these tools, the surf wears down and deepens the bottom and eats into the land, at the same time smoothing, rounding, and making smaller the tools themselves (Fig. 16—5).

The shallow surf zone, with a vertical thickness of no more than 30 feet, is therefore an erosional knife edge or saw, cutting horizontally into the land. Seaward beyond the surf zone, fine rock particles are moved and loose sediment is redistributed, but little erosion of bedrock takes place.

Movement of sediment. The rock particles worn from the land are being continually moved a little and dropped in new positions. They are dragged or rolled along the bottom, lifted in irregular jumps, or carried in suspension, according to their diameters and the varying energy of waves and currents. In the surf zone, as can be seen on almost any beach, sediments are moved to and fro, shoreward and seaward. But because the bottom slopes down in the seaward direction, the net effect is to carry rock particles derived from the land gradually out to sea.

Seaward of the surf zone, in deeper water, bottom sediments are shifted by unusually large waves during storms but are believed to be moved mainly by tidal and other currents, again with net movement seaward. Each particle is picked up again and again, whenever the energy level of waves or currents is high enough to move that particular diameter; but as the particle gets into ever deeper water it is picked up more and more rarely. The result of these movements is a general tendency to sort the sediments according to diameter, from coarse in the surf zone to finer offshore.

Wave refraction. A wave approaching a coast at an angle can not "feel bottom" along all parts of its crest simultaneously. As each part "feels bottom," wave length at that part begins to decrease and wave height increases. As a result the wave gradually swings around, part by part, toward parallelism with the bottom contours; it is said to be *refracted* (Figs. 16–6, 16–10). Thus waves approaching the shore in deep water at an angle of 40 or 50° may, after refraction, reach the shore at an angle of 5° or less. Waves coming in over a submerged ridge off a headland will converge on the headland. Convergence, plus the increased wave height that accompanies it, concentrates wave energy on the headland. Conversely, refraction of waves approaching a bay will make them diverge, diffusing their energy at the shore. Because of refraction, headlands are eroded more rapidly than are bays, so that in the course of time irregular coasts become smoother and less indented (Fig. 16–18).

In summary, *wave refraction* is *the process by which the direction of a series of waves, moving in shallow water at an angle to the shoreline, is changed.*

The shore profile

Elements of the shore profile. Seen in profile, the usual elements of a coast (Fig. 16–7) are a wave-cut cliff and wave-cut bench, both the work of erosion,

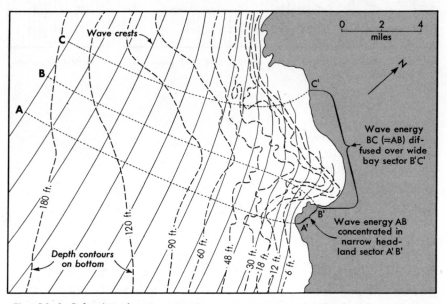

Fig. 16–6. Refraction of waves concentrates wave energy on headlands, diffuses it in bays. Contour lines on bottom show that shore profile (at right angles to contour lines and consisting of wave-cut bench and its patchy cover of beach) is smooth. Arena Cove, 100 miles north of San Francisco, California. (After Beach Erosion Board, U. S. Army Bulletin, Special Issue 2, 1953, p. A-46.)

309

and a beach and wave-built terrace, both the result of deposition.

The ***wave-cut cliff*** can be defined as *a coastal cliff cut by surf.* Acting like a horizontal saw, the surf cuts most actively at the base of the cliff. The upper part of the cliff is undermined and crumbles, furnishing rock particles to the surf. A cliff in which undercutting keeps well ahead of crumbling has a *notch* (Fig. 16–7) at its base. The notch is a concave part of the cliff profile, overhung by the part above. Other minor erosional features associated with cliffs are *sea caves, sea arches,* and *stacks* (Fig. 16–8). The cliff as a whole gradually retreats as the surf eats into the land.

The ***wave-cut bench*** is *a bench or platform cut across bedrock by surf.* It slopes gently seaward and grows wider in the landward direction as the cliff retreats. Some benches are bare or partly bare, but most are covered with sediment in gradual transit from shore to deeper water. This is the condition shown in Figure 16–7. At low tide the shoreward parts of some benches are exposed (Fig. 16–9). If the coast has been uplifted by movement of the Earth's crust, the bench can be wholly exposed (Fig. 16–10, 18–7). In some areas the bench is concealed and can be inferred only from maps constructed from soundings (Fig. 16–6).

The *beach* is thought of by most people as the sandy surface above water along a shore. Actually it is a much broader affair. We can define the ***beach*** as *the wave-washed sediment along a coast, extend-*

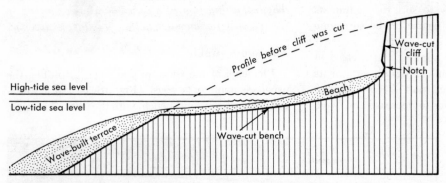

Fig. 16–7. Principal features of the shore profile. Not drawn to scale; vertical dimension exaggerated.

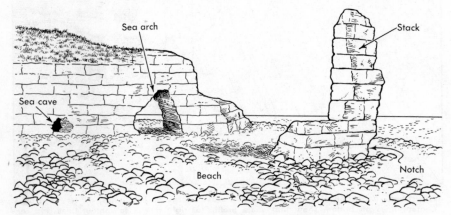

Fig. 16–8. Minor erosional features along coastal cliff, seen at low tide. Waves hollow out *sea cave* in erodible part of rock. Cave cut through narrow rocky headland becomes a *sea arch.* Waves cutting vertically jointed rock tear away parts, leaving isolated *stack.*

Fig. 16—9. Shoreward part of wave-cut bench, exposed at low tide, and wave-cut cliff 50 feet high. Beach here is scanty, consisting mostly of boulders, because high-energy waves carry finer rock particles seaward. North of Bonne Bay, Newfoundland. (R. F. Flint.)

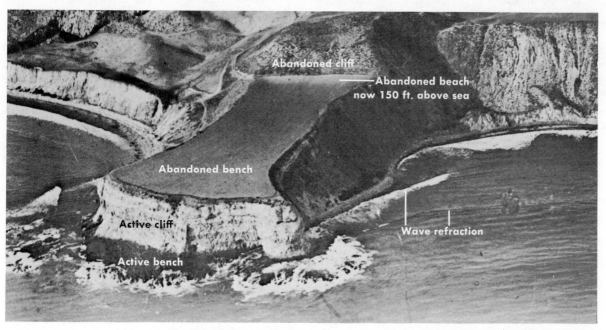

Fig. 16—10. Emerged and abandoned wave-cut cliff, wave-cut bench, and beach. Portuguese Point, San Pedro, California. Crustal movement has uplifted this part of the coast by 150 feet since the shoreline, now abandoned, was active. (Spence Air Photos.)

ing throughout the surf zone. In this zone, as we have seen, sediment is in very active movement. The sediment of a beach is derived in part from erosion of the adjacent cliff. It is derived also in large part from cliff erosion elsewhere along the shore, and, more important still, from alluvium contributed by streams. These latter sources can not be shown in Figure 16–7, but they are explained in a subsequent section.

The *wave-built terrace* is *the body of wave-washed sediment that extends seaward from the breakers.* Its extent in the seaward direction is indefinite. "Terrace" is not a particularly good name for the feature because it is not everywhere a real terrace or embankment. In places it is hardly more than a sort of carpet. Shoreward, it merges with the beach, as shown in Figure 16–7.

Stability principle along coasts. We have learned that the long profile of a stream is shaped by the adjustment of several factors to each other to create approximate stability. In an analogous manner the principle of stability shapes the shore profile as well.

This principle operates on the beach part of the shore profile, for gravel beaches have steeper seaward slopes than have sand beaches; in fact, there is an evident relationship between grain size and slope. The relationship is reasonably explained in this way: wave uprush on the beach moves sediment upslope, but the component of gravity down the beach causes sediment to move downslope. The two opposed movements establish a slope just steep enough to balance them. Because more energy is required to move pebbles than to move sand grains downslope, the slope established is steeper on a beach built of pebbles than on one built of sand.

During storms, increased surf energy erodes the exposed part of the beach and makes it narrower. During calm weather, the exposed beach is likely to receive more sediment than it loses and consequently becomes wider. But at all times the beach profile represents approximate equilibrium of energy among the forces operating at those times.

In the surf zone, on the wave-cut bench, the principle of stability operates also, again through two opposed tendencies. Waves have a resultant tendency to move sediment shoreward in the direction of wave motion. Opposed to this is the gravitational tendency of sediment to move downslope—in this case, sea-

ward. The two tendencies together establish a bottom slope just steep enough to permit slight net movement of sediment down it in the seaward direction.

As erosion causes the cliff to retreat, as the wave-cut bench widens correspondingly, and as sediment is gradually shifted seaward and sorted in the process, the principle of equilibrium of energy is in continuous operation. The form of the shore profile is not necessarily smooth. It may vary in response to the work of special currents, variations in sea level, and movement of the Earth's crust, and, although irregularities of profile due to such causes will always exist, they will tend gradually to be smoothed out. Widening of wave-cut benches and deposition of sediment beyond their seaward margins are among the processes by which continental shelves are made (Fig. 15–12).

Storm damage. The retreat of wave-cut cliffs occurs mainly during storms. Although the cliffs along the south shore of Cape Cod retreat at a rate that may amount to no more than one foot per year, a two-day hurricane in September 1944 cut them back in places as much as 50 feet. Such storm peaks of work are analogous to the peaks of deflation during wind storms in dry regions and to conspicuous channel erosion during seasonal stream floods. During storms and floods, energy levels in the moving fluids, water and air, are at their highest.

When shore property is sufficiently valuable to justify the expense, erosion of a cliff can be stopped, temporarily at least, by a *sea wall, a wall constructed of wood pilings, stone, or concrete along the foot of the wave-cut cliff.* Sea walls must have foundations so deep that they can not be undermined by storm waves. Well-built sea walls have been found to give complete protection against ordinary storms and some protection against exceptional storms. They are coming increasingly into use.

Beaches, bars, and other depositional shore features

Beaches and beach drifting. The most common depositional shore features are beaches. Figure 16–7, because it shows only two dimensions, might give the impression that the sediment constituting a beach is derived entirely from the cliff behind it. This is not true. Streams discharging at the shore contribute much sediment—more, on most coasts, than cliff

CURRENT

Fig. 16–11. Beach drifting. Dashed line shows path of typical sand grain offshore. Sand is shifted back and forth in surf while wave-generated current moves it alongshore. Dotted line shows path of typical sand grain at the shoreline. Uprush of wave washes sand up face of beach diagonally; backwash carries sand back at right angles to shoreline. Resulting path is a series of parabolas. Half Moon Bay, California. (L. Graff from A. Devaney, Inc.)

erosion contributes.

Regardless of source, the sand and gravel that remain in the surf zone are moved *along* the shore, on some coasts over great distances. *Along-the-beach movement of sediment*, known as **beach drifting,** occurs in this way: despite refraction, most waves reach the shore at an angle, however slight (Fig. 16–11).

This results in a component of motion along the shore, expressed as a slow current that moves parallel with the shore. Turbulence (for our current is in the surf zone) keeps sand grains in suspension, and the current moves them along the shore. Each grain follows a zigzag path because of the back-and-forth motion of the water in the surf.

On the beach, at the shoreline, the uprush of each wave is oblique, but the backwash flows straight down the beach slope. The result, for the rock par-

Fig. 16–12. Groins at Coney Island beach, Brooklyn, New York. Effective beach drifting transports sand from lower right to upper left, as shown by the pattern of sand piled against the up-current sides of the groins. (Fairchild Aerial Surveys.)

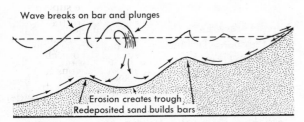

Wave breaks on bar and plunges

Erosion creates trough
Redeposited sand builds bars

Fig. 16–13. Development of longshore troughs and bars by breakers. Actually there should be more waves in the surf zone than those shown—perhaps as many as 8 or 10. (After O. F. Evans and Beach Erosion Board.)

ticles rolled and suspended in the water, is a zigzag movement, with net progress along the shore. Large pebbles have been observed to drift at a rate of more than half a mile per day. The volume of sediment drifted along the beach past Santa Monica, California, amounts to about 800 cubic yards daily.

Any unusual condition—natural, such as a hurricane, or artificial, such as the construction of a breakwater offshore—can change the equilibrium between net erosion and net deposition that keeps a beach nearly stable. Net erosion, which has been known to destroy some beaches completely within a matter of 2 or 3 years, can be checked by building groins at short intervals along the beach. A *groin* is *a low wall, built on a beach and crossing the shoreline at right angles* (Fig. 16–12). Most groins are spaced at short intervals, and many contain openings to permit some water to pass through them. Groins act as a check on the rate of beach drifting and so cause sand to accumulate against their up-drift sides. Some erosion, however, occurs beyond their down-drift sides.

Walls built out into the sea for other purposes act as groins and sometimes create enough erosion on their down-drift sides to destroy whole segments of beach. For this reason detailed studies, to determine the economy of a beach, are usually necessary before groins or other structures are erected.

Other kinds of depositional shore features. Several kinds of sedimentary shore features other than beaches, usually long, narrow, and composed of sand, are built up by waves and currents along or near shores that yield abundant sand. A grand example is the Atlantic and Gulf coast of North America from Cape Cod southward into Mexico. In contrast with the rocky coast of Maine and Canada farther north, this coast consists mostly of low, sandy plains. Eroded and reworked by waves, the sand is built into a host of bars and barriers.

As a result of the detailed study of shores induced by World War II, the classification and terminology of depositional shore features began to undergo a change. In fact, no single classification and terminology is generally accepted at present. Therefore, we shall describe such forms only in broad terms and use as few names as possible, realizing that as research progresses a somewhat different scheme may be adopted.

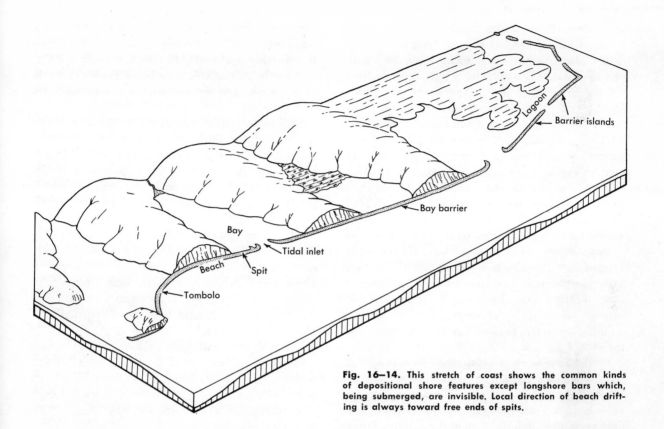

Fig. 16–14. This stretch of coast shows the common kinds of depositional shore features except longshore bars which, being submerged, are invisible. Local direction of beach drifting is always toward free ends of spits.

We can begin by following a recent proposal that depositional features whose tops are below sea level, at least at high tide, be called *bars* and that features whose tops stand above high-tide level be called *barriers*. We can then distinguish four chief kinds of bars and barriers.

Longshore bars (Fig. 16–13) are *low ridges of sand, nearly parallel with the shore, within the surf zone, and generally submerged.* There are generally two or more, separated by shallow troughs. Although bars of this kind have been given special study because landing craft stranded or capsized on them during operations in World War II, their origin is not yet well understood. One explanation is this.

Along the line on which each wave breaks, plunging turbulent water erodes the bottom and shifts the sand both landward and seaward, heaping it up. The eroded bottom becomes a trough; the deposited sand forms bars. Each bar is approximately as high as the height of the waves responsible for it. Series of bars are the work of waves of various heights;

that is, storm waves break on an outer, deeper bar, small waves on an inner, shallower one. Longshore bars shift with changing wave energy. They tend to form during stormy seasons and to smooth out or disappear during calm seasons. Some bars lie far offshore and are a hazard to ships; those off Cape Cod and Cape Hatteras have been the cause of many wrecks.

Although longshore bars interrupt the smooth profile of the bottom in the surf zone, they do not deny the stability principle. Longshore bars are superposed on the shore profile at those places where the breaking of waves introduces abrupt, local changes in energy and are a direct reflection of those changes. In this respect, longshore bars are analogous to point bars in a stream channel, which interrupt the stream's long profile because of local reduction of energy at bends in the channel (Fig. 9–21).

Spits are *elongate ridges of sand or pebbles, projecting from the land,* usually from a headland, *and ending in open water,* usually a bay (Fig. 16–14;

also Revere "Beach," Fig. 16–17, **C**). Most spits are continuations of beaches and are built of sediment drifted along the beach and dumped into deep water at a headland. When the ridge is built up to sea level, the waves act on it just as they would on a beach. Much of a spit, therefore, is likely to be above sea level, although the tip of it can not be; hence some spits are part bar, part barrier. Well-known examples are Sandy Hook at the entrance to New York Harbor, the northern tip of Cape Cod at Provincetown, Massachusetts, and Presque Isle peninsula in Lake Erie at Erie, Pennsylvania. The free ends of all three curve landward because wave energy on their seaward sides is greater than on their landward sides.

Bay barriers (Figs. 16–14; 16–17, **D**) are *ridges of sand that completely block the mouths of bays.* They are believed to be spits greatly lengthened by beach drifting across bays in which tidal and river currents are incapable of keeping the bay open by scouring away the sand as fast as it is dumped at the end of the spit.

Barrier islands are *elongate sand islands offshore parallel with the coast, with which they are not connected* (Fig. 16–14). Some of them are scores of miles long, and many are crowned with rows of sand dunes resulting from deflation of the beaches. Large-size examples are Coney Island and Jones Beach (New York City's shore-playground areas), the long chain of islands on one of which Atlantic City (Fig. 11–9) stands, the long chain centering at Cape Hatteras, North Carolina, and Padre Island, Texas, 80 miles long. How barrier islands originate is not known with certainty, but it seems likely that some of them at least are former spits severed from the mainland by wave erosion during hurricanes and other exceptional storms. Barrier islands create lagoons. A *lagoon* is *a bay inside a line of barrier islands or inshore from a coral reef.*

Openings between spits and barrier islands are

tidal inlets (Fig. 16–14), so called because tidal currents play an important part in keeping them open by removing sand brought to them by beach drifting.

A **tombolo** (tŏm′bōlō) is *a bar or barrier that connects an island to the mainland or to another island* (Fig. 16–14).

Sediments and stratification. Beaches, bars, and related features consist of the coarser sizes of whatever range of rock particles is contributed by erosion of cliffs, by streams, or even moved in temporarily from offshore. Since quartz is the most durable of common minerals in the rocks of the continental masses and since in most rocks it occurs in grains having the diameters of sand grains, it is not surprising that the majority of beaches consist chiefly of quartz sand. Bedrock that breaks down into larger pieces, along joints and other surfaces, makes beaches of gravel (Figs. 16–5, 8–17). Along an irregular coast, the change of grain size from place to place on a beach can be abrupt.

Dragged back and forth by the surf and turned over and over, particles of beach sediment become rounded by abrasion, much as do comparable particles in streams. In fact, we know of no easily recognized difference between the shapes of stream-worn and wave-worn particles.

There are, however, some differences in stratification. Spits, bay barriers, and the exposed parts of beaches, examined where natural erosion or man-made cuts expose them in section, generally are cross-stratified (Fig. 16–15). Their *seaward* parts consist of thin layers, gently inclined at many different angles. By watching calm-weather waves on a beach, we can see that the layers are deposited because part of the uprushing water infiltrates the beach, leaving the backwash unable to remove all the sediment brought by the uprush. The varying angles of the layers mostly represent the varying slopes related to sediments of varying diameter. In contrast, the *shoreward* parts usually consist of foreset laminae, deposited by high waves that wash entirely over the beach, spit, or barrier and deposit on the far side much of the load carried in the uprush. The result is not unlike the stratification of a sand dune (compare Fig. 16–16 with Fig. 14–26), but the foreset laminae are less variable in direction than in a dune because, owing to refraction, the angle the

Fig. 16–15. Ideal cross section through a small beach, spit, or bay barrier, showing lamination of sand. (Drawn from photographs by W. O. Thompson.)

Fig. 16—16. Trench dug through a small spit shows foreset laminae dipping to the right (shoreward side). End of spit is visible near top of view. Handle of shovel is 18 inches long. Cockenoe Island, Westport, Connecticut. Compare Figure 16—15. (C. W. Ellis.)

waves make with the beach varies less than the angle between wind direction and the crest of a dune.

Classification of coasts

The classification of coasts is more difficult than it would seem to be at first thought. A former classification, widely used, subdivided coasts into two groups, according to whether the shore attacked by waves and currents was *submerged* or *emerged* at the time the attack began. A submerged coast was thought of as being very irregular because of the drowning of its valleys. An emerged coast was thought of as nearly straight because it should consist of a nearly flat former sea floor.

However, we saw in Chapter 13 that as the last glacial age came to an end worldwide rise of sea level submerged most coasts, placing them in the first of the two groups mentioned above. Therefore, the classification formerly used is rather impractical.

The current practice is to classify coasts according to whether the topographic features of the land being attacked are mainly depositional or mainly erosional in origin. Examples of depositional land forms are alluvial plains and plains made by lava flows. Examples of erosional land forms are mountains dissected by streams and hills worn smooth by ice sheets.

Regardless of the classification we use, the basic principle, we must realize, is that no matter what the form of the land at the outset the surf will eventually convert it into a coast that is smooth in outline, as we shall see in the following section.

Sculptural evolution of coasts

Close observation tells us that a coast, as it is eroded by the surf, will gradually evolve through a sequence of forms to an ultimate form that is rather smooth and straight. An example of the geologic evidence on which this generalization is based is found in the three short segments of the Atlantic coast of the United States shown in Figure 16–17. Although the three segments are alike in having been gradually submerged by rise of sea level since the latest glacial age, they differ from each other as to the extent to which waves and currents have altered them by erosion and deposition.

The coast at Boothbay Harbor, Maine, **B**, consists of metamorphic rocks, very resistant to erosion, and covered in places with thin glacial drift. Hilltops stand 200 to 300 feet above the sea. Damariscotta "River," Johns Bay, and the other bays are stream valleys drowned by rise of sea level. A few minor coves have beaches so small that they can not be shown on the scale of the map, and there are no obvious wave-cut cliffs and benches. In short, the amount of geologic work performed by waves here is very slight.

The coast at Boston, Massachusetts, **C**, consists mainly of tough, compact till and other glacial sediments, all much more erodible than the rocks at Boothbay Harbor. Most of the islands are streamlined, ice-molded hills of till, and the land areas are generally less than 100 feet above sea level. Like the coast of Maine, that at Boston owes its broad features to the submergence of river valleys. Even though the Boston area is less fully exposed to the open sea than the Boothbay area, much more wave work is evident. The seaward shores of islands have been cliffed, and beaches and spits have been built. Revere "Beach" is a spit grown so long that it is almost a bay barrier. Small former islands have been reduced to shoals (not visible on the map). Rates of wave erosion here have been measured. During a 48-year period between two surveys, the cliff at Winthrop Head retreated at an average rate of 9 inches per year; during two shorter periods, Grovers Cliff retreated 9 inches and 12 inches per year, respectively. The greater amount of wave work accomplished at Boston than near Boothbay must result mainly from the more erodible character of the material exposed to the surf.

The coast near Edgartown, Massachusetts, **D**, consists of loose, uncemented sand and gravel (glacial outwash) whose surface forms a plain only 10 to 20 feet above sea level. It is more fully exposed to wave attack than the Boston area. The combination of highly erodible material and full exposure to the Atlantic Ocean has resulted in rapid erosion by surf. From their shape it is evident that Edgartown Great Pond and its neighbors are small, shallow stream valleys, with tributaries, that have been submerged. Yet the straight shoreline and the short lengths of the ponds imply that the interstream areas, which originally must have been headlands, have been cliffed and cut back through a considerable distance. During a 40-year interval between two surveys, high cliffs west of Edgartown, cut into till, retreated at an average rate of 66 inches per year; it is likely, therefore, that the low, sand-and-gravel cliffs in the area of **D** retreated even more rapidly. Whatever the rate, the coast has been simplified to a straight line in which beaches alternate with bay barriers to form a continuous deposit.

These three coastal segments constitute a natural sequence, involving progressive retreat of cliffs, creation and widening of a wave-cut bench, and smoothing of the shoreline. The effect is to distribute wave energy more and more uniformly along the shore. By comparing the three segments, we can predict that, barring interruptions, the Boston coast in time will reach a condition comparable to the Edgartown coast and that in a far longer time the Boothbay coast should do so as well.

By comparisons of this kind geologists have developed the concept that a broadly similar evolution should characterize coasts generally and that such evolution is analogous to the sculptural evolution of a land mass as it is eroded by streams and mass-wasting. In other words, just as there are cycles of erosion characteristic of the lands under a moist climate (Fig. 10–11) and under an arid climate (Fig. 14–11), so also there is a cycle of erosion characteristic of the effect of waves and currents along coasts. As with the stream cycle, the stages described as youth, maturity, and old age represent a continuous transformation of the coast and are not

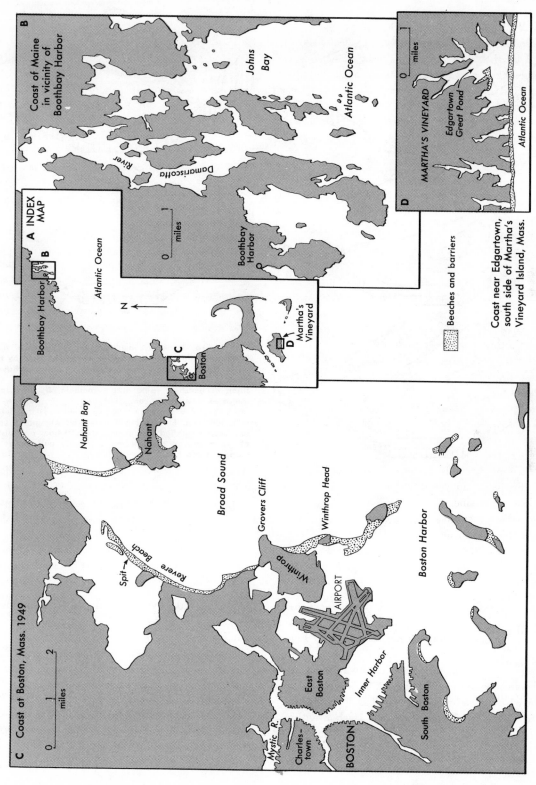

Fig. 16–17. Sculptural alteration of coasts by waves and currents. (Shore features in **C** after L. La Forge, 1932, U. S. Geol. Survey Bull. 839, pl. 1; in **D** after J. B. Woodworth, and Frank Wigglesworth, 1934, Mus. Comp. Zoölogy Mem. 52, pl. 13.)

319

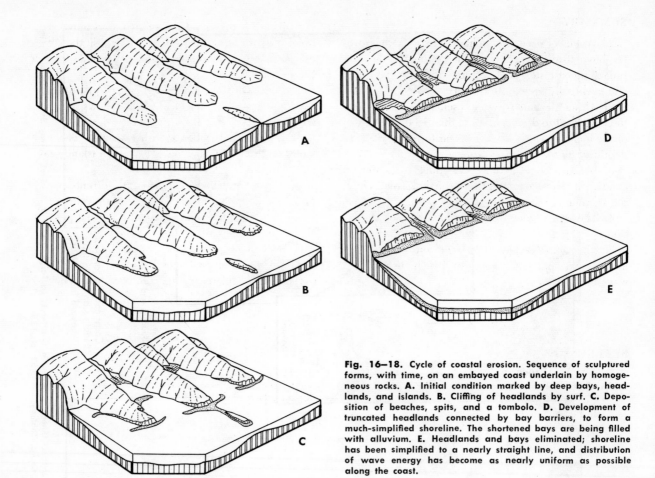

Fig. 16–18. Cycle of coastal erosion. Sequence of sculptured forms, with time, on an embayed coast underlain by homogeneous rocks. **A.** Initial condition marked by deep bays, headlands, and islands. **B.** Cliffing of headlands by surf. **C.** Deposition of beaches, spits, and a tombolo. **D.** Development of truncated headlands connected by bay barriers, to form a much-simplified shoreline. The shortened bays are being filled with alluvium. **E.** Headlands and bays eliminated; shoreline has been simplified to a nearly straight line, and distribution of wave energy has become as nearly uniform as possible along the coast.

sharply marked off from each other. They serve merely to emphasize the fact of unbroken evolution. A typical sequence, through time, is shown in Figure 16–18.

Theoretically, the surf could eat away the world's lands entirely and convert them into broad platforms slightly below sea level. On a small scale this has happened to small islands in Boston Harbor within a rather short period, and it seems to be what planed off the guyots (p. 288). Actually, however, we believe this has never happened to the continents because the sedimentary rocks of all ages imply that as far back as we can decipher Earth history there has not been a time when lands have not existed. This is hardly surprising, in view of abundant evidence that sea level keeps changing and that repeated upbending of parts of the Earth's crust works against effective erosion by surf. Except for some islands, therefore, the cycle of erosion along coasts does not seem ever to have destroyed the lands.

SUMMARY

1. Waves of oscillation, characteristic of deep water, have little or no effect on the bottom. As they approach a coast and "feel bottom," they are deformed and eventually break to form surf.

2. Although some waves of oscillation can stir bottom sediment to depths of more than 1,000 feet, most of the geologic work of waves is performed by surf at depths of 30 feet or less.

3. Because of refraction, surf attack is greater on headlands than along the shores of bays. As a result the shoreline becomes smoother.

4. The surf erodes by hydraulic action and abrasion.

5. The shore profile consists of four related elements: wave-cut cliff, wave-cut bench, beach, and wave-built terrace.

6. There is a general net tendency to move sediment seaward from the shore and to deposit the coarsest particles near shore; the sediment becomes finer in the seaward direction.

7. Beach drifting transports great quantities of sand along coasts; each sand grain follows a zigzag path.

8. Depositional shore features include beaches, longshore bars, spits, bay barriers, barrier islands, and tombolos.

9. A coast attacked by waves and currents passes through an orderly sequence of forms—a cycle of erosion—ending with a nearly straight form that permits almost uniform distribution of wave energy.

10. Because of movement of the crust and change of sea level, lands of continental size apparently have never been completely reduced to wave-cut benches.

REFERENCES

Bascom, Willard, 1960, Beaches: Sci. American, vol. 203, p. 81–94.
Bulletins of the Beach Erosion Board (Corps of Engineers, U. S. Army), Washington, D. C. Appearing at irregular intervals, these publications contain a large body of information, much of it quantitative, on the effects of waves and currents on the shore.
Inman, D. L., 1954, Beach and nearshore processes along the southern California coast: Calif. Div. Mines Bull. 170, Chap. 5, p. 29–34.
Johnson,, D. W., 1919, Shore processes and shoreline development: New York, John Wiley and Sons.
King, C. A. M., 1959, Beaches and coasts: London, Edward Arnold.
Shepard, F. P., 1948, Submarine geology: New York, Harper & Brothers.
Steers, J. A., 1954, The sea coast: London, Collins.

CHAPTER 17. SEDIMENTARY ROCKS

Nature of sedimentary rocks   *Kinds of sedimentary rocks*   *Stratification*   *Special features of sedimentary rocks*   *Stratigraphy*

Grand Canyon. (Harrison from Monkmeyer.)

Nature of sedimentary rocks

Sedimentary rocks, as we read in Chapter 3, are simply *rocks formed from sediment.* There is a close similarity between sedimentary rocks and the sediments being deposited today. Applying the principle of uniformity of process, we reason that the activities of erosion and deposition that are operating now have been acting in the same way throughout the Earth's history. When we look at the sedimentary rocks exposed in the side of a mountain or in the walls of a great canyon, we gain some concept of the enormous length of time in which sediments have been accumulating on the Earth's crust. We say "*on* the crust," although perhaps "in the crust" would be better. For as new sediments were deposited on older ones, the latter became more and more deeply buried and at the same time were slowly converted into rock. The buried rocks became an actual part of the crust itself. The thickness of sedimentary rocks in the crust varies greatly from place to place. Thicknesses of several thousand feet are not uncommon, and in a few places such rocks are believed to approach or exceed 50,000 feet. Sedimentary rocks lie at the surface of about 75 per cent of the area of the continental masses, but in terms of the Earth's crust they are superficial, for they constitute only a very small percentage of the volume of the crust.

The most obvious characteristic of sedimentary rocks as a group is that they are layered, or stratified. After describing the various kinds of rocks, we shall return to the stratification they possess because from stratification much can be learned about how the rocks originated.

Kinds of sedimentary rocks

Basis of classification. In examining any group or collection of natural objects, a scientist tries to classify them so that he can study them in an orderly way. Sedimentary rocks are no exception. If we examine a representative collection, we soon realize that there are a number of different kinds but not a bewildering variety. Before long, we find that a fundamental basis of classification is the texture of the rock, which, as we noted in Chapter 3, is determined by its component particles. On the basis of texture we can sort our rocks into two principal groups, clastic and non-clastic.

1. **Clastic rocks** are *rocks consisting of particles of other rocks (or fossils) that have been transported.* The particles were deposited as sediments, which were converted into new rocks. We call such rocks clastic because they were made from clastic sediments. An example of a clastic rock is sandstone. Clastic rocks are subdivided on the basis of grain size and mineral composition. Grain diameters are determined by separating the individual grains in a sample of rock of known weight and shaking them down through a series of screens, each with a finer mesh than the screen above it. The group of grains caught on each screen is then weighed and its percentage of the weight of the whole sample is calculated. The diameter of the group of grains constituting the greatest percentage determines the rock. If the grains are a mixture of various diameters, the mixture is named according to some standard scheme, which is not discussed further here.

Grain diameters can also be measured directly on a thin section under a microscope.

Many minerals, among which are quartz and clay minerals, occur only in clastic rocks. Other minerals occur only in non-clastic rocks, but calcite and dolomite occur in rocks of both groups. This is because these minerals are the principal constituents of lime-

TABLE 17–1. Principal kinds of sedimentary rocks
(Clastic rocks are shaded to distinguish them from non-clastic rocks)

GRAIN SIZE ↓ / COMPOSITION →		Fragments of, or minerals derived from, pre-existing rock	Carbonate minerals (mostly calcite and dolomite): Whole and fragmental shells, skeletons, etc.[1]	Carbonate minerals (mostly calcite and dolomite): Chemically precipitated; then transported	Chloride minerals, sulfate minerals, etc.: Chemically precipitated	Nonmineral substances: Accumulated mechanically in place
Limiting diameters of dominant particles	Name of equivalent sediment	Clastic rocks	Clastic rocks	Clastic rocks	Non-clastic rocks: Evaporites	Non-clastic rocks
More than 2 mm.	Gravel	Conglomerate Breccia	Limestone and Dolostone	[no rocks[2]]	Salt (mineral: halite), Gypsum (mineral: gypsum), etc.[3]	Coal[3]
2 mm. to $\frac{1}{16}$ mm.	Sand	Sandstone Arkose Graywacke	Limestone and Dolostone	Limestone and Dolostone	Salt (mineral: halite), Gypsum (mineral: gypsum), etc.[3]	Coal[3]
$\frac{1}{16}$ mm. to $\frac{1}{256}$ mm.	Silt	Siltstone	Limestone and Dolostone	Limestone and Dolostone	Salt (mineral: halite), Gypsum (mineral: gypsum), etc.[3]	Coal[3]
Less than $\frac{1}{256}$ mm.	Clay	Shale	Limestone and Dolostone	Limestone and Dolostone	Salt (mineral: halite), Gypsum (mineral: gypsum), etc.[3]	Coal[3]

[1] Some skeletal material is composed of silica.
[2] No rocks having this grain size, composition, and origin are known.
[3] Salt, gypsum, and coal are set vertically to emphasize the fact that they are unrelated to the particle diameters shown at the left.

Fig. 17–1. This conglomerate, of Triassic age, exposed in a wave-cut cliff in Hants County, Nova Scotia, was deposited by a swift stream. Imbrication of cobbles in middle and upper layers shows current flowed from right to left. (G. deV. Klein.)

stone and dolostone, which include both clastic and non-clastic varieties.

2. *Non-clastic rocks.* In this group are (*a*) rocks consisting of matter precipitated from chemical solution, and (*b*) coal. Most of the chemically precipitated rocks have a texture, consisting of interlocking mineral grains, developed during crystallization of the substances coming out of solution. The most common minerals represented in them are calcite and dolomite and the most common rocks are limestone and dolostone. Precipitation can be inorganic or can result from the chemical activity of organisms.

As tiny crystals of calcite settle to the bottom of a sea or lake, they are free at first. But as they lie at the bottom in a saturated environment, covered ever more deeply by newly precipitated crystals, they continue to grow, and eventually they form a solid mass of interlocking crystals like those of many igneous rocks.

Principal kinds. The two basic groups of sedimentary rocks, then, are clastic and non-clastic. Now we can examine the kinds of rocks that make up these

groups. We can best begin with a table (Table 17–1), remembering, however, that among most sedimentary rocks there is complete gradation from one kind to another. Descriptions helpful in identification of the rocks are given in Chapter 3 and Appendix B.

Conglomerate and *breccia.* The common coarse-grained clastic rocks are conglomerate and breccia. Although finer sizes are present, the dominant particles can include any sizes from pebbles up to huge boulders. In conglomerate the constituent particles are at least somewhat rounded by the action of streams or surf (Fig. 17–1). *Conglomerate* is therefore *a clastic rock in which rounded pebbles or larger particles are numerous.* In *breccia* the coarse particles have angular, fractured surfaces (Fig. 17–2), produced by mechanical weathering and other mechanical processes. Many breccias are merely consolidated sliderock (Fig. 7–3). *Sedimentary breccia*, therefore, is *a clastic rock in which angular pebbles or larger particles are numerous.*

Sandstone, arkose, and *graywacke. Sandstone* is the

Fig. 17–2. Breccia, consisting of angular fragments of black chert and colorless quartz, bound firmly together with siliceous cement. The angular shapes suggest former sliderock, possibly at the base of a cliff from which the fragments were derived.

Fig. 17–3. Shale, of Ordovician age, exposed in Black River region, New York. The many ledge-like layers are siltstone interbedded with the shale. Because of its erodibility, pure shale is rarely exposed so well as to show its stratification. We see the stratification here because of the siltstone layers. (C. O. Dunbar.)

medium-grained clastic rock. It is defined as _a clastic rock consisting predominantly of sand-size particles_. In most sandstones the constituent sand grains are quartz. The cementing material is usually calcium carbonate (Fig. 17–20, **B**), but in some sandstones it is iron oxide, silica, or some other substance.

Two unusual varieties of sandstone deserve special mention. Both are characterized by containing an appreciable proportion of feldspar along with the quartz. As we learned in Chapter 7, feldspar is attacked by chemical weathering much more readily than quartz. Therefore, feldspar does not ordinarily survive to become part of a sediment or a sedimentary rock. Hence a sandstone containing feldspar implies that it was derived from mechanically weathered source rocks, that the source rocks were eroded mechanically before they could be weathered chemically, or that some other special situation existed. _A light-colored sandstone containing at least 25 per cent feldspar as well as quartz_ is called _arkose_. _A poorly sorted sandstone, generally dark, containing rock fragments as well as_ quartz, is called _graywacke_ (Fig. 17–8). Feldspar is a common, though not essential, constituent in graywacke.

Siltstone and _shale_. The clastic rocks with finer grain than sandstone are siltstone and shale, identified by the dominant particle sizes silt or clay. _Siltstone_, then, is _a clastic rock consisting predominantly of silt-size particles_. _Shale_ is _a clastic rock consisting predominantly of clay-size particles_. The silt-size particles in siltstone are usually quartz; the clay-size particles in shale (Fig. 17–3) are commonly various clay minerals, but they include quartz and other minerals as well. The particles constituting these rocks are so very small that thorough study of them requires an electron microscope.

Limestone and *dolostone*. The broadest definition of **limestone** states merely that it is *a sedimentary rock consisting predominantly of calcite*. Some limestones are clastic, some are chemical precipitates (either inorganic or organic), and still others are mixtures of clastic and precipitated sediments. Clastic limestones (and dolostones) occur in all grain sizes, parallel with the other clastic rocks. However, as shown in Table 17–1, they are traditionally separated from the other clastic rocks because of their special composition.

A variety of limestone that is mainly clastic is **coquina** (Fig. 17–4), *an aggregation of shells and large shell fragments cemented with calcium carbonate*. Another variety, **chalk**, is *limestone that is weakly cohesive*. **Fresh-water limestone** is *limestone that formed in a lake*. Still other limestones form on or beneath the ground by evaporation in an environment of air rather than under water. The dripstone in caverns, described in Chapter 11, is an example. Another is **calcareous tufa**, *a light, spongy limestone precipitated by the evaporation of springs and small streams*. **Travertine** is used by some as *a name for both dripstone and calcareous tufa*.

Dolostone is *a sedimentary rock consisting chiefly of the mineral dolomite*. Hence it resembles limestone, except that its carbonate mineral is the double carbonate of magnesium and calcium. Dolostone and limestone are very intimately related. Not only is there a complete gradation between them, but a single sample of rock can consist of both varieties. Probably most dolostone has been formed by the alteration or conversion of limestone; hence it is a secondary rather than a primary rock. In such rock, alteration results from replacement, by magnesium, of some of the calcium within the limestone.

Evaporites. **Evaporites** are *non-clastic sedimentary rocks whose constituent minerals were precipitated from water solution as a result of evaporation*. The most common evaporites are salt (consisting of the mineral halite, $NaCl$), gypsum (consisting of the mineral gypsum $CaSO_4 \cdot 2H_2O$), and anhydrite (consisting of the mineral anhydrite, $CaSO_4$). As beds of salt and gypsum occur interlayered with sedimentary rocks of marine origin, they are believed to have been formed mainly on the floors of shallow seas, usually in an arid climate. However, some evaporites have formed in lakes and are forming today in the Great Salt Lake in Utah. Some limestones and dolostones formed as evaporites.

Coal. **Coal is a black sedimentary rock consisting chiefly of partly decomposed plant matter and containing less than 40 per cent inorganic matter.** Unlike most other sedimentary rocks, coal is made of substances that were not transported to areas of deposition. The substances accumulated in the same places in which the source plants grew. The process of coal formation is described in Chapter 22. The sediment equivalent of coal is peat, which represents an early stage in the making of coal. Peat is defined on page 225.

Stratification

Causes of stratification. *Stratification* in a rock is *the arrangement of the constituent particles in layers*. It is an obvious feature of most sedimentary rocks. Although it is true that a series of lava flows, which are not sedimentary rocks, is layered, we speak of stratification only in connection with sediments and sedimentary rocks. A *single sedimentary layer* is a **stratum** (plural: *strata*). For convenience in description, strata are subdivided into **beds** (*strata 1 cm. or more in thickness*) and **laminae** (*strata less than 1 cm. thick*). From these terms are derived the commonly used words *layering, stratification, bedding,* and *lamination*.

What is the cause of stratification in a sedimentary rock? If we look closely at a distinctly stratified rock, we can usually see that strata differ from each other because of differences in size, shape, composition, or arrangement of the particles that compose them. Very commonly one stratum consists of particles of different diameter from those in another. In a clastic rock such changes of diameter result from fluctuations of energy in a stream, in surf, in wind, in a lake current, or in whatever agency is responsible for the deposit. Such energy changes, usually small, are not the exception but the rule.

Fig. 17—4. Coquina. The shell fragments are weakly cemented with calcite. Anastasia Formation, St. Augustine, Florida. (Yale Peabody Museum.)

Fig. 17—5. Parallel stratification in weakly cemented sandstone, siltstone, and shale of Pliocene age, exposed in a dry valley northeast of Las Vegas, Nevada. The sediments were deposited in a lake that occupied a former basin, now within the Colorado River drainage area. (C. R. Longwell.)

Apart from differences in diameter, the particles in one stratum can differ in mineral composition from the particles in another stratum. For example, in some beaches laminae of quartz sand alternate in places with laminae consisting of sand grains of magnetite or some other heavy mineral. Grains of magnetite sand, being twice as heavy as the grains of quartz sand, are concentrated at times when the energy level of the waves, as they rush up the beach and wash back, is relatively great. The quartz grains are carried away, leaving the magnetite on the beach as thin patches of dark-colored sand.

Again, successive layers that do not differ from each other in grain size, composition, degree of compaction, or kind of cement between the particles can still be separated from each other by surfaces of easy splitting representing minor intervals when no deposition occurred.

In summary, each stratum usually has definite characteristics by which it differs from the stratum beneath or above it. With this in mind, we can describe two chief kinds of stratification and then discuss three obvious kinds of arrangement of the particles within a stratum.

Parallel stratification and cross-stratification. There are two principal kinds of stratification that involve the relation of successive layers to each other. _Parallel stratification_ is _stratification in which the individual layers are parallel throughout their extent_ (Fig. 17–5). Parallelism of the layers indicates that deposition of the sediment probably took place in water, either sea or lake, and that the activity of currents and waves was at a minimum. Indeed, the sediment of some lakes and the sediment brought up by coring devices from beneath the deep-sea floor rather commonly have parallel laminae. Although they appear to be parallel, foreset layers in deltas (Fig. 9–26) and dunes (Fig. 14–26) are special cases because, if traced toward one of their ends, they are seen to be not truly parallel.

A distinctive variety of parallel stratification is represented by repeated alternations of laminae of unlike grain size or mineral composition. Such alternation suggests the influence of some naturally occurring rhythm, such as rise and fall of the tide, seasonal change from winter to summer, or the slight climatic fluctuation related to the sun-spot "cycle" of about 11 years. _A pair of laminae deposited during the cycle_

329

Fig. 17–6. Fine-grained sediments showing varves, deposited in a glacial lake during the last glacial age, South Hadley Falls, Massachusetts. Each varve consists of a layer of (light-colored) silt deposited during the summer season of glacial melting and an overlying thinner layer of (dark-colored) clay deposited in winter. More than 25 varves are visible. (R. F. Flint.)

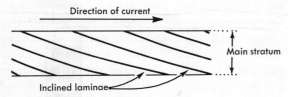

Fig. 17–7. Geometry of cross-stratification.

of the year with its seasons is a **varve** (Swedish: *cycle*). Such varves occur in glacial-lake sediments deposited during the last glaciation (Fig. 17–6); they are so young that they have not yet been converted from sediments into firm rock. They form especially well in glacial lakes because close to an ice sheet the contrast between summer and winter weather is very strong. Very similar pairs of laminae occur in ancient rocks. For example certain shales in South Africa have been interpreted as varves deposited in glacier-dammed lakes during a glaciation more than 200 million years ago.

Varves of different origin characterize rocks of the Green River Formation, which underlies thousands of square miles in Wyoming, Colorado, and Utah. In each varve one lamina consists of calcium carbonate; the other includes dark-colored organic matter. The rhythm is explained as follows: the sediments were deposited in a lake, which warmed in summer, therefore lost carbon dioxide, and precipitated calcium carbonate from solution. During the same warm season floating microscopic organisms reached a peak of abundance. The relatively heavy carbonate sank promptly and formed a summer lamina; the lighter organic matter sank much more slowly to form an overlying winter lamina. Thus the pair of laminae is a varve. It has been estimated from sample counts that between 5 and 8 million varves are present in the Green River formation; hence we reason that an immense lake occupied the Green River Basin for millions of years under remarkably uniform conditions.

In contrast to parallel stratification, *cross-stratification is stratification inclined to that of a larger stratum within which it occurs.* The term, of course, includes both cross-bedding and cross-lamination, depending on the thickness of the strata. The geometry of cross-stratification is shown in Figure 17–7. All such stratification is the work of strong flowing movement of water or air, as in streams, wind, and waves on a shore. We have seen examples of these movements in fans, outwash sediments (Fig. 13–21), deltas (Fig. 9–26), dunes (Fig. 14–26), and beaches (Fig. 16–15). Cross-stratification in sedimentary rocks implies ancient currents. From the down-current direction in which the inclined layers dip we can infer the direction of movement of the currents.

Arrangements of particles within a stratum. In addition to the two relationships of layers to each other, there are several types of arrangement of the particles within a single layer. Each type gives information about the conditions under which the sediment was deposited. Chief among them are uniform beds, graded beds, and nonsorted beds.

Uniform beds. A bed that consists of particles of about the same diameter is called a **uniform bed** because it is not laminated. A uniform bed of clastic rock implies deposition, from suspension, of particles of a single size, with little change in the energy of movement of the surrounding water or air. This might occur, for example, in the bottomset layers of a delta. A uniform bed of non-clastic rock implies uniform precipitation from solution, which produces crystalline particles of a single size. In contrast, a bed that is laminated because of grain-size differences implies that sediment was carried in water or air that was subject to fluctuation of energy.

Graded beds. If you put a quantity of small solid particles of different diameters and about the same specific gravity into a glass jar of water, shake the mixture well, and then let it stand, the solid particles will settle out and form a deposit on the bottom of the jar. The heaviest and largest particles settle first, followed by successively smaller particles; the finest ones, if small enough, may stay in suspension for hours or days, keeping the water turbid, before finally settling out. The whole deposit is sorted, in that particle size decreases gradually from the bottom upward. This kind of stratification characterizes a **graded bed**, defined as *a bed in which the particles grade upward from coarse to fine* (Fig. 17–8). The deposit is, as it were, a one-stroke affair. The water receives energy from the shaking of the jar and becomes turbulent; as a result, the sediment is lifted above the bottom. When the shaking stops, abrupt loss of energy results in continuous deposition.

Although a graded bed produced by simple shaking in a jar is graded only in the vertical dimension, those produced in nature are also graded laterally because they are made by currents that are moving from one place to another. Because the heaviest particles settle first, the sediment in a graded bed becomes finer not only from bottom to top but laterally in the down-current direction.

Graded beds are apparently widespread beneath

Fig. 17–8. Graded bed in graywacke of Triassic age, Branford, Connecticut, seen in a polished hand specimen 4 inches high. Rock grades from sandstone at base, where it overlies black shale, through siltstone to shale at top. It is thought to have been deposited by a turbidity current in a small lake at the edge of an ancient floodplain. (J. E. Sanders.)

Fig. 17–9. Tillite, representing a very ancient glaciation, overlying a smooth surface of dolerite, on which many glacial striations are visible. The tillite lacks stratification. The pebbles, and cobbles in it are mostly dolerite, further indicating glacial erosion of the underlying dolerite. Nooitgedacht, Cape Province, South Africa. (R. F. Flint.)

smooth parts of the deep-sea floor and are present in many sediments and rocks on the lands. Some of the processes that create graded beds are (1) turbidity currents in the sea and in lakes, (2) streams, as they lose energy and deposit bed-load sediment during the rapid subsidence of floods, (3) nuées ardentes, and (4) dust storms, as they subside. All four processes represent rapid, continuous loss of energy, an essential condition for the creation of graded beds.

Nonsorted beds. Some sedimentary rocks have no sorting at all. They consist of mixtures of particles of various sizes, arranged chaotically, without any obvious order. Particles carried in air and water are not deposited in this chaotic way. Processes that do create sediments of this class include landslide, earthflow, mudflow, solifluction, and transport by glaciers, and floating icebergs. Widely recognized among nonsorted sediments is tillite (Fig. 17–9) of glacial origin.

Special features of sedimentary rocks

Rounding, sorting, imbrication. We have noted at various points in our discussion that as streams, wind,

and surf, each in its characteristic way, transport rock particles the particles tend to become rounded. Figure 17–10 shows what can happen to pebbles on a beach, and Figure 17–11 shows how sand grains become shaped during transport. Degree of rounding therefore gives an idea of distance or time involved in transport.

Transport in water or wind results in *the selection of rock particles according to their size, shape, specific gravity, durability, and other characteristics.* This selection is called *sorting* and is evident in sediments after they have been deposited. Sorting according to specific gravity is seen in mineral placers (p. 462). Particles of unusually heavy minerals, such as gold and platinum, are quickly deposited on stream beds and on beaches, whereas the lighter particles are carried onward. Most of the particles carried in water and wind, however, consist of quartz and other minerals with specific gravity rather similar to quartz. Commonly, therefore, these particles are sorted according to size. In a stream gravel is deposited first; whereas sand and silt are generally carried farther

Fig. 17–10. Rounding of pebbles during transport by surf on a beach. These fragments of basalt were collected at random from a talus and an adjacent beach near Clarence, Nova Scotia. They are arranged here to show what can be expected to happen to a plate-shaped piece (*upper left*) and to a spindle-shaped piece (*upper right*) during progressive abrasion. The end product of each could be the same—a spherical pebble. Although this rounding is the work of beach drifting, stream transport produces a similar result. (J. E. Sanders.)

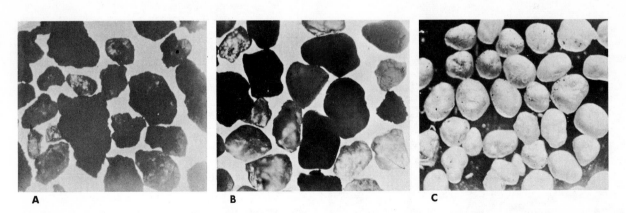

A B C

Fig. 17–11. Rounding and sorting of mineral grains during transport. About 9 times natural size. **A.** Mineral grains loosened and separated from igneous and metamorphic rocks by mechanical and chemical weathering before transport. The angular shapes of the individual grains, slightly altered by weathering, are the forms assumed by the minerals as they crystallized from a magma. The aggregate of grains is an unsorted sand. **B.** Sand carried from an area of rocks similar to those which yielded the sand in **A.** Some of the less durable mineral grains have been broken up and lost, leaving a larger proportion of grains of the durable mineral quartz. Battering in transit has partly rounded the grains. **C.** Sand transported over a long distance. Grains have become well rounded and consist almost entirely of durable quartz. Weaker minerals did not survive transport.

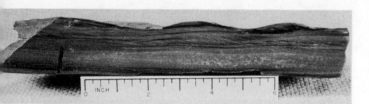

Fig. 17–12. Ripple marks preserved in the upper surface of a layer of sandstone of Paleozoic age. The ripples were made by a current moving from left to right. (Yale Peabody Museum.)

Fig. 17–13. Ripple marks seen in section as ripple lamination in fine-grained sandstone of Devonian age, from central New York. The current flowed from left to right. The fine inclined laminae mark successive positions of the front of the advancing ripple and are comparable with the forest laminae in a delta. The black vertical mark at the left is the mud filling of a worm burrow in the sea floor. (J. E. Sanders.)

Fig. 17–14. These mud cracks are preserved in sandstone of Mississippian age (more than 250 million years old), near Pottsville, Pennsylvania. The hammer handle is about 2 feet long. This is the underside of a slab of sandstone turned up on its edge. The sand was deposited over a layer of river mud in which the cracks had formed and then hardened. The shale (the former mud) has been destroyed by recent weathering, but chips of it litter the foreground. Most ancient mud cracks, like these, are really fillings of cracks by sand that was deposited in them. (Joseph Barrell.)

before deposition. Thin, flat particles are carried farther than spherical particles of similar weight. Long-continued handling of particles by turbulent water and air results in the gradual destruction of the weaker particles. In this way rocks and minerals that are soft or that have pronounced cleavage are eliminated, leaving as residue the particles that can better survive in the turbulent environment. Very commonly the survivor is quartz, which is hard and lacks cleavage. In this case sorting is based on durability.

Swift streams with bed loads of pebbles or cobbles that are platy or disk-shaped, as are some of those shown in Figure 17–10, tend to deposit them at an angle, with their flat sides sloping steeply downward in the upstream direction. This arrangement of the particles in a stream-transported gravel is called imbrication. It is visible in Figure 17–1 and, like cross-bedding, is useful in determining directions of flow of former streams. We can define *imbrication* in sedimentary rocks as *the slanting, overlapping arrangement of flat pebbles, like shingles on a roof.*

Ripple marks and mud cracks. Earlier we discussed the making of ripples in sand by the wind (Fig. 14–22). Although the mechanics of their formation differ, ripples in sand and silt are made also by currents in streams, lakes, and the sea, and by waves of oscillation in seas and lakes. Ripples are preserved in some sandstones and siltstones as *ripple marks* (Figs. 17–12, 17–13).

Some shales and siltstones contain layers that are cut by polygonal markings. By comparison with sediments forming today, such as those in roadside puddles following a rain, we infer that these are *mud cracks, cracks caused by the shrinkage of wet mud as its surface became dry* (Fig. 17–14). The presence of mud cracks in a rock generally implies at least temporary exposure to the air and therefore suggests tidal flats, exposed stream beds, playa lakes, and similar environments. Occurring with some ripple marks and mud cracks, and preserved in a similar manner, are the footprints of ancient animals. Even the impressions of large raindrops made during short, hard showers are preserved.

Fossils. One of the most significant features of sedimentary rocks is that many contain *fossils.* The word *fossil* (Lat. *fossilis,* from *fodere,* to dig) was used by ancient Romans for anything remarkable,

Fig. 17–15. Marine fossils in slab of sandstone of Devonian age, central New York. (A. L. McAlester.)

minerals included, that was dug up from the ground. Today, although we still use the word in the old sense when we speak of fossil fuels (p. 443), we think of fossils in a stricter sense. We define them as *the remains or traces of animals and plants preserved in sediments or rocks by natural means.* Plants and animals, or parts of them, were buried as sediments accumulated, and those that were protected against oxidation and against erosion were preserved through the long process of conversion of sediments into rocks (Fig. 17–15). Fossils are used in geologic science in many ways, of which two are outstanding. (1) Fossils in a sedimentary layer can be an important clue to the environment in which the sediments accumulated. To take a most obvious example, fossil clams of certain kinds indicate a shallow-water marine environment, whereas fossil horses indicate an environment of grassy plains. (2) Fossils are the chief basis of correlation, the tracing of strata from one place or region to another. Correlation is discussed later in this chapter.

Concretions and geodes. Inclosed in some sedimentary rocks are bodies called *concretions.* They range in diameter from a fraction of an inch to many feet and in shape from spherical through a variety of odd shapes, many with remarkable symmetry (Fig.

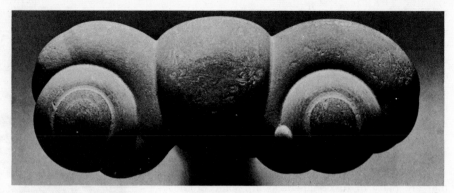

Fig. 17–16. Concretion, 3 inches long, consisting of calcium carbonate. It was imbedded in shale. (Andreas Feininger.)

17–16), to elongate lenses that parallel the stratification of the inclosing rock. Concretions are composed of many different substances, of which the commonest include calcite, silica, hematite, limonite, siderite (iron carbonate), and pyrite. Small concretions are dredged up from the sea floor, showing that they are forming there today as sediments are being deposited. This origin, contemporaneous with the inclosing sediments, is indicated also by the shapes of some concretions and by their relation to the lamination of the surrounding sedimentary rock. Others formed after the deposition of the sediments, as for example those that retain the stratification of the surrounding rock (Fig. 17–17).

The substances of which concretions are made show that they are the result of localized chemical precipitation. Some of them obviously formed by chemical separation of dissolved substances from sea or lake waters. Others developed later by precipitation from connate water with which the accumulated sediments were saturated. Once chemical precipitation starts around a fossil or other body that differs from the inclosing rock, it continues around the growing concretion instead of elsewhere. Indeed, in some rocks perfectly preserved fossils are found at the centers of concretions.

It is always hard to define a class of objects whose characteristics and origin are not fully understood, and we still do not fully understand concretions. The best definition we can suggest is that a *concretion is a localized body having distinct boundaries, inclosed in sedimentary rock, and consisting of a substance precipitated from solution, commonly around a nu-*cleus. Some geologists use the word *nodule* as a synonym for concretion; others restrict it to concretions of small size.

A feature somewhat related to concretions is a *geode* (Fig. 17–18). This is *a hollow rounded body having a lining of inward-pointing crystals*. The linings are usually quartz or calcite, and the rocks in which geodes occur are generally limestones. There is no question that geodes developed after the sedimentary rocks were formed. One explanation of these features is that they are essentially tiny caverns, excavated by solution, somewhat as are the caverns described in Chapter 11. Later, owing to changes in physical-chemical conditions, they were partly refilled with mineral substances crystallized from water solution.

Colors. The colors of sedimentary rocks vary considerably. Some rocks, exposed in cliffs, are colored only skin deep by a product of chemical weathering. For example, a sandstone that is pale gray on freshly fractured surfaces may have a surface coating of yellowish-brown limonite. This mineral is secondary, having been developed during weathering by the oxidation of sparse, iron-rich minerals included with the grains of quartz sand.

The color of fresh rock is the combination of the colors of the minerals that compose it. Iron sulfides and organic matter, buried with the sediment, are responsible for most dark colors in sedimentary rocks. Microscopic examination of red and brown rocks shows that their colors result mainly from the presence of ferric oxides as powdery coatings on grains of quartz and other minerals or as very fine particles

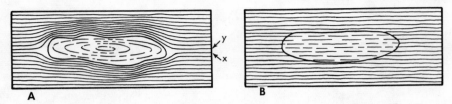

Fig. 17–17. Vertical cross-sections of two concretions, each several inches long, in shale, showing different times of origin relative to the deposition of the inclosing sedimentary rock. **A.** Concretion formed after lamina x was deposited but before lamina y was laid down. Hence the concretion is contemporaneous with deposition of the body of sediment. **B.** Concretion transected by laminae of the inclosing rock. Hence it was formed after all the laminae shown had been deposited.

mixed with clay. Apparently these oxides were derived from the erosion of red-clay soils, which today are characteristic of a warm, moist climate like that of southeastern United States. Some rivers of that region are red with suspended loads of eroded soil. Part of the load of sediment is deposited on swampy flood plains. There decaying plant matter, creating strong reducing agents, reduces the ferric oxide to ferrous oxide, which lacks the red color. The rest of the sediment goes into the sea, where the organic matter on the sea floor likewise reduces it. It is thought likely, therefore, that although red sediments result from decay of older rocks under warm, moist conditions, their color can be preserved only if they escape chemical reduction after deposition. This they could do if deposited in basins having either (*a*) little rainfall and sparse vegetation or (*b*) strongly seasonal rainfall, a condition unfavorable for the accumulation of organic matter in amounts sufficient to reduce the ferric iron.

Conversion of sediments into rocks. We noted at the beginning of this chapter that sedimentary rocks are rocks converted from sediment. *The complex process by which sediments are converted into rocks is known as lithification* (literally, "rock making"). The main activities in lithification consist of compaction, cementation, and crystallization. In *compaction* the individual particles gradually settle under the weight of sediments deposited on top of them and become packed more closely together. In Figure 17–19 compaction has reduced the original pore space by almost 50 per cent. This would also reduce the thickness of the sediment and would make it

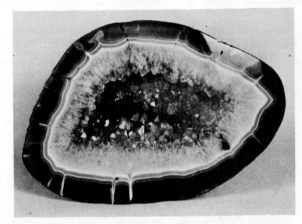

Fig. 17–18. Geode, about 8 inches in diameter, resulting from the partial filling of a cavity in rock, first with agate and later with crystals of quartz. Erosion has removed the surrounding rock, but the resistant quartz that lined the cavity remains. (American Museum of Natural History.)

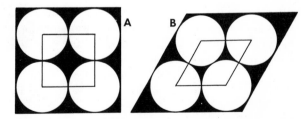

Fig. 17–19. Compaction in sediments (modified from C. S. Slichter.) Sections of four contiguous spheres of equal size: **A.** Packed in the least compact manner; pore space (shaded) 47.6 per cent of total volume. **B.** Packed in the most compact manner; pore space 25.9 per cent of total volume. As the individual grains in natural sediments are neither perfect spheres nor of equal diameter, these sections illustrate only the principle involved.

A   B

Fig. 17–20. Sediment and sedimentary rock compared. A. Sediment (sand) composed of grains of quartz. The grains are in the loose condition in which they were deposited. Twenty-five times natural size. B. Sedimentary rock (sandstone) composed of grains of quartz bound together with cement consisting of calcium carbonate. The photograph shows a transparent slice of the rock, about 0.03 mm. thick; 13½ times natural size. (R. W. Powers.)

more difficult for ground water to percolate through it. Compaction is generally the chief process of lithification of the fine-grained sediments, clay and silt.

In *cementation* the spaces between the grains of a sediment are gradually filled with substances, such as calcium carbonate, silica, and iron oxides, chemically precipitated from solution in connate water and later in other ground water (Fig. 17–20). Cementation is generally the chief process of lithification in the coarse-grained sediments, sand and gravel, because of ease of percolation of water through the relatively large openings between the particles.

Crystallization is the least-well understood of the activities of lithification. In some bodies of quartz sand, lying buried at depth in the zone of saturation, each grain of quartz grows by crystallization to form a texture of interlocking crystals, like that of an igneous rock. In bodies of fine sediment in similar environments new minerals, different from those in the original sediment, are known to have formed by crystallization.

Stratigraphy

Stratigraphy is *the study of stratified rocks.* Its aim is to learn the sources of the sediments, the agencies that transported and deposited them, the environments in which they were deposited, and their relation to each other both horizontally and vertically. Our best introduction to stratigraphy is an example of how the geologist goes about this study in the field.

Field study of a sequence of strata. Figure 17–21 shows a sequence of strata exposed in a steep slope. We examine the rocks systematically by climbing up the slope, taking notes as we go. We identify the kinds of rock present and determine the thickness of each of the layers or strata, of which there are five (numbered A to E in the figure). The surfaces of contact between any two units are not alike. The contacts between D and E and between C and D are sharp and distinct, whereas those between A and B and between B and C are transitional—that is, they represent a gradation between the layer beneath and the layer above. Looking for fossils to help determine the origins of the rocks, we find fossils of marine animals in units A, B, C, and D and the fossil bones of land animals in unit E.

Examining sandstone A, we find it is made up of grains of quartz and other minerals. All the minerals in this group occur in igneous rocks; so we infer that the sandstone was built of the sediment resulting from the erosion of igneous rocks. The sediment might have been derived from its parent rocks either directly or remotely, for it could have formed part of one or more sandstones older than the one we are examining. In either case the sandstone shows sorting, for the proportion of quartz to other minerals is far greater than in most igneous rocks. Probably this means that the durable quartz grains survived their trip from the region of erosion to the region of deposition in much greater numbers than did their less resistant associates. However, under a hand lens we can see that even the quartz grains have become moderately well rounded. From this we judge roughly that the journey involved considerable distances, long periods of time, or both.

Stratification of the sandstone is indistinct; the rock lacks well-marked laminae. This is because all the sand grains have nearly the same diameter; hence there is little distinction between one layer and the next. Yet the faint laminae that are present lie flat and nearly parallel. From this we infer that the sand was deposited in water deep enough to be beyond the reach of waves and strong currents. We can suppose that the sand was either derived from wave erosion of cliffs of an older sandstone or brought into the sea by rivers that carried some of the products of weathering of rocks lying inland. In the latter case the streams must have possessed considerable energy, enough to enable them to move sand grains over their beds; this in turn suggests that the slope was fairly steep—that the tributary region was one of hills or mountains. These are only suggestions, and they could hardly be verified from a study of this one exposure. Verification could come only from wide study of the sandstone and of the tributary region.

We note that in the upward direction the sand becomes finer and begins to be accompanied by silt. The silt then increases and is accompanied by clay, so that as we go upward we pass from sandstone through siltstone into shale (unit *B*). In the shale we find the same near-parallelism of the laminae and much the same kinds of marine fossils. Hence the only properties that have changed, as compared with the sandstone beneath, are the size and shape of grains and the kind of minerals present, because the

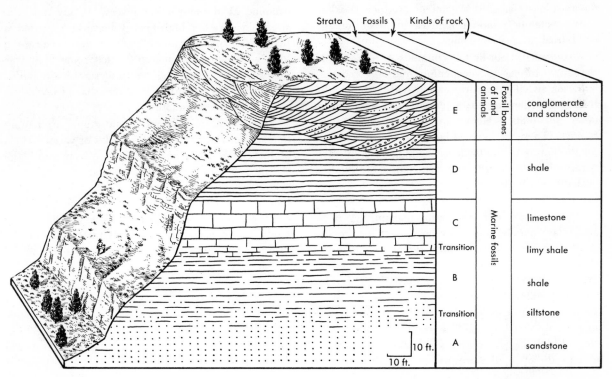

Fig. 17–21. Ideal sequence of strata exposed in a steep slope. Compare Fig. 5–2, A.

fine particles that constitute shale consist not of quartz but of clay minerals. We can explain the change in one of two ways. Either the water deepened, shifting the zone of sand deposition farther toward the shore and causing the deposition of mud here, or the contributing streams lost energy and deposited their sand before reaching the sea. To determine the cause, much wider study would be required.

The upper part of the shale becomes calcareous, that is, it begins to include calcite along with the clay minerals, and by transition it passes upward into nearly pure limestone (unit C) containing the same general kinds of fossils as those beneath. On close inspection the limestone is seen to be a mechanical deposit of fragments of shells. We can infer with confidence that mud ceased to be supplied to this part of the sea, the water cleared, and marine organisms became abundant. This could have been brought about by continued deepening.

Examining unit D, we find no transition from C but instead an abrupt change from limestone to shale. Here we find the same kinds of fossils and the same flat-lying, parallel laminae; only the composition of the rock has changed. We infer a sudden shoaling of the water or a sudden increase in stream energy rather than a gradual change.

A summary of our findings on units A, B, C, and D suggests a former sea, deepening gradually and perhaps somewhat irregularly or fed with sediment by rivers with changing characteristics; or there may be other possibilities. Hence we are left with uncertainties. These are something a geologist expects, for the nature of the evidence he must rely on often permits him to do no more than judge the relative probability of alternative explanations of the same feature.

However, from our observation that units A, B, C, and D are parallel and show no sign of intervening breaks we can infer with little doubt that together they represent continuous, unbroken sedimentation on the sea floor. The strata are *conformable* (p. 371).

Unit E differs from those below it. It is part sandstone and part conglomerate and is cross-stratified in wedge-shaped units. The repetition of wedge-shaped beds suggests currents that shifted in position and in direction; the occurrence of both sand and gravel indicates changes in energy as well; and finally the common direction of inclination of the laminae suggests general flow from right to left.

Also, this unit contains the fossil bones of land animals. This fact rules out the sea; the presence of conglomerate rules out the wind. Accordingly, we conclude that probably E was deposited by a stream or streams, and the dimensions of the wedge-shaped beds give a clue to the size of the stream channels. Streams today are seen to deposit just such beds.

Evidently E overlies D with a contact that is notably irregular and that cuts through some of the uppermost laminae of D. This relationship could result only from erosion of D before or during the deposition of E. It is *disconformable* (p. 373).

From these facts we infer that the sea floor emerged for some reason not shown by the evidence at this place. Unit D thereby became land, and a stream flowed over it, eroding an unknown amount of its upper part. To determine how much of D was removed during this erosion and whether to attribute all of the erosion to the stream or part of it to some agency that antedated the stream, we should have to examine D at many other places. At any rate, the stream had rather high energy because it carried a bed load of pebbles as well as sand and because the load was abundant enough so that some of it was deposited. Evidently the stream was gradually building up its bed because the wedge-shaped layers are superposed one on another.

The sand grains, like most sand grains, are mainly quartz, but the pebbles are samples of various kinds of rock. Here is a clue to the region from which the stream brought the pebbles. To make use of it, we should have to identify the kinds of rock in the pebbles and to search (probably in the direction to the right of Figure 17–21) for areas in which those same kinds of rock occur as bedrock. A further clue to the distance the sediment has been transported is found in the shapes of the grains.

This is the way in which sedimentary rocks are commonly studied in the field. From such a study it is possible to recreate a general sequence of events, but, as we have seen, not all our inferences are firm; we cannot always rule out other possibilities; and the study leads to questions that can be answered, if at all, only by extending the inquiry into the surrounding region.

Rock units: formations. We identified unit *A* (in Figure 17–21) as a sandstone, but a thorough study of it must go much further. The unit must be distinguished from other sandstones. One respect in which it differs from all others is its position in the vertical sequence of strata. It is given a designation by which its position is fixed and by which it can be catalogued and referred to by all those who have to do with it. The basic rock unit to which such a designation is applied is the *formation* (p. 66). A formation must constitute a mappable unit—that is, it must be (1) thick and extensive enough to be shown to scale on a geologic map and (2) distinguishable from the strata immediately above and below it, not just at one exposure, but generally, wherever the unit is exposed. Within these requirements a formation can be thin or thick, to suit the geologist's convenience. Its thickness is likely to depend on the degree of detail of the field study and correspondingly on the scale of the map to be made. In North America each formation is given a name, typically the name of a locality near which it is exposed (Lexington Limestone, Fox Hills Sandstone, Green River Formation). Not only sedimentary rocks but igneous and metamorphic rocks as well are identified as formations for mapping purposes (examples: San Juan Tuff, Conway Schist). Figure 5–9 is a geologic map showing several formations.

Formations can be subdivided and also grouped into larger rock units. But, since we are concerned here only with the way in which strata are identified, the formation alone serves our purpose.

Matching of rock units by physical characteristics. Once the layered rock units have been identified in vertical sequence, the extent of each—that is, the area it underlies—must be determined as closely as possible. With few exceptions, layers of sediment are deposited in basins located on land, beneath lakes, or in the sea. A layer of sediment may cover an entire basin or only a part of it. If deposited in the sea or in a lake, the stratum is likely to extend over the whole basin floor. However, during the time, perhaps very long, since its conversion from sediment into sedimentary rock, it may have been eroded and its

original extent may have been reduced, so that only parts or remnants of it may now be preserved. An example is the Pittsburgh Coal Seam, an easily recognized formation, whose original area of perhaps 20,000 square miles has been reduced by long-continued erosion to 5,729 square miles. It is one of the tasks of the geologist to study the remnants so thoroughly that he can determine as nearly as possible the original extent of each formation.

A pile of strata deposited in a roughly circular basin might be crudely likened to a stack of hot cakes on a plate (Fig. 17–22). If the steaming pile is cut through with a knife from top to bottom, the individual cakes can be traced continuously from one side of the plate to the other. The same could be done with a pile of strata transected by a single stream valley. If the hot cakes were eaten except for a few forkfuls carefully left in the positions they occupied as parts of the stack on the plate, reconstruction of the stack would be more difficult, especially if the cakes had been irregular in size and shape. Yet it could be done, at least approximately, and in a similar way the geologist matches the strata preserved in the hills left by erosion. Matching is accomplished by means of physical characteristics such as grain size, grain shape, mineral content, kind of stratification, and color. Matching on this basis is likely to be reliable over short distances but generally becomes less reliable over longer distances because the physical characteristics tend to change in lateral directions. We shall return to this change after showing how strata are correlated by means of their fossils.

Fig. 17–22. Stack of hot cakes, a simple analogy with a pile of sedimentary strata in a circular basin of deposition. The single knife cut shows how individual layers can be traced continuously along a valley cut through the rocks after sedimentation ceased.

Fig. 17–23. Cross-stratification in sandstone (Monument Valley, Arizona) built by currents flowing right to left. Although the foreset laminae are inclined steeply, the bedding (emphasized by dotted lines) is nearly horizontal. Hence cross-stratification does not violate the principle that sedimentary rocks are deposited in nearly horizontal layers. The cavities result from solution (a part of the general process of weathering) at places where calcium carbonate cement between the (quartz) sand grains is specially soluble. (Tad Nichols.)

Correlation by means of fossils. The usefulness of matching by physical characteristics is virtually limited to the area of the basin in which the strata were deposited originally. In order to determine equivalence in the ages of strata in different basins, and even in different continents, geologists generally compare the fossils contained in the strata. Fossils are the chief basis of stratigraphic *correlation,* which we define as the *determination of the equivalence, in geologic age and stratigraphic position, of stratigraphic units in different areas.*

Correlation involves also the acceptance of two principles, the principle of original horizontality and the principle of stratigraphic superposition. The means by which strata can be correlated consist of fossils and, secondarily, radioactive isotopes. We first

state the principles and then describe the means of correlation.

Principle of original horizontality. The first principle on which correlation is based was stated on page 45. It is that *sedimentary strata are horizontal, or nearly so, when deposited.* This is true even of strata that are cross-stratified (Fig. 17–23). From this *principle of original horizontality* it follows that strata that are not broadly horizontal have been deformed by movements of the crust, like those described in Chapter 18.

Principle of stratigraphic superposition. The second basic principle was first fully set forth by William Smith (1769–1839), an observant land surveyor in southern England, whose profession gave him an ideal opportunity to observe the terrain and rocks in that region. He soon realized that the strata lie "like slices of bread and butter" in a definite, unvarying sequence, with the oldest at the bottom and the youngest at the top. From this arrangement we derive the *principle of stratigraphic superposition,* which says that *in any sequence of strata, not later disturbed, the order in which they were deposited is from bottom to top.* Using this principle, Smith got to know the sequence of strata so well that by looking at a piece of sedimentary rock collected almost anywhere in southern England he could tell the formation from which it had come and, of course, its exact place in the sequence.

The principle of superposition encounters a difficulty, which, however, is apparent rather than real. In some mountain districts the sedimentary rocks have been so greatly bent, buckled, or faulted that in places older strata lie on top of younger, as we can see in Figure 21–9. If such exceptions exist, it is fair to ask whether the principle itself is really valid. The answer is yes, and it is based on direct evidence. In some of the exceptional cases the older rocks are separated from the younger by a fault (Fig. 18–26), which demonstrates that the original sequence has been altered. In other cases special features within some individual stratum demonstrate which is the top and which the bottom of that stratum (Fig. 18–14), and the demonstration is independent of the position of the stratum in the sequence as a whole. Such features include cross-stratification, ripple marks, mud cracks, footprints, graded beds, and some kinds of rhythmic lamination. Turn Figures 17–8, 17–21, and 17–23 upside down and note the differences between bottom and top. Therefore, although we must take care to identify places in which disturbances have folded or faulted the rocks, such disturbances do not violate the principle of superposition.

In some places we find an exposure in which one sedimentary stratum overlies another. The special features that might indicate top and bottom are not present, but the problem of which stratum is the younger is solved in this way: close examination shows that the overlying unit contains fragments of the underlying unit incorporated in it as part of its original sediment. Hence the upper unit is the younger of the two, and at this place, therefore, the sequence is not upside-down but right-side-up. This too, can be stated as a general principle: *if one of two rock bodies contains fragments of the other, it is the younger.*

Fossils and evolution. His close observation as a surveyor told William Smith another thing: most of the strata he saw contain sets of fossils that are peculiar to those strata. In other words the fossils are identification tags by which the strata can be recognized and correlated. Smith made this revolutionary discovery in 1796, and later wrote: ". . . The organised Fossils (which might be called the antiquities of Nature), and their localities also, may be understood by all, even the most illiterate: for they are so fixed in the earth as not to be mistaken or misplaced; and may be . . . readily referred to in any part of the . . . Stratum which contains them. . . ."

Smith's discovery was an empirical one; at the time neither he nor others understood why this relation of fossils to layers of rock is invariable. But the principle was verified and confirmed, and it constitutes a cornerstone of stratigraphy. While Smith was studying the strata in southern England, French geologists, working in the Paris region, discovered that the differences among the various sets of fossils are systematic. They found that the higher and younger the strata, the more nearly their contained fossils resemble living animals and plants. Charles Darwin's great study of evolution, published in 1859, coupled with an increasing general realization that the time required for deposition of the strata has been vast, made clear the explanation of these systematic differences in the fossils. It was seen that from the time of deposition of very old strata animals and plants have been evolving toward the kinds that are living today; the fossils in any one stratum are records of the stage of evolution reached at the time when that stratum was deposited as sediment. Viewed broadly, this principle applies not only to a single basin but to the whole world. In other words, by study of its contained fossils not only can the eroded remnants of a stratum be correlated within the limits of a single former basin of deposition, but also layers of rock can be correlated broadly from one basin to another and even from one continent to another. Thus correlation by means of fossils can be used to establish not only the former continuity of a single stratum or formation but also the general time-equivalence of widely separated strata that never possessed physical continuity or physical similarity. This is possible only because time has been so long and the evolution of organisms so slow that broad evolutionary changes have been able to penetrate throughout the world before being superseded by other later ones.

It is therefore common practice to correlate widely separated erosion remnants of sedimentary rocks by recognizing similar assemblages of fossils in each remnant (Fig. 17–24).

Sedimentary facies. Let us return now to the physical characteristics of strata. If these characteristics were uniform throughout the broad lateral extent of a layer, correlation could be accomplished without the use of fossils. However, most strata change character from one area to another. A simple example consists of the marine deposits made along a coast, at the shore and offshore. The coarsest sediments are found in the beach; offshore the sediments become gradually finer. This distribution reflects the fact that fine sediments remain in suspension longer than coarse.

A *distinctive kind of sediment within a single stratum* is a sedimentary *facies* (Lat. "aspect") (Fig. 17–25). The beach represents a coarse-grained facies; when converted into rock, it would probably form a sandstone. The offshore part of the deposit would be a finer-grained facies; as a rock it might be a siltstone or a shale, and still farther seaward the shale might pass gradually into limestone. Two facies grade laterally into each other, gradually or rather abruptly, according to the conditions of deposition.

If a sedimentary unit were exposed in section from end to end of its extent, it could be identified as a unit despite changes in its facies. But if, as is usual, only widely separated parts of it are exposed and each part represents a different facies, its contained fossils would be needed for correlation. There are difficulties because the assemblages of fossils in two facies may differ somewhat, even though the organisms they represent lived at the same time. This happens because the environments in which the organisms lived were different. In the same sea deep-water shellfish differ in some respects from shallow-water kinds, just as on land animals living in deserts differ from those living at the same time in moist, forested regions.

However, the variations of fossils with varying facies do not prevent correlation; they only make correlation more difficult than it would be otherwise.

Correlation by means of radioactive isotopes. In Chapter 4 we explained how some igneous rocks can be dated by measurement of radioactive isotopes contained in them. Sedimentary strata, having known relations to dated igneous rocks, can therefore be correlated in a general way from one region to another. This method, however, depends upon so many conditions that it can not be used widely as yet.

Stratigraphic column and time scale. By common agreement, geologists have grouped the strata into a *stratigraphic column* (also called *geologic column*).

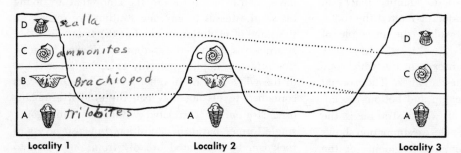

Fig. 17–24. Correlation of strata exposed at 3 localities, many miles apart, on a basis of similarity of the groups of fossils they contain. The fossil groups show that at locality 3 stratum B is missing because C directly overlies A. Was B never deposited there, or was it deposited but later removed by erosion, before the deposition of C?

This is *a table* (Table 4–1) *which shows the succession of rocks from the bottom upward.* It has been generally adopted and is used in most parts of the world. Its subdivisions are based on the groups of fossils that are found in them. A standard column of this kind is an essential convenience in the correlation of strata between one continent and another because it makes possible the use of the same terms, having standard meanings, no matter where the rocks occur geographically and no matter what names are used for them locally. Thus two units, one in the United States and one in western Europe, established as approximately equivalent in time because the fossils they contain are closely similar, might both be referred to the Paleocene Series, although each has its own distinctive local name.

The standard stratigraphic column also serves as a standard time scale. The same names that are applied to the standard groups of strata are used also for the corresponding time intervals during which the strata were deposited. For example, in Tables 4–1 and 4–2 the Cretaceous *System* (a sequence of strata) is shown as having been deposited during the Cretaceous *Period* (a time interval); similarly, the Miocene *Series* (a subdivision of a system) was deposited during the Miocene *Epoch* (a subdivision of a period). The standard column and time scale is thus both a catalog and an index, a flexible filing system that can be used in discussing rock units or units of geologic time. Like all filing systems, it can be altered to suit changing needs brought about by increasing knowledge of the strata. It is essentially a patchwork,

which has been evolving for more than 150 years through the common effort of geologists in all parts of the world.

The standard time units are arranged in correct relative order because they are based directly on the order of superposition of the strata. In themselves they give no information as to the absolute time, as measured in years, represented by each. However, the time scale in Table 4–2 has been calibrated crudely by isotopic dating of igneous rocks occurring in determinable positions with respect to the sedimentary-rock units.

SUMMARY

1. Sedimentary rocks underlie three-quarters of the area of the continental masses.

2. Sedimentary rocks are classified as (*a*) clastic and (*b*) non-clastic.

3. The most obvious characteristic of sedimentary rocks is that they are stratified. Stratification includes parallel stratification and cross-stratification. Different arrangements of the particles are seen in uniform beds, graded beds, and nonsorted beds.

4. Sediments become rounded and sorted in transport in water and air but not in transport by glaciers and mass-wasting.

5. Ripple marks, mud cracks, fossils, and red color in sedimentary rocks give evidence of the environment of deposition.

6. Sediments are converted into rocks by compaction, cementation, and crystallization.

7. Stratigraphy is the study of stratified rocks.

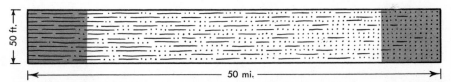

Fig. 17–25. Vertical section of a stratum showing change of sedimentary facies from sandstone (*right*) through siltstone (*center*) to shale (*left*). The direction of increase in grain size indicates that the source of the sediment was to the right. If only the shaded parts of the stratum remained, the intervening part having been lost through erosion, correlation by physical character would be impossible, and correlation by the use of fossils would be necessary.

From it most of our knowledge of the Earth's history has been learned.

8. The basic rock units are formations, each with a locality name.

9. Strata are correlated from place to place by means of fossils and in some instances by radioactive isotopes.

10. Correlation is based on the two principles that strata were horizontal when deposited and that they were formed in sequence from bottom to top.

11. The stratigraphic column is the basic catalog of rock layers used by geologists.

REFERENCES

Dunbar, C. O., and Rodgers, John, 1957, Principles of stratigraphy: New York, John Wiley and Sons.

Hatch, F. H., and Rastall, R. H., 1938, The petrology of the sedimentary rocks, 3d ed., revised by Maurice Black: London, Allen and Unwin.

Krumbein, W. C., and Sloss, L. L., 1951, Stratigraphy and sedimentation: San Francisco, W. H. Freeman and Co.

Pettijohn, F. J., 1957, Sedimentary rocks: New York, Harper & Bros, 2d ed.

Shrock, R. R., 1948, Sequence in layered rocks: New York, McGraw-Hill Book Co.

CHAPTER 18. DEFORMATION OF THE EARTH'S CRUST

Terra firma in motion   *Records in land forms*   *Bending and breaking of bedrock*   *Varied effects on rock masses*   *Mechanism of deformation*   *Superposed structural effects*   *Major gaps in the geologic record*

Cobbles and boulders marking a former shore zone, now 200 feet above sea level. Northeast Greenland. (A. L. Washburn.)

General evidence

We have looked briefly at several kinds of evidence pointing to large movements of the Earth's crust, both up and down. Layers of sedimentary rock that abound in fossils of marine organisms lie far above sea level in high mountains and plateaus; large bodies of igneous rock that must have cooled deep underground are widely exposed in high country; distinctive features that match closely those seen along present seashores are found on high terraces (Fig. 16–10); petrified trees and the bones of land animals are imbedded in shales underneath thick marine deposits, all now exposed to view in valley walls (Fig. 4–2). We have reasoned, also, that repeated uplifts of continents have been required to maintain the lands, which otherwise would have been consumed by erosion long ago.

Let us now examine parts of the evidence in some detail to determine whether there are distinctive patterns in the movements, how they have been distributed in time, and what lasting effects they have had on the visible bedrock.

Movements detected in progress

Abrupt movements. In 1915 the arid region of central Nevada was shaken by an earthquake that would have brought disaster to a populous city. Along the west base of the Tobin Range a steep cliff (*scarp*) was formed, as high as 16 feet and extending for 17 miles along the mountain front (Fig. 18–1, **A**). This scarp marks the upper part of a fault (Fig. 18–1, **B**), along which the crustal block under Pleasant Valley has moved down in relation to the range (though, as far as we know, the range may have been moved up). Many parts of the Basin and Range province (Pl. 1, inside front cover) are subject to earthquakes, and

several shocks recorded since the region was settled have been accompanied by displacements of the ground. A scarp in Owens Valley, California, made at the time of an earthquake in 1872, is more than 20 feet high. Perhaps the Sierra Nevada a short distance west of it grew by that amount in relation to the desert basin east of it; but we do not know how either of these crustal blocks moved in relation to sea level, since no reference points giving precise altitudes had been established in those immediate areas. Only the relative movements of blocks along many faults are known (Fig. 18–1, **C**).

The largest known displacement at the time of an earthquake occurred in 1899 at Yakutat Bay, Alaska, where a stretch of the shoreline, with beach deposits, barnacle-covered rocks, and other telltale features was lifted as much as 47 feet. This visible measure may not be complete because the presumed fault is hidden offshore and the crustal block on the other side of it, entirely under the sea, possibly went down and so increased the total displacement. This locality is at the western base of the St. Elias Range. Is this range still growing, and was the movement in 1899 just the latest of innumerable upward pulses that have made this mountain mass high? At least we know that the landward block went up at the time of the earthquake because our standard surface of reference, sea level, is right there for an accurate check.

During the San Francisco earthquake of 1906 there was abrupt horizontal movement along the San Andreas fault. Roads and fences that crossed the fault were offset as much as 21 feet (Fig. 18–2, **A**). In 1940 another earthquake occurred with horizontal movement along a branch of the same fault in Imperial Valley, nearly 500 miles southeast of San Francisco;

A

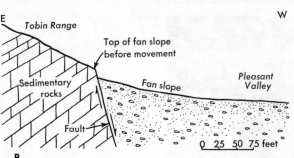

E
Tobin Range

Top of fan slope before movement

Sedimentary rocks

Fan slope

Pleasant Valley

W

Fault

0 25 50 75 feet

B

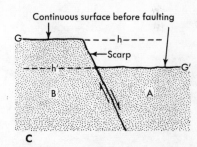

Continuous surface before faulting

G

h

Scarp

h'

G'

B

A

C

Fig. 18—1. A. Scarp at west base of Tobin Range, Nevada, formed in 1915 with attending earthquake. The whitish band marks a displacement at the top of the fan slope, several miles from the camera. (Eliot Blackwelder.) **B.** Vertical section across lower part of range and adjoining slope. Half-arrows indicate relative movement of crustal blocks. **C.** The scarp made by displacement of a level surface G-G' may mean that block *A* dropped from the position *h*, that block *B* moved up from the position *h'*, or that both blocks moved in some measure to give the net displacement we see.

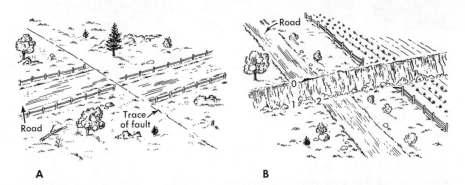

Road

Trace of fault

Road

0
1 2

A

B

Fig. 18—2. Varied movement on faults. **A.** Horizontal movement on the San Andreas fault in 1906, shown by offsetting of a road and fences. **B.** Movement with both vertical and horizontal components, as at Mino-Owari, Japan, in 1891. Edge of road moved diagonally between **0** and **2**. Movement wholly in a vertical plane would have placed edge of road at **1**.

Fig. 18–3. A. Scarp along slope near Fairview Peak, Nevada, made at time of an earthquake in 1954. View looking south. Scarp is 10 to 12 feet high. Ridge in middle distance was offset about 12 feet horizontally. B. Close view of the Fairview Peak scarp. Note the loose debris in the scarp, subject to rapid erosion. The Tobin Range scarp (Fig. 18–1), somewhat higher, exposes bedrock. (C. R. Longwell.)

the displacement, as much as 17 feet, was registered accurately by offset rows of fruit trees as well as by broken fences. Horizontal movement, then, seems to be a habit of this fault (p. 367). Possibly there was some horizontal as well as vertical movement at Yakutat Bay and the Tobin Range, but no road or other linear feature crossed the fault at either of those places to show a lateral shift. During an earthquake

in Japan in 1891 a road was broken and offset both vertically and horizontally (Fig. 18–2, B). In 1954 an abrupt movement near Fairview Peak, Nevada, caused a strong earthquake. The line of fracture is marked by a prominent scarp, similar to the break in slope at the base of the Tobin Range. A ridge transverse to the Fairview Peak scarp was offset laterally, thus demonstrating that the movement had a hori-

Clam borings

High-water mark

Fig. 18—4. Columns in a Roman ruin at Pozzuoli, Italy, as they appeared in 1828. The measure of former submergence is indicated by borings of marine clams. (Drawing copied from Lyell, Principles of Geology, 12th Edition, 1875.)

zontal component (Fig. 18–3, **A**).

Scarps that record recent faulting generally expose loose regolith (Fig. 18–3, **B**). Unless these scarps are renewed by repeated movements, they are short-lived, though in arid regions some are recognizable through several human generations.

Slow movements. Abrupt crustal movements that are measurable are known only along faults and have been attended by earthquakes, but it does not follow that all movements on faults are abrupt. A notable exception has claimed much attention because it interfered with production in an oil field. Near Bakers-field, California, the steel-tube linings in a number of oil wells were slowly bent, and some of them finally were sheared off, by movement on a fault with rather low dip. The rate of movement averaged a little more than one inch per year over a period of

17 years. From our viewpoint this is a slow rate, but the total movement would be a third of a mile if it should continue for 20,000 years, which is only a moment in geologic time.

Example in Italy. A classic example of slow changes in level of the land is supplied by the ruins of a Roman market place known as the Temple of Serapis, west of Naples. Three columns that are left standing have been bored by a peculiar marine clam to a height about 20 feet above the floor (Fig. 18–4), and the shells of the animals still line some of the borings. Along the shore near the ruin are sediments that contain abundant shells of ordinary clams like those now living in the adjoining bay; these deposits are exposed in bluffs as much as 23 feet above present sea level. An obvious suggestion to explain these exhibits is a world-wide rise and later withdrawal

Mean tide, 1839

A

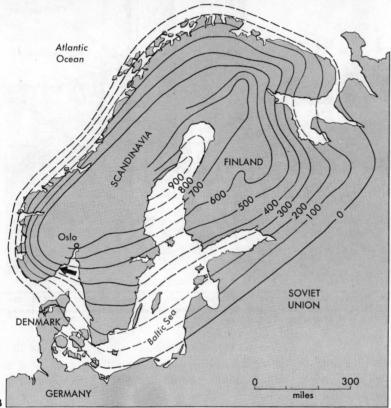

Atlantic
Ocean

SCANDINAVIA

FINLAND

900 800 700 600 500 400 300 200 100 0

Oslo

DENMARK

Baltic Sea

SOVIET
UNION

GERMANY

B

0   300
miles

Fig. 18–5. A. Evidence of change in relation of land to sea level near Oslo, Norway. A horizontal line cut into granitic
rock, marking position of mean tide in
1839, was 12 inches above mean tide in
1939, though sea level had risen measurably during the same period. Location is
indicated by arrow on map, B, southwest
of Olso. (Olaf Holtedahl.) B. Evidence of
differential uplift, shown on map of region
around Baltic Sea. Dashed lines indicate
rise of land, in feet, since disappearance
of latest Pleistocene ice cap. Lines are
projected across water-covered areas and
omitted on parts of Scandinavia where no
evidence in emerged shorelines has been
reported (From R. A. Daly, Our Mobile
Earth, Charles Scribner's Sons, 1936.)

of sea water while the land remained stationary.
But such fluctuations would have left a record in
coastal belts everywhere. As the evidence cited above
is found only within a limited area near the old ruin,
we conclude that this part of the Italian coastal belt
sank and was re-elevated within very recent time.
According to human records, part of the uplift occurred after A.D. 1500.

Record in the Baltic region. Uplift on a more impressive scale has been noticed for a long time by
dwellers along the Baltic and North Seas. Old sea-
men have pointed out low rocky islets in harbors
where a few generations earlier only shoals were re-

ported, and farmers have been impressed by the
large numbers of marine shells scattered over the
fields in coastal areas. More than a hundred years
ago students of this problem were convinced that
the Baltic shores were rising as much as 3 or 4 feet
per century; this figure has been confirmed by observations on markers set up for the purpose and by
systematic surveys with modern tide gages (Fig.
18–5, A). The rate is at a maximum in northeastern
Sweden and decreases southward to zero in northern
Denmark. How long has this widespread movement
been going on?

A convincing answer is given by those whose curiosity has led them to study all the evidence related to the latest glacial age in the Baltic region (Chap. 13). At its greatest extent the ice sheet covered Scandinavia, the present Baltic Sea, and Finland, and its southern edge touched northern Germany. Not until much of the ice had wasted away, leaving mere remnants in the Scandinavian highlands, could the sea re-enter the Baltic area. Yet we now find clearly marked shorelines, with beaches and marine shells, at many heights up to about 900 feet above present sea level (Fig. 18–5, **B**). These marks of the sea were made on the deposits left by the latest glaciation. Clearly, then, when the ice disappeared, the whole region was lower and the Baltic sea larger than it is now. Uplift, still going on, has carried part of the land up at least 900 feet, and perhaps considerably more because upward movement may have started while the ice still covered the northern part of the Baltic area, where the highest shorelines are developed. The upwarp has the form of an elongate dome, highest in the central part of the area covered by the ice sheet.

The latest ice sheet was disappearing from the Baltic lands about 10,000 years ago. Archeologists have established that many people lived in Europe at that time, south of the glacier ice. The uplift around the Baltic, then, occurred during the human history of the region, though we find no indication in written records that early peoples were conscious of this important geographic change. The first of the Vikings must have seen the Baltic lands with out-

lines different from those of today, and no doubt the succeeding generations of seafarers were aware of continuing changes, which probably were more rapid in the earlier stages.

North American examples. The Earth has been writing its own record of uplift in the Baltic region. The elevated shorelines described above outline the size and shape of the surface that has moved up and give a minimal measure of uplift since the weight of the ice was removed. Similar uplift occurred in a large area of Canada and northern United States when the great ice sheet in that region wasted away. Emerged shorelines similar to those in Scandinavia are recognized along the St. Lawrence Valley and the coast of Labrador at altitudes ranging up to hundreds of feet.

Lakes Superior, Michigan, and Huron are bordered by several old shorelines which in the northern part of the area are high above the present lakes. All these well-marked features slope southward and are near the present water surface along the southern part of Lake Michigan (Fig. 18–6). The angle of slope of each shoreline increases toward the north, and each higher (and older) line is inclined more steeply than the one next below it. These old shores cannot be followed continuously, for they have been destroyed by erosion in some stretches, and doubtless they were less clearly developed in some areas than in others. But careful regional study is the basis for a confident restoration, and the essential relations, shown diagrammatically in Figure 18–6, clearly re-

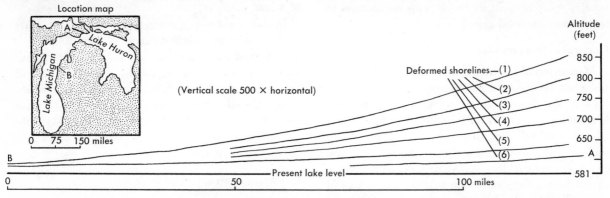

Fig. 18–6. Diagram representing, with greatly exaggerated vertical scale, tilted shorelines in the Great Lakes region. Features represented are along sides of Lakes Michigan and Huron, between points A and B on small location map. Note that the older shorelines are not only tilted but also warped to profiles that are concave upward. (Modified from J. W. Goldthwaite, Journal of Geology, 1908, vol. 16, p 459–476.)

cord repeated uplifts increasing in amount toward the north. Human records through several centuries are not available for this region, as they are in northern Europe; therefore we cannot say that uplift in North America has been actually "observed" by man. But precise surveys have detected a slow tilting in the region of the Great Lakes, similar to the differential uplift to which the lake terraces bear witness. Thus we have good grounds for including broad uplift in that region as a movement detected in progress.

The elevated marine shorelines along the southeast coast of Canada also indicate increase of uplift toward the north and northwest, that is, toward the central part of the area that was blanketed with thick ice during the glacial ages (Chap. 13). The marine shorelines, and also those bordering the Great Lakes, were developed on deposits left by the glacier ice. Therefore, the uplift recorded by these elevated and deformed shorelines has occurred since, and probably in part during, the melting away of the continental ice sheet.

Thus we can reason logically that removal of great ice caps in northern Europe and in North America has resulted in strong unwarping in the areas that were freed from those great loads. The postglacial uplifts in the two regions, as we shall consider later (Chap. 20), represent recovery from downbending of the Earth's crust under the weight of the great ice caps. It appears, then, that shifting of great masses at the Earth's surface, as in the building up and wasting away of great ice sheets, imposes changes in the form of the solid globe.

General evidence in land forms

Marine terraces. The raised shorelines around the Baltic are for the most part faintly marked, probably because the rising land did not stay in one position long enough for the waves to sculpture a wide bench and pronounced cliff. In many parts of the world there are well-developed wave-cut benches standing one above another like stairsteps (Fig. 18–7). Some of the lowest steps terminate inland against typical wave-cut cliffs, decorated with barnacle shells and rising above characteristic beach deposits. In higher terraces these critical markings have been dimmed or removed by erosion, but the close similarity in gen-

eral form indicates a like origin for all the steps in a series. Along the California coast the highest recognizable terraces are more than 1,400 feet above the sea. Because these terraces are found along only a part of that coastal area, we reason that a segment of the Coast Ranges has risen in a succession of pulses, separated by pauses long enough to allow development of distinct shore profiles. No one terrace can be followed continuously for a long distance because later erosion has been more destructive in some places than in others and because the wave work that shaped a terrace was not uniformly effective. The altitude of a terrace also varies appreciably from place to place, thereby telling us that the uplift was irregular.

Drowned lands. Accurate surveys of the sea floor north of the Aleutian Islands, Alaska, reveal a submarine topography of high ridges and hills separated by valleys that unite in what appears to be a well-developed drainage system. The only reasonable explanation seems to be the submergence of a wide landscape that was shaped by stream erosion. Was this drowning of a former landscape caused by rise of sea level or by sinking of the land? We know the level of the sea was raised by the return of water that was locked up in ice sheets during the glacial ages. The total rise from this cause is estimated to have been about 300 feet; but the drowned hills and valleys near the Aleutian Islands are at depths greater than 1,200 feet. We infer, therefore, that a large part of the submergence was caused by the sinking of a land mass.

Drowned shorelines are recognized in many parts of the world; the embayed coast of New England is an excellent example (Fig. 16–17), and San Francisco Bay, California, is another. Irregularities in the New England shoreline are explained largely by postglacial rise of sea level. The effect of this rise was of course world-wide and must be taken into account in estimating amounts of actual uplift and depression of lands.

Evidence in structure of bedrock

Only those crustal movements that have occurred fairly late in geologic time are still recorded in surface features because all parts of a land surface are doomed to destruction by erosion. Disturbance of

Fig. 18–7. Successive marine terraces, Palos Verdes, southern California. The lowest terrace (1) in the view is about 150 feet, the highest (5) more than 800 feet above present sea level. (Fairchild Aerial Surveys.)

rocks beneath the Earth's surface gives a more lasting effect. Sedimentary beds are especially useful in preserving records of disturbance because they are essentially horizontal at the start and even a slight bending or breaking is easily detected. Lavas and ash deposits also are layered but as a rule less regularly than sedimentary beds.

Deformation by bending

Broad warping. In the plateaus of Utah and Arizona a thick section of old marine formations lies thousands of feet above sea level and is dissected by deep canyons (Figs. 4–2, 5–5, **A**). In general these rocks are flat-lying, but if any layer is followed in detail it is found to bend upward into irregular domes and downward to form broad, saucer-like basins. Evidently this mass of sedimentary rock, many hundreds of miles across, was not lifted uniformly but was somewhat deformed. The original surface of the uplifted mass has been entirely destroyed by erosion,

but a record of the deformation is preserved in the form of each sedimentary layer to great depth.

*Gentle bending of the crust up or down is **crustal warping**.* The effects of warping are seen clearly in arid plateaus, where deep dissection by streams has exposed the rock layers in wide areas. In the broad lowlands between the Rocky Mountains and the Appalachian Region (Pl. 1), bedrock is visible only in scattered exposures because of widespread soil cover. Geologic field study, aided by records from thousands of wells, has established that sedimentary formations, horizontal or with low dips in large areas, have been warped upward and downward to form a number of large structural domes and basins. Generally these features are not recognized in a single view of exposed rocks. Inclinations of 1 or 2° are not conspicuous, but a layer with a persistent average dip of 2° over a horizontal distance of 5 miles has its altitude changed nearly 1,000 feet.

Structural domes and basins in an area that has

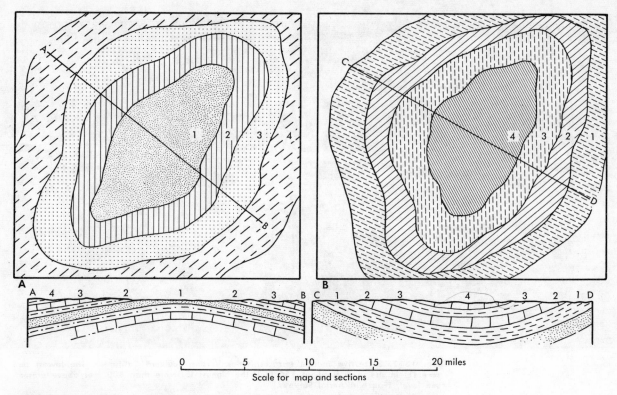

Fig. 18–8. A, B. Broad upwarping and downwarping of sedimentary formations, followed by erosion to nearly flat surfaces, result in strikingly similar patterns on a geologic
map. Over the structural dome A the inner part of the pattern is on the oldest exposed
formation, 1; over the structural basin B the inner area is on the youngest exposed formation, 4. These idealized diagrams resemble many actual examples, some of vast size. On
the Nashville dome in Tennessee the outcrop corresponding to the area 1 in A of this diagram
is 125 miles long, 50 miles wide. Most of the State of Michigan is on a structural basin
measuring about 200 miles east-west, 300 miles north-south. On those large structures the
layers dip at lower angles than in this figure. C. A great dome in French West Africa is almost circular in plan. On the present surface of low relief the more resistant sedimentary
formations form low asymmetric ridges. (U. S. Air Force.)

been much eroded make distinctive patterns on a geologic map (Fig. 18–8).

Folds. *A pronounced bend in layers of rock is a fold.* In many places, especially in mountain zones, stratified rocks have been buckled into more or less regular folds. Some are on a small scale and can be seen directly, but many folds are so large, and exposures of bedrock so scattered, that it is necessary to study and piece together the structure of distinctive layers over many miles before the exact forms of the folds become clear. In parts of central Pennsylvania, where natural exposures are supplemented by cuts along highways and railroads, some folds of large size are clearly displayed (Fig. 18–9).

An upfold in the form of an arch is an **anticline.** *A downfold with trough-like form is a* **syncline.** These terms are of Greek derivation. Anticline means "inclined oppositely"; in this form of fold the layers normally dip in opposite directions from a crest. In a syncline, which means "inclined together," the layers dip from two sides toward the line of flexure.

During the growth of folds, and presumably for some time afterward, anticlines form ridges, synclines form valleys. After erosion has made large progress, the streams tend to seek out the belts of weakest rocks. In the Appalachians many of the high ridges are on synclines and many valleys are along anticlines (Fig. 18–9). Such a reversal of original surface forms is an indication that this mountain belt has gone through a long history since the folds were formed. As we shall see (p. 419), more convincing evidence shows that the Appalachian Mountains are indeed very old.

Elements of folds. In a description of folds several special terms are required. *The sides of a fold are the* **limbs** (Fig. 18–10), *and the median line between the limbs, along the apex of an anticline or the lowest part of a syncline, is the* **fold axis.** This line extends along a bedding surface or along the surface restored if it has been partly eroded. When folds that have horizontal axes are deeply eroded, the ridges made by the edges of resistant layers are near-

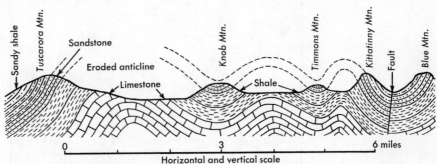

Fig. 18–9. Folds along the Turnpike in central Pennsylvania. Note that most of the valleys are on anticlines, whereas mountain ridges follow synclines except at extreme right where weak shale lies above resistant sandstone. (Modified from A. B. Cleaves and G. H. Ashley, Penn. Geol. Survey, Guidebook to the Geology of the Pennsylvania Turnpike, 1942.)

Fig. 18–10. Elements of simple upright folds. Note that youngest layer (6) has its upper surface facing *toward* the axis of the syncline, *away from* the axis of the anticline.

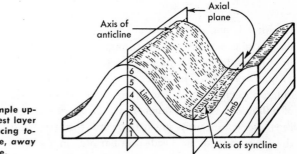

357

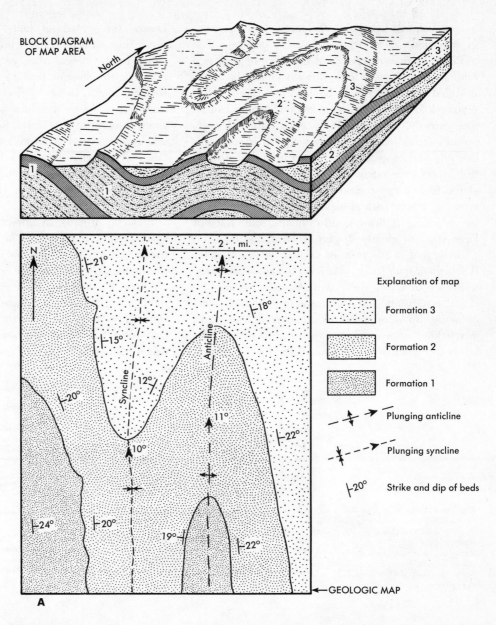

BLOCK DIAGRAM
OF MAP AREA

North

Explanation of map

Formation 3

Formation 2

Formation 1

Plunging anticline

Plunging syncline

Strike and dip of beds

GEOLOGIC MAP

A

ly parallel; but, if the axes are inclined, on a nearly flat erosion surface the outcropping edges of beds in opposite limbs of a fold converge and finally meet (Fig. 18–11, **A**). The result is a hairpin turn in the outcrop in either kind of fold; but there are two ways of telling one from the other. In the ordinary syncline dips are consistently inward toward the axis, and the *younger* beds lie inside the hairpin; in an ordi-

nary anticline dips are outward from the axis, and the *older* beds lie inside the hairpin (Fig. 18–11, **B**).

*A fold with inclined axis is a **plunging fold,** and the angle the fold axis makes with the horizontal is the **plunge** of the fold.*

The **axial plane** of a fold *is an imaginary plane through the middle of the fold and including its axis* (Fig. 18–10). In a regular fold this plane is one of

B

Fig. 18–11. A. Plunging folds as they appear on a geologic map and in a block diagram. Folds similar to these are common in parts of the Appalachian belt in central Pennsylvania. **B.** Airview northwest across Sheep Mountain, a high ridge 15 miles long in the Bighorn Basin, Wyoming. The ridge is at the axis of a doubly plunging anticline. The older formations are resistant and form the ridge. Younger formations, largely shale with some sandstone layers, have been eroded from the top of the fold but make some low ridges in the lower ground. These low ridges bend around each end of the mountain, thus registering the plunge. Bighorn River has cut a deep canyon across Sheep Mountain. (John S. Shelton.)

symmetry; each point on the left of the plane is the mirror image of a corresponding point on the right of it. In an upright fold the plane is essentially vertical; but many folds have been pushed over until their axial planes are strongly inclined and even deformed into curved surfaces (Fig. 18–12).

Some variations in folds. A fold with limbs that diverge at an obtuse angle is an open fold. Folds with acute angles between limbs are *closed folds. Folds whose limbs are essentially parallel* are *isoclinal* ("equally inclined") *folds.* In many mountain zones the sedimentary formations have been closely folded and isoclinal folds are not uncommon. Where erosion has cut away the crests of such folds, some skill is required in working out the structure because in limited outcrops the anticlines and synclines look

Fig. 18–12. Overturned syncline in the Coast Ranges of California, exposed in a cliff about 75 feet high. Weak sedimentary layers are locally broken, offset, and crumpled. The axial plane is much deformed, and at the upper right it is nearly horizontal. (John S. Shelton.)

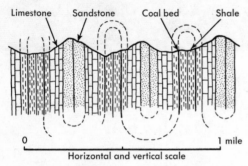

Fig. 18–13. Isoclinal folds, deeply eroded. Exposed beds are essentially parallel and vertical.

alike (Fig. 18–13). The general principle to keep in mind is that the tops of layers face *outward* from the axial plane of an anticline, *inward* toward the axial plane of a syncline (Fig. 18–10). Tops of layers are indicated by a number of peculiar markings made while the sediments in the beds were being deposited (Fig. 18–14). Under extreme deformation some folds have been completely overturned. *A fold of which the axial plane is essentially horizontal* is a *recumbent fold* (Fig. 18–15). In this fold the layers in one limb are upside down. Huge recumbent folds are common in the Alps and some other mountain belts (Fig. 21–9).

A *monocline* (Gr. "one inclination") is *a one-limb flexure, on either side of which the layers are horizontal or have uniformly gentle dips* (Fig. 18–16). In other words, a monocline is a local steepening of an otherwise uniform dip. Monoclines of large size are well developed, as isolated features, in the generally flat-lying beds of the Colorado Plateau.

Fractures in bedrock

The rocks of the Earth's crust are cut by innumerable fractures, ranging in size from microscopic crevices to breaks hundreds of miles long. These fractures have large geologic and practical importance; they aid weathering and erosion, the circulation of ground water, and the formation of some ore deposits. On

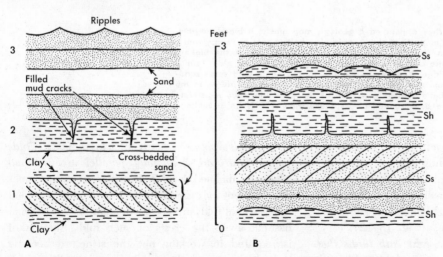

Fig. 18–14. Use of ripple marks, mud cracks, and cross-bedding in determining original tops of sedimentary layers. **A.** Layers in place as they were formed, with sedimentary markings in normal relation. **B.** Similar layers, essentially horizontal but upside down in a deformed section of sedimentary rocks.

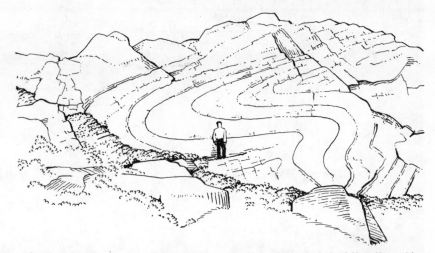

Fig. 18—15. A small recumbent fold exposed in the White Mountain belt of New Hampshire. Under great stress, far beneath the land surface at that time, the beds were thinned on the limbs, thickened at the bends of folds. (Modified from M. P. Billings, Structure and Metamorphism in the Mount Washington area, New Hampshire, Geol. Soc. America Bull., 1941, pp. 863–936, Fig. 7.)

Fig. 18—16. A sharp monocline that interrupts the generally flat-lying sedimentary formations in the wide Colorado Plateau, in southern Utah. The high mass at the left is the Monument Upwarp. Note that the exposed layers are nearly horizontal on both sides of the monocline. View looking south. (John S. Shelton.)

Fig. 18–17. A. Two vertical sets of joints, (1) and (2), essentially at right angles, cutting horizontal sedimentary layers. Drummond Island, Michigan. (U. S. Geol. Survey.) **B.** Two sets of vertical joints, intersecting at right angles, in thick sandstone on the dissected Colorado Plateau, southern Utah. The joints control the drainage pattern. Air view looking south, near junction of Colorado and Green Rivers. (John S. Shelton.)

Fig. 18–18. Curved joints separating thick shells of fresh granite. Top of cliff is 500 feet above foreground. Individual shells are 10 feet or more thick. Half Dome, Yosemite National Park, California. (F. C. Calkins, U. S. Geol. Survey.)

some large fractures movements recur, giving rise to earthquakes (Chap. 20).

A fracture in bedrock on which there has been no appreciable movement parallel to the fracture is a *joint.* Faults are fractures along which movement has occurred (p. 22). Along many fractures there has been barely visible or even microscopic movement, and so there is no sharp distinction between joints and faults.

Joints. Many joints in igneous rocks were caused by contraction on cooling (Fig. 6–20) and so have no connection with crustal movements. But large numbers of joints cutting rocks of all kinds probably are effects of strain connected with warping, folding, and faulting. Commonly, these joints are in definite *sets; a joint set is a group of nearly parallel joints with a considerable distribution. A combination of two or more intersecting sets of joints makes a joint system* (Fig. 18–17). Combined with bedding planes, joint systems simplify quarrying operations, but abundant joints are undesirable if exceptionally large blocks of quarried stone are wanted. Perfect monoliths 50 to 100 feet long are to be had from very few localities.

Curved joints that separate great shells of granite, as on some of the high masses in the Sierra Nevada

(Fig. 18–18), call for a special explanation. They cut fresh rock into slices 10 feet or several tens of feet thick and so are not to be explained as a result of exfoliation in weathering (Fig. 7–6). It has been suggested that erosion of thousands of feet of material since the Sierra Nevada block was uplifted has removed so much weight that the remaining bedrock has expanded appreciably, with separation of large sheets parallel to the surface.

Faults. Generally, there is no way of telling how much actual movement has occurred on either side of a fault. Even if a crystal or pebble in the rock has been cut through by the fracture and the halves carried apart a measurable distance, we cannot know whether one block stood still while the other moved past it or whether both sides shared in the movement (Fig. 18–1, **C**). Conceivably, we might know from precise surveys the exact positions of critical points on the ground before the faulting and later check the positions on each side of the break. Such a check is being attempted along some large faults in California that are known to be active. But most faults with which we have had to deal are old features whose former expression at the Earth's surface was long ago destroyed by erosion.

In classifying fault movements, then, we speak of

apparent and *relative* displacements. Most faulting occurs along inclined fractures. Many veins of metallic ore lie along faults, and we have inherited some terms used by miners working in tunnels, the *walls* of which are on opposite sides of the mineral vein. From the miner's viewpoint, one side overhangs him, the other is beneath his feet. The *hanging wall of an inclined fault* is *the block above the fracture. The block below an inclined fault is the footwall.* These terms, of course, do not apply to exceptional faults that are essentially vertical.

A *normal fault* is *an inclined fault with apparent downward movement of the hanging wall* (Fig. 18–19, B). A *reverse fault* is *an inclined fault with apparent upward movement of the hanging wall* (Fig. 18–19, C). *Large reverse faults with dips considerably less than 45° are thrust faults,* generally known as *thrusts* (Fig. 18–26). An *oblique-slip fault* is *a fault on which movement has both vertical and horizontal components* (Fig. 18–2, B, 18–3). A *fault on which displacement has been chiefly or wholly horizontal is a strike-slip fault,* or a *lateral fault* (Fig. 18–2, A). Horizontal layers of rock can give no measure of such a movement, but displacement of a nearly

vertical dike would record both the direction and the amount of the offset. If an observer, looking directly across this type of fault, sees evidence that the block on the opposite side has moved to his right, it is a *right-lateral fault;* if that block has moved to his left, it is a *left-lateral fault.*

The simplest possible examples are shown in Figure 18–19. Beds and other features of bedrock commonly are more or less inclined and so are likely to be offset by either vertical or horizontal movement. Therefore, the offsetting of rock layers in itself is not a safe guide in solving fault problems. For example, in central Connecticut sheets of old basaltic lava between layers of sandstone form ridges that are offset along a large fault (Fig. 18–20, A). A logical first guess about the faulting would be strike-slip movement of nearly 2 miles, the distance measured along the fault between offset parts of corresponding ridges. We see another possibility; perhaps long ago the block south of the fault was moved up, and as erosion slowly wore it down the outcrops of the lava sheets were shifted steadily eastward. We now look for other evidence and find a large dike of dolerite, essentially vertical, with its outcrop crossed by the

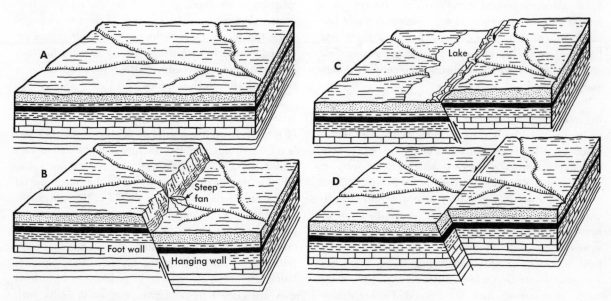

Fig. 18–19. Three principal kinds of faults. A. Unbroken block. B. Simple normal fault, making scarp which stream descends in cascade. C. Reverse fault; projecting edge of hanging-wall block has slumped under its own weight. D. Strike-slip fault, with no expression in topography. Fresh nature of surface features indicates that faulting was recent. Surface expressions of faults are quickly modified by erosion. Each block is about 1,000 feet long.

fault nearly at right angles. The dike is shattered where the fault crosses it but it is not appreciably offset. The dike is chemically identical with the lavas and may well represent a fissure along which some of the magma came up. We conclude that the dike was in place when the faulting occurred and movement must have been vertical, not strike-slip. The lavas and sandstone beds dip about 20° east, and a simple calculation gives about 2,450 feet as the vertical distance the block on the south was lifted above the one on the north (Fig. 18–20, **B**). Several exposures of the fault show a steep dip northwest; therefore, it is a normal fault.

Surface expression of faults. A displacement with a vertical component forms a cliff or scarp (Fig. 18–19, B). Many mountain fronts, hundreds or thousands of feet high, are recognized as fault scarps, but it is extremely unlikely that any were formed by a single movement. What we have learned from faults now active indicates that the stress causing movement is relieved temporarily by displacement of a few feet or tens of feet and then builds up slowly for tens or hundreds of years before movement is repeated. Hence a mountain face such as the west front of the Wasatch Range (Fig. 18–21) may represent countless slips, each accompanied by an earthquake, in a time interval of vast length judged by human standards, though short in the geologic scale of time. Erosion starts modifying such a scarp from its beginning. The upper part is much dissected because that part has been longest under attack, and the attack has been especially vigorous since the top of the block moved to high altitude. Two features at the base indicate that the fault is still alive: the blunt triangular ends of divides between mountain valleys suggest that erosion is not keeping up with displacement, and low scarps breaking the fan slope testify to recent movement.

After stresses along a fault have been fully relieved and movement has ended, erosion has full

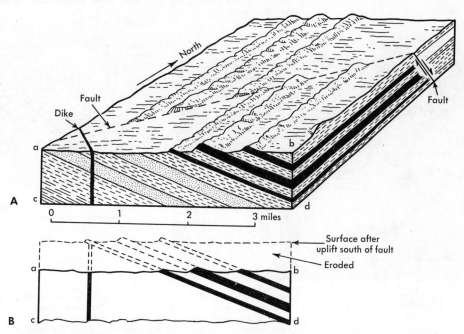

Fig. 18–20. Effects of faulting and later erosion. A. Fault offsetting three buried lava sheets in central Connecticut. Block on southeast side of fault was uplifted and eroded, as shown in B. With erosion, outcrops of lava sheets were shifted eastward, "downdip." This explanation of the offset, rather than strike-slip movement on the fault, is favored because the vertical dike has not been appreciably offset. The dike has same chemical composition as the lavas and presumably was formed at essentially the same time.

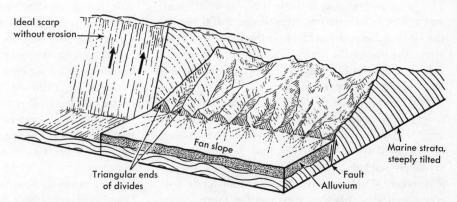

Fig. 18–21. West front of the high Wasatch Range south of Salt Lake City, Utah. The fault marking the nearly straight west base of the range is still active, as indicated by prominent breaks in the fan slope. The triangular ends of stream divides indicate that erosion is not keeping up with movements on the fault. (Modified from A. N. Strahler after W. M. Davis.)

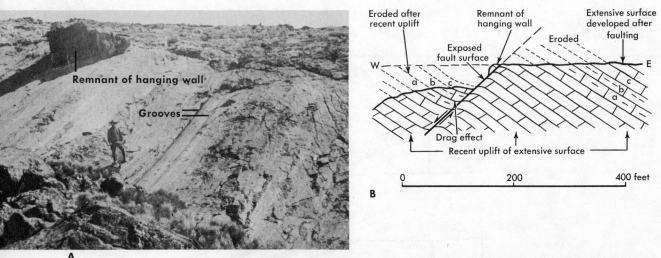

Fig. 18–22. Part of the history of a fault. A. Surface of an old fault in the Spotted Range, southern Nevada, exposed by erosion. The surface is polished and grooved. B. The layers a, b, c, identical on opposite sides of the fault, indicate the measure of displacement. The even surface of erosion on the upthrown block indicates widespread beveling of the layers by erosion before the latest regional uplift. (C. R. Longwell.)

Fig. 18–23. Air view southwest along great fault at McDonald Lake, near Great Slave Lake, northwestern Canada. Maximum height of scarp within view is about 900 feet. This is an old fault, and the scarp was formed by differential erosion, not directly by displacement. This fault can be traced about 300 miles. (Royal Canadian Air Force, Courtesy A. W. Jolliffe.)

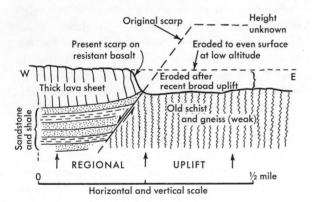

Fig. 18–24. Present scarp facing opposite the original scarp along a great fault in central Connecticut. The side of downthrow is indicated clearly by drag effect. Erosion produced a regional surface of low relief. Later broad uplift stimulated erosion on belts of weaker rocks, producing the present east-facing scarp. The sandstone, shale, and lava, youngest rocks in the area, were laid down in the Triassic Period, more than 150 million years ago.

sway and the scarp, however high, is doomed to destruction. Many an old fault can be traced across nearly level ground, though before the faulting the rocks on one side must have been hundreds or thousands of feet above those on the other. If an area crossed by an old fault is uplifted, renewed erosion attacks the weakest rocks and parts of the old fault may be exposed (Fig. 18–22). With continued erosion a new scarp may come to mark the course of a very old fault (Fig. 18–23). If, when erosion is renewed along an old fault, the more resistant rocks are on the side that was downthrown, a new scarp may be developed facing exactly opposite the original scarp (Fig. 18-24).

A fault with habitual strike-slip displacement is marked by a furrow because the ground-up rock along the fault is weak and yields easily to erosion. The course of the San Andreas fault in California follows a conspicuous trough-like depression for hundreds of miles (Fig. 20–4). This fault is not a simple fracture but a group of nearly parallel fractures separating long splinter-like blocks; it is a *fault zone* as much as a mile wide. Irregular movement of adjacent blocks has made knobs and ridges separated by depressions, some of which are occupied by ponds and small lakes. These marks of interrupted drainage are characteristic of an active fault zone.

Important special features of faults. The masses of rock involved in large-scale faulting move against each other under strong frictional resistance, and the surfaces of movement are smoothed, scratched, and grooved. *Highly polished surfaces on hard rocks abraded by movement along a fault* are **slickensides.** Parallel scratches and grooves on such surfaces record the direction of the latest movement (Fig. 18–22). A clear indication of the relative movement is given also by **drag,** *the bending of rock layers by frictional resistance to a movement on a fault* (Fig. 18–22, **B,** 18–24).

*A fault on which the displacement dies out perceptibly along the strike and ends at a definite point is a **hinge fault.*** Some hinge faults pass gradually into monoclinal folds (Fig. 18–25).

Thrust faults. Low-angle reverse faults are put into a special class because they have large importance in the great mountain belts in which, together with folds, they indicate many miles of shortening in belts of deformation (Chap. 21). Moving of the hanging wall over the footwall through a horizontal distance of 10 miles or more is not exceptional among the larger thrusts in the southern Appalachians, some of which can be traced hundreds of miles along the strike (p. 419). In most cases the mass above the thrust surface, thousands of feet thick, is made of

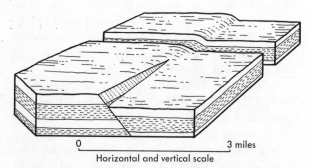

Fig. 18–25. A hinge fault (foreground) passing into a monoclinal fold (rear block). Examples of this structural relationship are found in the Colorado Plateau, in Utah, Arizona, and New Mexico.

rocks much older than those directly below the surface (Fig. 18–26). Some thrusts in thick sedimentary rocks have beds above nearly parallel to those beneath, giving a deceptive appearance of an unbroken sequence, but generally the movement under great frictional resistance has folded and broken the beds both above and beneath the thrust surface. In the Alps, where some of the largest thrusts have been recognized and described in detail, rocks involved in the movements have been fantastically crumpled and sheared (Fig. 21–10).

Relations of thrusts and folds. Both folding and thrusting appear to reflect strong stresses that compressed the rocks horizontally. Many thrusts in sedimentary rocks developed from anticlines that became overturned and broke under the strain. Folds that were overridden by thrust masses are strongly overturned and even recumbent, apparently smeared out by the weight that moved over them. Under continued compression in mountain zones, many of the great thrusts themselves became strongly folded (Chap. 21).

Numerous large thrust masses have the relations shown in Figure 18–27, **B,** which represents reconstruction of a thrust in southern Nevada. The original extent of the overriding mass (or *plate*) is not known because erosion has removed much of it; isolated remnants show a minimum earlier extent. In the forward part of this thrust, an older sedimentary unit moved over a much younger unit, whereas several miles to the west the rocks in the plate are younger than those beneath it. Figure 18–27, **A** shows the situation before the faulting. A strong plate made up chiefly of limestone was forced to move over the underlying weak shale. The moving plate buckled; it was sheared across and continued forward several miles over the land surface of that time.

How rocks are deformed

The preceding discussion of structural features has been chiefly descriptive. In a study of these features, the first requisite is to classify them according to form so far as possible and to examine their relations to each other. We may then reason about the mechanics of their development and speculate about the ultimate forces that were responsible.

Most of us find the breaking of rocks, as in devel-

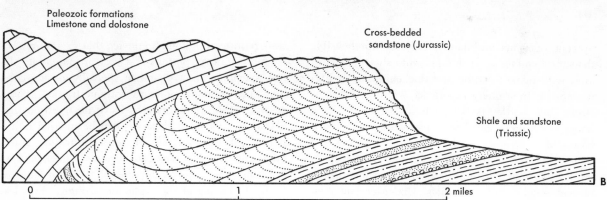

Fig. 18–26. A. Air view northward along the Keystone thrust fault, west of Las Vegas, Nevada. The cliff, on light-colored Jurassic sandstone, is 2,000 feet high. Dark rocks at left of view are older formations of limestone and dolostone in a plate that was thrust over the sandstone. The thrust contact is clearly defined by contrast in color between older and younger rocks. B. Vertical section along line A-B-C in photograph and extending somewhat farther east and west. Canyons crossing the thrust reveal that the contact steepens downward, toward the west, and crosses overturned layers of the sandstone. Farther forward the contact is essentially parallel to the sedimentary layers, both below and above. (John S. Shelton.)

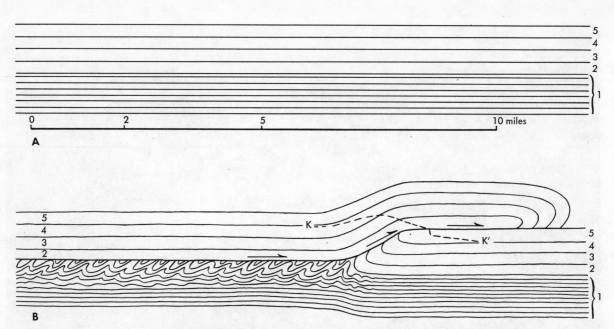

Fig. 18–27. A common type of large thrust fault in southern Nevada. A. Thick section of sedimentary formations before they were deformed. The figures, 1 to 5, indicate relative ages of large units, oldest at the base. The thick formation 1 is in large part weak shale; higher formations consist largely of strong quartzite, sandstone, and carbonate rocks. B. Under compression the strong formations were buckled and sheared across. As indicated by arrows, the western part of this mass moved eastward over the older weak shale, then upward and horizontally over the younger formations. The Keystone thrust is a thrust of this kind. The dashed line K-K' represents the present profile of the section shown in Figure 18–26, B. All the rock above this profile has been eroded.

opment of joints and faults, more comprehensible than the bending of thick layers into sharply curved arcs, with much thinning and thickening, as in Figure 18–15. In ordinary experience we regard rock as strong but brittle. Building stone keeps its shape under heavy loads but breaks like glass under sharp blows of a hammer or with forcible bending. To understand the reactions of rock materials deep in the Earth's crust, we must have in mind some principles of engineering mechanics. Under certain conditions, rock that ordinarily is strong and brittle can be deformed as if it were a mass of stiff dough. The essentials to bring this about are (1) confining pressure and (2) time. A third helpful factor, commonly present in many parts of the Earth's crust, is rising temperature.

In mechanical laboratories specimens of strong rock have been shortened and thickened under high pressures, without fracturing or loss of strength. Such tests require an automatic device that exerts uniform compression over periods of a year or more, with the test specimen in a chamber specially designed to maintain confining pressure without friction. These results within a few months leave no question that a thick section of rock layers can be molded into a pattern of smooth folds under compression maintained for tens of thousands of years. Effects of flow are conspicuous in the thinning of layers in limbs of folds, thickening at the crests and troughs (Fig. 18–15).

In other specially designed laboratory experiments, parallel fractures are developed in test specimens, with patterns that imitate closely the sets and systems of joints common in bedrock. In a testing device that allows adjustments by movement, fractures formed experimentally become faults; by studied manipulation, these appear as normal, reverse, or strike-slip faults. Realistic patterns of folds also are produced in small-scale experiments. To make the results of these small laboratory products really trustworthy, as representatives of the structural features in the Earth's crust, the strengths of the testing materials used are scaled down in proportion to the size of the model and the short time involved in the experiment.

Many structural features, and especially faults, reveal that shearing stress has been responsible for much crustal deformation. The operation of shearing stress is illustrated simply by placing a deck of cards on a table, holding a flat ruler upright against it and, with the end of the ruler in place on the table, pushing the upper end toward the deck, causing the individual cards to slide differentially. By careful study of deformed rocks, we can recognize effects of compressional, tensile, and shearing stresses, but we should like to know also the fundamental source of these stresses, the actual forces involved. This major problem is considered in connection with the structure of mountains in Chapter 21.

Unconformity

When we see in contact two groups of layered rocks that diverge widely in dip, we think first of faulting as a possible explanation. On examining closely the contact between the two formations shown in Figure 18–28, we find it highly irregular in detail and with no suggestion of any movement along it. In the lower layers of the upper group we see pebbles and cobbles made of distinctive rocks in the steeply dipping layers beneath. Marine fossils, abundant in the tilted layers, show that these layers were formed on the sea floor during the Cambrian Period; whereas bones of land mammals, together with the nature of the sediments around them, tell us that the flat-lying layers were deposited by streams in the Pliocene Epoch (Table 4–2, p. 63). It is clear, then, that sometime after the thick marine deposits were formed a strong crustal disturbance tilted the layers and raised them above sea level. After a large part of the uplifted mass was destroyed by erosion, a blanket of nonmarine sediments accumulated. Erosion now in progress reveals a part of the record.

Nothing at this locality provides a clue to the exact date of the crustal disturbance to which the tilted layers bear witness. By study of exposures in a

Fig. 18–28. A. Angular unconformity between nearly horizontal strata and much older strata that were strongly deformed and eroded to a nearly even surface before the younger deposits were laid down. **B.** Detail of the unconformable contact shown in **A.** The older, tilted layers are marine limestone; the younger layers are gravelly stream deposits. Meadow Valley Wash, Lincoln County, Nevada. (C. R. Longwell.)

large surrounding area, we learn that the deforming movements occurred while strata dated as Cretaceous were being laid down. Therefore, the disturbance occurred more than 70 million years ago, erosion removed a large thickness of the deformed rocks, and the blanket of stream deposits was laid down about 10 million years ago.

The upper group of deposits shown in Figure 18–28 does not *conform* with the lower group. The relation is one of *unconformity, a lack of continuity between units of rock in contact, corresponding to a gap in the geologic record.* The example shown in the figure illustrates *angular unconformity,* which is *unconformity marked by angular divergence between older and younger rocks.*

371

Unconformity of sedimentary deposits to older rocks beneath them is commonly a record of crustal movement. This record may give few details; it tells us that the older rocks were brought into the realm of erosion (this suggests some kind of uplift) and that at some later time conditions became favorable for laying down of sediments, possibly because the land sank, but perhaps because movement, lava flows, or landslides obstructed drainage and started deposition by streams or in a lake. If marine beds lie above and below the contact, the information is more definite: (1) the older beds were uplifted and eroded, (2) submergence brought back the sea, and (3) another uplift made possible the erosion which has exposed both sets of beds to our view.

Kinds of unconformity. Possible combinations of crustal movement, erosion, and sedimentation are almost countless, and there are many variations among the unconformities we find in rocks. But we recognize only a few differences that are of major importance. The angular unconformity has been presented first because the divergence of beds above and below makes it especially clear. More common but less conspicuous are unconformities between beds that are essentially parallel. In the walls of the Grand Canyon limestone that is dated by marine fossils as Devonian lies on marine limestone containing fossils of Cambrian age (Fig. 18–29, **A**). This is not a local matter—it holds through nearly the full length of the canyon, about 200 miles. On close inspection, we find the contact between the two limestones slightly irregular, with shallow, valley-like depressions cutting across the top Cambrian beds. Hence there was erosion before the Devonian beds were laid down, and surely there was ample time, since the combined lengths of the Ordovician and Silurian Periods total more than 80 million years (Table 4–2). Were sediments deposited in that area during those periods and completely eroded before the Devonian sea came in? Or was the area above

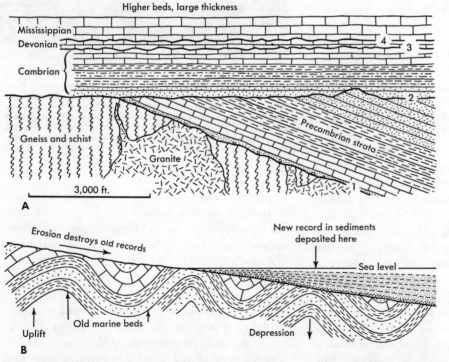

Fig. 18–29. Meaning of unconformities. A. The sedimentary record in the Grand Canyon has large gaps. Angular unconformities indicated at (1) and (2) represent large-scale crustal movements followed by long intervals of erosion. Surfaces of erosion indicated at (3) and (4), nearly parallel to the sedimentary layers, record broad upwarping followed by erosion and renewed deposition. **B.** While erosion destroys or prevents formation of a record in some areas, sediments build up to write a new record elsewhere.

sea level and not receiving deposits during two long periods? Whatever the reason, the unconformity between Cambrian and Devonian formations in the Grand Canyon represents a gap in history greater than that between Cretaceous and Pliocene records in Neveda, though less conspicuous. *Disconformity* is *unconformity that is not marked by angular divergence between the two groups of rocks in contact.*

Every unconformity testifies to a "lost interval" in the geologic record at the locality—an interval of time in which no deposition of sediments occurred in the area and erosion destroyed part of an earlier record. Critical evidence for recognition of any unconformity, then, is of two kinds: absence of any record for a part of geologic time, long or short, and presence of a buried erosion surface. Recognition of this surface is made easier by a difference in structure on the two sides, but this difference is not essential. In some large continental areas there has been no strong folding through long ages. This is true of the Colorado Plateau and also of the wide lowland between the Rocky Mountains and the Appalachians. In both regions many disconformities have developed in broad warping movements, and locally there has been perceptible tilting of layers in two formations that are separated by important disconformities.

In many places we find sedimentary beds overlying metamorphic and igneous rocks (Fig. 18–29, **A**). The contact of sandstone on igneous rock of intrusive origin is recognized as sedimentary if the sandstone fills small valleys and contains pebbles and mineral grains clearly derived from the underlying bedrock. Rock of any kind, then, may be involved in an unconformity. Deposition of younger rock material on older is the essential fact. Superficially an intrusive or fault contact may look like the contact at (1) in Fig. 18–29, **A**, but close examination should give evidence of the true relation.

Volcanic as well as sedimentary rocks are commonly found unconformable on older rocks. In southern Nevada, where crustal movements and volcanic eruptions have been numerous in long geologic periods, lavas and ash beds lie with unconformable contact on rocks of several ages between Precambrian and Cenozoic. Fossils useful for dating are found in some of the ash beds and also in sedimentary layers interbedded with the volcanic rocks.

Proper definition of the term. The term unconformity is not easily defined in a short sentence, as we realize on analysis of some published definitions. Some textbooks state categorically that an unconformity is "a buried erosion surface" and in diagrams label the surface separating rock units as "the unconformity." But if this is accepted, an *angular* unconformity must be a surface that has angles, not in the plane of the surface but in planes cutting across the surface. This does violence to basic principles of geometry.

The buried erosion surface is, of course, an essential part of any unconformity, but not the whole of it. Unconformity is not a simple geometric feature; it is a *relationship.* To learn the relationship between rocks under and above the surface, we must explore in the third dimension; what we learn there may be all-important in determining that an erosion surface exists and whether it represents a significant or a negligible lapse of time. Surely, in an outcrop such as that shown in Figure 18–28 the evidence for unconformity between the two rock masses goes beyond their surface of contact; and though in the erosion surface (3) of Figure 18–29, **A**, the critical evidence is less visible, this is supplied when we learn how much of the record is missing because of erosion or nondeposition.

The *contact between two unconformable rock masses* is properly called the **surface of unconformity.**

Unconformities and Earth history. Presumably, out in the ocean basins sediments have been building up during much or all of geologic time, making a continuous record. On the continents the record has had numerous interruptions by uplift and erosion, and it is by its partial destruction that the record is available to us for study. In the Appalachians, the Rocky Mountains, and the Alps we see great thicknesses of sedimentary beds, folded, faulted, and cut by deep valleys, full of information about geologic history. These three mountain chains were formed at different times, and so the records they reveal partly supplement each other. But every thick sedimentary section has unconformities, each representing a gap in the record. This is not altogether a loss because each unconformity is itself a record of some important event, such as folding and thrusting in a mountain belt or upwarping of a wide continental area.

Within certain limits, we can date the events that

caused unconformities. If the youngest beds in a folded series are Permian and the oldest nonfolded beds above are Triassic, we know that the folding occurred near the close of the Paleozoic era. But the time brackets for some events are much farther apart. In central Connecticut the youngest beds in the hanging wall of a great normal fault are of late Triassic age, and the oldest beds deposited across the fault are Pleistocene. Without further information, the date of faulting can not be fixed within 150 million years.

A study of unconformities brings out the close relationship between crustal movements, erosion, and sedimentation. Vigorous erosion is now going on where there has been recent uplift. Cutting by streams is laying bare the records in old rocks, and, in doing this, it is slowly destroying some of the records. Meanwhile, the eroded material is carried away and deposited somewhere else, perhaps on a land surface recently sunk below sea level (Fig. 18–29, **B**). And so building up in one place compensates tearing down in another. The many unconformities within the geologic column testify that this making and destroying of records has been going on through the Earth's long history.

SUMMARY

1. Abrupt movements on faults, with displacements ranging up to tens of feet, have occurred within recent years at widespread localities.

2. Broad areas that were covered with ice sheets in northern Europe and North America have been rising slowly since the latest glacial age. The cumu-lative uplifts are measurable within a human generation.

3. In coastal belts, at many latitudes, differential uplift of lands is recorded by old shoreline terraces at altitudes ranging up to many hundreds of feet. Erosion is destroying this surficial evidence.

4. More durable evidence of crustal movement is registered in deformation of bedrock. The bending and breaking of layered rocks give the clearest records of these movements.

5. Structural domes and basins record ancient crustal warping. Horizontal compression is registered in strong folding of layered rocks, most pronounced in mountain belts.

6. Shearing stresses in the crust have produced faults, many with large displacement. Joints, fractures without appreciable displacement, result from various kinds of stresses.

7. Vertical or horizontal movement on a fault is cumulative in successive small increments. Some measured total displacements are thousands of feet vertically, many miles horizontally.

8. Thrust faults, involving great crustal blocks that have moved on low-dipping surfaces, commonly are related to folding in mountain belts.

9. Some mechanical principles of crustal deformation are clarified by well-designed laboratory tests, which produce in miniature some effects seen in deformed bedrock.

10. In many areas new rock materials have been laid down after parts of the older deformed bedrock were removed by erosion. The resulting unconformities are clear records of crustal movements.

REFERENCES

Anderson, E. M., 1951, The dynamics of faulting and dyke formation: Edinburgh, Oliver and Boyd.

Billings, M. P., 1954, Structural geology, 2nd ed.: Englewood Cliffs, New Jersey, Prentice-Hall.

Daly, R. A., 1936, Our mobile Earth: New York, Charles Scribner's Sons.

Hills, E. S., 1953, Outlines of structural geology, 3rd ed.: London, Methuen and Co.; New York, John Wiley and Sons.

Hubbert, M. K., 1945, Strength of the Earth: Amer. Assoc. Petroleum Geologists Bull., vol. 29, p. 1630–1653.

Lahee, F. H., 1961, Field geology, 6th ed.: New York, McGraw-Hill Book Co.

CHAPTER 19. METAMORPHISM

Changes in coals   Causes of change in rocks   Shale to schist   Varied response in rock types

Heat a potent agent   Minerals provide clues to history   What is granite?

Banded gneiss formed by extreme metamorphism of sedimentary rocks in southern Norway. (R. V. Dietrich, 1959.)

Geologic definition

To *metamorphose* is to change or transform. Constant change, slow but persistent, is a common rule on and within the Earth's crust. Weathering changes rocks profoundly, and logically it could be included among processes of metamorphism. Radical changes result also when large masses of rock within the crust are heated above melting temperatures, with formation of magmas. In geology the accepted meaning of *metamorphism* is the *changing of one kind of coherent rock into another kind, below the zone of weathering and without* the complete *fusion* that leads to igneous activity. Some examples will make the usage clear.

Changes in coal

Western Pennsylvania is rich in high-grade soft (*bituminous*) coal; a hundred miles or so farther east, in the Appalachian Mountain chain, is the district that supplies most of our hard coal (*anthracite*), which the early colonial fathers found unusable—they could not make it burn. Anthracite truly is very different from ordinary coal; it is harder and more lustrous and breaks into smooth-surfaced, irregular fragments instead of nearly rectangular blocks. On analysis, we find that soft coal gives off a third or more of its weight in gases (hence the black smoke when it burns), whereas anthracite loses only about 5 per cent. Tests to determine the amounts of volatile matter in coal are carried out at a temperature of 950°C and at atmospheric pressure. When the gases are driven off, the residue is chiefly black carbon, amounting to 90 or even 95 per cent of the original weight of the hard coal, whereas in the soft coal the residue amounts to about 40 to 60 per cent. The high concentration of carbon and low content of combustible gas explain the difficulty in making hard coal start to burn.

Both the anthracite and the soft coal of Pennsylvania occur in layers between beds of shale and sandstone. All the coal in the state was laid down in the same geologic period, the Pennsylvanian. Why, then, are the coals of the two districts so different? The chief difference that meets the eye is in the structure of the beds, which in western Pennsylvania are nearly horizontal or gently dipping but in the hard coal region are buckled into tight folds (Fig. 19–1). Was soft coal turned into anthracite by squeezing during the growth of folds in the Appalachian Mountains? A look at coal fields in other lands favors an affirmative answer. Anthracite is commonly found in mountain belts where the rocks are much deformed, whereas formations containing layers of soft coal have been less disturbed. We infer that anthracite was developed from coal of lower rank by strong compression, perhaps with some rise in temperature caused by friction as the layers of rock were bent and crushed. Under this treatment, the gases were slowly expelled and the coal was changed both in composition and in physical properties.

Because of these large changes, anthracite is classed as a metamorphic rock. But why in the anthracite fields of Pennsylvania was there no noticeable change in the shale and sandstone layers, which were folded as strongly as the coal beds? We know, from laboratory studies, that coal is much more sensitive to changing conditions than ordinary rock material. With very strong deformation, especially if it is accompanied by a rise in temperature, all kinds of rocks are noticeably changed. Thus in the small coal field of Rhode Island, where the rocks were severely folded and also invaded by igneous bodies, all the sedimentary formations were affected radically. Quartz pebbles in conglomerate layers were squeezed into long lenses (Fig. 19–2), shale was turned into

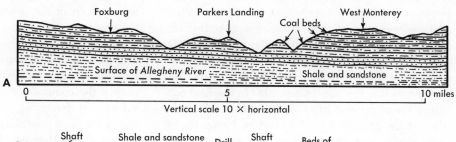

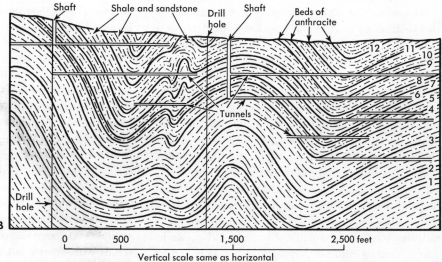

Fig. 19–1. Contrasting occurrences of coal. **A.** These 9 layers of bituminous coal, and the layers of shale and sandstone inclosing them, have been little deformed since they were deposited. Near Pittsburgh, Pennsylvania. **B.** Twelve layers of anthracite coal between layers of shale and sandstone, all strongly folded. Eastern Pennsylvania. (A, from Folio 178, U. S. Geol. Survey; B from Coal Investigations Map C3, 1950, U. S. Geol. Survey.)

Fig. 19–2. Pebbles, chiefly of light-colored igneous rock, were squeezed into flat lenses by strong compression that folded layers of conglomerate, now vertical. View obliquely downward on nearly horizontal surface. These metamorphosed sedimentary rocks, widely exposed in southern Canada, resemble some rocks in the coal basin of Rhode Island. (J. W. Ambrose, Geol. Survey of Canada.)

lustrous phyllite and fine-grained schist, and much of the coal went beyond the anthracite stage so that carbon took the form of the mineral graphite (p. 34). This mineral will not burn, and people who tried using the anthracite from that field expressed their opinion of it in the testy statement: "In the final conflagration of the world the Rhode Island coal will be the last thing to catch fire." In eastern Pennsylvania, then, folding was severe enough to force out most of the volatile material of the coal but caused no perceptible alteration of the shale and sandstone. In Rhode Island deformation and temperature were sufficient to change the mineral content of the coal and of the inclosing rock as well.

Some anthracite has developed in beds that are not folded. In west-central Colorado dikes and thick laccoliths were intruded into coal-bearing beds of late Cretaceous age (Fig. 19–3). This coal, then, is less than half as old as that in Pennsylvania (Table 4–2), but around some of the laccoliths there are quantities of good anthracite, and close to the igneous bodies the coal has been turned into coke; the high temperature drove off all the volatile substance. Where shale was in contact with the hot magma, it was baked to a hard flinty rock, with no resemblance to shale, through a thickness as great as several tens of feet.

Agents of metamorphism

The examples from Appalachian and Rocky Mountain coal fields indicate that high pressures and heat play important roles in the metamorphism of rock materials. This is amply confirmed by wide and intensive study of metamorphic rocks in many environments. Circulating solutions, both liquid and gaseous, serve as a third major agent of metamorphism.

Some effects of this agent are revealed in studies of hot springs and fumaroles at natural laboratories such as Yellowstone Park, the geyser fields of New Zealand and Iceland, and a number of active volcanoes. Hot fluids, carrying active chemicals in solution, change the composition of rocks by dissolving some substances, depositing others, and causing reactions that form new minerals. Hot vapors are especially effective, since they penetrate the most minute openings and cause radical changes of mineral composition within rock masses that look impervious. Under high confining pressures deep in the crust, hot solutions doubtless are more potent than under low pressure at the Earth's surface.

Some terms used by students of metamorphic rocks recognize the dominant role of one or another agent in causing specific changes. *Thermal metamorphism is metamorphism attributed chiefly to heat.* These effects are especially pronounced in masses of rock adjacent to igneous bodies, and *contact metamorphism is change that has occurred in rocks at or near contacts with magma.* A major effect of circulating solutions has been the replacement of some rock materials with others; but no appropriate term, such as *replacement metamorphism* is in common use for specific recognition of this process. *Dynamic metamorphism, change in rocks caused chiefly by deforming pressure,* is a term commonly used. *Dynamo-thermal metamorphism, changes in rock that combine effects of heat and directed pressure,* is an appropriate designation for some metamorphic effects.

Although specific types of metamorphism are recognized in limited areas, commonly the metamorphic rocks are extremely complex and reflect combined operations of two or more processes. Clearly, the

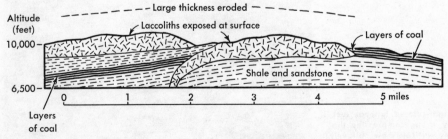

Fig. 19–3. Anthracite was developed by high temperature near large igneous masses intrusive into a coal-bearing formation of Cretaceous age. Anthracite region, Colorado. (Modified from Folio 9, U. S. Geol. Survey.)

most extensive metamorphism has occurred at considerable depth in the crust. The best and widest exposures of metamorphic rocks lie along the axial zones of old mountain belts from which erosion has removed great thicknesses of bedrock. As temperature rises with increasing depth, a location deep in the crust is in itself favorable for chemical change. More important, during the development of a mountain belt strong pressures have operated, as indicated by close folds, thrusts, and other structural features. Also, intrusive igneous bodies, some of great size, were emplaced at some stage of the deformation. Thus changes caused by heat and fluids given out by masses of magma are added to the effects of deforming pressures.

Metamorphism that extends over a wide area is **regional metamorphism.** Metamorphic rocks underlie large areas of the Appalachian belt from southeastern Canada to Alabama. This is in strong contrast with major parts of the wide Mississippi Valley, where we see only sedimentary rocks, little deformed. Obviously, the two regions have had very different histories.

Grades of metamorphism

We recognize in some rocks the marks of *strong* or *intense* metamorphism; other rocks are described as moderately or slightly metamorphosed. Examples to illustrate these degrees of change should include only rocks that were basically alike before metamorphism. Materials differ in susceptibility to physical and chemical changes. Rocks of some kinds show no signs of alteration, though they are interlayered with other rocks that bear strong marks of metamorphism.

Slaty cleavage. If pressure that has deformed beds to make folds has also caused metamorphism, then logically we should find the metamorphic effects best developed where the deformation is strongest. In the Appalachian region the intensity of folding increases generally toward the southeast. In western Pennsylvania the thick section of shale and sandstone, inclosing layers of coal, is nearly horizontal. Farther east, in the anthracite district, folds are strongly developed, but otherwise the shale is unchanged (Fig. 19–1). Some miles east of this district the sedimentary section is buckled into close, overturned folds, and the layers of shale are much obscured by *slaty cleavage, a close-spaced, plane foliation that divides the*

rock into thin plates (Fig. 19–4, **A**). This is one of the districts that for many years supplied quantities of slate for shingles and blackboards. Development of slate is an early stage in the metamorphism of shale. And just what is slate? Chemically, it is like the parent shale; but the plates of slate, remarkably even, are bounded by planes that are essentially parallel to the axial planes of folds (Fig. 19–4, **B**). Under strong compression that caused folding, something happened that set up this uniform and closely spaced cleavage. A key to the riddle is given by study with the most modern magnifying equipment, which shows that the slate consists in large part of tiny mica flakes in parallel arrangement. We reason that these mineral flakes formed while the rocks were under strong compression. Probably some rise in temperature also favored the conversion of clay minerals to mica. But why did these flakes develop in remarkably parallel arrangement?

Orientation of the cleavage planes parallel to axial planes of the folds is significant. Folds are formed in response to compressive stress, with axes generally at right angles to the direction of greatest compression. In the Appalachian chain the axes of folds extend generally northeast-southwest, parallel to the chain itself. Thus the maximum compression had the general direction southeast-northwest. Crests of folds, pointing upward, indicate the direction of easiest relief. This structural arrangement marks an unbalanced pattern of stresses, favoring failures under *shearing stress.* Overturning of folds toward the northwest emphasized this tendency, and in many parts of the Appalachian belt large folds were sheared across and important thrust faults were formed, striking parallel to fold axes and dipping to the southeast. While the folds were growing, shearing stress pervaded the entire rock mass. Planes of slaty cleavage represent planes of *potential failure* and the direction of easiest relief. Mineral flakes in their growth responded to this mechanical advantage.

Rocks with slaty cleavage are abundant in the Appalachian chain from eastern Canada to Alabama and indeed in all great mountain belts of the world. Shale, the most abundant and the weakest kind of sedimentary rock, is the chief parent of slate, but limestone impure with clay also takes on slaty cleavage with folding, as do layers of volcanic ash.

A

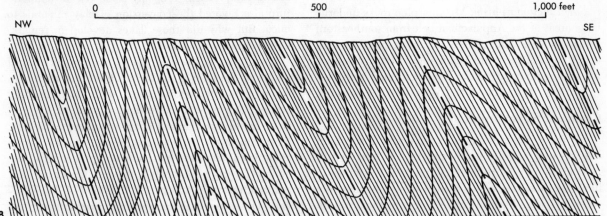

NW   0   500   1,000 feet   SE

B

Fig. 19–4. A. Slaty cleavage parallel to the axial plane of a syncline in the Appalachian Mountains, eastern Tennessee. Similar slate occurs in a wide belt directly east of the Pennsylvania anthracite district. (U.S. Geol. Survey.) **B.** Slaty cleavage commonly is parallel to axial planes of strongly folded layers of shale and impure limestone. In many parts of the Appalachian Mountains the axial planes are overturned toward the northwest, as indicated in this diagram. Sections of the planes, represented by the most prominent lines in this drawing, of course are not actually visible in the rock. Scale of folds showing these relations varies widely, from inches to hundreds of feet in height and width.

Phyllite and schist. In many parts of the Appalachians slate grades southeastward into *phyllite,* which has the habit of slate but is more lustrous. Under high magnification, the reason for the luster is found in discreet flakes of white mica. Thus phyllite represents a somewhat more advanced stage of metamorphism than slate. In turn, phyllite grades perceptibly into mica schist, in which flakes of mica are discernable without the aid of a lens. The schist also has visible grains of quartz, which with the mica is a product of the chemical change from clay minerals.

For further illustrations of advanced stages in metamorphism of shaly rocks we turn to the Alps, where there are enormous masses of lustrous mica schist. Fossil shells of squids and other marine animals, much distorted but still recognizable, tell us that the schist was once a sedimentary rock; this is made clear also by recognizable layers of sandstone, which have resisted metamorphism. In their careful studies Alpine geologists have found that over a distance of several miles the schist made largely of visible mica plates grades laterally into phyllite, which grades into slate, which, in turn, grades into ordinary shale. From these studies it is inferred that metamorphism of shale proceeds through stages (shale to slate to phyllite to mica schist) and that different stages were reached in various parts of a mountain belt because the intensity of deformation varied from place to place. In large parts of the Swiss Alps the deformation by folding and thrusting was extreme, and in those parts the thick deposits were largely changed to mica schist.

In southern Nevada a clear demonstration of metamorphism in shale by deforming pressure can be seen in limited exposures beneath a thrust plate (Fig. 19–5). A thick section of strong sedimentary rocks moved over a formation made of weak layers of shale and sandstone. By frictional drag these layers, in a thickness of 200 or 300 feet, were forced into folds, isoclinal and overturned, with well-developed cleavage parallel to the axial planes. Within this folded zone the shale became slate, which grades upward into lustrous, crumpled phyllite. Thus is displayed in miniature the grading of metamorphic effects commonly shown on a larger scale in zones of regional metamorphism.

Chemical analyses of typical shale, slate, phyllite, and mica schist from the Alpine belt are remarkably alike; each shows 60 per cent or more of silica and more than 15 per cent of aluminum oxide, with small amounts of iron, calcium, potassium, magnesium, and sodium. This composition is much like that of clay minerals, which, of course, made up most of the original shale. In the metamorphism, then, these chemical substances stayed in the rock but shifted into different combinations (that is, formed new minerals) that were stable under the new conditions. Clay is formed only near the surface, and under high pressures and temperatures it is changed into other minerals, such as muscovite, which are suited to the conditions deep in a mountain zone.

Study of the shale-schist series has particular interest because it illustrates well the principle of equilibrium (Chap. 2) and the changes that are continually under way in the Earth's crust in obedience to this principle. Minerals and rocks tend toward adjustment to their surroundings. The mica schist now exposed over large areas in the Alps was brought to the surface only yesterday in geologic time by rapid uplift and vigorous erosion. The minerals formed at depth and under great pressures of folding will now be broken up and in part weathered to make new combinations that are stable at the Earth's surface.

Varied effects of metamorphism

Changes in sedimentary rocks. Conglomerates that contained clay and silt between the pebbles have been changed by folding pressure into distinctive gneiss; the pebbles are drawn out ("stretched") into long lenses (Fig. 19–2), and the clay between has become thin, irregular bands of mica schist. Sandstones made of quartz grains persist stubbornly under metamorphic pressures because quartz is stable under a wide range of conditions. Solutions have deposited silica between the grains of some strongly folded sandstone layers to produce a rock that is almost totally quartz but keeps ghostly shapes of the old grains; this is quartzite. Limestone and dolomite

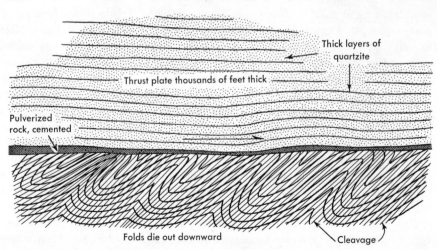

Fig. 19–5. Deformation of shale beneath a thrust plate, with development of slate and phyllite. The plate was thousands of feet thick, and in the movement the rocks beneath were subjected to very strong shearing stress. Near Johnnie, Nevada.

Fig. 19–6. These old sedimentary rocks in southern Sweden retained their general layered structure, but the layers were deformed and radically changed in composition by dynamic and thermal metamorphism. White bands are marble; dark bands are schist. (P. J. Holmquist.)

layers keep their chemical composition, but the grains of calcite and dolomite have grown larger and the resulting rock is marble. Carbon in some marbles poses a problem. Lumps and lenses of coarse graphite in very old marbles of the Adirondack region and parts of Canada probably represent plants or animals that lived in the seas while the sediments were being laid down, long before the Paleozoic era (Table 4–2).

In deformed rocks widespread around the Baltic Sea we find layers of quartzite, conglomerate with stretched pebbles, mica schist, and marble intermixed and very strongly folded (Fig. 19–6). We see in this combination an old sedimentary section made up of conglomerate, sandstone, shale, and limestone, folded together, deeply buried in an ancient mountain chain, and metamorphosed. Erosion through long ages has literally removed the mountains and has exposed rocks that provide unmistakable clues to their origin.

Metamorphosed igneous rocks. Metamorphic products of igneous rocks are as varied as the igneous rocks themselves, and a few of the common kinds will serve as examples. Most volcanic ash is made of light-colored igneous material with the general composition of rhyolite or andesite. Therefore, most of the fine particles in ash are feldspar. Beds of volcanic ash have little resemblance to beds of shale, yet these two kinds of rock are similar in basic composition because shale is made chiefly of clay, which is the chief product of weathered feldspar. It is not surprising, then, that metamorphic rocks developed from ash beds are much like those derived from shale. Folded beds of volcanic ash commonly have good slaty cleavage, and in some mountain belts these slates clearly grade into phyllite and mica schist. When metamorphism has been extreme there may be no way of telling whether schists came from ash beds or from shale. But usually with careful study of a wide area the schist can be traced into less-altered material in which there are telltale traces of the original rock. Some large bodies of schist in New Hampshire have been identified as metamorphosed volcanic ash. This kind of problem offers one of the best opportunities for geologic detective work by using every bit of evidence to be found in field examination, study with microscopes of the highest power, and exact chemical analyses.

Metamorphic rocks of a very different kind have come from basalt and its dark-colored relatives (Fig. 3–17). These dark igneous rocks contain an abundance of the mineral pyroxene, which in belts of strong folding has been changed into the green mineral chlorite; the resulting metamorphic rocks are aptly called *greenstone*. Great thicknesses of greenstone in parts of Canada are known to have been accumulations of basaltic lavas because in many of the layers we can distinguish the forms of typical pillows (Fig. 6–19) and of mineral-filled vesicles (Fig. 3–16) that have survived the effects of pressure. With continued metamorphism, some of these rocks have become coarse-grained chlorite schist.

In folded mountain belts many large bodies of granite have become coarsely banded gneisses. Clearly, some of these bodies were deformed after the igneous minerals were fully crystallized because the feldspar grains have been squeezed into flat lenses and many of them minutely fractured (Fig. 19–7) in much the same way as the pebbles in a deformed conglomerate (Fig. 19–2). On the other hand, many granite gneisses must have taken on their banded structure while much of the original granitic magma was soft and mushy, since the individual mineral grains are not cracked, though they are arranged in irregular layers. We reason that strong pressure squeezed the body of magma while the mineral grains were forming and forced the plastic mass to flow slowly in the direction indicated by the layered pattern (Fig. 19–8).

Thermal metamorphism

Bodies of magma at some depth in the crust lose temperature very slowly because the solid rock around them is a poor conductor of heat. In time this older rock becomes heated, with temperatures highest near the magma and decreasing outward. With

Fig. 19–7. Hand specimen of gneiss formed by deformation of granite porphyry containing large phenocrysts of feldspar. These mineral grains were compressed into lenticular forms parallel to the gneissic banding (*upper left* to *lower right* of specimen). The German term for such a rock is *augen gneiss*, from fancied resemblance of the lenticular grains to eyes.

Fig. 19–8. This evenly banded gneiss has the mineral composition of granite, but the minerals, especially the feldspar grains, have the form of irregular thin layers. Length of specimen about 4 inches. From Uxbridge, Massachusetts. (Courtesy of the American Museum of Natural History.)

slow loss of heat, the magma finally reaches the critical temperatures at which igneous minerals crystallize, and the body becomes solid. Even after this stage is reached a large igneous mass a mile or more below the Earth's surface must remain hot for a long time and share its heat with the rocks around it.

In long and careful studies in specially equipped laboratories we have learned much about the temperature at which igneous rocks fuse. Under atmospheric pressure, ordinary granite fuses at about 800° C, ba-

salt at just under 1,100° C. These melting points would be higher under the great pressures deep below the Earth's surface, though this increase may be at least partly offset by the presence of much water vapor and other gases which we know are dissolved in magmas and help keep them fluid. Fortunately, the temperatures at which certain minerals crystallize under given pressures have been determined accurately, and one of these minerals found in a rock provides valuable information. For example, quartz

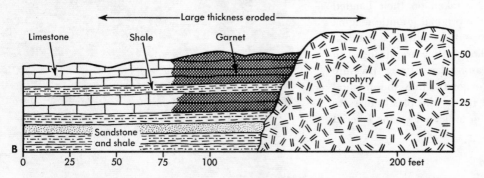

Fig. 19–9. A. Contact of a granite mass (*at left*) and some of the intruded rock, which now is banded gneiss but probably was once part of a thick section of sedimentary layers. Near right of view, left of the road sign, a dike that branches from the intrusive body cuts across the layers. Telemark area, near Kristiansand, Norway. (R. V. Dietrich.) **B.** Beds of limestone were entirely replaced with garnet by chemical action when the igneous body was fluid magma at high temperature. The shale and sandstone were hardened near the contact but show no chemical changes. Near Breckenridge, Colorado.

occurs in low-temperature and high-temperature varieties, each with its own crystal structure by which it is recognized. A very delicate relation between temperature and pressure governs the crystal growth of the mineral *wollastonite,* a calcium silicate. At a pressure equal to that under a 5-mile thickness of rock, this mineral forms at about 800° C. Hence, if we find evidence that rock containing wollastonite has been exposed by erosion to a depth of about 5 miles, we know approximately the temperature of the rock at the time the mineral formed. Such a mineral is a *geologic thermometer* (p. 456). On the same general principle, we use the boiling time of an egg in estimating our height above sea level; the time required to cook the egg to a given stage tells us the boiling temperature, which depends on the air pressure, which in turn tells us the altitude.

The estimated temperature for changing bituminous coal into the anthracite in Colorado (Fig. 19–3) is 300 to 350° C, for changing it into natural coke, 500 to 700° C. At higher temperatures, many minerals have formed in solid rock, some by new combinations of elements already there, others by introduction of new materials sent out in gases or liquids from bodies of magma. The most intense metamorphism of this kind occurs close to an igneous mass, in the *contact zone* (Fig. 19–9, **A**), both because temperatures are highest there and because fluids from the magma reach into this zone most readily. Of the common rocks, limestone is the most easily changed by contact metamorphism because of its solubility. Close to many igneous masses beds of limestone have been entirely *replaced* by garnet (Fig. 19–9, **B**), hematite, and other minerals, although the bedding and even the forms of fossil shells may be perfectly preserved. The chemistry of the replacement process is complex and varied. Usually, some elements in the original rock are removed, others are combined with elements brought by fluids from the magma. The new rock may have almost exactly the same volume as the old but a very different specific gravity and entirely new minerals. Some large ore deposits have been formed by replacement near contacts with igneous masses (p. 455).

A common product of contact metamorphism is *hornfels, a fine-grained, hard, siliceous rock, usually massive and with scattered crystals of high-tempera-* ture *minerals*. It is developed by thermal metamorphism of various rocks, commonly shale, sandstone, and some dark igneous kinds.

Dynamic and thermal effects combined

In belts of close folding that are not cut by igneous bodies the metamorphic effects result largely from pressure. Thermal changes alone are displayed where igneous bodies have been intruded into nonfolded beds as in the Colorado Plateau. But in nearly all great mountain chains deep erosion has exposed deformed rocks that were changed during folding into slate, schist, quartzite, and marble and later were intruded by igneous masses. The results are highly complex, in some places fantastically so. Changes caused by the high temperatures and the fluids given out by magma are added to the effects of high pressure. Near some of the large igneous bodies innumerable thin sheets of fluid rock were forced along surfaces of bedding and cleavage, giving rise to *injection* gneisses in which bands of the igneous rock, a few inches or commonly fractions of an inch thick, alternate with thin layers of the intruded metamorphic rock (Fig. 19–10). In these older layers, which were highly heated and also soaked in "juices" from the invading magma, grains of garnet and other minerals grew profusely.

In the cores of old mountain chains great volumes of rock have gone through this kind of double metamorphism. An excellent example is the folded belt of Rhode Island containing the metamorphosed beds of coal. West of the entrance to Narragansett Bay the closely folded sedimentary beds come to an end in a mass of younger granite, which when it was a body of magma invaded the core of the mountain chain and engulfed the older rocks (Fig. 19–11). The former shale beds, which some miles north and east of the granite body are now slate and phyllite, were changed by the invading magma into coarse-grained schist filled with minerals that indicate high temperature. Intense thermal effects were added to the earlier dynamic changes.

Metamorphic facies

We have considered the kinds of evidence in sedimentary rocks that point to the environments in which the sediments were deposited (Chap. 17). Met-

Fig. 19-10. The light-colored bands are marble; the darker bands have granitic composition. Magma was injected in thin layers between layers of ancient limestone, which crystallized to form marble, not a common constituent of injection gneiss. (Geological Survey of Canada.)

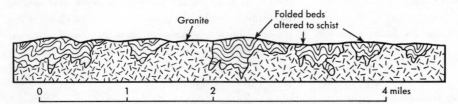

Fig. 19-11. Closely folded sedimentary rocks surrounded and injected by granite. The folded layers are intensely metamorphosed. Near Narraganset Pier, Rhode Island. (After G. F. Loughlin, American Jour. Sci., v. 29, 1910, p. 447-457.

amorphic rocks as a whole are much more complex than those of sedimentary origin. Moreover, we can watch many sedimentary processes in operation and can easily recognize in old sedimentary rocks features that are now being developed before our eyes. Sediments are deposited within the zone of observation; even those being laid down on ocean floors are studied in some detail with the aid of modern mechanical devices. Metamorphism occurs at varied depths in the crust, and we see the products only where they have been brought into view by long-continued erosion. Studies of these diverse products, in many lands, aim at a logical classification that will have general application. What critical features in a group of metamorphic rocks will tell us the conditions responsible for the metamorphism and the nature of the rocks before they were drastically changed?

Agreement on some significant aspects of metamorphic rocks has not been difficult. The progressive change from shale to slate and phyllite to mica schist is obvious in many belts of regional metamorphism. Masses of hornfels containing crystals of peculiar minerals have long been recognized as a product of thermal change near intrusive igneous bodies. But only within the present century has there been encouraging progress toward classification of all metamorphic rocks according to mode of origin.

Significant metamorphic minerals. The association of some peculiar minerals with metamorphic rocks has long been recognized. For example, sillimanite, a rather rare aluminum silicate, occurs characteristically as thin, blade-like crystals in zones of contact metamorphism. Metamorphic rocks are especially prominent in Finland, and in 1921 Eskola, a Finnish geologist, announced significant results from a study of mineral assemblages. In a succession of zones he found that the rocks have almost identical chemical composition but that each zone has its own peculiar assemblage of minerals. Some of these minerals are known to form only at high temperatures, others are characteristic of low-temperature environments, still others of moderate temperature conditions. Eskola suggested that these mineral assemblages are trustworthy indicators of distinctive *metamorphic facies,* based on average temperatures under which the rocks as we see them were evolved.

Recognized facies. Research stimulated by Eskola's concept is bringing some order into a field of geology that was long considered hopelessly complex. This is not to say that the complexities have been resolved; only a hopeful beginning has been made. A major difficulty stems from the greatly varied compositions of the parent rock materials. Eskola worked with rocks that have composition close to that of basalt. His results, in diagrammatic form, are outlined in Table 19–1.

Needless to say, parent bedrock consisting of sandstone, shale, and limestone will yield mineral assemblages different from those listed in the table. The important point is the range of temperatures indicated by the distinctive minerals. The estimated approximate temperatures are, for the four metamorphic zones (1) greenschist, 150–250°C; (2) epidote-amphibolite, 250–450°C; (3) amphibolite, 450–700°C; (4) hornfels, above 700°C.

A metamorphic facies, then, is *a kind of metamorphic rock containing minerals that indicate conditions under which the metamorphism occurred.*

The problem of granite

Rocks of granitic composition make up an important percentage of the exposed bedrock in continental masses. The great batholiths, and many plutons of smaller size, consist of granitic rocks. As explained in

Table 19—1. Metamorphic facies

Original rock: Basalt, dolerite, or gabbro			
Increasing temperature →			
Greenschist facies	Epidote-Amphibolite facies	Amphibolite facies	Pyroxene-hornfels facies
Chief minerals: albite, epidote, chlorite, biotite	Chief minerals: albite, hornblende, epidote, almandite	Chief minerals: plagioclase, hornblende, staurolite	Chief minerals: plagioclase, augite, olivine
Regional metamorphic zones			Contact zone

Fig. 19–12. Common pattern of a migmatite. The dark bands are in large part biotite; the light bands consist chiefly of feldspar and quartz. The original rock was intensely metamorphosed and crumpled; the feldspar and quartz were developed later. (Courtesy of American Museum of Natural History.)

Chapter 6, no one of these major plutonic bodies was formed as a unit. Each of them is made up of segments, varied in size and shape and formed at different times. A common supposition has been that each of these fractions represents an upsurge of magma, with displacement of older rocks to make room for the invading mass.

Relations at the margins of many plutons suggest strongly that the granite in those zones invaded the older rocks as a mobile fluid. Irregular offshoots, large and small, extend from the pluton into the surrounding rock. Blocks of the older rock are surrounded by the granite at varying distances from the main contact. On the other hand, the margins of some plutons are very indefinite. The granite fades into a wide, irregular zone of *migmatite* ("mixed rock"),

a rock in which thin stringers and threads of granitic material are intertwined with dark schistose bands (Fig. 19–12). Stringers of schist fade imperceptibly into the granite as if they were dissolved. In schistose rocks, far outside borders of some plutons, pockets and clots of feldspar and other minerals like those in the granite are completely isolated. Apparently, the rock that occupied these pockets has been replaced bodily by material identical with granite in the pluton.

Migmatites, which form wide zones bordering granitic plutons, make up a large fraction of all bedrock exposed in Finland. In an effort to explain these puzzling complexes, some Finnish geologists were among the first to favor the hypothesis of *granitization, the replacement of older rocks, in the solid state, by mineral ions moving up from a deep source.* Some parts of this concept seem mysterious, but it has many adherents. They maintain that formation of the great plutons by replacement of older rock offers the most plausible solution of the "room problem" (p. 110). If these great masses of granite were intruded as magma, what became of the enormous volume of older rock that was displaced?

Many advocates of granitization concede that some granites have formed from intrusive magma. Clear evidence of this is displayed in many places, but this kind of igneous action is regarded as secondary and minor in comparison with the products of granitization. In their view, only a small fraction of the granitic rocks is of igneous origin. Granitization, if it is a reality, proceeds generally without fusion of rock materials. It is a process of replacement, and the product is metamorphic rock.

This major problem regarding the origin of granite has given rise to two schools of thought. Geologists who do not favor the concept of granitization are referred to as "magmatists." The opposed point of view is illustrated in attempts to explain some features of a batholith in the Inyo Range of California. In a wide zone the granite is interlayered with remnants of dark schist (Fig. 19–13, **A**). On close inspection shreds of schist can be seen that fade ghost-like into the granite (Fig. 19–13, **B**). Advocates of granitization suggest that the layered zone is a good exhibit of partial conversion to granite, with

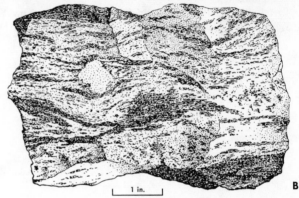

Fig. 19-13. Granite in the Inyo Range, California. A. Much of the granite appears to have irregular layering. The dark bands consist of schist, apparently formed by metamorphism of sedimentary rocks. Granite in lower part of cliff is massive, has no schistose bands. B. Sample of the layered rock. Stringers of schist (dark) are intimately mixed with the granite. (G. H. Anderson, Bull. Geol. Soc. Am., v. 48, 1937, p. 1–74.)

1 in.

gradation into a lower zone in which conversion was complete. The opposing view regards the bands of schist as remnants of roof rocks that were detached and partly assimilated during the time the pluton was a mass of magma deep in the crust.

As the study of granitic bodies proceeds, conviction grows that both magmatic intrusion and granitization are important processes. Relative importance of the two mechanisms remains as a major issue, with impressive arguments on each side.

It is not surprising that the metamorphic and igneous processes present many puzzles. Great changes have taken place below the limit of direct observation, and we have only indirect evidence of conditions and activities in critical zones at great depth. Yet some baffling problems have been solved, and rigorous testing of hypotheses on the origin of granite may eventually give a satisfactory answer.

SUMMARY

1. Soft coal is changed to anthracite by loss of combustible gases, caused by (a) strong pressure, (b) high temperature.

2. Agents of metamorphism are (a) pressure, (b) heat, (c) circulating solutions. Commonly at least two of the three agents work together.

3. Deformation in a mountain zone produces regional metamorphism, extending over a wide area.

4. Slate, phyllite, and mica schist represent progressive stages in metamorphism of shale. Volcanic

ash yields similar products.

5. Quartzite is metamorphosed sandstone; marble is metamorphosed limestone or dolostone. Metamorphism of igneous rocks yields varied gneisses and schists.

6. Dynamic and thermal effects in combination result in high-grade metamorphism.

7. Zones of progressive metamorphism are indicated by significant assemblages of minerals. Three regional zones and a contact zone are recognized.

8. The concept that granite has its source solely in magmas is challenged by the hypothesis of granitization, which assigns a major role to replacement in the solid state by mineral ions ascending from a deep zone.

REFERENCES

Fyfe, W. S., Turner, F. J., and Verhoogen, J., 1958, Metamorphic reactions and metamorphic facies: Geol. Soc. America, Mem. 73.

Read, H. H., 1957, The granite controversy: London and New York, Interscience Publishers.

Tyrrell, G. W., 1927, The principles of petrology: New York, E. P. Dutton & Co.

Williams, H., Turner, F. J., and Gilbert, C. M., 1954, Petrography: San Francisco, W. H. Freeman and Co.

CHAPTER 20. EARTHQUAKES: THE EARTH'S INTERIOR

Records in human history   Search for causes   Analysis by modern instruments   Geographic distribution   Seismic sea waves   Density distribution   Probing inside the Earth   Terrestrial magnetism explained   Why continents and ocean basins?   Evidence of crustal balance

Wreckage of a school building in Long Beach, California, by the earthquake of 1933. Fortunately school was not in session when earthquake occurred.

Examples of earthquakes

In the year 1960 world attention was directed repeatedly to Chile, the long, narrow country between the southern Andes Mountains and the Pacific Ocean. This interest had both human and scientific aspects. Strong earthquakes, starting on May 21 and recurring at irregular intervals through several months, brought widespread disaster in a north-south belt hundreds of miles long. At least 2,000 lives were lost, and the property damage is estimated at about 500 million dollars.

The Chilean experience of 1960 is remarkable for the number of major shocks that were recorded within a short time. Five destructive earthquakes occurred within 2 days, and more than forty shocks recorded within 11 days were of large magnitude. A great sea wave generated by the first larg movements added to the damage caused directly by the major shocks (Fig. 20–1). Large changes in landscape features occurred abruptly. Massive landslides rushed down some mountain slopes, and in large coastal areas the surface subsided several feet (Fig. 20–2)

The western coastal belt of North America also is subject to strong earthquakes. April 18, 1906, is a memorable date in the modern history of central California. At about 5 o'clock that morning the people of San Francisco Bay region were rudely awakened, and some of them actually thrown from their beds, by abrupt and violent shaking of the ground. In downtown San Francisco guests in some hotels found their rooms wide open to the street, and in the dim light they looked across at other dazed figures in night attire, robbed of their privacy by the collapse of outside walls. Some buildings were totally wrecked, and the unfortunate occupants were buried in the ruins. Soon the rubble-heaped streets were filled with throngs in panic, and the situation rapidly worsened as fires spread out of control. The city's water mains were broken, and fire raging unchecked for days destroyed vastly more than the earthquake itself. The toll taken by quake and fire together totaled hundreds of human lives and property valued at hundreds of millions of dollars.

Disasters like those in some Chilean cities and in San Francisco have plagued the human race throughout its history. Every year we read reports of strong earthquakes in some parts of the world, and the occasional wreckage of a populous city is set down as a historic event. Actually, many of the most violent shocks occur in sparsely inhabited regions, as in central Nevada in 1915 and at Yakutat Bay, Alaska, in 1899 (p. 348). In 1958 a strong shock at Lituya Bay, Alaska, started a landslide with an estimated volume of 40 million cubic yards. On striking the water, the slide raised a gigantic wave that swept away the forest trees to a height 1,720 feet above sea level (Fig. 20–3) Such events make the headlines briefly and are soon forgotten by the general public, but some of the belts most subject to strong earthquakes have been thickly settled since ancient times and so have become proverbial as sites of recurrent human misery.

A few examples in modern times will serve to highlight the nature, scale, and persistence of this natural scourge. In the summer of 1953 the islands of western Greece were shaken violently time after time, and many towns were reduced to ruins. In August 1950 an area estimated at 100,000 square miles in

Fig. 20–1. In addition to damage caused directly by the earthquakes of 1960, this street at Ancud, Chile, was blocked by a building washed in by a great sea wave that was generated by one of the shocks. (Courtesy C. Ruiz, Reifscheider, Santiago, Chile.)

Fig. 20–2. A road south of Valdivia, Chile, was below sea level at low tide after the earthquakes of 1960. Earlier this road was well above sea level, even at high tide. (Courtesy C. Ruiz, Reifscheider, Santiago, Chile.)

Fig. 20–3. Lituya Bay, Alaska, looking NNW. This valley, partly filled by glacier ice, marks an active fault zone. In 1958 a movement on the fault caused a strong earthquake, which started a major landslide on the slope R. The landslide generated a wave that swept away the forest trees to the point T, 1,720 feet above the level of the bay. (Don J. Miller, U. S. Geol. Survey.)

the mountain land of Assam, near the east end of the great Himalaya chain, was convulsed with major shocks that were almost continuous for 5 or 6 minutes and were repeated at intervals, with lessening intensity, for several weeks. Deep rumbling sounds like the bursting of antiaircraft shells filled the air during the initial shocks. The shaking started enormous landslides that stripped all the regolith with its cover of forest from many steep mountainsides and blocked the adjacent valleys with great heaps of waste. Later breaching of these dams by the backed-up water caused disastrous floods. This earthquake is especially notable because just 53 years earlier, in 1897, one of the greatest shocks ever recorded had its center in the same part of India and was felt over an area estimated at 1,750,000 square miles. India has had numerous great earthquakes, some of which have wrought great havoc in populous centers.

Among the many destructive shocks recorded in Japan, one of the most memorable occurred September 1, 1923, with greatest intensity south of Tokyo. The first warning was a rumbling like thun-

Fig. 20—4. The San Andreas fault zone extends from the vicinity of San Francisco (opposite S. F. on map) northwestward along the coast, southeastward to an area near the Mexican border where it is hidden by alluvium. C, Carrizo Plain. **B.** Air View WSW, across the Carrizo Plain (point marked C on the map, A). Movement along the San Andreas fault, F-F', has offset small valleys cut into weak materials. Probably this offset resulted at the time of the earthquake in 1857. Movement of 1906 occurred farther north. (John S. Shelton.)

der, faint at the start but rapidly swelling to large volume. Then came the powerful shaking of the ground, which wrecked the weaker buildings and caused all others to rock violently. The captain of a large liner in Tokyo Bay saw "the whole flat city of Yokohama billowing like the surface of the ocean under a great storm, and all the houses and vehicles seemed exactly like ships drifting about at the mercy of the waves. The next moment clouds of dust caused by the falling of the houses covered the scene, and then the smoke from the fire which followed blotted the whole city out of sight." Tokyo, somewhat farther from the earthquake center, had fewer buildings thrown down but was in large part destroyed by the resulting fire. In the entire area affected by the earthquake about 140,000 persons were reported killed or missing, and the property damage totaled nearly 3 billion dollars. An earthquake that affected the same general area in 1703 caused about 200,000 deaths. But the all-time record in human toll is reported from the province of Shensi, China, where in 1556 an earthquake claimed more than 830,000 lives.

Italy has had its share of destructive shocks. In the Christmas season of 1908 a great earthquake destroyed Messina, a city in eastern Sicily and Reggio across the strait on the mainland. Cities on these same sites had been wrecked by earthquakes in 1509, 1599, and 1783, and severely shaken at several other times. Much of the destruction in 1908 was caused by a great sea wave that reached heights up to 38 feet above normal sea level and swept over large lowland areas. Such waves have accompanied other earthquakes in coastal belts. At Lisbon, Portugal, in 1755 a wave estimated as 50 feet high added vast damage to that caused directly by one of the most disastrous shocks on record.

Cause of earthquakes

Immediate cause. Aristotle's teaching, in the Fourth Century B.C., that earthquakes are caused by air struggling to escape from underground cavities had at least the merit of attempting to explain by natural causes events that were generally regarded with superstitious awe. The explanation of earthquakes as an outrush of wind, like many other ideas starting with Aristotle, carried through to Shakespeare's day. We read in Shakespeare's play, King Henry the Fourth, Part I:

". . . oft the teeming earth
Is with a kind of colic pincht and vext
By the imprisoning of unruly wind
Within her womb; which for enlargement striving
Shakes the old beldam earth, and topples down
Steeples and moss-grown towers."

The Roman scholar Lucretius in the First Century B.C. supposed that roof collapse in vast caverns set the Earth shaking. Not until the middle of the Nineteenth Century did engineers recognize earthquakes as the expression of elastic-wave motion, and geologists then reasoned that the origin must lie in abrupt movements of large blocks in the Earth's crust. Studies connected with the San Francisco disaster of 1906 support this view and throw a flood of light on the behavior of moving crustal blocks.

Years before the event of 1906 the San Andreas fault was recognized as a zone along which recent movement had occurred. This zone is clearly marked over a distance of several hundred miles, from northern to southern California (Fig. 20–4). Starting in 1874 the U.S. Coast and Geodetic Survey, by precise mapping in central California, fixed the positions of many points near the fault zone with relation to other points some tens of miles farther east. Repetition of the mapping soon after the earthquake revealed that points along the east side of the fault had moved southward, points along the west side had moved northward, and *the amount of movement decreased rapidly with distance of points from the fault*. These consistent facts are explained logically by the mechanism outlined in Fig. 20–5. Suppose that in the early mapping the seven points, *A* to *G*, were located along a straight line across the fault. The crustal block beneath the country east of the fault was moving slowly southeastward; the block on the west was moving northwestward. Frictional resistance where the two blocks were in contact prevented slipping along the fault, and the line became strongly bent from *A'* to *G'*. Elastic strain was building up and enormous potential energy was being stored in the deformed zone. On April 18, 1906, the growing strain suddenly overcame friction, and energy was released as in the springing of a steel trap. The bent line parted at *D,* and the two segments straightened

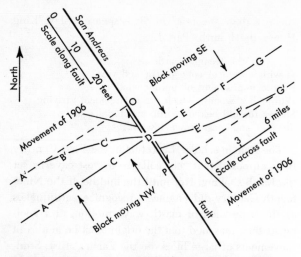

Fig. 20–5. Abrupt movement along the fault in 1906 relieved the bending strain. Crustal blocks separated and segments straightened, D to O and D to P. (Note the exaggerated scale along the fault in comparison with scale across the fault.)

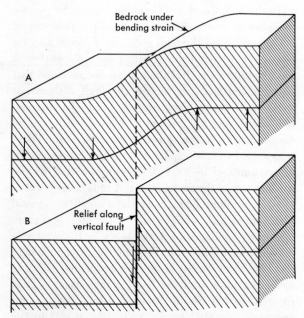

Fig. 20–6. Vertical movement along a fault, forming a steep scarp. A. Deformation by slow bending before displacement. B. Appearance after slipping of blocks along fracture relieves bending strain. (Vertical scale exaggerated.)

to *OA'* and *PG'*; near San Francisco the total offset, *O* to *P*, was 21 feet (Fig. 18–2, **A**).

Vertical movements on some faults, with formation of scarps, also occur abruptly and cause strong earthquakes, as at Pleasant Valley in 1915 (Fig. 18–1). Though we have no evidence from fixing of points by precise surveying near such a fault, we infer that the great energy released in an abrupt movement was stored up during a long period of deformation by bending (Fig. 20–6). There is strong inference that every great earthquake is the result of rupture, though there may be no visible fault in the shaken area. Every fault must be of limited extent, in the vertical as well as the horizontal direction, and many displacements at considerable depth in the crust may die out below the Earth's surface.

Basic cause. Tracing the origin of earthquakes to movements of crustal blocks raises the more fundamental problem of forces that make these blocks move. Many earthquakes occur around active volcanoes, and we infer that pressures from molten rock and the associated gases set up strains that are relieved by jarring movements. But volcanic shocks are local and of small or moderate strength. Some of the greatest earthquakes have occurred far from any active volcanoes. Repeated displacements on faults such as the San Andreas suggest that major adjustments are going on in the body of the Earth, but we do not know how or why. This is the riddle we face in our study of the great mountain belts (Chap. 21).

Analysis of earthquake motion. The physics of elastic vibrations in gases, liquids, and solids is well understood from long and intensive study. A tuning fork set in vibration imparts energy to the surrounding air, which is compressed and expanded in alternate layers (Fig. 20–7). The particles of air oscillate back and forth over very short distances, but the impulse is carried progressively outward as a *sound wave*, at the rate of nearly 1,100 feet per second. Such waves travel even more effectively through water, as is shown to the satisfaction of boys in a swimming hole; one boy, with his head under water, hears sharp clicks when another boy at some distance holds his hands under water and taps two cobbles together. Sound waves move through water nearly a mile a second, or more than four times as fast as through air. Some solids transmit sound still more rapidly. A gentle tapping on a long steel rod can be heard at a great distance, and miners trapped by caving in mines often send out code messages by rapping on the steel rails of tracks, on pipes, or even on bedrock in tunnel walls. The *waves of alternate compression and expansion,* known as **longitudinal waves,** move through steel about 3 miles per second and through rocks at even higher speeds.

Abrupt release of energy in movement on a fault sets up strong vibrations in bedrock. Waves of alternate compression and expansion move out in all directions. These are true sound waves and are often audible as deep rumblings or even as loud reports in the early stages of earthquakes. Because of their superior speed, these waves are *the first impulses to reach points distant from the place of earthquake origin* and are therefore called **primary waves** or simply **P waves.** But another and wholly different type of vibration is caused by the faulting movement. The rock particles are set in oscillation at right angles to the direction of the wave transmission, as in the familiar experiment of fastening a rope at one end and shaking the other end vigorously up and down (Fig. 20–8). These *transverse waves in an earthquake,* usually called *secondary* or *S waves,* move less rapidly than *P* waves, hence lag farther and farther behind them as they move outward. Transverse waves are formed only in rigid materials, *not in gases or liquids;* this fact has considerable importance in

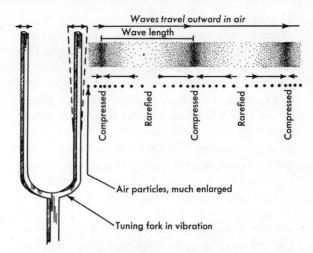

Fig. 20–7. A sound wave moving out from one arm of a tuning fork. Pulses of compression and rarefaction alternate. (Modified from O. H. Blackwood, Introductory College Physics, by permission of John Wiley & Sons, Inc.)

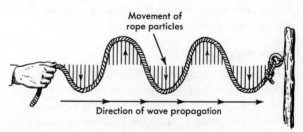

Fig. 20–8. In transverse waves the particles in a rope are displaced at right angles to a median axis, as indicated by short lines and arrows. (Modified from R. M. Garrels, A Textbook of Geology, by permission of Harper and Brothers.)

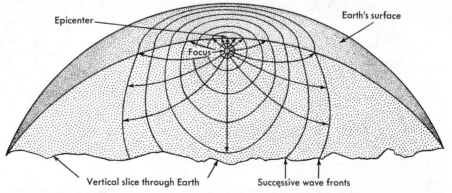

Fig. 20–9. Assumed vertical section through the Earth. From an earthquake focus (small circle) P and S waves spread out with elipsoidal fronts because their speed increases with depth. Only a few wave paths are shown. Note that they bend, keeping at right angles to the wave front.

the study of the Earth's interior.

Both *P* and *S* waves move outward in all directions from the place of origin, spreading with a generally spherical front and affecting all particles in the bedrock through which they move (Fig. 20–9). The place of origin is not a point but probably is a limited area on a fault surface where the faulting movement starts. This *center of the spreading vibrations of an earthquake* is the **earthquake focus.** For a large earthquake the focus is many miles or tens of miles below the Earth's surface. As the front of the *P* wave moves rapidly outward, it first reaches the surface at *a point vertically above the focus;* this point is the **epicenter** (Gr. "above the center"). From the epicenter, elastic waves of a third type spread outward, the *long* or *L* waves, so called because they have much greater wave length (and amplitude) than the *P* and *S* vibrations. **Long waves,** *generated from energy brought to the surface by the P waves, travel around the outer part of the crust* at comparatively low speeds.

Seismology

Recording instruments. *The science of earthquakes,* **seismology** (sīs-mŏl′o-jĭ; Gr. "earthquake study"), has developed rapidly with the perfection of **seismographs,** *instruments for accurate recording of all components of earthquake vibrations.* Many ingenious types of seismographs are in use, but a common basic feature is a heavy mass of metal suspended so that it remains comparatively at rest while the bedrock beneath it vibrates in an earthquake. For a complete record of every important shock a recording station requires three units: two set up at right angles to each other, to register all possible horizontal components of motion, and a third for vertical components.

In a horizontal unit the heavy mass commonly is mounted on a horizontal bar (Fig. 20–10, **A**), with flexible attachment to a supporting post that is firmly anchored in a concrete base. This base, secured to bedrock, must be free on its sides from any regolith that may transmit jarring from traffic or other local sources. A paper-covered drum, mounted on a frame fastened to the concrete base, is rotated slowly by precise clockwork, and time intervals are marked mechanically on the paper. In older instruments the heavy mass carried an arm with a delicate pen point that rested on the drum and traced a continuous line, but it is more satisfactory to use photographic paper onto which a continuous beam of light is reflected by a mirror; the resulting line appears when the paper is developed. A worm gear shifts the revolving drum laterally, to keep all parts of the line in the clear. When the earthquake waves make the bedrock and the attached drum vibrate, the steady beam of

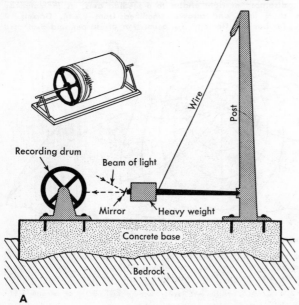

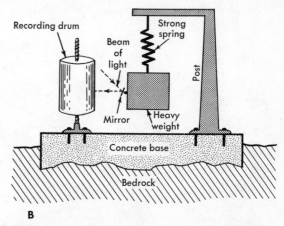

Fig. 20–10. Units of a seismograph. **A.** One of two horizontal units. Drum with part of record shown at upper left. Record would be visible only after photographic development of the sensitized paper. **B.** The vertical unit. (Modified from R. M. Garrels, A Textbook of Geology, by permission of Harper and Brothers.)

light traces on the paper a zigzag path that is the *graphic earthquake record*, or **seismogram** Fig. 20–11). Seismographs at stations far away from an epicenter are equipped to write the record with considerably exaggerated scale because the actual movement of particles in vibrating bedrock decreases with distance, though the pattern of movement remains distinct. At a station near an epicenter the oscillations are so large they sometimes throw parts of the seismogram off the edge of the recording paper. A fully equipped station, therefore, has some machines designed to record earthquakes near at hand, others to record shocks at a great distance.

The unit of a seismograph that registers vertical components of wave motion commonly has the heavy mass suspended by a coiled spring that absorbs the movement of the supporting post and leaves the mass, with its attached mirror, almost unmoved (Fig. 20–10, **B**,).

Speeds of seismic waves. *Waves generated by an earthquake* are **seismic waves.** Arrivals of the waves at each seismograph station are timed to a small fraction of a second. As soon as the location of the epicenter and the time of the shock are known, the average speeds of waves between the place of origin and each station are determined. For both *P* and *S* waves the average rates of travel increase steadily with distance out to more than 100°—about 7,000

miles[1] from the epicenter. Therefore, a line through points on a chart showing arrival times of a wave at a series of stations is a curve that flattens outward (Fig. 20–12). These waves move through the body of the Earth, and the paths followed to more and more distant stations lie at correspondingly greater depths (Fig. 20–9). Increase of speed with depth is logical because compression under great load makes rock more rigid. For this reason the path followed by a *P* or *S* impulse to a distant station can not be a straight chord through the Earth but must curve, concave-up. The increased length of the path is more than offset by the gain in velocity.

Long waves travel at a nearly uniform speed to all distances because these waves move in a shallow zone in which the elastic properties of the rocks are almost uniform. Therefore, on a chart a nearly straight line connects points that represent arrival times of long waves at a series of stations (Fig. 20–12).

Meaning of seismograms. In its simplest form a seismogram has three distinctive parts, each a series of zigzag lines (Fig. 20–11). Thousands of these records are made every year and are studied in many countries by specialists who exchange their informa-

[1] Angular distances are reckoned along a *full circumference* or *great circle of the Earth.* The average linear distance corresponding to 1° is about 69 miles (p. 14).

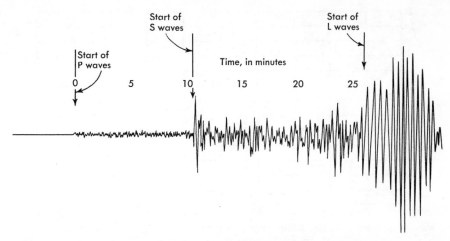

Fig. 20–11. Record, made at Harvard station, of an earthquake with epicenter at Erzincan, Turkey, December 26, 1939. Time interval between *P* and *S*, 10 minutes and 45 seconds, determines the distance between seismograph and epicenter as 88° 30', or about 6,100 miles. (Modified from *Geophysics at Harvard.*)

tion. Comparative studies have convinced these *seismologists* (students of earthquakes) that the first segment of the record represents the *P* waves, the second segment the *S* waves, which travel less rapidly but have somewhat greater amplitude, and the third segment the *L* waves, slowest of the three but with the largest amplitude. A critical part of the record is the interval between the starting points of the *P* and *S* segments. The time represented by this interval is read from the seismogram with great precision and can be used to determine the distance of the station from the epicenter. If each type of wave moved at a constant velocity, this computation would be simple. For example, if the difference in arrival times read from a seismogram were 9 minutes and 10 seconds, or 550 seconds, and the velocities of the waves were $P = 7.5$ miles per second, $S = 4$ miles per second, we could express the unknown distance as *X* miles, and the time required for *P* to travel to the receiving station would be $X/7.5$ seconds, the time for *S* would be $X/4$ seconds. We could then write $X/4 - X/7.5 = 550$. Solution of this simple algebraic equation would give the distance in miles from the station to the epicenter.

Actually, the waves start from an earthquake focus at velocities considerably less than those we have assumed and steadily speed up as they strike deeper into the body of the Earth. Therefore, the problem outlined above is one for calculus and not simple algebra. Fortunately seismologists, in their long and arduous studies, have made accurate tables and charts that give distances for all values of *S* minus *P*. The time interval 9 minutes and 10 seconds tells us that the epicenter is 70°, or about 4,800 miles away from the recording station. With accurate scaling, this value can be read from Figure 20–12.

Location of epicenters. After the distance to an epicenter has been found at three or more widely spaced stations, circles drawn on a globe, with these distances as radii, intersect at the epicenter (Fig. 20–13). As soon as an important earthquake is recorded, many stations get in touch with each other and announcement of the location often is made before any direct news comes from the epicentral area itself. This was true of the 1950 Assam shock, which centered in remote mountain country with no means of rapid communication. The great majority of all earthquakes originate beneath the Pacific Ocean, where epicenters can be located only from seismographic records.

Complicating waves. Nearly all seismograms are more complex than Figure 20–11 because the body of the Earth is not a uniform elastic medium. At every surface between unlike materials, a part of the wave energy is reflected, just as an ordinary sound wave is reflected by a cliff to make an echo.

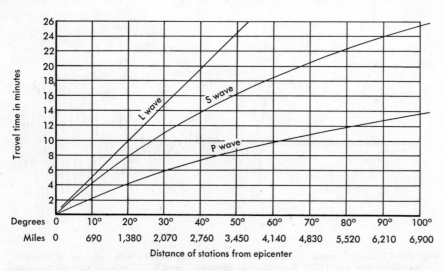

Fig. 20–12. These curves indicate distances traveled from an epicenter, in given times, by the *P*, *S*, and *L* waves. Note that the *L*-wave curve is essentially a straight line. (Data from Perry Byerly, *Seismology*, Prentice-Hall, Inc.)

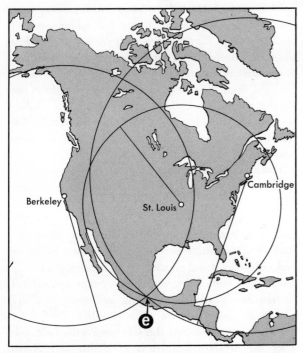

Fig. 20–13. The epicenter (e) of an earthquake in southern Mexico is located at the intersection of circles drawn from stations at Berkeley, Saint Louis, and Cambridge, with the radius at each station determined by the time interval between starts of *P* and *S* waves.

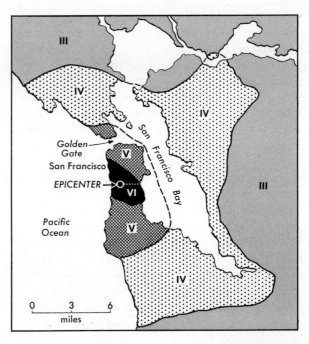

Fig. 20–14. Intensity map of a moderate earthquake near San Francisco, October 2, 1934. The bounding lines, passing through points of equal intensity, are isoseismals. This map shows intensities on the Mercali scale. Note that zone IV is widest in areas near the bay that are on thick alluvium. (After Perry Byerly, Seismology, Prentice-Hall, Inc.)

Wherever *P* and *S* waves reach the Earth's surface, some energy is reflected back to produce new wave motions. Both reflection and refraction occur at a contact between bodies of unlike rock, such as granite and basalt. Many of these incidental waves are too weak to be registered at distant stations; others make characteristic marks on a seismogram that are recognized and cause no confusion.

Reflection and refraction of seismic waves have been turned to good use in study of the Earth's interior and in the search for oil and gas (p. 404).

Earthquake intensity. Generally, the effects of an earthquake are strongest near the epicenter and decrease gradually outward. We like to have a convenient way of comparing *intensities* in different areas during any one shock and in the epicentral areas of different shocks. Several intensity *scales* have been proposed, and one now commonly used, the Mercali scale, recognizes degrees ranging from I, the weakest, up to XII. *Earthquake intensity* is expressed by *a number related to observed destruction or disturbance and to human sensations*, and the

scale is therefore qualitative rather than exact. For example, intensity I is felt only by a few people, favorably located; III is felt noticeably indoors, especially on upper floors of buildings; V is felt by nearly everyone, breaks some dishes and windows; VII makes everybody run outdoors, breaks some chimneys; IX damages well-designed buildings, cracks the ground, breaks underground pipes; XI destroys nearly all masonry structures, bends rails (of railroads); and XII causes total damage, throws objects into the air.

After a strong shock the area affected is studied carefully and an intensity map is made (Fig. 20–14). *A line on a map through points of equal earthquake intensity is an* **isoseismal line.** Some of the isoseismal lines are highly irregular because effects at the surface reflect not only the strength of vibrations in bedrock but also differences in the regolith. Thick water-soaked alluvium shakes like jelly and causes exceptional damage even at considerable distances from an epicenter.

Newspaper reports of an earthquake usually quote

a seismologist who states the magnitude of the shock in terms of the *Richter scale,* which has a more scientific basis than the Mercali scale of local intensities. The Richter scale of magnitude is based on a comparison of graphic records made by seismometers of a standard type. The figures expressing magnitudes are logarithms of maximum trace amplitudes registered by the standard instrument at a distance of 100 kilometers from the epicenter. Critical values on this scale are explained in Table 20–1.

Shocks of magnitude 7 or greater cause major damage in the epicentral area. As the values are logarithmic, differences between successive classes are very large. A shock of magnitude 8 releases more than 3,500 times the energy of a shock classed as 6, and more than 200,000 times the energy of one rated as 5. The San Francisco earthquake of 1906 is listed as 8¼, the Assam earthquake of 1950 as 8.6. By this quantitative method, *earthquake magnitudes* are expressed in *numbers related to actual energy released in the bedrock.*

Depth of focus. If an earthquake focus is only a few miles below the surface, the *P* and *S* waves will rise to the epicenter considerably before these waves reach points 50 or 100 miles away; but, if the focus is 100 or 200 miles deep, the waves will arrive almost simultaneously at all points inside a large circle around the epicenter. In effect, then, the epicentral area increases rapidly in size with increasing depth of focus. This fact, together with careful study of the intervals between arrivals of *P, S,* and *L* waves, makes it possible to estimate quite accurately the depth of focus for every earthquake. The greatest depth so far recorded is about 700 kilometers (435 mi.), and all *earthquakes with foci at least 300 kilometers*[1] (186 mi.) *deep* are classed as *deep-focus*

[1] The metric system is used almost exclusively by seismologists, and some of their critical measurements in that system are reported here because translation into the United States-British system produces awkward values.

earthquakes. Intermediate-focus earthquakes have depths of focus between 70 and 300 kilometers (44 and 186 mi.). Earthquakes with foci at depths less than 70 kilometers (a large majority) are *shallow-focus earthquakes.* Deep-focus earthquakes, about 3 per cent of all recorded, have been noted only in the Pacific region and the Andes Mountains. Intermediate earthquakes have the same restricted distribution, except for some recorded in southwestern Asia and in Mediterranean lands.

Earthquakes that start at great depth are of interest in the study of young mountain belts (Chap. 21).

Distribution of earthquakes. No part of the Earth's surface is exempt from earthquakes, but since the start of systematic recording many large areas have had only occasional shocks of small or moderate intensity. By contrast, several large *tracts* are *subject to frequent shocks,* both strong and weak, and are known as **seismic belts** (Fig. 20–15). The most prominent, aptly called the Circum-Pacific belt, follows the western highlands of South and North America from Cape Horn to Alaska, crosses to Asia, extends southward along the eastern coast and related island arcs, and loops far to the southeast and south beyond New Zealand. Next in prominence is the broad east-west zone extending through the high mountains of southern Asia and the Mediterranean region to Gibraltar. A third long belt follows the Mid-Atlantic Ridge from Arctic to Antarctic waters, and a fourth runs along the Mid-Indian Ridge to unite with a belt in eastern Africa. Smaller seismic areas include island groups in the Pacific and Atlantic.

In a general way, the chief lines of active volcanoes coincide with belts of frequent earthquakes, and this may suggest that volcanic activity is an important cause of earthquakes. The seismic belts coincide closely with young mountain systems, and probably both earthquakes and volcanoes are re-

Table 20–1. Richter scale of earthquake magnitudes

Class	a	b	c	d	e
Magnitude	7¾–8½	7.0–7.7	6–6.9	5.3–5.9	below 5.3
Distance recorded	world-wide		up to 90° (10,000 km.)	up to 45° (5,000 km.)	not beyond 10°

lated to zones of crustal disturbance. When the seismic belts lie directly along the continental borders, as in Chile, the Alaska Peninsula, and Japan, the edges of the continental masses slope steeply and are bordered by deep troughs that appear to be sinking as the adjacent lands are rising. We infer that these are zones of disturbance in which stresses are being relieved by frequent movements, the cause of strong earthquakes.

Fully 80 per cent of all earthquakes occur in the Circum-Pacific belt and 15 per cent in the belt that includes the Himalayan and Alpine mountain zones. Thus the greater part of the Earth's surface is comparatively free from shocks, and most of those that occur in this great area are of low intensity.

Seismic sea waves. A majority of strong earthquakes occur beneath the Pacific, and that ocean has been the scene of many gigantic waves, commonly but mistakenly called "tidal waves." In April 1946 an earthquake occurred in the Aleutian Trench, near the Alaska Peninsula. Great waves that started near the epicenter spread across the Pacific and caused widespread destruction in low coastal areas of the Hawaiian Islands, 2,000 miles from the point of origin. A wave that started at an epicenter near the islands in 1868 is said to have reached above the tops of cocoanut trees. Waves set up during a great Peruvian earthquake in 1877 carried more than 10,000 miles to Japan, where their measured amplitude was as much as 8 feet. A giant wave set up by the Chilean earthquake in 1960 not only did vast damage locally (Fig. 20–2) but also wrecked a considerable part of Hilo, a city on the Island of Hawaii, nearly 6,000 miles from the epicenter. The velocity of these great waves in the Pacific is about 450 mph.

A sea wave generated by an earthquake is a *tsunami* (tsōō-nah'mē, the Japanese term). We can only conjecture how these waves are started. They do not accompany most of the strong sub-Pacific shocks, and perhaps only a vertical fault displacement on a considerable scale will set up the kind of disturbance and supply the great energy peculiar to tsunamis.

Seismic prospecting. Principles learned from study of earthquakes have been turned to practical account, especially in the world-wide search for petroleum. Small artificial earthquakes are produced by setting off explosive charges in holes drilled at

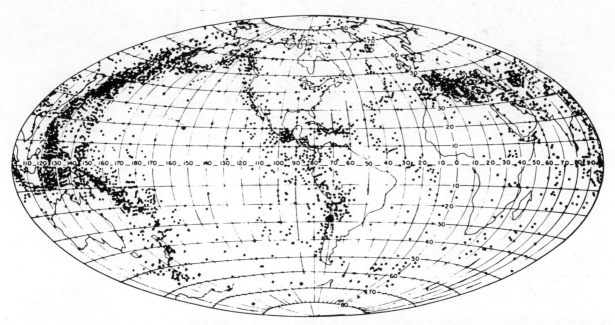

Fig. 20–15. Epicenters of more than 3,700 earthquakes that were recorded between 1899 and 1930. The base map is Aitoff's equal area projection. Note the areas and belts of maximum concentration. (L. Don Leet and Sheldon Judson, Physical Geology, 2d. ed., 1958. Prentice-Hall, Inc., Englewood Cliffs, N. J. By permission.)

selected points, and records of the resulting elastic waves are made by seismographs that are highly sensitive and mounted in trucks for convenient transportation (Fig. 20–16). In wide areas covered with alluvium, such as the San Joaquin Valley of California and the coastal plain of Texas and Louisiana, seismic waves reflected from key beds at some depth may reveal structures favorable for the accumulation of oil and gas.

The *use of seismic techniques in a search for valu-able subsurface deposits* is known as **seismic prospecting**.

The Earth's interior

Seismologists estimate that as many as a million earthquakes occur in a year, most of them weak but some strong. The average for the world is about two earthquakes per minute. This almost constant trembling confirms other evidence that the Earth is not a stagnant mass bearing only the marks of past activ-

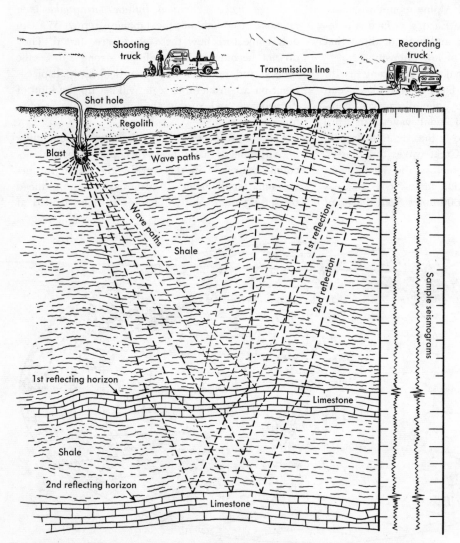

Fig. 20–16. Use of portable equipment in a search for underground structure favorable for accumulation of oil and gas. Abrupt changes in kinds of rock give strong reflections of seismic waves. (Modified from C. A. Heiland, Geophysical Exploration, Prentice-Hall, Inc.)

ities; it is full of energy and undergoing continual change. The fact that earthquakes are attended by growth of fault scarps and yet have their origin far beneath us makes us realize that what goes on in the Earth's interior plays a large part in shaping the surface on which we live. How much do we know about the depths of the Earth and in what ways do we hope to learn more?

Earthquakes themselves provide a sort of X-ray mechanism with which we can "see" all the way to the Earth's core. This study is in a growing state and will go forward only with the help of all other known methods of attack and all the information that has been won. Let us look at this problem in brief outline.

Weighing the Earth. Handbooks that list the Earth's vital statistics give as its total mass 5.976×10^{27} gm. (5,976 billion billion metric tons) and its average density, 5.516 gm./cm.[3] This value of density, carried to the third decimal place, suggests a confident solution. How is it known that an average sample of the whole Earth weighs 5.516 times as much as an equal volume of pure water? And where has anyone found scales for weighing the Earth?

Isaac Newton showed the way to the solution in his universal law of gravitation: *Every particle in the universe attracts every other particle with a force directly proportional to the product of their masses and inversely as the square of the distance between them.* This is expressed compactly in the familiar equation $F = (Gm_1m_2/d^2)$, in which m_1 and m_2 are any two masses, d is the distance between their centers, F is the force of attraction, and G is the *gravitational constant,* the precise value of the attractive force between two masses of one gram each, exactly one centimeter apart. In Newton's day there was no equipment with the delicate precision required for working out the value of G. In the nineteenth century the German scientist von Jolly measured with a highly sensitive balance the attraction between 5 kilograms (11 lb.) of mercury and a lead ball weighing more than 5 tons (Fig. 20–17). After the mercury was precisely balanced, the lead ball was placed below it, and the downward pull was found to be offset by a tiny weight, 0.589 milligram. Therefore, F in the equation became 0.589 dyne; and with the distance between the centers of the lead and mercury spheres

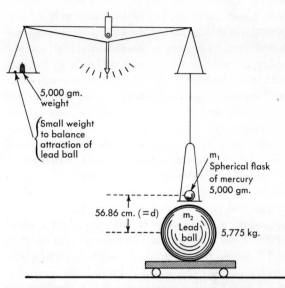

Fig. 20–17. Von Jolly used this method to determine the gravitational constant, as an essential quantity for computing the mass of the Earth. (From O. H. Blackwood, Introductory College Physics, 1939, p. 99, by permission of John Wiley & Sons, Inc.)

accurately measured, von Jolly solved for G. His result was 6.47×10^{-8} dyne-cm.^{2}/gm.^{2} Later refinements have increased the 6.47 to 6.664. Measurements show that the Earth exerts a force of about 980 dynes on a mass of one gram at sea level, and the average length of the Earth's radius (= d of the equation) is 637 million centimeters.

If the mass of the Earth is W, then 980 dynes (F) = (6.664×10^{-8} dyne-cm.^{2}/gm.^{2}) (G) × (1 gm. × W)/637,000,000^2, and W = 5,976 billion billion metric tons.

We know the Earth's form and dimensions (p. 14) and, therefore, its volume, V. Thus we have $W/V = 5.516$, the average density.

This average is fully twice that of rocks that make up the visible part of the crust; the density of granitic rock is less than 2.7 and of basaltic rocks somewhat less than 3. Then why is the Earth as a whole so heavy? As one speculation, we might picture a thin outer shell of the ordinary rocks, and material with density somewhat above 6 from this shell down to the center. But this guess fails to meet a simple test of astronomers. The Sun and Moon exert a pull on the Earth's equatorial bulge, causing a slow change in the tilt of the axis of rotation. The measure of this effect, known precisely, can be explained only by supposing that a large part of the Earth's mass is concentrated near its center; in other words, that material of low or moderate density extends far down to a core with much higher density. This view is strongly in accord also with the known shape of the Earth. If there were fairly uniform density through a large part of the radius, the mass in the outer part of the globe would cause much greater equatorial bulging and polar flattening under rotation than we actually find.

Using earthquake data. Every strong earthquake sends out messages that are picked up by seismographs widely distributed. These records, studied together, tell a consistent story. All stations out to about 103° (7,100 mi.) from an epicenter receive the P, S, and L waves. In long study of records made by earthquakes all over the world seismologists agree that the P and S waves coming through to stations just inside the 103° limit reach to a maximum depth of about 1,800 miles (2,900 km.; Fig. 20–18). Stations farther away receive no S wave, and in a zone between 103 and 143° from the epicenter seismograms show neither P nor S records; only the L waves and complicated reflections are recorded in this *shadow zone,* about 2,750 miles wide (Fig. 20–18). Between 143° and the point exactly opposite the epicenter (180° from it), seismograms record P and L vibrations but the primary waves arrive late; they are slowed down beyond the 1,800-mile depth. A radical change occurs at that depth.

We conclude that there is a definite *core of the Earth, an inner spherical mass below a depth of 1,800 miles* (2,900 km.). This core must differ radically from the outer part of the Earth in physical condition and probably in chemical composition. The abrupt disappearance of the S wave on reaching the core boundary indicates a change from the solid to a fluid state because transverse waves move only through a rigid medium (p. 397). P waves continue through the core, but at the boundary their velocity drops abruptly from about 8 to 5 miles per second, and the paths are sharply refracted toward the center of the core, just as rays of light are bent in passing from air into a slower medium such as glass or water. On emerging at the far side of the core, the P waves are refracted again, in the direction to increase still

further the width of the shadow zone.

Behavior of the two waves in their course downward is shown graphically in Fig. 20–19, **A**. The velocity of each wave increases rapidly in the first 600 miles, then at a considerably slower rate to the 1,800-mile level, where the S wave stops. After its radical drop at the core boundary, the speed of the P wave rises gradually, mounts abruptly beyond 3,200 miles in depth, then levels off to the center.

Reasoning about the deep zones. The steady rise in speed of elastic waves from the surface down to the 1,800-mile level suggests that this large part of the Earth—more than 80 per cent of its entire volume—is made of material that is generally the same in composition but compressed more and more with increasing depth. It must be in the solid state; otherwise the S waves would not go through it. Stopping of these waves at a sharp boundary must mean a change from solid to fluid. The best guess is that inside the core boundary the temperature is high enough to keep the material there fluid in spite of the enormous pressure that raises melting points. But how is it possible to have molten matter confined to the deepest zone where pressure is highest and to keep solid matter

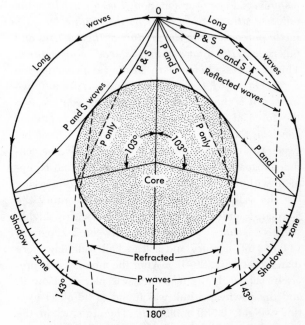

Fig. 20–18. Information given by critical seismic waves, used as a basis for determining the structure of the Earth's interior.

just outside in a zone of lower pressure? Only one answer seems to make sense: the chemical composition changes abruptly at the core boundary, and the material in the core has a lower melting point than the material directly outside it.

Our reasoning must also take account of evidence that the inner part of the Earth is exceptionally heavy (p. 406). In meteorites, which perhaps represent a fair sample of the Earth and its neighbor planets, iron and oxygen are the most abundant elements. If, in the infant Earth, material of this kind was heated above the melting point, logically most of the iron, with nickel and some other minerals, would have settled toward the center, forcing the lighter elements oxygen, aluminum, silicon, and others into higher zones. As cooling went on, some of the silicate minerals with a somewhat higher melting point than iron may have formed a thick solid shell that insulated the hot core, keeping much of it fluid to this day. This general theory has become so acceptable that we often speak of "the Earth's iron core" as if it were an established fact.

A point still calling for explanation is the abrupt rise in velocity of P waves deep within the core (Fig. 20–19, A). Perhaps the inner part of the core is solid; at a critical depth the pressure may be high enough to prevent fusion even at temperatures somewhat above those in the outer part of the core. Following this proposal, then, we picture an inner solid ball, 1,700 miles in diameter, made up of iron and other metals, and an outside layer, about 1,300 miles thick, in which the metals are fluid (Fig. 20–19, B). Under the enormous pressures at those depths, the average density of the whole core probably is above 12. According to one hypothesis now much in favor, the fluid part of the core is continually stirred by convection, like boiling water in a kettle; and this motion generates electric currents that in turn produce the Earth's magnetic field. This provision of a dynamo may finally solve one of the greatest scientific puzzles, the cause of terrestrial magnetism. Turbulence in the core may cause the continual slow shifting of the magnetic poles.

Temperatures in the Earth. Volcanoes and hot springs indicate that at least in some places temperatures at depth are high, and direct measurements in deep mines and wells suggest a universal increase in temperature downward. At some localities this in-

Wave velocity, kilometers per second

Fig. 20–19. A. Critical changes in velocity of seismic waves with depth. Note that the S wave is not recorded below a depth of 2,900 kilometers, the periphery of the core, and the velocity of the P wave, sharply decreased at 2,900 kilometers, increases within the core. **B.** Dimensions of the three major zones below the thin crust of the Earth. Evidence suggests a gradation from outer to inner parts of the core, instead of the abrupt separation shown in this diagram.

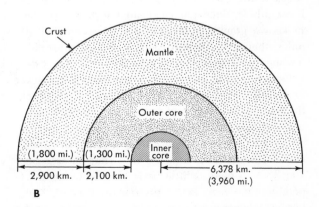

crease is as high as 1° F every 30 feet; at others, as in the deep gold mines of the Transvaal, South Africa, it is only 1° F every 250 feet. At a depth of slightly more than 16,000 feet, in a hole drilled for oil in California, the measured temperature was 400° F. The average for all observations is about 1° F every 60 feet.

The change in temperature in the Earth for a given vertical unit distance is known as the **geothermal gradient.** If the gradient determined in mines and boreholes should continue downward unchanged, the temperature at the center would exceed 350,000° F; but for several reasons the average rate of change in the shallow zone cannot be extended to great depths. The length of the deepest opening used in estimating the gradient is only about one thousandth of the Earth's radius; and the value obtained for this thin skin can not be accepted for the whole body. Rocks such as granite are poor conductors of heat. Therefore, if the temperature at a depth of several miles should be high (say, 1,000°), heat would flow out very slowly through the overlying granite, and the change in temperature for each 100 feet would be considerable. Probably the heat conductivity improves with depth, both because compression of the rocks increases and because metallic elements, notably good conductors, are more abundant in deeper zones. Therefore, in those zones the change in temperature for each 100 feet should be less than in rocks directly under the continents; how much less we have no way of knowing.

All confidence in guesses about the geothermal gradient was destroyed by the discovery of radio-activity (p. 56). Uranium, thorium, and potassium break down, each at a constant rate, with development of heat. If the average content of these elements in known granitic rocks extended to a depth of 10 miles, they would supply more heat than is actually flowing up to the surface of the continents. Basalt develops only about one-third as much radioactive heat as granite but enough to cause permanent fusion of the crust if the content of radioactive elements were constant to a depth of some tens of miles.

We infer, therefore, that these elements, in appreciable amounts, are confined to a thin outer zone; and, though there is little basis for calculating temperatures in deeper zones, presumably they are high because the core behaves as a fluid toward the S

waves from earthquakes. We reason that the heavy core is made of metal (p. 407) and that very high temperature is required to keep metals fluid under the enormous pressures on the core. Heat must be conducted outward, and, in all parts of the deep interior, temperatures probably are above the melting points for the materials under surface conditions. Yet, as we have seen, earthquake waves testify that no considerable part of the globe is molten in the outer 1,800 miles of its radius. Therefore, in this outer portion there is not enough heat to cause general fusion under the great pressures that prevail. At depths of a few tens of miles the rocks, though "solid," probably have very little strength. Even though high pressures maintain the rigidity that is indicated by fast-moving S waves, the rock at high temperature would flow under long-continued unbalanced stresses.

Outer part of the Earth

Reality of the crust. Glimpses into the deep parts of the Earth are fascinating, but some problems in the shallow zones concern us more closely and hold promise of early solution. Sensitive portable seismographs in critical positions record large quarry blasts and give us the speeds of seismic waves through basalt in Washington and Idaho and through large bodies of granite in New England and Canada. These small but measurable differences in speed then serve to identify the general type of bedrock concealed in ocean floors and beneath continents. The L waves sent out from an epicenter in Hawaii or Japan reach a station in California in travel times characteristic of basalt; waves that start in Nevada arrive in New

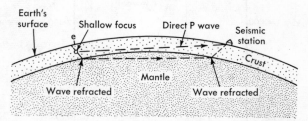

Fig. 20–20. Seismic records at stations within critical distances from a shallow epicenter e give information about thickness of the crust. Dimensions and relations in this figure are diagrammatic only.

England with speed more nearly like that known for granite. This evidence confirms our impression, resting on what can be seen only in widely scattered islands, that bedrock in floors of the oceans is basaltic and thus heavier than the common rocks exposed on continents.

More information about the crust beneath continents comes from study of records at stations fairly near epicenters. A seismogram made within 500 miles of a shallow earthquake focus shows distinct records of at least two P waves and two S waves. By comparative study from a number of stations, it is determined that one pair of waves has come by a direct route and another has been refracted in crossing a boundary into a deeper zone, then refracted upward to the surface (Fig. 20–20). Records from the several stations at differing distances from the epicenter give a basis for computing the thickness of the layer above the refracting boundary. Beneath plains and hill country in western Europe, New England, and California, thicknesses determined in this way vary from 10 to 20 miles. Under the Alps the refracting boundary is about 40 miles below the average surface.

From this evidence, then, the **crust** seems fairly well defined: it is *an outer shell with varied but measurable thickness.* By the interpretation now favored, beneath the continents sedimentary, granitic, and metamorphic rocks overlie basalt, and, below this composite crust, rocks that are considerably heavier and contain less silica extend to great depth. Beneath the oceans a crust made wholly of basalt lies on the heavier basement. According to the best seismic evidence now available, the average thickness of the

basaltic layer in the floors of the Atlantic and Pacific Oceans is only about 3 miles (5 km.). Above this layer is a variable thickness of marine deposits (Chap. 15).

The rocks forming the greater part of the continental masses consist of minerals with high content of the elements silicon and aluminum. The basaltic layer in the ocean floors and in the basal parts of continental masses is rich in minerals with a high content of silicon and magnesium. In the language of geology *the collective term for continental rocks is* **sial** (Si = silicon, al = aluminum); *the collective term for rocks beneath the ocean floors is* **sima** (Si = silicon, ma = magnesium).

The moho and the mantle. In the early years of the twentieth century a seismologist with the difficult name of Mohorovičić, in what is now Yugoslavia, observed that seismic records suggest a lower boundary of continental rocks at moderate depths. He used the method explained in Figure 20–20, and thus he was the first to announce definite evidence for what we now recognize as *the base of the crust.* Seismologists refer to this boundary as the **Mohorovičič discontinuity,** a ponderous term which by wide agreement has been shortened to **moho** (mō-hō) for use in conversation.

As shown diagrammatically in Figure 20–21, the computed depth to the moho beneath a continent is several times the average depth beneath ocean floors. It is seriously suggested by some scientists that with modern drilling equipment a test well could be sunk to the moho at some location on the ocean floor. Advocates of this project argue that it promises information of great scientific value and that it should have

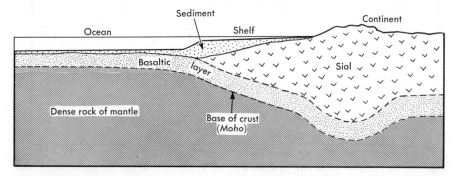

Fig. 20–21. The oceanic crust differs radically from the continental crust in composition and in thickness. Beneath continents there is considerable variation in thickness of the basaltic layer and also of the sialic plate.

priority over proposals for exploration in space. Of course, drilling a hole to the base of the crust would be very expensive and technical difficulties would be serious. Some wells drilled for oil on land are considerably more than 4 miles deep, but equipment for probing to the moho has to operate from a floating platform, over water thousands of feet deep, subject to agitation by rough seas and possible destruction by storm. Encouraging results have come from a first test of such equipment. Early in 1961 a drill operated over deep water off the west coast of Mexico passed through bottom sediments and into basalt.

What kind of material underlies the crust is, of course, a matter for speculation. Geophysical evidence indicates that the density of the material is about 3.3 and thus about 10 per cent heavier than basalt. The density increases steadily downward with increasing pressure (Fig. 20–22). According to a favored suggestion, the material may have a composition similar to that of the mineral olivine.

The zone between the crust and the central core, about 1,800 miles (2900 km.) thick, is known as the *mantle.*

Equilibrium in the crust. Even in man-made structures, the strength of rock is limited. In a mass as large as the Earth, which gravity has molded into nearly spherical form (Fig. 2–6), rock is extremely weak. If by some external force the Earth could be shaped momentarily as a cube, gravity would quickly restore the nearly spherical form of equilibrium. Yet the form seen in detail is not quite that of an oblate spheroid. Continents stand high above ocean floors, and great mountain chains tower above plains. Are these great relief features held up entirely by the strength of the crust? We see evidence that large loads are shifted from place to place on the Earth's surface. Continents and mountains are eroded, and great volumes of sediment are piled up in deltas such as those of the Mississippi and the Nile. More than once vast quantities of water have been removed from the sea and converted into thick ice sheets on the land. These shifts of load must set up stresses that tend to change the form of the Earth. Is there some mechanism for relieving these stresses?

This problem is attacked in several ways; one makes use of the plumb bob, an instrument familiar to builders and surveyors. A line holding the plumb bob is normally vertical; it points toward the Earth's center of mass. But on a plain near a great mountain range the bob is pulled a little to one side by the up-

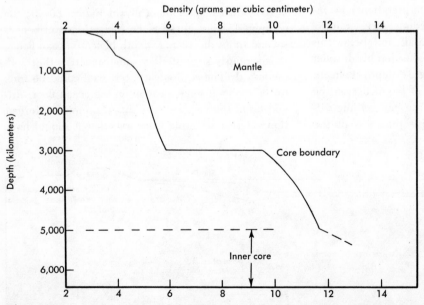

Fig. 20–22. Increase in density downward in the Earth, as reckoned by geophysicists. The sharp bend at top of curve marks the base of the crust. Note the large, abrupt increase in density from the mantle to the core. Maximum values, within the inner core, are uncertain, as indicated. (From K. E. Bullen, Introduction to the Theory of Seismology, Methuen, 1953.)

standing mountain mass. Knowing from maps the volume of the mountain unit, and assuming that the rocks in the mountains and under the plains have the same average density, we compute accurately the amount of lateral attraction to be expected. In precise tests made by geodetic surveys near the Himalaya and the Rocky Mountains the actual departure of the plumb line from the vertical is found to be only a small fraction of the expected value (Fig. 20–23). We infer, therefore, that the rocks in or under the mountains are on the average lighter than those under the plains. This inference is checked by using a delicate pendulum to measure the values of gravity on the high and low areas. The rate at which the pendulum swings is governed closely by the intensity of gravity, which varies with latitude and altitude. If the density of the crust were uniform, the value of gravity at any point could be closely predicted. For mountain stations the calculated values are generally higher than the measured values. Again the discrepancy is explained most logically by supposing that the excess *volume* represented by the mountains is offset by deficient *density* beneath. We infer, then, that great mountain chains are approximately balanced against adjacent lowlands and continental masses against the deep-sea floors. The *ideal condition of flotational balance among segments of the Earth's crust* is **isostasy** (ī-sŏs′tah-sĭ; Gr. "equal standing").

Figure 20–24 is an oversimplified illustration of the principle involved in isostasy. Blocks of copper, equal in cross section but of different lengths, float in mercury. The longer blocks sink deeper and also rise higher than shorter blocks, obeying the Archimedes principle just as icebergs do. If we cut some copper from the top of one block and add it to another, adjustment will occur by some sinking of the loaded unit and rising of the other. In a liquid this adjustment is immediate and perfect; but how can the principle operate in the solid crust? Although there is no continuous layer of liquid rock beneath the Earth's surface, we know from laboratory experiment that solid rock when subjected to high unbalanced pressure is deformed by plastic flow. We infer, then, that an overloaded part of the crust sinks, that parts lightened by long-continued erosion rise, and that the adjustment between them is made by very slow lateral flowage of rock in a deep zone. The operation is less

perfect and, of course, requires much more time than in a liquid.

A striking confirmation of the isostatic theory is furnished by the regions in North America and Europe that were covered by great ice sheets during Pleistocene time. As the ice melted, the sea invaded large parts of the glaciated regions but was excluded by later uplift. Emerged shorelines, associated with beach and offshore deposits that contain marine shells and bones of seals and whales, are found in the region of Lake Champlain and Montreal several hundred feet above present sea level; and similar evidence is found in Scandinavia (p. 352). The plain inference is that the masses of ice were overloads that depressed the land. After the loads were removed, some time was required for restoration of balance by slow flowage in the rocks at depth. During that time interval, the sea invaded the depressed regions, and as balance was gradually restored by regional uplift the sea was expelled. Although thou-

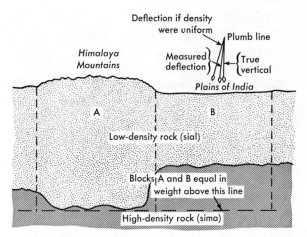

Fig. 20–23. A plumb line reveals that average density of rock beneath a high mountain chain is lower than beneath adjacent plains. Compare with Figure 20–24.

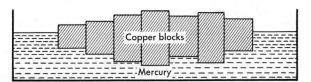

Fig. 20–24. Blocks floating in a liquid are in perfect isostatic balance. If the blocks have about equal density, those that extend to greatest heights reach to greatest depths.

411

sands of years have elapsed since the ice disappeared, the adjustment is not yet complete, for parts of Scandinavia are still rising (Fig. 18–5). Strong tilting of the Great Lakes basins in North America is ascribed to the postglacial uplift (Fig. 18–6), which seems to have been greatest in southern and eastern Canada where presumably the load of glacier ice was greatest. Frequent earthquakes of low intensity in northeastern United States and southern Canada probably reflect slow uplift still in progress.

The general fact of isostasy appears to be established, but many uncertainties remain. We do not know the depth at which flowage occurs during adjustment, the size of a load necessary to start the mechanism of adjustment, and the degree of completeness to which adjustment is carried.

The operation of isostasy has particular interest in connection with the growth of great mountain chains, followed by reduction in their height by erosion. These aspects of the problem are considered in Chapter 21.

SUMMARY

1. Destructive earthquakes have occurred in many lands throughout human history. Prominent breaks in land surfaces have occurred at the time of many strong shocks.

2. Abrupt displacements in the Earth's crust is the immediate cause of earthquakes. The basic cause of these displacements is speculative.

3. Seismology, the branch of geophysics devoted to study of earthquakes, is equipped with sensitive recording instruments at widely distributed stations.

4. Seismograms, graphic records of an earthquake, give information on location and depth of the point of origin and the amount of energy released.

5. Most earthquakes originate within a few tens of miles from the Earth's surface, but some have their origin at depths greater than 400 miles.

6. Ninety-five per cent of all earthquakes have their origin in the Circum-Pacific belt and a belt crossing southern Asia to Mediterranean lands. Those in the remaining 5 per cent are widely distributed.

7. Some earthquakes caused by displacements in ocean floors generate sea waves that cause widespread destruction.

8. The average density of the Earth is known accurately, and a general distribution of density is determined from geophysical and astronomic data. Densities increase downward to high values in a central core.

9. Study of seismograms reveals a thin crust on a denser mantle that extends to a depth about 1,800 miles. Failure of transverse seismic waves to extend deeper indicates that the central core is in large part fluid.

10. The fluid condition and the high density of the core suggest that it consists of metals, largely iron. Convection within the core may generate the Earth's magnetic field.

11. Seismic evidence indicates an outer crust, several miles to a few tens of miles thick, overlying the denser mantle. Low-density rocks such as granite are restricted to continental masses. The thinner crust in ocean floors consists largely of basalt.

12. Higher segments of the crust are generally in balance with lower segments because of differences in density. Large transfers of load, such as occur during waxing and waning of great ice sheets, result in vertical movements to restore balance.

REFERENCES

Daly, R. A., 1926, Our mobile Earth: New York, Charles Scribner's Sons.

Davidson, Charles, 1931, The Japanese earthquake of 1923: London, Thomas Murby and Co.

Gutenberg, B., and Richter, C. F., 1949, Seismicity of the Earth: Princeton Univ. Press.

Lawson, A. C., and others, 1908, Report on the California earthquake of April 18, 1906: Washington, D. C., Carnegie Institution Publication 87, vol. 1 and Atlas.

Macelwane, J. B., 1947, When the Earth quakes: Milwaukee, Bruce Publishing Co.

CHAPTER 21. ORIGIN AND HISTORY OF MOUNTAINS

Mountains defined   Structure of continents   The type geosyncline   Appalachian history

Mountains of western North America   The Alps, a classic example   Late stages in mountain

history   Maintaining crustal balance   Search for cause of orogeny   Have continents drifted?

Rocks made of deposits on sea floors are now at the greatest mountain heights. Kanchenjunga, third highest peak in the Himalaya.

(Burton Holmes, from Ewing Galloway.)

Mountains defined

In common usage the term *mountain* is applied to *any land mass that stands conspicuously above its surroundings*. No standard limits are set on minimal height and size of topographic features that qualify. In a region of low plains steep hills only a few hundred feet high are known as mountains. On the other hand, in the Rocky Mountain region and other rugged districts some features as high as 2,000 feet are known as buttes or hills. Whatever height is acceptable, an essential characteristic of mountains is comparatively limited width at the top. In northwestern Arizona, near the mouth of the Grand Canyon, a steep, rugged escarpment 4,000 feet high faces westward (Fig. 21–1). Some local inhabitants refer to this precipitous scarp as "the mountain," but at the top of the escarpment one looks eastward for tens of miles across nearly level ground. Therefore the west-facing scarp is the edge of an extensive *plateau*, not a mountain front. Bedrock beneath a plateau commonly consists of nearly horizontal layers of sedimentary or volcanic rock (Figs. 1–10, 2–11).

Many isolated high masses, such as Stone Mountain, Georgia, and high points of the Catskill Mountains, New York, are *residual mountains,* that is, *remnants that have survived long-continued erosion of extensive highlands.* Other high peaks, and some extensive ridges, are *large accumulations of volcanic materials* and are properly called *volcanic mountains.* Good examples are the Hawaiian islands and parts of the Cascade Mountains of Oregon and Washington. The great mountain belts of the Earth owe their origin primarily to massive disturbance of bedrock. The term *mountain making,* commonly used in geology, is applied to *creation of elongate highlands by large-scale deformation of rocks in the Earth's crust.* Effects of such deformation are fold-

ing, faulting, and metamorphism. These effects, widely displayed in all great mountain belts of the present, are conspicuous also on the sites of ancient mountain belts that have been reduced to low altitudes by erosion during long ages.

The term *orogeny,* in common use by geologists, has essentially the same meaning as mountain making (p. 435).

Mountains formed by deformation of the crust are the most informative but perhaps also the most puzzling of the Earth's major features. Their formation by uplift to great heights has allowed cutting by streams to unusual depths. As a result, mountain districts have the finest displays of bedrock, including great thicknesses of sedimentary beds that contain marine fossils. Mountains, then, stand on the sites of old seaways. Why have sea floors of earlier times become the lofty highlands of today? This riddle still remains unanswered, but under persistent study mountains are slowly giving up some of their secrets.

Descriptive classification of mountains

Generally, mountain masses are parts of distinct units that vary in size and plan, from irregular *groups,* such as the La Sal Mountains of Utah and the Adirondack Mountains of northern New York, to the enormous belt that extends more or less regularly from the Pyrenees eastward across Europe and Asia to the East Indies. Descriptions of the larger units or their parts employ somewhat loosely the terms *range, system,* and *chain.* As it is desirable to use descriptive terms with a definite meaning, the usage proposed many years ago by J. D. Dana is followed here.

A *mountain range* is either *a single large complex*

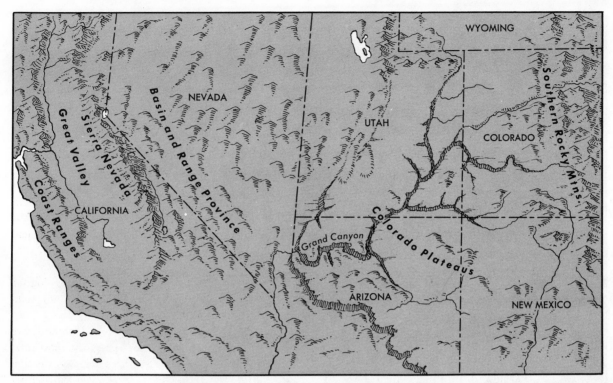

Fig. 21–1. Principal highlands of southwestern United States. The major features are, from east to west, the Southern Rocky Mountains, the Colorado Plateaus, the Basin and Range Province, the Sierra Nevada, and the Coast Ranges. Numerous sizable units are omitted.

ridge or a series of clearly related ridges that make a fairly continuous and compact unit. Excellent types are the Sierra Nevada in eastern California (Fig. 21–1) and the Front Range of Colorado. *A group of ranges that are similar in their general form, structure, and alignment, and presumably owe their origin to the same general causes,* constitutes a **mountain system.** Thus the Basin Range System in Nevada and adjoining states is made up of many distinct ranges that trend north or northwest and have similar form and structure. The Rocky Mountain System is a great assemblage of ranges, formed at approximately the same time, extending from near the Mexican border northward through the United States and western Canada (Pl. 1, inside front cover). The term **mountain chain** is used somewhat more loosely to designate *an elongate unit consisting of numerous ranges or groups, regardless of similarity in form or equivalence in age.*

Alexander von Humboldt, famous traveler of the late eighteenth and early nineteenth centuries, felt the need of a still more comprehensive term in referring to a series of systems or chains in a more or less unified belt of vast extent. For this purpose he borrowed the Spanish word *cordillera. All the mountain units in western North America, from the eastern border of the Rocky Mountains to the Pacific Coast,* are known collectively as the **North American Cordillera.** Similarly, *the entire broad mountain belt that extends almost continuously from Alaska to Cape Horn* is known as the **American Cordilleras.** Mountain units that comprise this great belt are diverse in kind and in date of origin.

Structure of continental masses

Distribution of mountains. The great mountain chains are not in haphazard arrangement; they form rather distinct belts, the largest of which are thousands of miles in length and hundreds of miles in width. (Pl. 2, inside back cover.) Three sides of the Pacific Ocean are framed with these persistent chains. Outside the Pacific area the dominant belt

415

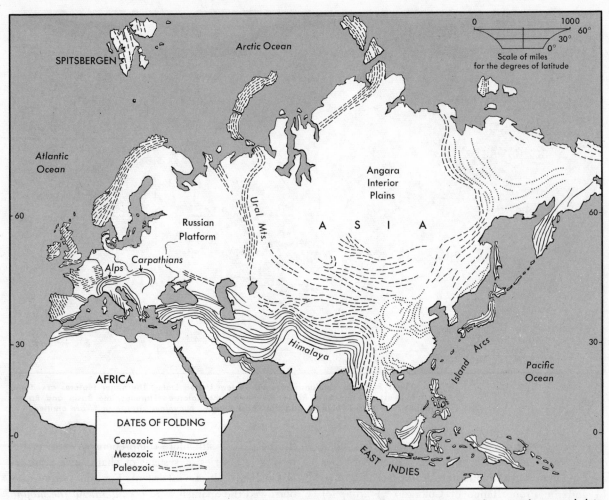

Fig. 21—2. Chief mountain belts of Asia and Europe. Patterns show trends, general dates of origin, and arrangements around old stable areas. (Modified from J. H. F. Umbgrove, *The Pulse of the Earth*, 1947.)

extends eastward from Spain and Morocco to southwest Asia and includes such familiar units as the Pyrenees, the Alps, and the Himalaya. Among the older chains with less imposing heights are the Appalachians of eastern North America, the Ural Mountains between Europe and Asia, and the Cape Mountains at the southern tip of Africa.

Each mountain chain is made up of many individual ranges, some tens and others hundreds of miles long, most of them generally parallel to the long dimension of the chain. Some of the largest units, notably the Alps and Carpathians of Europe,

Fig. 21—3. Numerous islands east and southeast of Asia are arranged in rows and groups with pronounced arcuate form. These *island arcs* are in belts of frequent strong earthquakes (Fig. 20—15). At least some of the groups appear to be growing mountain chains. Deep trenches in the ocean floor are parallel to the oceanward sides of prominent arcs. ►

the Himalaya and neighboring chains in Asia, appear on the map as great crescentic arcs (Fig. 21–2). The island chains from Japan southward through the East Indies form a succession of arcs, some with large radius, others sharply curved (Fig. 21–3). If their bases were above sea level and not on a sea

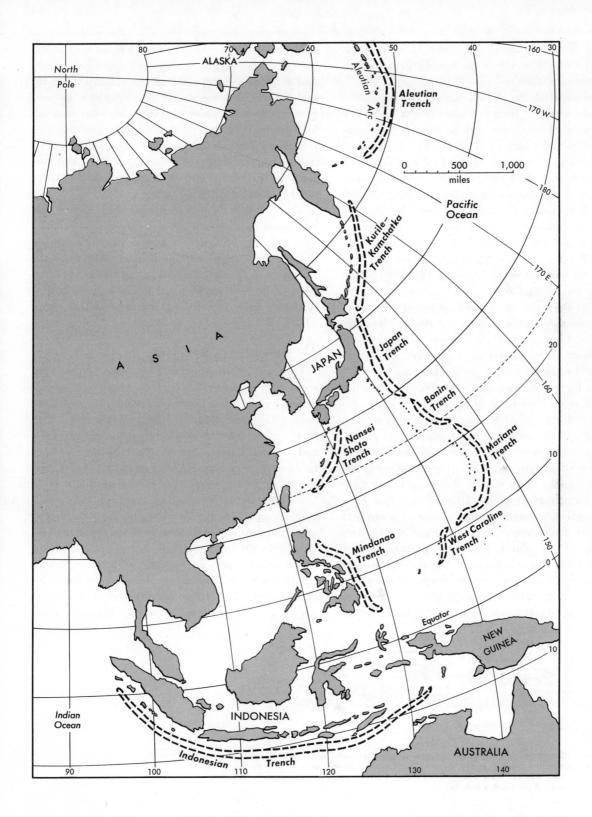

North
Pole

ALASKA

Aleutian Arc

Aleutian
Trench

Kurile–
Kamchatka
Trench

Pacific
Ocean

A S I A

JAPAN

Japan
Trench

Bonin
Trench

Nansei
Shoto
Trench

Mariana
Trench

Mindanao
Trench

West Caroline
Trench

Equator

NEW
GUINEA

Indian
Ocean

INDONESIA

Indonesian   Trench

AUSTRALIA

0   500   1,000
miles

floor at large average depth, these arcuate chains would be joined in one of the world's most impressive mountain systems.

Continental plates. Within each of the continents is a wide area free from mountain ridges. In Asia a vast region of plains lies well to the north, in central and western Siberia (Fig. 21–2). The eastern part of Europe, bounded by the Ural and Carpathian mountains and by the Black Sea and the Arctic Ocean, is a monotonous plain, the Russian Platform. Africa has mountain chains only along its northern and southern margins; otherwise it is a vast expanse of plains and plateaus. North America has a broad, rather flat interior, the Mississippi River drainage basin and much of central Canada (Pl. 1). Tourists looking for exciting scenery find monotonous landscapes in the 1,200- to 1,500-mile journey from the Appalachian Mountain belt to the Rocky Mountain front in Colorado and Wyoming. Farther west, through more than 1,000 miles, they see an endless variety of rugged forms in the Rockies, the wide Basin and Range province, the Sierra Nevada, and the Coast Ranges. How many of these travelers are concerned with the underlying cause of the wide interior lowland and the bordering highlands?

Surely this cause lies beneath the surface, and evidence of it must be in large part indirect, not actually visible. Early studies of seismic waves gave strong hints, now growing into assurance, that each continental mass has a bottom as well as a top and is in fact a relatively thin plate (Fig. 20–21). Deflections of the plumb line and measurements of gravity give strong indication that the lightweight rocks under mountains extend deeper than under plains (Fig. 20–24). This suggestion is confirmed convincingly by the refraction of seismic waves as they pass from one kind of rock into another at the base of a high range. Analysis of these waves at several stations in Europe shows that the crust directly under the Alps is more than 40 miles thick, as compared with thicknesses of 10 to 20 miles beneath lower areas to the north. A similar thickening under the Sierra Nevada of California is revealed when waves from earthquakes occurring a short distance west of that range are recorded on seismographs not far from its eastern base.

There is little danger, then, that our home on land will suddenly sink beneath the waves. It is "afloat," though firmly anchored. Under each continent is a plate of lightweight rock, in balance with the heavier floors of the adjacent deep-sea basins. Thinner parts of a continental plate underlie wide plains; thickened parts support high mountain chains (Fig. 21–4).

The Appalachian Mountains

Distinctive structure of bedrock. Sedimentary rocks give surest evidence of deformation that may have occurred since they were formed. Beds of limestone, shale, and sandstone that underlie the surface in the wide interior lowland of the United States and central Canada are nearly everywhere either horizontal or gently inclined. At a few exceptional places the layers are sharply bent along faults or in local folds, but in general there has been only broad, gentle warping. In the Ozark region of southern Missouri and northern Arkansas the beds dip a few degrees outward from a central area (Ozark dome) in which uplift has been enough to allow streams to cut through the sedimentary section into the older basement of granite. Two broad domes that are similar but eroded less deeply have their centers in Ohio

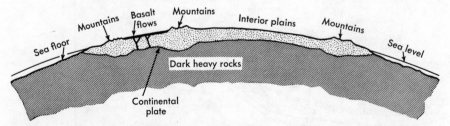

Fig. 21–4. Concept of a continental mass as a plate of rocks with relatively low density, mountains above the thicker parts, the whole "floating" above denser rock that underlies ocean floors also. Vertical scale exaggerated about 15 times. Basaltic rocks are included here with heavier rocks of the Earth's mantle.

and Tennessee. Between these wide upwarps are areas of downwarping, also with very gentle dips; one that covers most of southern Illinois is called the Illinois Basin. Despite these broad undulations, the formations in the interior lowland look almost undisturbed.

The layered rocks that cover this wide expanse are made of sediments deposited on the floors of shallow seas during the Paleozoic Era, hundreds of millions of years ago. Because of the slight disturbance during these long ages the region is aptly described as the *stable interior*. Farther east the evidence is strikingly different. In the Appalachian Mountains, from Alabama northeastward into Canada (Pl. 1), all the Paleozoic formations have been strongly deformed throughout a belt 75 to 150 miles wide. In some areas the layers are buckled into fairly regular folds (Fig. 21–5, **A**); in others there are many thrust faults along which great slices of the bedrock were driven one over another (Fig. 21–5, **B**). From gentle folds along the western margin of the belt the deformation increases eastward to folds that are overturned and isoclinal with strongly developed slaty cleavage (Fig. 19–4). Along the eastern margin many thrust blocks of Precambrian gneiss and schist were pushed westward and upward and now lie on the younger folded beds (Fig. 21–7, **B**).

The Appalachian Mountains, then, coincide with a zone of intense crustal deformation. Similar evidence is found in all other great mountain chains of the world.

Thickness of sedimentary rocks. In the Mississippi River drainage basin the total thickness of sedimentary beds is known from many places, widely distributed. Around the Ozark dome we find successively younger beds dipping outward from the exposed base of the section and can measure them directly. Many holes drilled for water and oil give exact measurements, and seismic reflections (Fig. 20–16) locate the top of the old basement rocks even where the sedimentary cover is thickest. In the Illinois Basin the complete section measures about 8,500 feet, and this is well above the average, which from Missouri to eastern Kentucky probably is no more than 5,000 feet.

By comparison, thicknesses in the Appalachian folds are astonishingly large. Erosion has cut across beds that are turned up steeply, enabling us to measure at the surface a thick succession of layers that before the folding lay one above another (Fig. 21–6). From Pennsylvania southward total thicknesses of 20,000 to 30,000 feet are common, and the maximum is nearly 8 miles. In the folded belt, then, the sedimentary section is four to eight times as thick as formations of the same age directly to the west. Before folding, the section must have had the general form of a great trough, as shown in Fig. 21–7, **A**.

In a large part of the section the beds contain marine fossils. Much of the deposition, therefore, occurred below sea level. Was there at the very start a trough several miles deep, from which sea water

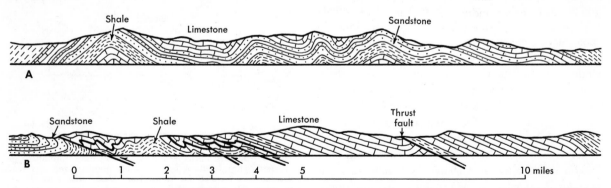

Fig. 21–5. Examples of Appalachian structure. A. This section in Virginia-West Virginia illustrates open folds that are common in the western part of the Appalachian Mountains. **B.** In southwestern Virginia, as in much of the southern segment of the Appalachians, the formations are sliced by thrust faults. One formation is shown in black to emphasize details of structure. (U. S. Geol. Survey, Folios 59 and 61.)

was gradually displaced by sediments? Certainly not, because layers at many levels in the section carry mud cracks, rainprints, and other evidence of deposition in shallow water or on floodplains. Some thick parts of the section have the characteristics of delta deposits and contain fossils of land plants; these deposits lie above and are overlain by beds of limestone full of marine shells. Therefore, the crust beneath a large part of the trough must have subsided slowly and irregularly, and sediments came in at a rate to keep the sea shallow and even to fill it up temporarily. Similar evidence is common in other mountain belts: the Rocky Mountains, the Coast Ranges of California, the Andes, the Urals, the Alps, and the high ranges of Asia. In some of these belts, however, small parts of the sediments are similar to those found on modern deep-sea floors, and probably there were local deep trenches between areas of shallow water, as we find today near the island arcs (p. 428).

A great trough that has received thick sedimentary deposits during slow subsidence through long geologic periods is a **geosyncline.** In connection with this definition, three points call for emphasis. (1) Geosynclines have been much deformed, and study of the sedimentary deposits over a wide area is required for reconstructing the original form. (2) The slow downwarping produced a very broad trough, with average floor inclinations of no more than a few degrees. (3) The term *geosyncline* applies not only to the trough-shaped basin but also to the accumulation of sedimentary formations.

The Appalachian geosyncline was filled chiefly with sand, silt, clay, and calcareous deposits. In some places, chiefly in the eastern part of the area, large quantities of lava and volcanic ash were included. Most of the clastic sediments came from the east, as shown by westward gradation from coarse to fine particles. Therefore there was land on the east, and it must have been rising steadily or at intervals, to keep up the supply of clastic sediments. There were centers of igneous activity, as indicated by the volcanic rocks. A shallow sea, most of it far from any land, covered the present Mississippi drainage basin during much of the long time in which the geosyncline was growing. We know this because the

thin section in the western area consists mainly of limestone instead of clastic sediments and has fossils representing all the Paleozoic periods that are recorded in the much thicker deposits of the folded belt. Near the end of the geosynclinal history the sea was gradually replaced with vast swamps in which grew the rank vegetation that built up the coal deposits of the Appalachian and Midwestern fields (Fig. 22–4).

Early stages of growth. The reconstruction of the geosyncline in Fig. 21–7, A may give an impression that the crust in this region was quiet, except for slow downbending, during the long ages in which the sediments accumulated. This impression is incorrect, for the sediments themselves tell quite a different story. Overlying marine shales in the eastern part of the folded belt are accumulations of conglomerate and sandstone containing fossils of land plants. A good example is the thick section of red beds, best exposed in the Catskill Mountains, which contain petrified stumps and logs of the earliest known forest trees. The volume of these clastic sediments, which extend from eastern New York as far south as Virginia, is thousands of cubic miles, equal to that of a great mountain range. This kind of evidence, repeated through the geosynclinal section, speaks eloquently of large uplifts east of the sinking trough. Eloquent also are large angular unconformities in the section, one of which is represented in

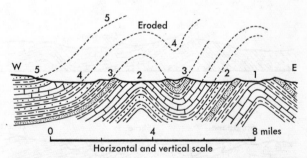

Fig. 21–6. This thick section of sedimentary formations in western Pennsylvania is open to study because long-continued erosion has beveled the folds. The oldest formations (1) exposed in this partial section are of Cambrian age. Toward the west younger strata are exposed. Those marked (5) are in the Pennsylvanian system. Thickness of section represented here totals more than 20,000 feet.

Fig. 21–7, **A.** Along the Hudson Valley and in eastern Pennsylvania the older beds of the geosyncline were strongly folded and the folds were deeply eroded before later sediments covered them. In the northern part of the Appalachian belt several widespread unconformities are recognized. We infer that mountain-making forces were at work while the geosyncline developed and that a chain of growing mountains east of the trough was furnishing the great volumes of clastic sediments.

The climax. In a final display of power (actually in several stages and over a long time), the deforming forces folded all the geosynclinal beds and sliced them with thrust faults (Fig. 21–7, **B**). Both the folds and the faults indicate large-scale horizontal compression. If we could grasp the eastern edge of the folded rocks in Pennsylvania and pull them out to their original flat attitude, as we would straighten a crumpled rug, the formations would cover most of New Jersey. On each of several large thrust faults in the southern Appalachians, thick rock sheets have been moved several miles westward; the total movement adds up to tens of miles.

By this compression the rocks of the geosynclinal belt were squeezed into a smaller area. In other words, the crust under the mountain belt was thick-ened. How much thickening there was depends on the depth to which the compression reached, and this we do not know. Any considerable thickening must have lifted the surface, and we find no record that the sea has ever returned to any large part of the folded belt since the folding occurred more than 200 million years ago. An examination of the eroded folds makes clear that enormous quantities of rock have been eroded from the belt. If the upper part of the Nittany Arch, a great anticline in central Pennsylvania, were restored by projecting the eroded limbs upward. the crest would stand 5 miles above the present land surface. But we can not assume that the youthful Appalachians were so high because vigorous erosion must have gone on while the fold was being formed, and the limbs have been cut lower with each of several later uplifts of the region.

Metamorphism and igneous intrusions. Slaty cleavage was developed widely in closely folded beds of the geosyncline, and large volumes of shale were converted into phyllite and even into mica schists studded with garnets. Some fossils have come through the metamorphism well enough to supply geologic dates of the inclosing rocks. The slates were formed by compression in folding, but the schists

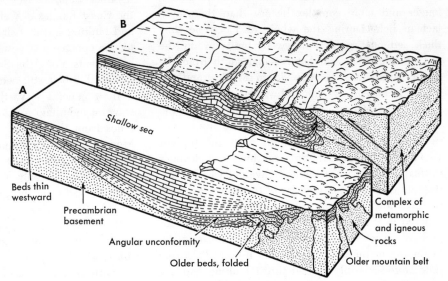

Fig. 21–7. Diagrammatic representation of the Appalachian geosyncline. Vertical scale greatly exaggerated. **A.** General restoration of the geosyncline before final deformation. **B.** An early stage of erosion during the final folding and thrusting. Overturned folds and large thrust faults are not shown.

are best developed near large intrusive bodies of granitic rock, many of which are exposed in New England and southeastern Canada and east of the folded belt from Pennsylvania southward. Near most of these bodies extreme metamorphism obscures the original nature of the rocks and their relation to the folded sedimentary formations. Analysis of radioactive minerals in a number of the igneous bodies dates their origin in several Paleozoic periods from Ordovician to Permian (Table 4–2). This strengthens other evidence which indicates that mountain-making forces were at work repeatedly during the growth of the geosyncline.

Comparison of mountain histories

Analysis of evidence in the Appalachian region reveals a complex history of repeated crustal movements, with resulting uplifts supplying vast quantities of sediment to a geosyncline that continued to subside but with changing pattern. Can this history be accepted as typical for great mountain chains? It is advisable to look at other examples. To mountains, as to living organisms, we must apply the principles of comparative study.

Western North America. A great geosynclinal belt along the western border of the continent had a longer and more complex history than the Appalachian belt. During the whole of Paleozoic time thick sedimentary deposits were built up on the sinking floor of a sea that reached south from the Arctic across western Canada to Mexico and extended as far east as Utah and western Arizona (Fig. 21–8). Part of the earlier sediment came from the continent on the east; much of it came from land, probably great chains of islands, near the present Pacific coast from California northward. Volcanoes in this western part of the belt gave out vast quantities of ash, cinders, and lava; these old volcanic products are prominent in some of the bedrock now exposed in the coastal belt. Mountain-making forces probably were active in this volcanic zone from the beginning of the geosyncline, and by mid-Paleozoic time large-scale folding and thrust faulting had advanced as far eastward as central Nevada.

Separate troughs then took definite form. One of these, covering much of California and extending far to the north, was folded in Mesozoic time, and

great batholiths were formed at the core of the folded belt in Lower California, in what is now the Sierra Nevada, and in the Coast Ranges of British Columbia. Sediments continued to accumulate farther east, and from Nevada northward we now measure sections of Paleozoic and Mesozoic beds that total as much as 8 miles thick. In the Cretaceous Period this belt was folded, and great sheets of rock were pushed many miles on thrust faults with low westward dips (Fig. 18–22). While mountains were growing in this belt, still another great trough was developing farther east on the site of the present Rocky Mountains. In this trough the sea extended from the Gulf of Mexico to the Arctic. Sediments washed from the growing ranges on the west kept the trough nearly full, and with local inclusions of volcanic materials formed a thickness totaling 20,000 feet. If we could spread these deposits out evenly, they would make a layer more than a quarter of a mile thick over the entire area of the United States. In turn, these deposits were deformed and are now exposed in the Rocky Mountains. The folding and faulting in this great chain continued from late Cretaceous through Eocene time. Meanwhile another trough had developed along the Pacific Coast, and its thick deposits were folded and faulted to form the Coast Ranges of California. Much of the folding and faulting in this belt took place during the Pleistocene epoch—just yesterday in geologic time—and movements along the San Andreas and other faults within this belt still occur (p. 395).

In a general way, then, but with variations, a wave of mountain making advanced eastward 1,000 miles from the Pacific coastal region to the Rocky Mountain front, deforming the crust throughout this Cordilleran belt except for the wide Colorado Plateau, which has only a moderate thickness of sedimentary rocks and was never part of a geosynclinal trough. Comparison of this western mountain belt with the Appalachians brings out differences as well as similarities. The western geosyncline was much the larger, lasted longer, and was more complex in its pattern and its history. Basically the two belts developed in strikingly similar fashion. In each a geosynclinal stage that was long and turbulent ended with strong deformation and uplift. In each belt crustal movement and volcanic activity continued

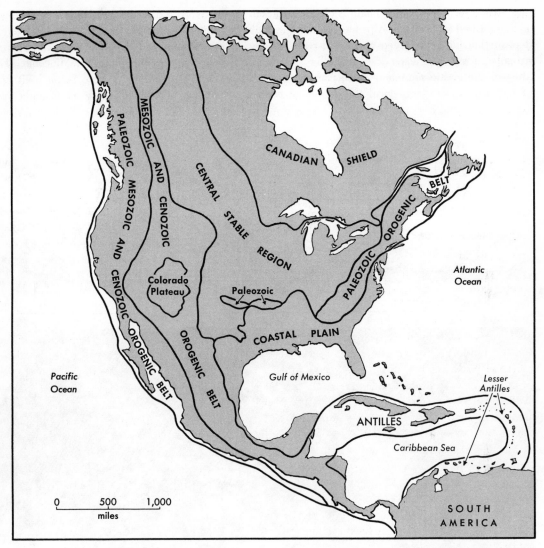

Fig. 21–8. Orogenic belts of North America, classified according to geologic eras in which they were active. In some belts there was activity in two or three eras. Some belts are partly covered by ocean waters, and therefore some of the boundaries are indefinite. In the Caribbean-Antillean region the boundaries are wholly submerged. Coastal Plain deposits conceal parts of the Appalachian belt. (From A. J. Eardley, Structural Geology of North America, Courtesy of Harper and Brothers.)

for a long time along the outer margin while the geosyncline was filling. The folds and great thrust faults in the two belts are much alike. Large intrusive bodies of granitic rock that formed deep down in each belt have been brought to light, as erosion, striving to keep pace with uplift, has cut thousands of feet below the earlier mountain summits.

The structural trends, present topography, and regional relations of the great mountain units in the middle part of North America are shown in Plate 1. General age relations of the major mountain belts are represented in Figure 21–8.

The Alps. The Alps have had more intensive study than any other mountains because their location is convenient to centers in which geology had much of its early development, and because much of the complex structure of the Alpine chain is clearly exposed. The deformed rocks of the Alps include thick marine deposits laid down in a geosyncline that had a very irregular form but extended generally east-west. Most of the clastic sediments came from land south of the trough, but large local thicknesses of coarse materials indicate that islands were rising within the trough itself. Most of the sediments were laid down in Mesozoic and early Cenozoic time, but some thick deposits are as young as Miocene (Table 4–2). While the sediments were being built up, deformation was already in progress, as indicated by some

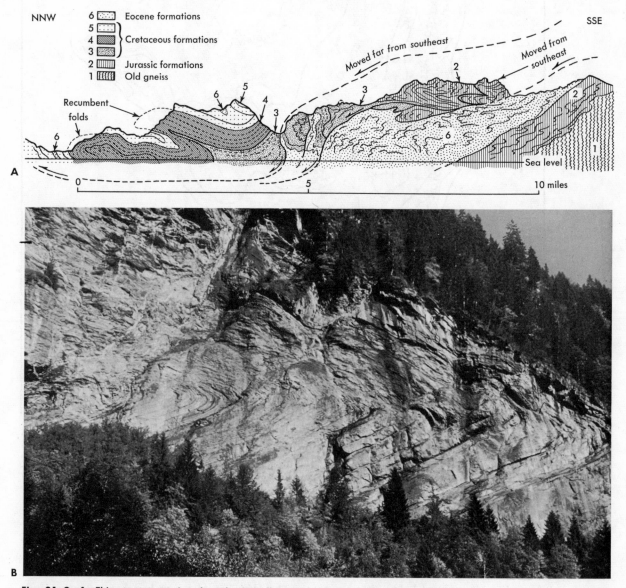

Fig. 21–9. **A.** This structure section through a small part of the Swiss Alps shows characteristic folding, thrusting, and duplication of rock formations. (Modified from Albert Heim, Geologie der Schweiz.) **B.** Jurassic limestone in a recumbent fold. East wall of Lauterbrunnen Valley, south of Interlaken, Switzerland. Some recumbent folds are vastly larger than this. (John S. Shelton.)

of the deposits that are chaotic, with bedding obscure. Some masses that contain large angular blocks of older rocks in a matrix of finer grain are interpreted as submarine slides on the steep flanks of rising islands.

Deformation by folding and thrust faulting continued from early through middle Cenozoic time. The resulting structure is almost incredibly complex, and even after generations of field study some of it is not fully understood. A sample of the structure, with many of the complicating details left out, is shown in Figure 21–9. Emile Argand, a Swiss geologist who made the Alps his lifetime study, expressed the evolution of the structure in a series of cross-sectional diagrams, three of which are shown in Figure 21–10. Evidence in the sediments and in the structure strongly supports his view that folding and faulting began at an early stage and that the resulting uplifts made chains of islands dividing the geosyncline into several troughs in which sedimentary deposits built up continuously. Under compressive stress, the rising masses under the island chains were moved together and finally were piled up, one above another. Argand's diagrams emphasize the development of immense recumbent folds, a conspicuous feature of Alpine structure, but to

avoid confusion these diagrams omit the large thrust faults by which the folds were sliced and moved northward.

Directly north of the Swiss Alps is the Swiss Plain, about 20 miles wide (Fig. 21–11). Bedrock beneath much of it consists of coarse deposits, dated as late Cenozoic, which contain large blocks of peculiar rock types that can be matched only in masses exposed tens of miles to the south in the high interior of the range. These masses are parts of thrust sheets, which no doubt had their forward edges near the high mountain front but have been in large part destroyed by erosion. North of the Swiss Plain are the Jura Mountains, a series of folds in a thin section of beds outside the geosyncline. The structure is noteworthy because of numerous steep faults transverse to the fold axes (Fig. 21–12). On opposite sides of a given fault the folds differ in form and spacing, and commonly there are more folds on one side of a fault than on the opposite side. Clearly, the faults were active while the folds were developing; they are strike-slip faults (p. 364), formed in response to shearing stresses during growth of the arc-shaped Jura as a secondary structural unit in front of the massive Alps.

In plan the Jura is bowed toward the northwest,

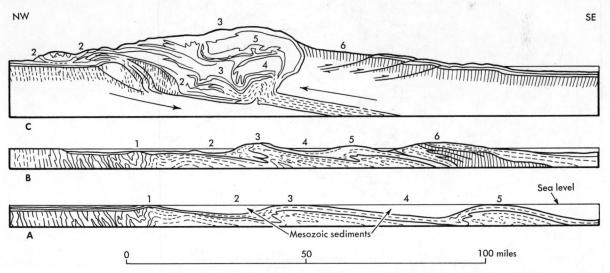

Fig. 21–10. Cross sections to illustrate development of the Alps. A and B represent stages in growth of the Alpine geosyncline in Mesozoic and early Cenozoic time. Note that deformation was in progress while marine sediments accumulated. C shows major deformation in mid-Cenozoic time. The numbers, 1 to 6, identify major units and emphasize the shortening of the section by folding and thrusting. (After Emile Argand.)

parallel to the curved front of the Alps (Fig. 21–11). This agreement in plan, and the fact that folding in the Jura dies out toward the northwest, indicate that the Jura folds were formed by pressure transmitted from the Alpine zone. Probably the deformed rocks exposed in the Jura are much more strongly folded under the Swiss Plain, where they are hidden under the great volume of waste eroded from the high Alpine mass as it grew. The strength of folding tens of miles out from the margin of the range testifies to

great horizontal compression, which is indicated even more clearly by the intense folding and the piling up of great thrust slices within the high mass itself (Fig. 21–9). Estimates of the shortening represented by this crowding together of the geosynclinal rocks run into scores of miles. During the deformation of the thick geosynclinal section shale was changed to lustrous mica schist on a stupendous scale.

Island arcs. The Appalachians completed their

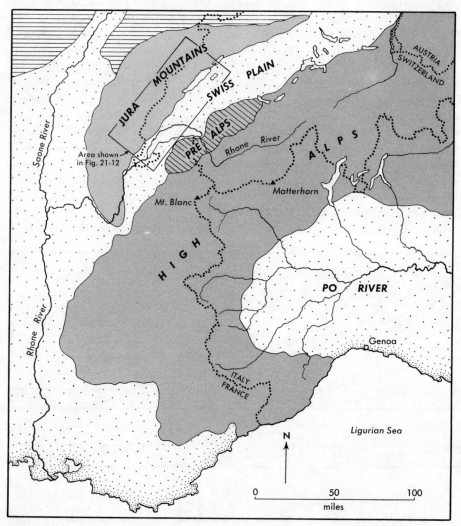

Fig. 21–11. The western part of the Alps, the Jura Mountains, and adjacent areas. The bend at the southwest end of the Alps is part of the strongly arcuate form of this great mountain chain. The rectangle marked on the Jura Mountains block is the area of the map, Figure 21–12.

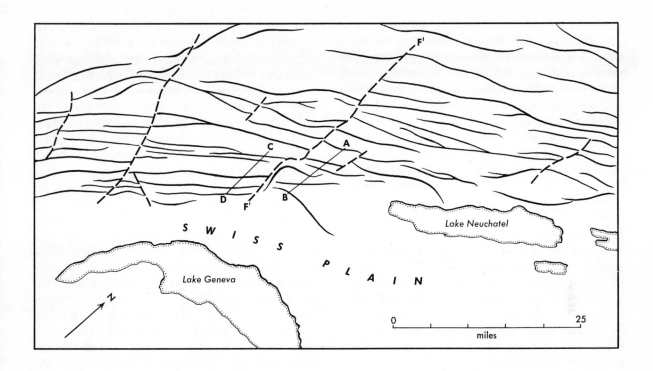

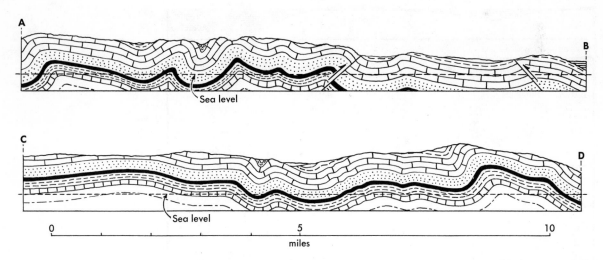

Fig. 21–12. Structural features of the Jura Mountains. (*Above*). Characteristic folds and faults (see Fig. 21–11 for location). Heavy continuous lines are traces of anticlines; heavy broken lines are large faults. Note that many anticlines end against faults. The largest fault, F′ was sharply bent by continued pressure. (*Below*). Structure sections along A-B and C-D of map, on opposite sides of the large fault F′. Though the sections are not far apart, they show large differences in details of structure, as do the patterns of folds on the map. (After Albert Heim, *Geologic der Schweiz.*)

growth in the Paleozoic Era. Deformation in a large part of our Cordilleran belt occurred in Mesozoic time. The California Coast Ranges and the Alps grew up in the present Era, the Cenozoic. In some of the island arcs we find convincing evidence of mountain growth now going on. And so once again we can use the present as a key to the past.

The long archipelagoes east of Asia (Fig. 21–3) and near Alaska, the East Indian islands, and parts of our own West Indies have much in common. In all we recognize the pattern of crescentic arcs like those of the Alps, Carpathians, Himalaya, and numerous other full-grown ranges. Inside many of the island arcs are rows of active volcanoes. Just outside a number of them are the greatest known oceanic depths, within long and narrow trenches. Some belts of frequent strong earthquakes coincide closely with these rows of islands (Fig. 21–13), and many islands in the arcuate chains are growing actively, as shown by marine terraces that go up like flights of stairs, the lowest and most recent treads almost untouched by erosion (Fig. 21–14).

The Lesser Antilles, a long row of islands curving eastward between Puerto Rico and Venezuela, are merely high peaks of a great range with its base on the deep-sea floor. Soundings show that a contour 6,000 feet below sea level lies far up the slopes of the range (Fig. 21–15) and that parts of the east base are at depths greater than 25,000 feet. Mont Pelée (p. 87) is one of numerous active volcanoes in this island arc, and frequent strong earthquakes indicate crustal movements that may be related to mountain growth.

The sea floors around some of the island arcs, especially in the East Indies, have been studied with the aid of echo-sounding and modern coring equipment (Chap. 15). Some of the sediments are strikingly like those exposed in the deformed beds of the Alps, the Appalachians, and other mountain belts, and on the insides of arcs these modern sediments are mingled with lavas and pyroclastic materials from the active volcanoes. Conviction is growing that island arcs and the sea floors around them represent active geosynclines and that mountain-making forces were at work throughout the history of the Alpine and Appalachian geosynclines, not just in the

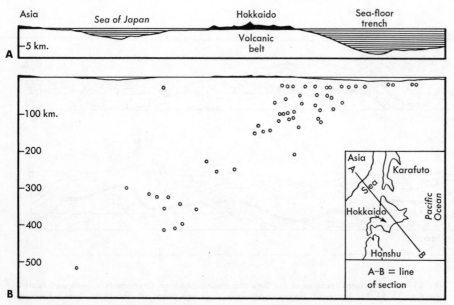

Fig. 21–13. A. Section across northern Japan, with vertical scale exaggerated 10 times, showing the deep trench on the ocean floor east of the island Hokkaido. B. Same section to true scale and extended to great depth. The foci of recorded earthquakes (small circles) have a distribution that suggests a fault zone inclined toward the northwest and emerging at the floor of the deep trench. The small map in inset, lower right, shows location. (After B. Gutenberg and C. F. Richter, Seismicity of the Earth, Princeton Univ. Press, 1949.)

Fig. 21–14. Emerged shorelines, forming prominent terraces on Aguijan Island, in the Marianas Group, southeast of Asia. Scale can be judged by trees and by graded road (*upper right*). (U. S. Army Air Force.)

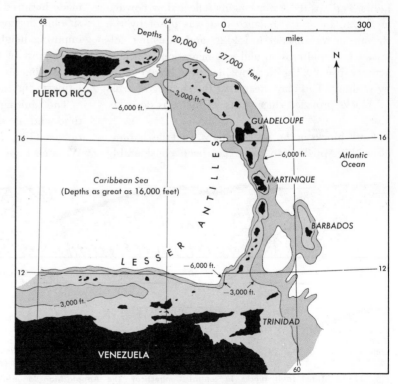

Fig. 21–15. Islands of the Lesser Antilles, eastern Caribbean region, are the protruding tops of peaks in a high mountain chain that is growing. Note the strongly arcuate pattern. Land areas are shown in black, and shading indicates extent of the continuous mountain mass at great depth. (After H. H. Hess. See Fig. 21–8 for general setting.)

closing phases. In this light the Alps and related mountains of southern Europe, completed just yesterday in the geologic time scale, are a logical connecting link between the older geosynclines and the active island arcs of today. This is not to say there has been a standard pattern, with exact repetition of events in all details. Each mountain unit has unique features that give it individuality. But the common trend running through the histories of mountain belts, one generation after another, must mean that there is a basic underlying reason for repeated mountain growth. By persistent study we may hope eventually to learn the source of energy and the mechanism of the mountain-building process.

Later chapters in mountain history

Block faulting and volcanism. In some of the old mountain belts the stage of deformation by compression, with growth of folds and thrust faults, has been followed by movement of blocks on large steep faults. Perhaps these movements reflect slow flowage at depth, to restore balance that was upset by the shifting of rock masses in folding and thrusting, followed by rapid erosion and sedimentation. Volcanic activity usually has accompanied the breaking up by faulting. This may mean that the shifting of crustal blocks provided easier exits for magmas deep below.

Fault blocks in the Appalachians. In Triassic time, after the Appalachian folds had been considerably

eroded, many large blocks sank along steep faults and were covered with thick deposits of sediments eroded from adjacent blocks that were rising. Floods of basaltic lava poured out and made widespread thick sheets that were then buried under sediments accumulating on the sinking blocks. Thick sills made from the same magma were injected into the lower beds of the new sediments. With later tilting and erosion, these sills, large dikes related to them, and the buried flows have come to form the prominent ridges of dark rock in Nova Scotia, southern New England, New Jersey, and several states farther south (Fig. 21–16). The edge of the largest sill exposed in these Triassic rocks forms the Palisades along the Hudson River.

The Basin Ranges. The Basin and Range province, extending south and southeast from southern Oregon through several states into Mexico, offers an exceptional display of crustal breakup by block-faulting. Movements along thousands of faults have made hundreds of ridges, many small or of moderate size but dozens of them are large mountain ranges of imposing height. Under the arid climate of the region, most of the drainage is interior (Chap. 14), and sediments eroded from the ranges are accumulating in the intervening basins.

The faulting went on through much of Cenozoic time and is still active along the bases of some ranges (Fig. 18–1). The high, steep scarps of the Wasatch Range in Utah (Fig. 18–21) and of ranges

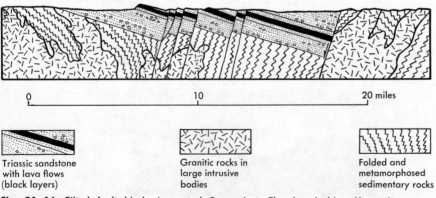

Triassic sandstone with lava flows (black layers)

Granitic rocks in large intrusive bodies

Folded and metamorphosed sedimentary rocks

Fig. 21–16. Tilted fault blocks in central Connecticut. The Appalachian Mountains were deeply eroded, and in the Triassic period thick sedimentary accumulations, with large flows of basaltic lava, filled deep local basins. These rocks were then broken and tilted by movements on large faults. Triassic rocks deformed in this way are in many parts of the Appalachian belt from Nova Scotia to South Carolina.

Fig. 21–17. Frenchman Mountain, east of Las Vegas, Nevada, is made of Paleozoic marine strata, now inclined about 60° eastward, between large faults that trend north. A fault across the range makes a conspicuous offset of strata in the right part of the view. Total thickness of exposed formations is more than 5,000 feet. View northeastward. (William Belknap, Jr.)

overlooking Death Valley, California, give the impression that movements were rapid and catastrophic. Probably this is not so. We infer from studies of recent faulting that the growth of a high scarp occurred in a succession of spasmodic jumps, each adding no more than a few tens of feet, and that long pauses intervened between movements. The steep faults trend north or northwest, in part parallel to the older grain made by folding and thrusting. Some of the range blocks have been lifted quite uniformly between parallel faults; more have been strongly tilted, one side going up to make a steep scarp, the other down to be buried by basin sediments. Lavas and volcanic ash were erupted in enormous quantities, and in many parts of the province these volcanic rocks were faulted and made into sizable ranges.

The ranges have wide variety in kinds of rocks and types of structure. Many consist of marine beds in thick sections, steeply tilted (Fig. 21–17). The largest of all, at the western limit of the province, is the Sierra Nevada, a block 400 miles long and more than 50 miles wide, its eastern side a high fault scarp and its western side deeply buried by sedimentary deposits (Fig. 21–18). Its complex bedrock consists partly of closely folded and metamorphosed sedimentary beds, partly of granitic rocks in a large batholith. The folding and igneous intrusion occurred in the Mesozoic Era, the resulting high mountains were eroded to low altitude, and the present range was made by tilting uplift that started late in Cenozoic time.

Erosional features of a folded belt. The topographic forms in a region of folded bedrock reflect the details of fold structure, the arrangement of strong and weak beds, and the stage of development.

431

Figure 21–19 shows some of the characteristic forms that result. Anticlines that rise slowly across the courses of some vigorous streams are cut through as fast as they come up, just as a log is cut when it is pushed against a circular saw. The stream comes to flow through deep gorges cut into the anticlines, as in Figure 21–19; it is then an antecedent stream (p. 192). The Columbia River in central Washington has cut through growing folds that might have diverted a weaker stream. With passage of time, resistant beds in anticlines are breached by general erosion, and tributaries to a main stream may develop in weak beds along anticlinal axes, as in diagrams **C** and **D**. If crustal movement ends, long-continued erosion may reduce the entire surface to low relief, as in diagram **E**, and the large streams will take on meandering courses in wide valleys.

Some of the large valleys in the Appalachian Mountains have stream terraces flanking their sides. These features probably indicate repeated uplifts of rather recent date, separated by time intervals when conditions were more stable.

Analysis of surface features in the Appalachian folded belt shows that the region has been arched up, perhaps more than once, since the deposition of Cretaceous strata that now lie along the southeastern flank of the mountain belt. The Rocky Mountains and mountain chains in other continents bear unmistakable marks of strong upwarping long after an earlier mountain topography had been cut away. It appears that mountain belts can not be kept down; they have an urge to rise even in extreme old age. This common tendency must have a rational explanation.

Keeping isostatic balance. The continental crust is thickest under mountain belts (p. 418). But the mountains stand where once were sea floors; they have come into existence, one belt after another, in various geologic periods, and therefore the crustal thickening must be part of the mountain-making process. Gravity measurements tell us that the Himalaya, the Alps, and other high ranges are essentially in balance with the much lower country around them. Erosion is attacking these high masses vigorously, and we reason that eventually they will be brought lower, as have the Appalachians and other old mountains. As weight is removed, the present balance with the surrounding crust will be impaired unless there is a mechanism for adjustment.

When an iceberg is thinned by melting of its top, the part under water must move upward. Similarly, if a metal block floating in mercury has its upper part cut off, its base rises. By the same principle, erosion of much rock from a high mountain mass sets up strains in the underlying crust, and eventually uplift must occur to relieve strain and restore balance. This reasoning is borne out by the uplift that has occurred in glaciated areas since the ice sheets vanished. We know also that when these sheets formed in the glacial ages the crust was depressed under

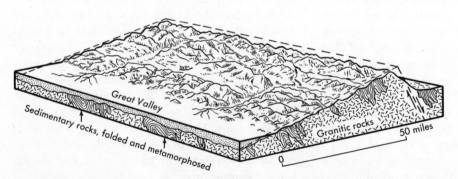

Fig. 21–18. Part of the Sierra Nevada, California, a tilted crustal block. An older mountain mass, formed by folding of thick strata and intrusion of granitic magmas, was almost leveled by erosion. The later tilting uplift has stimulated vigorous erosion by streams and glaciers. Broken lines suggest approximate form of the block before this erosion. (Modified from F. E. Matthes, U.S. Geol. Survey, Prof. paper 160.)

their weight. Uplift since glaciation is merely bringing the surface back toward the position it had before
the ice sheets formed.

The load removed by erosion from a mountain
range is carried away and added to other areas. In
deltas of major streams this load grows to large proportions. Deep drilling in the Mississippi delta reveals that sediments bearing marks of deposition at
or above sea level extend to great depths. Subsidence
has kept pace with delta growth, and presumably
much of the sinking was caused by the growing load.
With some large parts of the crust going down,
others up, there must be a transfer of material at
depth. If there were a liquid layer under the crust,

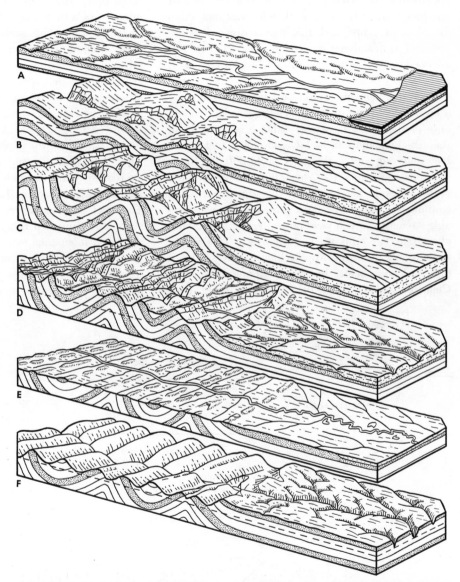

Fig. 21–19. Block diagrams suggesting the development of surface forms on folded formations like those in the Appalachian Mountains. **A.** Before folding. **B.** Early stage of folding,
with a vigorous stream maintaining its course. **C.** and **D.** Erosion breaches the anticlines and
tributary valleys are developed. **E.** Surface reduced essentially to a peneplane. **F.** Forms developed after broad uplift of the peneplaned surface. Note the ridges on synclines, valleys
on anticlines.

this would be a simple matter; but seismic evidence rules this out (p. 406). We infer, therefore, that at some depth the rock is very weak, even though high pressure keeps it rigid, and that the weak rock flows slowly from beneath sinking areas toward areas that are rising (Fig. 21–20).

Because the lightweight continental crust is thin, presumably the flowage is in the heavier rock at greater depth. If this is true, then heavier rock takes the place of lighter rock that moves upward in adjustment as mountains are eroded (Fig. 21–20). The assumed densities are in the ratio 2.7 to 3.3 (9 to 11), and the loss of a layer 11 feet thick from the entire surface of a highland would be balanced exactly by a layer 9 feet thick of the heavier rock added at the base of the crust. If perfect balance is to be kept, then the highland will be lowered only 2 feet for 11 feet removed, and a thickness of 11,000 feet must be eroded to reduce the Alps 2,000 feet below their present average height. Surely the adjustment is not continuous because the crust probably has considerable strength and will yield only after a great amount of erosion has built up large stresses. This would explain how the entire Appalachian region was worn to low altitude before broad upwarping occurred in Cenozoic time (Fig. 21–19). This upwarping, once

it started, must have been interrupted by long pauses, each of which allowed the cutting of wide stream terraces.

Records of ancient mountains. In all continents sedimentary rocks as old as Cambrian are unconformable on still older rocks that are much deformed and in part metamorphosed. Bedrock showing this relationship is widely exposed in Scandinavia and in eastern Canada. In a belt extending eastward from Lake Superior across southern Canada to the Adirondack Mountains large thicknesses of limestone and other kinds of sedimentary rocks, as well as old lavas, are closely folded and partly engulfed in bodies of granite. All these older rocks were eroded to form an even surface on which Cambrian sediments were deposited (Fig. 21–21). Carrying our thread of reasoning back from the modern island arcs through the Alps, Appalachians, and still older mountain units, we recognize in these deformed rocks of Scandinavia and Canada mountain belts of Precambrian time. The thick sedimentary rocks indicate a geosynclinal stage, the truncated folds and thrust sheets suggest that high mountains were developed, and the widespread granite and associated metamorphic rocks tell us the old mountains were worn down, probably after repeated uplifts, until the deep inner core of

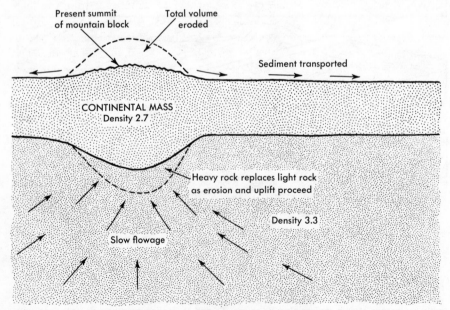

Fig. 21–20. Supposed mechanism to maintain general equilibrium in the crust during erosion of a mountain mass and transportation of sediments to distant areas.

the mountain belt was exposed. As the geologist Le Conte said, "We see only the bones of the extinct mountains."

In summary, then, the geologic evidence indicates that the principle of uniformity of process applies to mountains as to other features of the Earth. Successive generations of mountains have developed through the stages of geosynclinal accumulation, deformation, igneous activity, uplift, and slow reduction by erosion. All available evidence indicates that these processes are as vigorous today as they have been through hundreds of millions of years. What is the secret process of mountain making?

Possible cause of orogeny

In the parlance of geology *orogeny* (ŏr-ŏj'ĕn-ĭ; Gr. "mountain genesis") is *the deformation of the crust in the development of mountains.* As indicated in the foregoing analysis, this is a complex process which, however, proceeds through a fairly definite succession of steps. The fundamental cause and mechanism are hidden, and we grope for them by speculation. Several hypotheses have been framed, but critical evidence for testing them builds up slowly and no one of the suggestions has yet become a favored theory.

Concept of a shrinking Earth. Before the development of seismology, it was generally accepted that the body of the Earth, inside a comparatively thin crust, was molten. Under that view, both igneous activity and crustal deformation had logical explanations. Magmas were ready made, and they came up to disturb the outer world even less than might have been expected. Loss of heat by conduction through the

crust and by volcanic action was supposed to cause slow but continuous shrinkage of the interior. The solid crust, in adjusting to a circumference always growing smaller, would, of course, be crumpled just as the skin wrinkles on a drying apple. The source of energy for the folding and thrusting would be gravity, and "gravity never rests."

This comfortable doctrine had to be modified drastically when it was found that the secondary earthquake waves (S waves), which move only through a rigid medium, are transmitted freely to a depth of 1,800 miles (Fig. 20–18). Confidence in the concept of a shrinking interior was shaken also by the discovery that radioactive minerals generate at least a considerable part of the heat flowing upward to the Earth's surface; if *all* this heat is from radioactivity, the Earth's interior is not cooling now. But the idea of a contracting interior, revised to accord with all that is known, can not be dismissed. The radioactive minerals, in amounts sufficient to generate considerable heat, may be restricted to a thin outer part of the crust. Locally, the heat from this source may raise temperatures to the melting point, but once a large mass becomes fused it tends to move upward in the crust, carrying the self-heaters—the radioactive elements—with it. In this way, it is argued, nearly all these elements must have moved out from the interior, even from the deeper parts of the crust, during geologic time. There is growing evidence that a large part of the Earth's core is liquid, in spite of enormous pressures at that depth (p. 407), and its temperatures must be very high. If the core is made of metal —a favored theory—then the Earth in its early history probably went through a molten stage, during

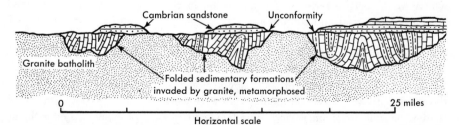

Fig. 21–21. Sedimentary strata widely exposed in southern Canada and northern New York are strongly folded, metamorphosed, and engulfed in batholiths of granitic rock. This complex assemblage is unconformable beneath formations of Cambrian age.

which most of the iron and some other metals settled toward the center.

Harold Jeffreys, an English scientist long a champion of the contraction concept, has estimated the measure of shrinkage to be expected since the Earth became solid in the outer 1,800 miles of its radius. Heat is conducted through silicate rocks at a very slow rate, but geologic time is long. To direct shrinkage from cooling, Jeffreys adds loss of volume from crystallization and from slow "sweating out" of water, assuming that a large part of the water in the seas has come slowly but steadily from the deep interior through the Earth's long history (p. 110). He recognizes the large uncertainties but considers as "reasonable" a shortening of the Earth's radius by as much as 85 kilometers (53 mi.) in 2 billion years. This would give a reduction in the circumference by 330 miles and would account for a large amount of folding and thrusting. Presumably, this would be distributed more or less evenly through time and would account for about 80 miles of shortening along every circumference since the start of the Paleozoic era.

The strongest objection to the contraction concept is seen in the distribution of mountain belts during any time interval. The Cenozoic belts extend in many directions, as they should under the theory, but why are they so widely spaced? Those crossed by any circumference are thousands of miles apart, and only the one including the Alps and Himalaya extends east-west. In a collapsing crust the compressive stresses should be distributed uniformly, and because rock in large masses is weak it is hardly conceivable that these stresses would be transmitted halfway around the Earth to concentrate all the crumpling in a single zone. Another objection is based on features that suggest large-scale pulling apart of the crust, which would not be possible if compression in the crust were universal and continuous.

Suggestion of an expanding Earth. The old assumption that the Earth is slowly contracting, long tacitly accepted as a reasonable doctrine, is now challenged by the diametrically opposed suggestion that the Earth is growing larger. Proponents of this concept remind us that astronomers find abundant evidence of expanding stars and argue that we have no dependable clues to the condition of matter inside the Earth, which may be swelling in volume, not shrink-

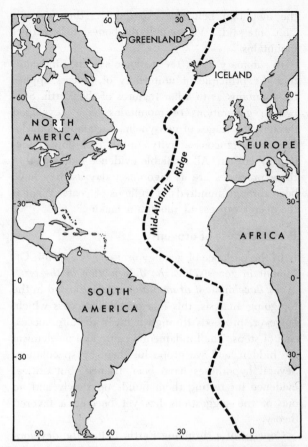

Fig. 21–22. The basin of the Atlantic Ocean would be nearly closed if the continental masses on opposite sides could be moved bodily to the Mid-Atlantic Ridge. The general plan of this submarine ridge is strikingly similar to the forms of opposed continental shorelines.

ing. They cite recent announcements by students of ocean basins that great trenches, suggestive of tensional rifts, are extensive in the floors of the Atlantic, Pacific, and Indian oceans. They indorse a suggestion that the American continents have separated from Europe and Africa, as indicated by the matching of opposed margins (Fig. 21–22), and propose that since the start of the Mesozoic Era the expansion of the globe has disrupted the crust in a measure equal at least to the width of the Atlantic basin.

An obvious argument urged against the hypothesis of expansion cites the apparent shortening by folding and thrust faulting in mountain belts. Deformation of this sort seems to require large-scale compression of the crust. In reply, the proponents of expansion

Fig. 21–23. This gigantic pattern of folds, outlined by bands of debris in the ice of the Malaspina Glacier, Alaska, was formed as the ice spread by flowage after it emerged from narrow valleys in the St. Elias Range. Axial planes of the folds are almost vertical. The extent to which ice moving from valley glaciers spreads on a piedmont slope is shown in Figure 13–2. (Bradford Washburn.)

cite the close folds outlined by debris in the ice of a piedmont glacier (Fig. 21–23). These fold patterns develop while the area of the ice is enlarged five to ten times by flowage as the glaciers emerge from the confines of valleys onto an open slope. Therefore, folds in a mountain belt may reflect large-scale deformation by flowage, not shortening by regional compression.

Although these arguments by the expansionist school may not be convincing, they are not demolished by any counter arguments now available. Many regard the idea of an expanding Earth as radical, and truly it conflicts with some older concepts that were long in favor. But in our present state of ignorance about the Earth's interior we must give a hearing to every constructive suggestion.

Theory of convection currents. In a vessel of boiling water the hot liquid rises and cooler liquid sinks to form currents that circulate up and down. The Earth outside the central core is not liquid, but its strength may be very low, and temperatures near the core probably are much higher than at the base of the crust. It is argued that convection may go on by solid flow at the rate of less than an inch in a year, with millions of years required for a round trip between core and crust. The theory pictures great convection cells, each thousands of miles across. Two adjacent cells that turn away from each other at the base of the continental crust may pull the crust apart and carry the fragments long distances. When two cells meet and turn downward, they press parts of the crust together and also exert a downward pull. The compression may buckle parts of the crust upward, but directly over the descending currents the crust should be bent down to form a trough. Thus the stage is set for a geosyncline, to be filled with sediments from bordering lands, perhaps islands, that keep rising under pressure. The entire geosyncline is finally crushed to make mountains.

Some have used the convection mechanism in a bold hypothesis of "continental drift," in which the Atlantic Ocean basin is represented as a great rift, opened and continually widened by drifting apart of the continental masses east and west of it. This concept had its origin in the remarkable matching of the opposing shorelines as seen on a map; the ocean basin would be almost filled if the Americas were pushed eastward, Africa and Europe westward, to meet along the Mid-Atlantic Ridge (Fig. 21–22). The Appalachian belt, which breaks off abruptly along the east coast of Newfoundland, would then be almost continuous with mountains of nearly the same date in western Europe. Other geologic features that are similar on opposite sides of the Atlantic are urged as evidence for the separation. Advocates of the expanding-Earth concept point out that opening of the Atlantic basin by global expansion avoids a strong mechanical objection urged against the concept of drifting continents. In the supposed lateral movement how has a continent displaced the strong crust in front of it? One suggestion has been that deformation at the forward edge of a moving continent produces mountains. The American Cordilleras are cited as an outstanding example.

With continued study, the hypothesis of continental drift raises fully as many questions as it appears to answer. The hypothesis of convection currents also faces serious physical difficulties, even if it is considered without any relation to the concept of continental drift. These difficulties do not at present condemn either concept, but both concepts are in the category of *hypotheses on trial.*

Gravitative movements. Far down the flanks of the Alps, on both the north and the south sides, large isolated masses of sedimentary rocks that are folded and sliced with thrust faults are far removed from their original positions. The largest of these puzzling masses, 60 miles long and as much as 20 miles wide, forms a group of ridges known as the Prealps at the south side of the Swiss Plain (Fig. 21–11). All the rocks in the Prealps mass are out of harmony with the bedrock beneath and around them and are closely related to folded rocks exposed tens of miles away in the high part of the range. Long study of this problem has convinced some geologists that the Prealps and similar masses became detached during the final great deformation and uplift in the Alps (Fig. 21–10, C) and were moved by gravity down the steep slopes, inch by inch for thousands of years, to their present strange positions.

This problem has focused attention on the part played by gravity in deforming the crust. According to one speculation, folding and thrusting are caused by the moving rock masses down the flanks of great *welts* or *blisters.* Potential energy is provided by these uplifts, and the pull of gravity does the rest. Whatever the primary source of energy may be in crustal deformation, gravitative adjustments surely modify mountain structure in important measure. Slow movement in response to the pull of gravity appears to explain best the displacements, through many miles, of some large thrust plates in the Alps, in central Nevada, and in many other mountain belts.

Studies of magnetism in rocks. Since 1950 a number of investigators in the field of terrestrial magnetism have been concerned with the history of the Earth's crust. Magnetite and related minerals are widely disseminated in igneous and sedimentary rocks. When particles of these minerals crystallize in a body of magma, they behave as tiny magnets and become oriented with the Earth's magnetic field. Particles settling from water with other sediments are oriented also, though less accurately than the igneous particles. Unless these mineral grains of a rock are subjected to high temperature or some other radical disturbance, they will keep a record of the magnetic field in which they were deposited. Study of many such particles in favorable bodies of rock, with the aid of special sensitive equipment, should indicate the location of the magnetic pole at the time the rocks were formed.

Thick sills of dolerite in the Island of Tasmania (part of Australia) are particularly favorable for this kind of study. The rock is rich in magnetic particles, and the sills, almost horizontal, have been little disturbed since their formation during the Jurassic Period, about 150 million years ago. The location of the magnetic pole corresponding to the record given by minerals in the sills is about 10° of arc (700 miles) southeast of Tasmania. At present the magnetic pole is fully 45° (3,100 miles) from the island. Similar studies of rocks formed during other periods of Earth-history give equally startling results. One ancient position of the north magnetic pole, as located by these studies, is in the Pacific Ocean near the Hawaiian Islands. As the magnetic field presumably has always been closely related to spinning of the Earth on its axis, this evidence indicates that the position of Hawaii, now in the tropics, was at a much earlier date inside the Arctic Circle.

Magnetic effect retained in mineral particles long after their orientation in the Earth's magnetic field is **remanent magnetism** *or* **paleomagnetism.** Although broad studies of remanent magnetism are in an early stage, a number of results give strong suggestion that positions of the poles have changed widely during geologic time. What can this mean? According to a favored hypothesis, the crust of the Earth has shifted bodily, slowly but in large measure, so that in the course of tens of millions of years the latitude of a given area has changed radically. This may appear incredible, but it is in general accord with some geologic evidence that is unquestioned. Near the close of the Paleozoic Era, more than 200 million years ago, great ice sheets covered parts of the African continent that are now within the tropics. This is but one example of many radical climatic changes to which the geologic record bears witness.

Studies of paleomagnetism are not far enough advanced to be used as a basis for firm conclusions. The method and some tentative results are outlined here to emphasize that study of the Earth's crust is in a pioneering stage and that hopeful new lines of attack are in operation.

Batholiths in mountain belts. Another subject of much speculation is the origin of large granitic batholiths and related igneous bodies that are exposed in nearly all deeply eroded mountain belts. Relations of these masses to the structure show that some were intruded before folding started, some during the folding, and others after the folds and thrusts were fully

developed. Generally the intruded rocks are much metamorphosed, and many ore deposits are associated with the intrusive bodies.

According to one theory, the rocks carried to great depths by geosynclinal sinking and forced still deeper by deformation come into a zone of high temperature. More heat is developed by radioactive elements in these rocks and large masses become fused. Fusion may extend to a high level, or the deforming pressures may squeeze some of the magma up into the folded zone. Wide differences in view remain on the relative importance of magmas and granitization in the formation of large plutons (p. 388).

The puzzle of orogeny. The wide diversity of ideas on the origin of mountains shows clearly that we have no trustworthy answers to the basic questions. A survey of several intelligent guesses reminds us of the varied opinions of the blind men about the overall appearance of an elephant. The problem of mountain making is too big and too much of the essential information is still hidden for any confident solution now. The challenge of the problem will stimulate more intensive efforts, and the architectural features of mountain belts will always be worthy of study for their own sake.

SUMMARY

1. Mountains of greatest significance in geology are those formed by large-scale deformation of the Earth's crust.

2. Deformation that has produced large mountain chains on each continent has had little effect on wide continental plates to which these chains are marginal.

3. Rocks in the Appalachian Mountains are in large part sedimentary formations deposited in a geosynclinal trough. These deposits, largely marine and as much as several miles thick, were laid down chiefly in shallow water during slow subsidence.

4. Deformation and volcanic activity were continuous or recurrent in the eastern part of the geosyncline during the long history of its development.

5. A climax of deformation near the close of the Paleozoic Era marked the end of Appalachian orogeny.

6. A succession of geosynclines in western North America had a similar but longer and more complex history than the Appalachian geosyncline.

7. The Cordilleran geosyncline was deformed repeatedly during the Paleozoic and Mesozoic Eras. A later Rocky Mountain geosyncline was ended in early Cenozoic time. A geosyncline on the site of the Coast Ranges was active until climactic orogeny occurred late in the Cenozoic Era.

8. The Alps and related mountain chains record a long history of crustal unrest that ended with strong orogeny late in the Cenozoic Era.

9. Island arcs around the margins of the Pacific basin and in the Caribbean region appear to be examples of orogenic belts now in process of development.

10. Large-scale block faulting, with accompanying igneous activity, succeeded the climax of orogeny in the Appalachian region and in the Basin and Range province.

11. All available evidence indicates that general isostatic balance is maintained through the several stages of orogeny and later widespread erosion.

12. The basic cause of orogeny remains a major problem in geology. Some current hypotheses present major contradictions. Active studies in paleomagnetism are an example of new methods of attack on basic problems of the Earth's crust.

REFERENCES

Bailey, E. B., 1935, Tectonic essays, mainly alpine: Oxford, The Clarendon Press.
Eardley, A. J., 1951, Structural Geology of North America: New York, Harper & Brothers.
Jeffreys, Harold, 1953, Earthquakes and Mountains: London, Methuen and Co.
King, P. B., 1959, The evolution of North America: Princeton, Princeton Univ. Press.
Umbgrove, J. H. F., 1947, The pulse of the Earth, 2nd ed.: The Hague, Martinus Nijhoff.

CHAPTER 22. GEOLOGY IN INDUSTRY

Our high-energy industry   Sources of energy   Coal   Petroleum   Nuclear energy   Sources of materials: minerals used in industry   Natural concentrations   Origin of mineral deposits   Future of mineral use and mineral exploration

Drilling ore in a New Mexico mine. (American Smelting & Refining Co.)

Our high-energy industry

Muscles and machines. When people speak of the present epoch in western civilization as "the industrial age," they really mean the age of suddenly and enormously increased use of fuels and metals, the age of high-energy industry. Stone-age man, 30,000 or more years ago, had an industry: he chipped and flaked mineral substances (mostly pieces of quartz) to make tools and weapons. But his was a low-energy industry, with the energy supplied by human muscle. Although he was limited by this fact and by a very narrow choice of materials to work with, we must not underestimate him. He was as intelligent as we, lacking only our accumulated experience and the know-how that comes from experience.

The lack was gradually, though not steadily, overcome by him and by his descendants. Here are a few of their accomplishments, discovered and dated by archeologists:

4000 B.C.: Chaldeans had become skilled workers in metals such as gold, silver, copper, lead, tin, and iron.

3000 B.C.: Eastern Mediterranean peoples were making glass, glazed pottery, and porcelain.

2500 B.C.: Babylonians were using petroleum instead of wood for fuel.

1100 B.C.: Chinese were mining coal and drilling wells hundreds of feet deep for natural gas.

These were arts, learned by experience, and they implied the substitution of metals, glass, and other substances for stone. But most of the energy with which these arts were pursued came from wood fuel and from the muscles of men and animals. This was still true, even in Europe, as late as the seventeenth century A.D., and of the majority of the world's people it is still true today.

With the eighteenth century came the substitution of coal for wood as an energy source and of iron for wood as a construction material, and with the nineteenth century came the steam engine. Thereupon, at an almost incredible speed, a minority of the Earth's peoples substituted machines for muscles, with the result that between 1800 and 1960 the industrial consumption of energy *per person* in the United States increased about 5 times. Today each person in the United States has working for him about 20 horsepower of energy, equivalent to the labor of more than two hundred slaves. This explosive industrial revolution has conferred upon its many beneficiaries a leisure and an opportunity for cultural development that could be enjoyed only by the richest people in slave-owning ancient Rome or Greece, Babylon, or Egypt.

Rapid emancipation from heavy labor has its bad aspects as well as its good, but for better or for worse the most highly industrialized nations enjoy its fruits. In the effort to maintain and increase the high consumption of energy, machines, and structures on which our comparative industrial freedom is based the geologist plays an important part. For we depend on him to find beneath the surface the oil and gas, the coal, and the metals necessary to build machines and to power them.

The supply of materials and energy. Metals and other materials to build machines and energy to power them are complementary. The increasing availability of machines makes it possible to do more things with energy. Furthermore high-energy industry demands also a host of nonmetallic mineral products, such as shale and limestone for making concrete, gypsum for making plaster, and asbestos for insulation. All these demands, taken together, have bent up the curve of industrial production very steeply (Fig. 22–1).

Skilled geologists play an essential part in exploring for, finding, and bringing to the surface mineral substances for use in industry. This task is being accomplished by the application of the basic principles set forth in this book and by the use of a great body of specialized knowledge that has no place here. Much ingenuity has been expended by prospectors, geologists, and engineers in bringing the production of minerals to its present state, and more ingenuity will be required in the future.

Let us take a look at what every educated citizen of any industrial nation ought to know about the geology of industrial mineral deposits. We can begin with sources of energy and then continue with mineral sources of materials for machines and structures.

Sources of energy

The chief sources of the energy consumed in highly industrialized nations are few: the fossil fuels (coal, oil, natural gas), hydroelectric power, wood, wind, and a little muscle. Nuclear energy will become an important source, but at present it is just beginning to develop. Excluding wood (used mainly for space heating in dwellings) and muscle (a resource now getting very little exercise in industrial countries), the United States in 1955 used energy from these sources:

Fossil fuels {	oil	41%
	coal	32%
	natural gas	24%
Water power		3%

For oil-poor western Europe the breakdown is different, coal accounts for nearly two-thirds the energy consumed. For the world as a whole, with its hundreds of millions of agricultural workers, the breakdown would be different again; wood and muscle would be a substantial source of energy, and fossil fuels, especially oil and gas, would bulk less.

Coal

Coal as energy. The black, combustible sedimentary rock we call coal is the most abundant of the fossil fuels. These fuels are so called because they contain solar energy, locked up securely in chemical compounds by the plants or animals of former ages. Coal is also the world's greatest single present source of industrial energy, for most of the coal mined is

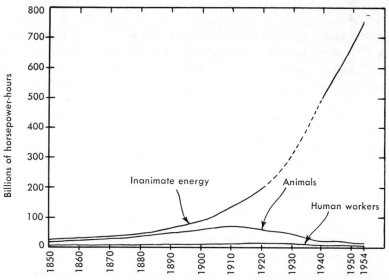

Fig. 22–1. Energy consumed industrially in the United States, 1850–1954. (After J. F. Dewhurst.)

443

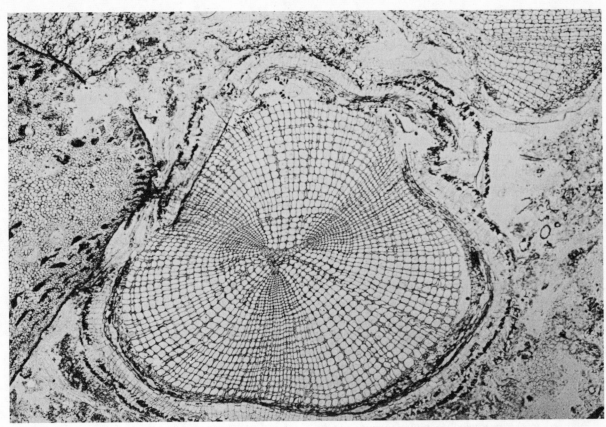

Fig. 22–2. Photomicrograph of coal of Pennsylvanian age from Illinois, showing cellular structure. Enlarged 10 times. (General Biological Supply House; Julius Weber.)

burned under boilers to make steam, and coke, a product of the burning of coal, is essential in making steel. Varying amounts of liquid fuel can be derived from coal, and, since internal-combustion engines are generally more efficient than steam engines, probably more and more coal will be used in this way. In addition to its uses as energy, coal is the chief raw material from which nylon, some plastics, and a multitude of chemicals are made.

Origin of coal. Coal occurs in beds or layers (miners call them *seams*) along with other sedimentary rocks, mostly shale and sandstone. A look at a thin slice of coal under the microscope shows that it consists of bits of fossil wood, bark, leaves, roots, and other parts of land plants, chemically altered but still identifiable. This composition leads at once to the inference that coal is fossil plant matter (Fig. 22–2). This is a characteristic that has been incorporated into the

definition of coal, which is given on page 328. Unlike most other sediments, coal was not eroded, transported, and deposited, but accumulated right where the plants grew, for coal beds include fossil tree stumps rooted in place in underlying shale, evidently a former clay soil. Furthermore, although coal is interbedded with inorganic sediments, it is not usually mixed with them, as inevitably it would be if it had been transported.

It was recognized as long ago as 1778 that the places of accumulation were swamps because (1) a complete physieal and chemical gradation exists from coal to peat, which today accumulates only in swamps, and (2) only under swamp conditions is the conversion of plant matter to coal chemically probable. On dry land dead plant matter (composed of carbon, hydrogen, and oxygen) combines with atmospheric oxygen to form carbon dioxide and water; it rots away.

Under water, however, oxygen is excluded from dead plant matter and oxidation is prevented. Instead, the plant substance is attacked by bacteria, which partly decompose it, splitting off oxygen and hydrogen. These two elements escape, combined in various gases, and the carbon gradually becomes concentrated in the residue. Although they work to destroy the vegetal matter, the bacteria themselves are destroyed first because the acid compounds they liberate poison them. This could not happen in a stream, whose flowing water would dilute the poisons and permit the bacteria to complete their destructive process.

With destruction of the bacteria, the biochemical phase of coal making comes to an end, the plant matter has been converted to peat, and a geochemical phase, so called because it involves geologic activity, begins. The peat is gradually buried and compressed beneath accumulating sand, silt, or clay (Fig. 22–3). Volatile matter continues to escape, leaving an ever-increasing proportion of carbon. The peat is converted successively into lignite, sub-bituminous coal, and bituminous coal. These coals are sedimentary rocks, but a still later phase, anthracite, is a metamorphic rock. As it generally occurs in folded strata, anthracite has undergone a further loss of volatiles and concentration of carbon caused by the pressure and heat that accompany folding. Because of its low content of volatiles, anthracite is hard to ignite but burns with almost no smoke. In contrast, lignite, rich in volatiles, ignites so easily that it is dangerously subject to spontaneous ignition (in chemical terms, rapid oxidation) and burns smokily. In certain regions where folding has been intense coal has been metamorphosed so thoroughly that it has been converted to graphite in which all the volatiles have been lost, leaving nothing but carbon. Graphite therefore will not burn.

Occurrence. We have said that coal occurs in layers or seams, which are merely strata of coal. Each seam is a flat, lens-shaped body corresponding in area to the area of the swamp in which it accumulated originally. Most coal seams are 2 to 10 feet thick, although some reach more than 100 feet. They tend to occur in groups; in Pennsylvania, for example, there are about 60 beds of bituminous coal. Their occurrence in the rocks of every period later than Devonian indicates that during the last 300 million years or so swamps rich in vegetal growth have been recurrent features of the land. Peat is accumulating today, at an average rate of about 1 foot in 30 years, in swamps on the Atlantic-Gulf coastal plain of the United States. The swamps now represented by coal beds must have been much the same as these. This relationship embodies the principle of uniformity, which underlies all of physical geology.

Distribution of coal. Coal is not only abundant but also rather widely distributed; it is present even in Antarctica. Although probably most of the world's coal fields have been discovered, world reserves have never been even closely estimated, but experts guess there may be 6 trillion tons, of which almost half is in the United States (Fig. 22–4). However, some of this coal would be impossible to mine, and mining much of the rest of it would be expensive, for some beds are thin, some are impure, and some lie far beneath the surface.

Coal mining. Thin beds and deep-lying beds are avoided wherever possible; the average thickness of all beds now mined in the United States is about 5

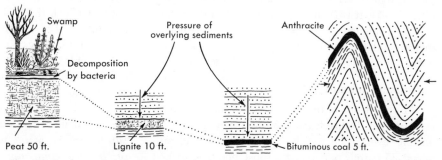

Fig. 22–3. Accumulating plant matter is converted into coal by decomposition and pressure.

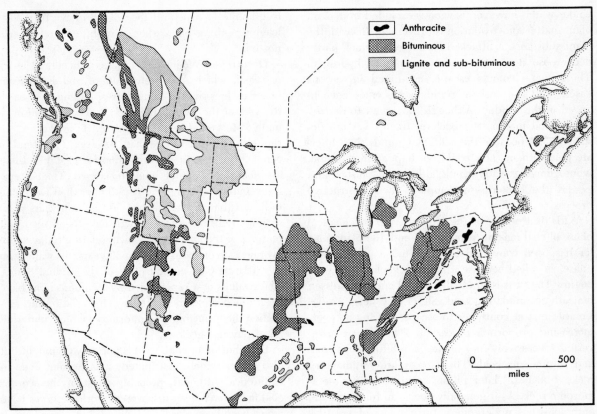

Fig. 22—4. Coal fields of United States and southern Canada. (Adapted from maps by U. S. Geol. Survey and Geol. Survey of Canada.)

feet. Increasing costs have stimulated the invention of increasingly efficient methods. In underground mining the automatic coal-cutting and loading machine, which eliminates drilling and blasting, has increased production per man-hour in thick beds 10 to 20 times. Coal within 100 feet of the surface is being mined, without ever going underground, by power shovels that take 10 to 50 cubic yards at a single bite (Fig. 22–5). It is thought possible that in the future beds too thin and too deep to mine can be burned in the ground to produce gas for industrial use. This technique would eliminate mining altogether.

Petroleum: oil and natural gas

The completion of the first oil well of modern times, at Titusville, Pennsylvania, in 1859, was an epoch-making event. The well was 69 feet deep and produced 25 barrels per day of a substance that spelled the doom of candles and whale-oil lamps. A hundred years later the United States was producing 7.5 million barrels of oil per day from nearly half a million wells, some of which were more than 3 miles deep and at least one of which was more than 4 miles deep. And the rest of the world produced an almost equal amount. Of the huge production, 90 per cent is actually used as fuel; the remainder goes into lubricants, without which the fuel would turn very few wheels, and into a thousand manufactured products of the chemical industry. New discoveries are continually being made, but most of these are in areas long recognized as being favorable for oil. Therefore, the search yearly becomes more difficult.

Oil and gas are the two chief kinds of petroleum. We can define *petroleum* as *gaseous, liquid, or solid substances, occurring naturally and consisting chiefly of chemical compounds of carbon and hydrogen. As*

Upper shovel removes overburden

Conveyor belt carries overburden to dump

Lower shovel digs coal
(man shows scale)

Conveyor belt loads coal

Fig. 22–5. This coal strip-mine at Wyodak, Wyoming, produces 300,000 tons a year from a seam 60 to 90 feet thick. The coal is intermediate in rank between lignite and bituminous coal. (U. S. Bureau of Mines.)

oil and gas generally occur together and are searched for in the same way, we can follow a rather general practice and talk about oil pools and oil exploration with the understanding that we mean not only oil but gas as well.

Oil pools. The accumulated experience of a century of exploration, drilling, and producing has taught us much about where and how oil occurs and not very much about how it originates. Oil possesses two important properties that affect its occurrence. It is fluid, and it is generally lighter than water. It is produced from pools. A *pool* is *an underground accumulation of oil or gas in a reservoir limited by geologic barriers.* The word gives a wrong impression because an oil pool is not a lake of oil. It is a body of rock in which oil occupies the pore spaces.

For oil or gas to accumulate in a pool four essential requirements must be met. (1) There must be a *reservoir rock* to hold the oil, and this rock must be permeable so that the oil can percolate through it, under pressure, into wells just as ground water does. (2) The reservoir rock must be overlain by an impermeable *roof rock*, such as a shale, to prevent upward escape of the oil, which is floating on ground water. (3) The pool must have the form of a *trap* that holds the oil and prevents it from moving laterally under pressure of the water beneath it (Fig. 22–6). These requirements are much like those of an artesian-water system (Fig. 11–8) but with the essential difference that the artesian aquifer connects with the surface, whereas the oil pool does not. Although these three features—reservoir, roof, and trap—are essential, they do not guarantee a pool. In many places where they occur together drilling has proved that there is no pool, generally because there is no source from which oil could enter the trap. So we must add

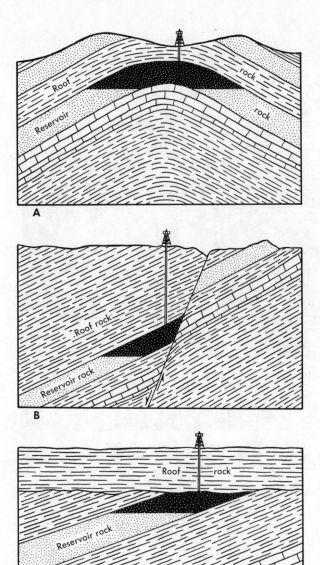

Fig. 22–6. Three of the many kinds of oil traps. Oil (black) floats on ground water, saturates reservoir rock, and is held down by roof of shale. Oil fills only the pore spaces in rock.

to the three requirements for a pool: (4) There must be *source rocks* to provide oil.

A group of pools, usually of similar type, or a single pool in an isolated position constitutes an **oil field.** The pools may be side by side or one on top of the other.

Origin of oil. The chemical composition of oil (95 to 99 per cent carbon and hydrogen) does not in itself imply an organic origin. Nevertheless, oil is generally regarded as organic mainly for two reasons: (1) Oil has certain optical properties that are known only in organic substances. (2) Oil contains nitrogen and certain compounds (porphyrins) that chemists believe could come only from organic sources.

Furthermore, oil is nearly always found in marine sedimentary rocks. Indeed, in places on the sea floors of the continental shelves sampling has shown that fine-grained sediments now accumulating contain up to 7 per cent organic matter, chemically good potential oil substance. In this fact we see still another application of the principle of uniformity.

Although the steps in the formation of oil are still poorly known, the following theory is rather widely held and is supported by enough facts to be at least somewhere near the truth.

1. The raw material consists of simple marine organisms, mostly plants, living in multitudes at and near the sea surface. Of such material there is certainly no lack. Measurements show that the sea grows at least 350 pounds of protein matter per acre per year, and in the most productive inshore waters as much as 1 ton is grown. The latter value represents more than could be harvested in a year from the most productive farm land.

2. The organic matter accumulates on the bottom, mostly in basins where the water is stagnant and deficient in oxygen and where, therefore, the substance is neither devoured by scavengers nor destroyed by oxidation. Instead, it is attacked and decomposed by bacteria, which split off and remove oxygen, nitrogen, and other elements, leaving residual carbon and hydrogen. Sediments, rich in organic matter, that are accumulating today, teem with bacteria.

3. Deep burial beneath further fine sediment destroys the bacteria and provides pressure, heat, and time for further chemical changes that convert the

substance into droplets of liquid oil and tiny bubbles of gas.

4. Gradual compaction of the inclosing sediments under the pressure of their own increasing weight reduces the space between the rock particles and squeezes out the oil and gas into nearby layers of sand or sandstone, where open spaces are larger.

5. Aided by their buoyancy and perhaps by artesian water circulation, the oil and gas move generally upward through the sand until they reach the surface and are lost or until they are caught in a trap and form a pool.

Exploration. The oil industry in the United States dates from about 1860, when commercial production in western Pennsylvania began. The first pools were discovered at places where oil and gas advertised their presence by seeping out at the surface. It soon became apparent that at all the producing wells the rocks were sedimentary and that at most wells the structure consisted of anticlines (Fig. 22–6, **A**). In 1861 the theory was advanced that oil had migrated upward into anticlines and lay trapped beneath their crests. In the 1880's this theory was tested and confirmed by drilling holes in certain anticlines where no oil had been found previously; the holes were successful wells.

Geologic exploration. Proof of the anticline theory led to a period (1890 to 1925) in which geologists searched for and mapped anticlines from surface outcrops. During this period traps other than anticlines were discovered (Fig. 22–6, **B**), and the search for pools rapidly widened.

The occurrence of buried traps such as the one in Figure 22–6, **C**, showed that mapping of outcrops would have to be supplemented by methods that would reveal structures not apparent at the surface. This was done first, and is still being done, by core drilling in a pattern beneath a suspected area. Study of the cores enables geologists to construct a graphic log (Fig. 5–13) from each core and to correlate the strata by physical character and contained fossils (Fig. 17–24) almost as well as though the rocks were exposed at the surface. The depths at which a recognizable bed is encountered by a series of drill holes give a strong clue to structure (Fig. 22–7).

Core drilling, however, is expensive. This stimulated the development of electric logging, which can be done in holes drilled by cheaper methods. Common salt and other dissolved substances are present in the ground water that saturates all deep-lying sedimentary rocks. As salt solution is a good conductor, the conductivity of a sedimentary layer at depth varies with water content. The conductivity or the resistivity at any desired depth is measured by devices lowered into the hole by a cable. The resulting electric logs (Fig. 5–13) are widely used in correlation.

Geophysical exploration. In the 1920's geophysical exploration began to be widely used. Twenty years later this kind of exploration was uncovering most of the new pools simply because the majority of those discoverable by geologic methods alone had been found already. Geophysical exploration is designed to detect variations in distribution, in the rocks, of some physical property such as specific gravity, magnetism, or ability to transmit or reflect seismic waves (Fig. 20–16). As most of these variations are related to structures, they help to indicate the presence of possible pools. If, for instance, a stratum having a high specific gravity has been raised during the making of an anticline, the value of gravity will be increased very slightly compared with that in the surrounding area. As the increase is not likely to be more than about one ten-millionth, the weighing instrument used, a gravity meter, has to be extremely sensitive.

Again, distortions of the Earth's magnetic field by rocks of varying magnetic susceptibility are measured

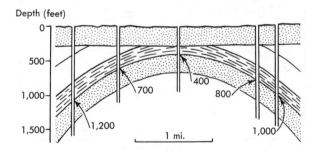

Depth (feet)

Fig. 22–7. Core-drill holes at 5 points show that flat-lying surface strata conceal an anticline lying unconformably beneath it. Numbers show depths in feet at which top of sandstone was encountered.

Fig. 22—8. Magnetometer, mounted on a helicopter, starting out on a subsurface-exploration traverse in northwestern Canada. Helicopter also carries a scintillation counter (not visible). A magnetometer can also be mounted on a truck. (Canadian Aero Service Ltd.)

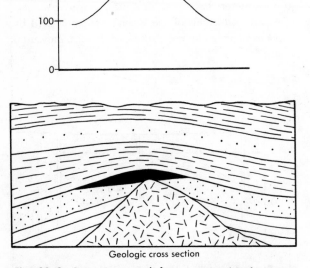

Fig. 22—9. Curve constructed from a magnetometer survey showed an abrupt local increase in magnetic intensity. Later test drilling disclosed a buried hill of relatively magnetic granite, with an oil pool just over its summit. (Courtesy Sharpe Instruments of Canada.)

with magnetometers (Fig. 22–8). Since igneous rocks, containing magnetite, are much more magnetic than sedimentary rocks, magnetometer surveys are most successful in areas in which igneous rocks project into overlying sedimentary rocks by intrusion, folding, or faulting or as erosional hills beneath unconformities (Fig. 22–9). But the magnetometer also shows differences among sedimentary rocks.

In the search for oil the most useful geophysical exploration method is seismic surveying. An artificial earthquake is created by exploding buried dynamite, and in the common method the waves reflected from the upper surfaces of rock layers with high wave-reflection potential are picked up at ground level by portable seismographs located half a mile or so from the explosion. Velocity of wave transmission being known, depths of the reflecting layers can be calculated from travel times. The principle involved is similar to that used in echo sounding of sea depth (Figs. 15–1, 15–2).

Areal pattern of exploration. Exploration proceeds by a process of elimination. Experience shows that, essentially, oil occurs only in sedimentary rocks and that the thinner the pile of such rocks the less likely they are to yield oil. Maps showing possibly productive areas are continually being made and revised by exploration companies. On them areas of igneous and metamorphic rocks are labeled improbable; areas of sedimentary rocks that are very thin or that have unfavorable structure are likely to be put into the same class. With these, too, go areas that, having the right rocks and structure, have been drilled and just have not yielded oil. Figure 22–10 is a 1960 map of this kind for North America. People who have to risk half a million dollars or more in drilling a hole do not rely solely on such general data; they prepare large-scale maps of small areas before making decisions.

The map shows in outline the continental shelf, which adds almost one-third to the potentially productive area of the United States. Geophysical exploration and some drilling close to shore have shown that in places at least the shelf is favorable territory. The hole at Hatteras Light, shown in Figure 15–12, was drilled primarily for exploring the strata of the shelf. In the Gulf Coast area, where considerable production has already developed, wells are being drilled as far as 50 miles offshore (Fig. 22–11). Wells

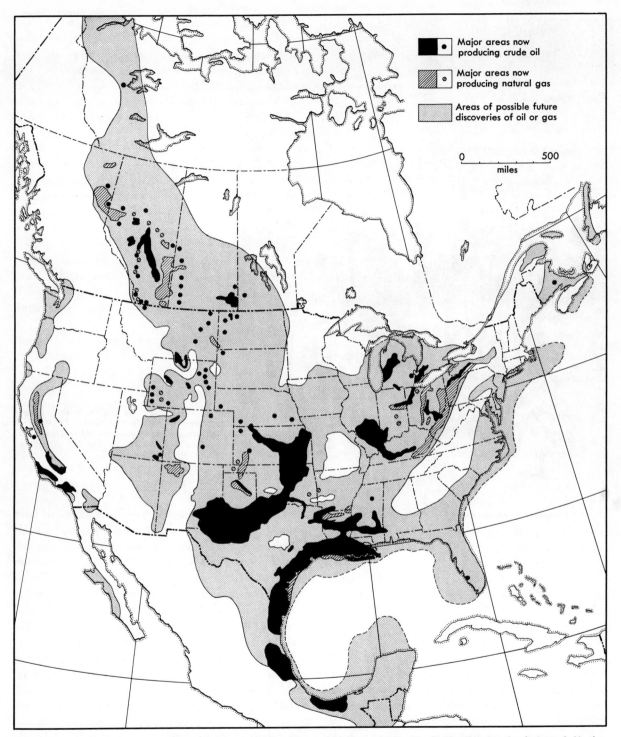

Fig. 22–10. Major petroleum-producing areas in North America (exclusive of Northern Canada and Alaska) and areas of possible future production. Compiled from American Petroleum Institute, Geological Survey of Canada, and other sources.

Legend:
- Major areas now producing crude oil
- Major areas now producing natural gas
- Areas of possible future discoveries of oil or gas

0   500
miles

Fig. 22–11. Drilling rig on a three-legged platform in 100 feet of water, 50 miles off the coast of Louisiana, in 1959. Crew of 45 lives on platform, which also has a heliport. (Shell Oil Company.)

drilled at water depths of 350 feet off southern California have produced oil. Continental shelves have large possibilities for future production, but how great they are is still unknown.

The production of oil and the distribution of known oil reserves throughout the world are shown in Figure 22–12.

Nuclear energy

Although most of the energy we use today comes from fossil fuels, the use of nuclear energy for industrial purposes has already begun and in time will play an important part in the world's economy. So far, such energy has been obtained only from the atomic nuclei of a few unstable, radioactive elements, chiefly uranium.

Like many other economic deposits described later in this chapter, some deposits containing uranium are basically related to magmas, whereas others were deposited by ground water. The most common uranium mineral is uraninite or pitchblende (Fig. 4–7), so called because it is "black as pitch." In some regions pitchblende has been altered, by weathering and redeposition by ground water, to secondary minerals, mostly vanadates and phosphates.

Because uranium is radioactive, prospecting for uranium-bearing deposits employs scintillometers, which sensitively record the presence of high-energy particles released by radioactive decay.

Deposits from which important North American production is now coming are located in the Colorado Plateau region and Wyoming and in the Blind River

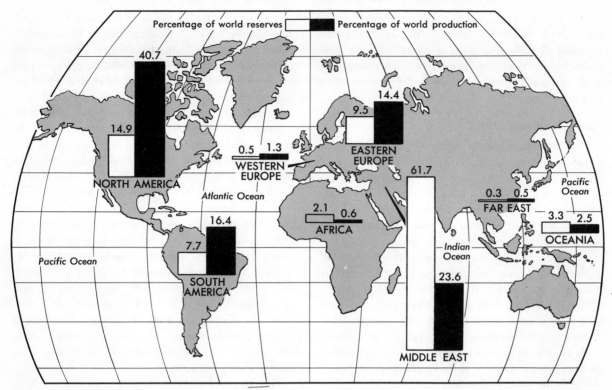

Fig. 22–12. Location of the world's proved oil reserves (oil known to be in the ground) compared with amount of oil produced, by regions, in 1959. In 1959 North America had 14.9 per cent of the world's known oil but contributed 40.7 per cent of the world's production (Source: World Oil, 1960.)

district in Ontario. Important foreign sources include the U.S.S.R., the Witwatersrand district in the Union of South Africa, and France.

Sources of materials: minerals used in industry

Some of the principal minerals used in industry are listed, according to use, in Table 22–1.

The table lists a natural mineral or a derivative if it is used industrially as such (example: fluorite), and the metallic element derived from minerals if only the metal is used (example: iron). The list, much generalized, shows only a few of the hundred or more minerals and metals that enter into commerce.

In the table subdivision according to use separates metals from nonmetals rather distinctly; but we are concerned here mainly with the *origin* of mineral de-

Table 22–1. Principal mineral substances used in industry
(Modified after A. M. Bateman)

Group (according to use)	Partial List of Mineral Substances
METALS	
Iron and steel	Iron ore
Metals used as alloys with iron	Manganese, chromium, nickel, tungsten, molybdenum, vanadium, cobalt
Other important metals	Copper, zinc, lead, tin, aluminum
Minor metals	Mercury, silver, platinum, gold
Fissionable isotopes	Uranium
NONMETALS	
Minerals used in metallurgy	Fluorite, bauxite, graphite
Minerals used in chemical industry	Salt, sulfur, borax, coal
Minerals used in building	Stone, cement minerals, gypsum, petroleum solids
Minerals used in fertilizer	Phosphates, potash, nitrates, calcite
Minerals used in ceramics	Clay, feldspar, quartz
Minerals used in abrasives	Diamond, garnet, quartz, corundum
Fossil fuels	Coal, oil, gas

posits, and in this respect metals are not easily separated from nonmetals because in many deposits minerals of both groups were formed side by side under much the same conditions. Therefore, we shall discuss the two groups together according to their origin.

Natural concentrations

Important though some nonmetals are, to most of us metals are inherently the more interesting group, partly because both the implements (including machines) and the structures on which our material civilization is based are built increasingly of metal. This has been made possible—in fact, the transition from the stone age to the age of metals was made possible—only because here and there metals have been *concentrated* in the rocks by natural processes. For if the metals present in the Earth's crust were scattered uniformly through the rocks their amounts everywhere would have been so small that it would have been impossible to use them. Whoever the ancient people were, thousands of years before the Christian era, who used metals first, we can be sure they found them in places in which the Earth's chemistry had brought together enough particles to be easily visible and easily extracted from the rocks. In many places metals like gold and copper occur and are mined as elements in the native form uncombined with other elements; metals such as iron and aluminum, on the other hand, occur in combination with other elements, usually oxygen.

What we mean, quantitatively, by concentrations depends on whether our point of view is pure scientific curiosity (in which case we are interested only in percentages) or economic (in which case we are interested also in costs and prices).

The curiosity of scientists has led to the chemical analyses of thousands of samples of igneous rocks of all kinds, and from the analyses the probable abundance of each of the chemical elements present in the crust has been estimated. Of all the useful metals, aluminum (8%), iron (5%) and magnesium (2%) are the only ones that make up more than 1 per cent by weight of the total rock matter. In fact, all the other useful metals lumped together constitute less than one per cent of the total. These amounts are so very small that only when they have been greatly increased by

natural concentration can metals be mined and used. The degree of concentration required varies with value, accessibility, and other factors. Minable aluminum ore ordinarily contains around 20 per cent pure aluminum; the iron ore now mined runs 25 to 70 per cent pure iron; because of its high value, minable gold ore can be less than 0.001 per cent pure gold. Each represents a concentration equal to many times the average abundance of the metal in the rocks.

Ores. We have just spoken of *ore* and of *value*. The two terms go together because the definition of ore is a quantitative one. An **ore** is *an aggregate of minerals from which one or more metals can be extracted profitably*. As both costs and market prices fluctuate, a particular aggregate of minerals may be an ore at one time but not at another. Associated with the ore minerals, from which the desired metals are extracted, are other minerals collectively termed the gangue (pronounced *gang*). We define **gangue** as *the nonvaluable minerals of an ore*. Familiar minerals common in gangue are quartz, limonite, calcite, dolomite, feldspar, and garnet, although no two ores are exactly alike as to gangue.

The ore problem has always been twofold: first, to find the ores (which altogether underlie an infinitesimally small proportion of the Earth's land area) and, next, to get rid of the gangue as economically as possible. Getting rid of the gangue is merely the completion by man of the process of concentration begun by nature.

Origin and classification of mineral deposits

Relation of most ores to magmas. One of the basic facts about ores is their obvious relation to igneous rocks. Ore deposits tend to occur in groups and clusters in or close to intrusive igneous bodies, especially stocks and batholiths. This relationship, coupled with observed occurrences of metallic deposits such as hematite and galena at active fumaroles and of deposits of gold, silver, copper, lead, and zinc minerals at active hot springs, has led to the opinion that most ores are closely related to magmas, the parent materials of igneous rocks. This idea was dimly suspected as early as the sixteenth century, was clearly set forth in 1788 by James Hutton, the author of the principle of uniformity of process, and, with increasing support, is held by almost all geologists today. Magma, therefore, is the parent not only of igneous rocks but of most ores as well.

The degree of kinship between ores and magmas varies. Some ores constitute an actual part of the magma itself. Others have been deposited by fluids percolating upward and outward from the magma far into the surrounding rock. Finally a minority of ore deposits is obviously unrelated to magmas, having been concentrated in altogether different ways.

Classification by origin. The search for new depósits is based to a considerable extent on the use of analogy with features characteristic of ores already being mined. Accurate analogy demands a thorough knowledge of known deposits, down to the minutest details visible only under a microscope. Knowledge of these details has made possible a systematic classification of ore deposits based on their conditions of origin. The list below is simplified, but it includes the more important ways in which ores are formed:

1. Concentration within cooling magma
2. Alteration of rock in contact with cooling magma
3. Deposition from hot waters coming from cooling magma
4. Deposition from solution in sea and lakes
5. Concentration by weathering and ground water
   A. Secondary enrichment
   B. Residual concentration
6. Mechanical concentration

1. *Concentration within magma.* When some kinds of metallic ore are melted in a smelter, the molten metallic compounds, being heavy, sink to the bottom, whereas the molten silicates, being light, rise to the top as a sort of scum. This simple concentration of metallic compounds occurs in nature as well. The separation and concentration of substances within a cooling magma is believed to explain the origin of some iron, chromium, nickel, and copper deposits. The huge deposit of magnetite iron ore at Kiruna, in northern Sweden, the site of one of the most important iron mines in Europe, seems to have been concentrated in a magma; this is true also of some of the much smaller magnetite ore bodies in the Adirondack region of New York. Among nonmetals, the diamonds from the famous mines in South Africa are believed to have originated through concentration within a magma.

2. *Alteration of rock in contact with magma.* In the Cananea mining district in Mexico, just over the border from Arizona, part of the large production of copper ore is in limestone at the contact of an intrusive body of igneous rock. The alteration of rock around igneous bodies, in a sort of halo (Fig. 22–13) surrounding the intrusive mass, is commonplace, but when conditions are favorable the halo includes ore. The deposit at Cananea illustrates the two important favorable conditions: first, the minerals composing the

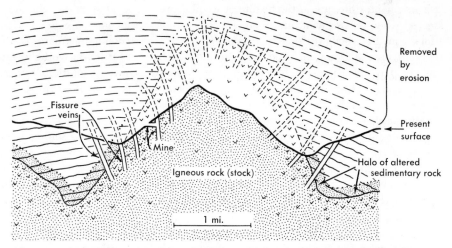

Fig. 22–13. Geologic examination at the surface and in mines shows that hot solutions from a cooling magma body altered sedimentary rocks and converted fissures into veins of ore. Relations before erosion, shown above present surface, are reconstructed by analogy with similar but less eroded masses elsewhere.

rock to be altered must be ready to react chemically when heated; this is especially true of calcite, the constituent mineral of limestone. Second, new elements must be introduced from the magma.

The copper ore consists of chalcopyrite and other sulfides; evidently the copper, sulfur, iron, and other constituents foreign to the unaltered limestone were brought in by hot, gaseous fluids emanating from the magma. The fluids were not magma, for the ore shows their composition was unlike that of any igneous rock; they consisted of relatively few elements. Temperatures were high—400 to 800° C. We know this because the temperatures at which many minerals form have been learned through laboratory experiments with melted igneous rocks that are allowed to cool under controlled conditions; hence the presence of certain minerals in the gangue is a geologic thermometer. Such thermometers suggest that in some deposits temperatures may have reached 1,100° C. Attempts to create some of these "magma-contact" minerals synthetically in the laboratory suggest that gases are required for their formation and that therefore the new elements introduced into the rocks were brought from the magmas in a gaseous state.

The chief way in which alteration is brought about is by replacement. In this process the substance of the mineral grains in the rock is replaced, volume for volume, by ore (and other) substances brought in by the gaseous fluids. This preserves the finest details of the original texture, just as the texture of wood is preserved when replacement, under much cooler conditions, converts woody tissues to petrified wood.

Some ores of iron, zinc, and lead, in addition to copper, have been created by alteration of rocks at igneous contacts (Fig. 19–9). Among nonmetals, garnet (used in abrasives) and rubies and sapphires (varieties of corundum) are recovered.

3. *Deposition from hot waters coming from cooling magma.* By far the most numerous and best-known ore deposits are those deposited in open spaces in rocks by hot water (perhaps with dissolved gases). Containing metals in solution, the waters percolate outward and upward from cooling magma. Large proportions of the world's gold (from such famous mining districts as the Mother Lode in California, Kirkland Lake in Ontario, and Kalgoorlie in Australia), silver, copper (as from Cerro de Pasco in Peru), lead,

and zinc are mined from deposits of this sort.

The most obvious deposits are *fissure veins* (defined simply as *fissures in rock, filled with mineral matter*) (Figs. 22–13, 22–14, 22–15). Originally they may have been joints, cracks, or faults; most of them are no more than a few feet in width, and they are generally lighter in color than the surrounding rock because their common gangue mineral is quartz. But the ores brought by magmatic waters fill openings of other kinds too: solution cavities in limestone, thin spaces between beds in sedimentary rocks, vesicles in lava flows, and angular openings in breccias. Water-deposited ores are formed also by replacement, but they differ from ore deposited in contact with magma in having their own characteristic set of geologic-thermometer minerals, which indicate a watery rather than a gaseous origin and point to lower temperatures prevailing at the time of deposition.

Although many fissure veins, replacements, and related deposits occur in wide zones extending outward away from batholiths and other intrusive igneous bodies, some of them penetrate far down into the igneous bodies themselves (Fig. 22–13). At Butte, Montana, an important copper district, veins extend more than 4,000 feet into a batholith; this fact tells us that the batholith had solidified through at least its outermost 4,000 feet before the thick shell began to fracture, permitting the escape of hot, watery solutions from the still-fluid magma within.

Despite their variation in detail, these deposits have a common general origin in hot waters escaping from cooling magmas.

Why do we believe that these fugitive fluids were watery solutions rather than magma itself? Here is some of the evidence. (1) Many of the minerals occurring in ore deposits of this kind have been produced artificially in the laboratory by precipitation from *water* solutions. (2) Hot-spring waters that are partly of magmatic origin are observed to deposit minerals of gold, silver, copper, lead, and other metals, similar to the minerals found in fissure veins. (3) Some of the crystals in fissure veins contain trapped bubbles of water. This condition shows that when the crystal formed the fissure was filled with a water solution. Furthermore, analysis of the bubbles shows that the water contains dissolved constituents, such as chlorine, fluorine, and sulfur, that occur in the hot waters

Fig. 22–14. Quartz vein diagonally cutting across vertically foliated phyllite. Stratford, Connecticut. (S. C. Porter.)

Fig. 22–15. The native gold in this ore, from a mine near Alleghany, California, is worth several thousand dollars per ton of ore. The principal gangue mineral (white) is quartz. Several other minerals are present in small amounts. (A. M. Bateman.)

of volcanic regions and that would not, as a group, be expected in ordinary ground water.

If we try to reconstruct the probable conditions of origin of fissure veins and related deposits, we shall have to piece the story together from scattered evidence such as structure, texture, and composition of the ores, analyses of waters and gases at hot springs, observations at fumaroles and volcanoes, use of geologic thermometers, and laboratory models. The magma body in its fireless cooker, perhaps miles below the surface, holds quantities of gases in solution by virtue of the pressure under which it is confined. As the magma slowly cools and solidifies from the outside inward, the liquids and gases are confined within an ever-decreasing volume of magma in which also the mineral substances of potential ore deposits become concentrated. Fissures develop in the solidified outer part of the magma body and tap the gas-charged residual fluids within. Under great pressures the fluids escape outward and upward through the fissures into the surrounding rocks. Depending on the pressures and temperatures prevailing, the escaping solutions of metals could be either hot gases or hot liquids. But as they move up through fissures they encounter ever-decreasing pressures, react chemically with the rocks through which they pass, and commonly become mixed with ground water. Most important of all, they lose heat. These changes make various constituents successively insoluble and deposits result. Geologic-thermometer minerals indicate that deposition begins at around 500° C and that some minerals are deposited only when temperatures have been reduced to 50° C or less.

According to this reconstruction, which is still no more than a reasonable probability that meets the geologic facts we know, fissure veins are analogous to dikes, except that they form from watery solutions rather than solidifying from the magma itself.

Examination of ore samples under the microscope shows that fissure-vein minerals are generally deposited in sequence with later minerals filling spaces between, or even replacing, those formed earlier. For example, a sequence met with in some copper deposits is quartz, then pyrite, then sphalerite, and, last, chalcopyrite. The sequence records response to changes in the physical-chemical conditions with the passage of time, while the ore-forming solutions

moved outward through the fissures.

There are also wide differences in the kinds of minerals deposited in different regions. Why do the ore minerals in the fissure veins at Great Bear Lake, Canada, yield uranium compounds, whereas those at famed Cripple Creek, Colorado, yield chiefly gold? Some such differences may be the result, in part, of variations in the chemical composition of the crust from place to place. But changes may perhaps have resulted from the separation of compounds within the magma itself, creating successive natural liquors or broths from which the fissure-vein solutions were tapped off. This is still speculative and is merely a hypothesis that geologists, in their continuing curiosity, have suggested to explain an observed fact.

Despite these and other unsolved problems, the basic principle seems fairly certain that the source of the constituents of fissure veins and their relatives is magma.

4. *Deposition from solution in seas and lakes.* We have seen how sodium chloride and other nonmetallic compounds precipitated in Great Salt Lake are derived through tributary streams from the products of chemical weathering of the rocks within the lake's drainage area. This process of weathering → stream transport → precipitation in a water body, a prime example of natural concentration, has been responsible for a wide variety of mineral deposits. Many salts of sodium (including common salt), potassium, and boron are recovered from saline lakes and playas. Enormous quantities of common salt, and of the calcium sulfates gypsum and anhydrite used in making plaster, are recovered from sedimentary layers precipitated in shallow, cut-off arms of ancient seas. Much of the salt production in the United States comes from such layers in rocks of Silurian age, well over 300 million years old.

These and other nonmetallic substances have been concentrated by evaporation and are therefore evaporites. Metals, too, have been concentrated from solution in the sea, but their abundance in sea water is so slight that thick beds of iron ore, for example, could not have been concentrated by evaporation; some other process must have been responsible.

A good example is the Clinton iron ore, occurring as lenslike bodies in several sedimentary beds, one of them locally more than 30 feet thick, extending from

Fig. 22—16. Susquehanna location, a deep open-pit iron mine, Hibbing, Minnesota. (Sawders-Cushing.)

New York State southward for 700 miles into Alabama. The large steel industry of Birmingham, Alabama, is based on the convenient occurrence of this ore, coal, and limestone close together. Fossils in the ore beds show that the strata were laid down in a shallow sea during the Silurian Period. Ripple marks and mud cracks further indicate shallow water. Obviously these beds were units in the thick pile of sediments accumulated in the Appalachian geosyncline. The iron mineral is red hematite, and the ore is 35 to 40 per cent iron, except at outcrops where weathering has concentrated it to still richer proportions.

It is believed that the iron was dissolved from iron-bearing minerals in basic igneous rocks, carried by streams to the shallow sea, perhaps as a bicarbonate, and there precipitated as oxides. The Clinton ore concentrated in this way runs into billions of tons. The enormous iron-ore beds in the province of Lorraine, in eastern France, have a similar origin. The Lake Superior iron ores (Fig. 22–16), hitherto the mainstay of the North American steel industry, and the similar, newly developed ores in Labrador, on which Canada and the United States will depend increasingly, possibly were originally deposited in the same way, but both have been further greatly enriched by weathering.

The world's biggest deposits of manganese, in the U.S.S.R., originated in a similar manner by precipitation, probably organic, in ancient seas.

5. *Concentration by weathering and ground water:* A. Secondary enrichment. The related processes of sorting and concentration by ground water are chem-

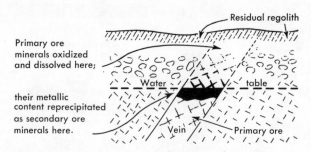

Primary ore minerals oxidized and dissolved here;

their metallic content reprecipitated as secondary ore minerals here.

Fig. 22—17. Descending ground water impoverishes ore above water table by removing soluble ore minerals; produces secondary enrichment below.

ical. They depend on the principle that change in the environment of a mineral may make it vulnerable to chemical attack. Many fissure-vein minerals, though stable at the high temperatures at which they crystallized from solution, become unstable in the zone of aeration at the Earth's surface. In many areas erosion has worn the surface down so that even the deep-lying minerals are brought within the shallow zone in which air and ground water can attack them and cause them to decay. Many metallic minerals are oxidized and dissolved, and the metallic elements are carried down through the zone of aeration. They enter the zone of saturation, an environment out of reach of air, and are there redeposited, commonly as sulfides. In a fissure vein the added sulfides enrich the ore already present or convert low-grade deposits into workable ore (Fig. 22–17). This process of addition is known to mining geologists as *secondary enrichment,* defined

Fig. 22—18. Utah Copper Mine at Bingham Canyon, Utah, in 1950. Terraced slope in background is 1,900 feet high. (Kennecott Copper Corporation.)

as *natural enrichment of an ore body by the addition of material of later origin.*

Secondary enrichment has been important at the Utah Copper Mine (Fig. 22–18) at Bingham Canyon, Utah, the world's second-largest copper producer. The ore body is in the upper part of an igneous intrusion, in which copper, gold, silver, and molybdenum were deposited by replacement from hot solutions coming from the magma underneath. In a zone more than 100 feet thick, secondary enrichment has improved the upper part of the primary ore (Fig. 22–19). This enormous, low-grade deposit is an ore only because low-cost surface mining, roughly similar to the surface mining of coal (Fig. 22–5), can be used instead of underground mining. The sides of the canyon have been cut into giant steps 50 to 70 feet high, making a huge pit resembling a Roman amphitheater. The ore is blasted out and loaded by power shovels into railroad cars. Waste is dumped into side can-

yons. The ore already mined exceeds 1¼ billion tons, and some ore containing as little as 0.4 per cent copper is being worked profitably.

B. Residual concentration. In secondary enrichment ground water adds new material to an existing body. Some ores, however, are developed by the subtraction of old material. This is **residual concentration,** defined as the *natural concentration of a mineral substance by removal of a different substance with which it was associated.* An example is bauxite, a hydrous aluminum oxide and the common ore of aluminum (Fig. 22–20).

Bauxite is a product of chemical weathering. Aluminum was present as a constituent of original, primary aluminum-silicate minerals in rocks, usually syenite, schist, or clay. During weathering, silica was carried away in solution, leaving a gradually increasing concentration of aluminum. We know this has happened because we can see bauxite grading down-

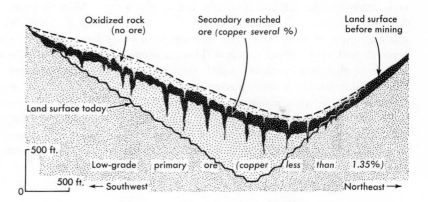

Fig. 22–19. Diagrammatic section across Utah Copper Mine at Bingham Canyon, Utah.

Oxidized rock (no ore)

Secondary enriched ore (copper several %)

Land surface before mining

Land surface today

500 ft.

500 ft. ← Southwest

Low-grade primary ore (copper less than 1.35%)

Northeast →

Fig. 22–20. Bauxite, the ore of aluminum, concentrated by deep, long-continued weathering of syenite. The rounded bodies are not pebbles but concretions, developed during weathering. Bauxite, Arkansas.

ward into the underlying rock just as any weathered regolith does. From the locations of bauxite ores we know that the weathering has taken place beneath peneplanes and other surfaces of low relief, with the water table close to the surface, with slow ground-water circulation, and always in tropical or subtropical climates. But the chemistry of the process is complex, and we still have much to learn about just what happens. Apparently ground water, charged with substances derived from the soil, decomposes the aluminum silicates in the fresh rock, carries away silica in solution, and leaves aluminum (and iron as well) behind as oxides. Whatever the chemical details, the resulting bauxite may reach a concentration of 20 per cent pure aluminum.

Although there is some difference of opinion about the matter, it is likely that the richer iron ores of the Lake Superior district, and those of the newly developed district in Labrador, originated in a somewhat similar way. The ore bodies are sedimentary beds much like the Clinton iron ores, but at depth they are siliceous, with only about 30 per cent iron, grading upward toward the surface into nonsiliceous hematite with up to 62 per cent iron. There is reason to believe that long-continued weathering has dissolved and removed the silica, leaving a residual concentrate of almost pure hematite.

6. *Mechanical concentration: placers.* The famous gold rush to California in 1849 resulted from the discovery that the sand and gravel in the bed of a small Sierran stream contained bits of gold. Indeed, most mining districts have been discovered by following trails of gold and other minerals upstream to their sources in bedrock. Pure gold is very heavy. Having a specific gravity of about 19, it is quickly dropped by a stream in preference to quartz, with a specific gravity of only 2.65. Particles of gold therefore are mechanically sorted out and concentrated in the lowermost parts of stream deposits, particularly in point bars where stream velocities are low. *A deposit of heavy minerals concentrated mechanically* is a **placer** (plăs-er). Besides native gold other heavy, durable metallic minerals form placers. These include platinum, tinstone (cassiterite), and native copper and the nonmetallic diamond and other gemstones as well.

Every phase of the conversion of gold in a fissure vein to placer gold has been traced. Chemical weathering of the vein at its outcrop releases the gold, which is then slowly moved downslope by mass-wasting (Fig. 22–21). In some places mass-wasting alone has concentrated gold or tinstone sufficiently to justify mining these metals.

More commonly, however, the mineral particles get into a stream, which concentrates them more effectively than mass-wasting can. Most placer gold occurs in grains the size of silt particles, the "gold dust" of placer miners. Some of it is coarser; pebble-size fragments are *nuggets* (Fig. 22–22), of which the largest ever recorded weighed 2,280 ounces and at the current price of gold would be worth $79,800. In following placers upstream, prospectors have learned that rounding and flattening (by pounding) increase downstream, just as does rounding of ordinary pebbles; when they find angular nuggets they know they

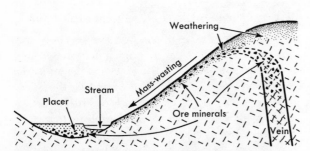

Fig. 22–21. Ore minerals from weathered fissure veins creep down slopes and are redeposited by streams as placers.

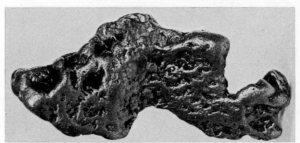

Fig. 22–22. Gold nugget, found near Greenville, California, is 7⅝ inches long and weighs 82 ounces. Its surface shows clearly the pounding it received during stream transport. (Photo Smithsonian Institution, courtesy George Switzer. Collection U.S. National Museum.)

Boom swings back and forth, dumping washed gravel in neat piles

Gravel washed here; gold removed

Gravel scooped up here

Pickup truck shows scale

Fig. 22–23. A gold dredge like this one in the Yukon Valley, Alaska, may cost more than half a million dollars, but it can profitably work gravel containing only 10 to 20 cents in gold per cubic yard. (H. Bradford Washburn.)

are close to the bedrock source. Mining was done first by hand, simply by swashing stream sediment around in a small pan of water. Later it was done by jetting water under high pressure against gravel banks and washing the sediment through troughs that caught the heavy gold behind cleats. Nowadays the more efficient method of dredging is used (Fig. 22–23).

The platinum placers of the Ural Mountains in Russia and the rich diamond placers of the Kasai district in the Congo are examples of other mechanical concentrations by streams. Gold, diamonds, and several other minerals have been concentrated in beaches by surf. Diamonds worth as much as 50 million dollars a year have been obtained from gravelly beach placers along a 200-mile strip of the coast of South West Africa. Weathered from deposits in the interior, the diamonds were transported by the Orange River to the coast and were spread southward by beach drifting. The beaches then emerged probably by uplift of the land.

Finally, gold is recovered in Mexico and in Aus-

tralia from placers concentrated by wind. Quartz and other light minerals have been deflated, leaving the heavier gold particles behind. Therefore, since mechanical concentration results from a variety of natural processes, the principles of erosion and deposition must be thoroughly understood by those who would discover new placers.

Future of mineral use and mineral exploration

A look at the future of the world's sources of energy and materials shows that the present pattern is changing and will continue to change. When the industrial revolution began, mankind had existed for thousands of years on an energy economy of wood fuel and muscle power, both of which are replaceable up to a point. Now, in the industrial age, which began only yesterday in man's long history and less than a minute ago in the vastly longer span of geologic history, man is rapidly using up the mineral riches stored in the Earth.

The steep curve of energy consumption shown in

463

Figure 22–1, and the very similar curve of consumption of materials, can not long continue to steepen if we employ only the materials and energy sources we are using today. The supply of these commodities is far from inexhaustible. Unlike agricultural products, they are "one-crop" products; that is, they are not renewable. By persistent search man has found a large proportion of the mineral deposits that are not well hidden. Probably, however, great quantities of ore lie concealed and undiscovered at depths no greater than a few hundred feet. The search for them will involve not old-fashioned surface prospecting but geologic research and will require more highly skilled and specialized geologists than have been needed in the easier past. The future, then, should see an increase in the supply of the kinds of materials and energy we are using now, the development of improved ways to apply them, and the addition of entirely new and different kinds.

In the field of energy water power can never become a major source, for probably little more than one per cent of the world's runoff can be made to generate power economically, and about one-tenth of this potential is harnessed and working for us already. Many new oil fields will be found, but their average depth will be greater than at present, and costs will therefore be higher. Eventually the production of petroleum will decline. The amount in the ground is limited, and once used it can not be replaced within the probable lifetime of the human race. It has been estimated that consumption of petroleum by the western world will be 60 per cent greater in 1975 than it was in 1960 but that the consumption of nuclear energy will be 100 to 1,000 per cent greater. In terms of energy, world reserves of uranium probably are greater than reserves of fossil fuels, and the cost of energy from this source may prove to be less than the average cost of energy from fossil fuels. Nuclear energy is likely to come not only from uranium but also from thorium, another unstable, radioactive element. Possibly it will come from still other elements as well.

For the longer future the most promising energy source is energy from the Sun—current energy, that is, not fossil energy—collected directly and concentrated at the Earth's surface.

When we consider the future of the western world's sources of materials for industry, we again find increasing use and increasing production. As we have seen, if iron, copper, and the other metals essential to our economy were distributed evenly throughout the Earth's crust, they would be irrecoverable, unminable. They can be recovered and used only from those few areas, trivial when compared with the area of the Earth, in which igneous activity, erosion and sedimentation, or some other geologic process has strongly concentrated them. When the existing phase of our industrial activity, marked by the consumption of stored-up concentrations of minerals begins to decline, as it inevitably will, man will have to look to materials of other kinds to supplant at least some of the metals now used to build machines and structures. The comparatively recent plastics industry, whose chief raw materials are petroleum, coal, and agricultural products, is an important step in that direction. It seems certain that chemists will play a large part in this future development. Whether their chief co-workers will be geologists or agriculturists, it is too soon to say.

SUMMARY

1. Ancient industry, based largely on wood and muscle, has given way to high-energy industry based mainly on fossil fuels and metals.

2. Coal originated as plant matter in ancient swamps and is both abundant and widely distributed.

3. Oil and gas probably originated as organic matter sedimented on sea floors and decomposed chemically. Later it moved through reservoir rocks and was caught in geologic traps to form pools.

4. Oil pools are found by the use of both geologic and geophysical methods. Of the latter the most useful is seismic surveying.

5. Nuclear energy is derived from atomic nuclei of unstable elements, chiefly uranium.

6. The mineral industry is based mainly on local concentrations of useful minerals, concentrated by natural processes far beyond their average abundance in the Earth's crust.

7. Most but not all ores are related directly or indirectly to magmas. The most numerous were deposited by hot water and gases moving outward from cooling magmas.

8. Many important iron ores were originally precipitated in ancient seas and probably later concentrated by ground-water removal of silica.

9. Secondary enrichment by weathering and ground water has been important in further concentrating many copper deposits.

10. Gold, platinum, tinstone, diamonds, and copper have been mechanically concentrated to form placers.

11. Geologic research, as distinct from conventional prospecting, will probably uncover many new ore deposits.

REFERENCES

Ayres, Eugene, and Scarlott, C. A., 1952, Energy sources—the wealth of the world: New York, McGraw-Hill Book Co.

Bateman, A. M., 1951 The formation of mineral deposits: New York, John Wiley and Sons.

Levorsen, A. I., 1956, Geology of petroleum: San Francisco, W. H. Freeman and Co.

Lovering, T. S., 1944, Minerals in world affairs: New York, Prentice-Hall.

McKinstry, H. E., 1948, Mining geology: Englewood Cliffs, N. J., Prentice-Hall.

Moore, E. S., 1940, Coal: New York, John Wiley and Sons.

Resources for freedom. A report to the President by The President's Materials Policy Commission: Washington, U. S. Govt. Printing Office, 1952. Vol. 2, The outlook for key commodities; vol. 3, The outlook for energy sources.

Van Royen, William, and Bowles, Oliver, 1952, Atlas of the world's resources, vol. II—The mineral resources of the world: Englewood Cliffs, N. J., Prentice-Hall.

Appendices

APPENDIX A. HOW TO IDENTIFY COMMON MINERALS

Minerals that are abundant in rocks or common as ores number only a few dozens, and most can be recognized without special equipment if sizable pieces are available. Each mineral species has peculiarities that appear on careful examination or by use of simple tests.

Special students of minerals, aided by technical equipment, learn to recognize hundreds of kinds. Some of the most common minerals are difficult to identify if they occur in very small grains scattered through a rock mass. Mineral laboratories are equipped for (1) examination with petrographic microscopes, by using thin sections (p. 30) or powder in special liquids, (2) photographing powdered material with an electron microscope, (3) X-ray analysis, and (4) chemical analysis. Such equipment is not always available and its use requires expert knowledge.

Physical properties

Form. Crystal form provides an excellent clue to the identity of a mineral. Evidence that a specimen belongs in one of the six crystal systems narrows by a large percentage the ground we must cover in tracking the mineral down. Usually the field is reduced much more because minerals within any system differ in their crystal habits. The cubes for which pyrite has a preference (Fig. 3–6, **A**, 2) the twelve-sided forms of garnet (Fig. 3–6, **A**, 3), and the eight-sided crystals common in magnetic iron ore are three different habits within the isometric system (p. 37).

The conditions favorable for perfect crystals are exceptional in nature; more commonly, the mineral grains in their growth crowd against and distort each other and the result is a granular mass. Some minerals take on characteristic forms not those of crystals. Asbestos is *fibrous* (Fig. A–1). Some ore minerals have *forms resembling grapes closely bunched*, described as *botryoidal* (bŏt-rĭ-ŏy′dăl; Fig. A–2). Several minerals are *micaceous*, that is, they form in thin sheets, and some iron ore is *earthy*, like crumbly soil. These habitual forms, once we have learned them, are very helpful in mineral identification.

Cleavage and fracture. The atomic structure of many minerals results in cleavage, a tendency to separate along planes in one or more directions. These planes are parallel to certain crystal faces and intersect others, provided these faces have formed (Fig. A–3). Even if a mineral occurs in irregular grains, with no recognizable crystal faces, the grains will break along cleavage planes characteristic of the mineral. Cleavage, then, is a real aid in identifying some minerals (p. 29).

The atomic structure of some minerals does not favor separation along plane surfaces. Certain minerals break with *uneven* or *irregular* fracture; others have *conchoidal* (kŏn-koi′dăl) *fracture, breakage resulting in surfaces that are curved like a clam shell* (Fig. B–3). Another type of fracture is *splintery*, like that of wood.

Color. The color of some minerals is a definite and constant property and therefore an aid to identification, provided we are dealing with fresh surfaces. Exposure to weather or to circulating ground water may change the color appreciably. Furthermore, many isomorphous minerals (p. 470) vary in color with change in composition, and others are given a wide range in color by inclusion of various impurities. Therefore caution is required in using this method of identification.

Streak. The *streak* is *a thin layer of powdered mineral made by rubbing a specimen on an unglazed porcelain plate.* The powder diffuses light and gives a color effect that for a given mineral may be quite different from the color of the specimen as a unit. For many minerals the streak is white and has no diagnostic value; for others, especially those with high content of metals, the streak is distinctive and helpful in identification.

Luster. *The quality and intensity of light reflected from a mineral* produce an effect known as **luster.** Two minerals with almost the same color can have totally different lusters. The more important are described as *metallic*, like that on a polished metal surface; *vitreous*, like that on glass; *resinous*, like that of yellow resin; *pearly*, like that of pearl; *greasy*, as if

Fig. A–1. Asbestos, a variety of serpentine, occurs in closely packed fibers. It separates into fine, cottony threads which are woven in manufacture of fireproof fabric.

Fig. A–2. This specimen of psilomelane has typical botryoidal form. It consists chiefly of hydrous manganese oxide and is common in manganese ore.

A

B

Fig. A–3. A. This crystal of orthoclase will break with one perfect cleavage parallel to the face *c,* a less perfect cleavage parallel to face *b.* **B.** In this cleavage fragment of orthoclase, which came from a crystal larger than *A,* cleavage planes on the side *c'* correspond to the crystal face *c,* those on side *b'* correspond to the crystal face *b.* All other fracture surfaces are irregular.

469

the surface were covered with a film of oil; and *adamantine,* having the brilliance of a diamond.

Hardness. Comparative *resistance to scratching,* or *hardness,* is one of the most noticeable ways in which minerals differ. A series of 10 minerals has been chosen as a standard scale, and any unknown specimen can be classified, 1 to 10, by trying it against the known specimens in the scale, which are arranged in order of increasing hardness as follows:

1. Talc	6. Orthoclase
2. Gypsum	7. Quartz
3. Calcite	8. Topaz
4. Fluorite	9. Corundum
5. Apatite	10. Diamond

Fractional values of hardness are common. If a specimen scratches calcite but is distinctly scratched by fluorite, the approximate value of its hardness is 3.5. This is only an approximation. With suitable equipment, values of hardness are found to small fractions of a point.

Several precautions are necessary in making tests. mineral softer than another may leave a mark that looks like a scratch, just as a soft pencil leaves its mark. A real scratch can not be rubbed off. The physical structure of some minerals may make the hardness test difficult; if a specimen is powdery or in fine grains or if it breaks easily into splinters, an apparent scratch may be deceptive.

If a hardness scale is not available, rough tests can be made by using the finger nail as 2.5, a copper coin as 3.5, and the blade of a pocket knife or a piece of ordinary glass as 5.5.

Specific gravity. In comparing unit weights, we use water as a standard. The *specific gravity* of any substance is expressed as *a number stating the ratio of the weight of the substance to the weight of an equal volume of pure water at 4°C.* Most minerals range between 2 and 4 in specific gravity, but some exceed 10 and platinum exceeds 20.

A Jolly balance or a delicate spring scale can be used for accurate determinations. With a little practice, rather small differences in specific gravity can be detected by comparing pieces of different minerals held in the hand.

Other tests. Some minerals have unusual properties that serve to distinguish them. One of the iron oxides is attracted to a magnet. A few minerals have on crystal faces or on cleavage surfaces fine parallel lines that indicate peculiar habits of growth. Dilute hydrochloric acid applied to some mineral surfaces or to the powdered mineral starts a bubbling that indicates chemical reaction. Several other tests that single out certain minerals require equipment that is not readily available.

Use of the mineral table. Among the minerals in Table A–1 more than half are abundant in the rocks of the Earth's crust. Others are important in ore deposits. Some are so distinctive they are easily recognized, but others require careful study. Some of them have definite and fairly simple chemical composition, but several that are isomorphous and contain a number of elements can be defined by chemical symbols in a general way only. This is particularly true of several silicate minerals that are abundant in common rocks. For example, the plagioclase feldspars are a group in which the elements sodium and calcium replace each other in all proportions. Only for the two "end members," one lacking calcium, the other lacking sodium, can we write chemical formulas that are simple and definite. The amphibole and pyroxene groups are solid solutions with varying proportions of several elements. Both groups are known as "ferromagnesian silicates" because iron and magnesium are prominent in both groups.

Generalized formulas for the solid-solution silicates use three symbols to designate elements with differing ionic radii (see Fig. 3–7). Thus in several formulas given in Table A–1

A = elements with large ionic radius, such as K, Ca, Na

B = elements with intermediate radius, such as Mg, Fe″, Fe‴, Al‴

C = elements with small radius, mainly Si, Al

Valences are shown by the symbols ′, ″, ‴.

Because silica is abundant in quartz and related minerals, these common oxides are listed alphabetically with the common silicates.

Chemical compositions are given in the table as a matter of interest, not as an aid to making identifications. Each laboratory specimen should be examined closely for critical physical properties. Its place in the table may be located by a process of elimination.

TABLE A–1. PROPERTIES OF SOME IMPORTANT MINERALS

(For explanation of A, B, C in chemical formulas, see text on facing page.)

Mineral	Chemical composition	Form	Cleavage	Luster	Hardness	Specific gravity	Other properties

1. Common silicates and oxides

Mineral	Chemical composition	Form	Cleavage	Luster	Hardness	Specific gravity	Other properties
Amphibole (complex group of minerals, *hornblende* most common)	Silicates of Ca, Mg, Fe, Al, Na. General formula: $A_{2-3}B_5C_8O_{22}(OH)_2$	In long, 6-sided crystals; also in fibers and irregular grains	Two, intersecting at 56 and 124° (Fig. A–4, **B**)	Vitreous on cleavage surfaces	5 to 6	2.9 to 3.8	Commonly black, dark and light green; rarely white
Biotite (black mica, "trioctahedral mica")	Complex silicate of K, Mg, Fe, Al. General formula: $AB_3C_4O_{10}(OH)_2$	In perfect thin flakes; 6-sided crystals	One cleavage direction; uniform flakes or sheets	Pearly to nearly vitreous	2.5 to 3	2.8 to 3.2	Black, dark brown, or green; nearly or quite opaque; flakes are flexible *and elastic*
Chlorite	Variable silicate of Mg, Fe, Al. General formula: $B_3C_4O_{10}(OH)_2 \cdot B_3(OH)_6$	In flaky masses or 6-sided crystals	One perfect cleavage	Greasy to vitreous	2 to 2.5	2.6 to 3	Light to dark green; flakes are weak, *inelastic*, easily separated
Epidote	Variable silicate of Ca, Fe, Al. General formula: $Ca_2B_3'''(SiO_4)_3(OH)$	In small prismatic crystals; also fibrous	One perfect cleavage, another imperfect	Vitreous	6 to 7	About 3.4	Yellow-green to blackish-green; commonly associated with chlorite
Garnet (complex group)	Isomorphous silicates of Ca, Mg, Fe, Mn, Al. General formula: $A,B'')_3B_2'''(SiO_4)_3$	Commonly in perfect crystals with 12 or 24 sides; also granular masses	None; fracture conchoidal or uneven	Vitreous to resinous	6.5 to 7.5	3.5 to 4.3	Color varies with composition; red, brown, yellow, green to almost black
Kaolinite (common clay mineral)	$Al_2Si_2O_5(OH)_4$	Soft, earthy masses. Crystals photographed with electron microscope	One perfect cleavage, submicroscopic	Dull	2 to 2.5	About 2.6	White if pure, usually stained yellow or other colors; plastic; has clay odor
Kyanite	Al_2SiO_5	In groups of blade-like crystals	One good, another imperfect	Vitreous to pearly	4 to 5 parallel to crystal, 7 across crystal	3.5 to 3.7	White, pale blue, or green; occurs in metamorphic rocks; compare with sillimanite
Muscovite (white mica, "dioctahedral mica")	Variable silicate of K, Al. General formula: $AB_2C_4O_{10}(OH)_2$	In uniform thin flakes; rarely in 6-sided crystals	One cleavage direction; perfect flakes or sheets (Fig. 3–5)	Vitreous to pearly	2 to 2.5	2.7 to 3	Colorless and transparent when pure but commonly greenish and mottled; flakes are flexible *and elastic*
Olivine	Varied proportions of Fe, Mg. General formula: $B_2''SiO_4$	In small grains or granular masses	None; conchoidal fracture	Vitreous	6.5 to 7	3.2 to 4.4	Olive green to yellow-green; transparent to translucent
Plagioclase feldspars (Na-Ca feldspars)	$NaAlSi_3O_8$(albite) to $CaAl_2Si_2O_8$ (anorthite) General formula: AC_4O_8	Commonly as irregular grains or cleavable masses; some varieties in thin plates	Two good cleavages, not quite at right angles	Vitreous to pearly	6 to 6.5	2.6 to 2.7	White to dark gray and also other colors; some cleavage planes show fine parallel lines; play of colors in some varieties

Mineral	Chemical composition	Form	Cleavage	Luster	Hardness	Specific gravity	Other properties
Potassium feldspars (orthoclase, microcline, and sanidine)	$KAlSi_3O_8$	In prismatic crystals (Fig. A–3) or grains with cleavage	Two good cleavages, at right angles	Vitreous	6	2.5 to 2.6	Commonly flesh-colored, pink, or gray; one variety green
Pyroxene (complex group, *augite* and *hypersthene* most common)	Silicates of Ca, Fe, Mg, Na, Al. General formula: ABC_2O_6	In 8-sided, stubby crystals; also in granular masses	Two cleavages, nearly at right angles	Vitreous	5 to 6	3.2 to 3.9	Light to dark green, or black; alternate crystal faces at right angles (fit into corner of a box)
Quartz	SiO_2	Six-sided crystals, pyramids at ends; also in irregular grains and masses	None; conchoidal fracture	Vitreous to greasy	7	2.65	Varies from colorless and transparent to opaque with wide range of colors
Chalcedony (crypto-crystalline quartz)	SiO_2	No visible crystals; commonly banded or in formless masses	None; conchoidal fracture	Dull	6 to 6.5	2.6	White if pure; variously colored by impurities
Opal (hydrous silica)	$SiO_2 \cdot nH_2O$	Amorphous; in irregular masses	None; conchoidal fracture	Waxy to vitreous	5 to 6.5	2.1 to 2.3	Various colors; translucent to opaque

Note: Other common varieties of silica, most of them containing impurities, are agate, flint, chert, and jasper.

Mineral	Chemical composition	Form	Cleavage	Luster	Hardness	Specific gravity	Other properties
Serpentine (fibrous variety is *asbestos*)	Variable silicate of Mg, with (OH). General formula: $B_6C_4O_{10}(OH)_8$	Massive or fibrous	Usually breaks irregularly, except in the fibrous variety	Greasy or resinous	2.5 to 5	2.5 to 2.65	Light to dark green; smooth, greasy feel; translucent to opaque
Sillimanite	Al_2SiO_5	In long crystals or in fibers	Perfect in one direction	Vitreous	6 to 7	3.2	White to greenish-gray; found in high-grade metamorphic rocks; compare with kyanite
Staurolite	$Al_4Fe''(SiO_4)_2(OH)_2O_2$	Stubby crystals, commonly twinned in form of cross	Distinct in one direction	Vitreous to resinous	7 to 7.5	3.7 to 3.8	Red-brown to nearly black; associated with sillimanite, kyanite, garnet
Talc	$Mg_3(OH)_2Si_4O_{10}$	In small scales and compact masses	One perfect cleavage	Greasy, pearly	1	2.8	White to greenish; has greasy feel

2. Common carbonates, chlorides, and sulfates

Mineral	Chemical composition	Form	Cleavage	Luster	Hardness	Specific gravity	Other properties
Barite	$BaSO_4$	Crystals tabular or prismatic	Two perfect, one imperfect	Vitreous to pearly	2.5 to 3.5	4.3 to 4.6	Translucent to opaque
Calcite	$CaCO_3$	In tapering crystals, or granular form	Three perfect, at oblique angles	Vitreous to dull	3	2.7	Colorless or white; effervesces in dilute HCl

Mineral	Chemical composition	Form	Cleavage	Luster	Hardness	Specific gravity	Other properties
Dolomite	$CaMg(CO_3)_2$	In crystals with rhomb-shaped faces; also in granular masses	Perfect in three directions, as in calcite	Vitreous to pearly	3.5 to 4	2.8 to 2.9	White, gray, or flesh-colored; some crystals have curved faces; must be scratched or powdered to effervesce in cold dilute HCl
Gypsum	$CaSO_4 \cdot 2 H_2O$	In tabular, diamond-shaped crystals; also granular, fibrous, or earthy	One perfect cleavage, two imperfect	Vitreous to pearly	2	2.3	Usually white or colorless, transparent or translucent; cleavage plates flexible, *inelastic*
Halite (rock salt, common salt)	NaCl	In cubic crystals or granular masses	Perfect in three directions at right angles	Vitreous	2.5	2.1	Colorless or white when pure, transparent to translucent; strong salty taste

3. Ore minerals

Mineral	Chemical composition	Form	Cleavage	Luster	Hardness	Specific gravity	Other properties
Azurite	$Cu_3(CO_3)_2(OH)_2$	In crystals, in form of stalactites, in formless masses, or earthy	One perfect, another imperfect	Vitreous	3.5 to 4	3.7 to 3.8	In upper zone of copper deposits; generally with malachite and limonite; secondary ore mineral of copper; blue
Bauxite	Mixture of hydrous aluminum oxides	In earthy, clay-like masses; also in small spherical forms	None; uneven fracture	Dull, earthy	1 to 3	2 to 3	Product of tropical weathering; has strong clayish odor
Carnotite	$K_2(UO_2)(VO_4)_2 \cdot 3H_2O$	Earthy powder	Not visible	Earthy	Very soft	4 to 4.7	Occurs in powdery form, with brilliant canary-yellow color; ore of vanadium and uranium
Cassiterite (tinstone)	SnO_2	Granular masses; well-formed crystals common; rounded pebbles in stream gravels	Two, indistinct; conchoidal fracture	Adamantine to dull	6 to 7	6.8 to 7	Yellow to red-brown; principal ore of tin, in part from placer deposits
Chalcocite	Cu_2S	Usually massive, fine-grained; crystals rare	None; conchoidal fracture	Metallic	2.5 to 3	5.5 to 5.8	Steel-gray to black; dark gray streak; an ore of copper
Chalcopyrite	$CuFeS_2$	Massive or granular	None; uneven fracture	Metallic	3.5 to 4	4.1 to 4.3	Golden yellow to brassy color; streak dark green to black; an ore of copper
Cinnabar	HgS	In veins; also in disseminated grains	One perfect cleavage	Adamantine to dull	2 to 2.5	8.1	Red to red-brown; scarlet streak; chief ore mineral of mercury
Copper (native)	Cu	Forms of twisted leaves and wires; also irregular nodules	None; hackly fracture	Dull-metallic	2.5 to 3	8.9	Not now common as an ore; copper color, but commonly stained green; ductile and malleable

Mineral	Chemical composition	Form	Cleavage	Luster	Hardness	Specific gravity	Other properties
Diamond	C	In octahedral or cubic crystals; faces commonly curved	Good, in four directions	Adamantine to greasy	10	3.5	Used as abrasive; now a synthetic as well as natural product; high-quality stones used as gems
Galena	PbS	In cubic crystals and granular masses, coarse- or fine-grained	Perfect in three directions at right angles	Bright metallic	2.5	7.6	Lead-gray color; streak gray to gray-black; common ore of lead; in many deposits it contains silver
Gold (native)	Au	Massive or in thin irregular scales	None; hackly fracture	Metallic	2.5 to 3	19.3	Quite malleable; commonly scattered in quartz veins; nuggets occur in stream gravels
Graphite	C	In scaly masses	Perfect, in flakes	Metallic to dull	1 to 2	2 to 2.3	Gray to nearly black; black streak; greasy feel; high melting point
Hematite	Fe_2O_3	Varied: massive, granular, micaceous, earthy	None, uneven fracture	Metallic to earthy	5 to 6	4.9 to 5.3	Red-brown, gray, to black; red-brown streak; most important ore of iron
Limonite (impure oxide)	Mixture of several hydrous oxides of iron	Compact to earthy masses; irregular nodules	None, irregular fracture	Dull to vitreous	1 to 5.5	3.5 to 4	Yellow, brown, black; streak yellow-brown; an ore of iron
Magnetite	Fe_3O_4	Varied: massive, granular	None, uneven fracture	Metallic	5.5 to 6.5	5 to 5.2	Black and opaque; black streak; strongly attracted to a magnet; important ore of iron
Malachite	$Cu_2(CO_3)(OH)_2$	Rarely in crystals; massive, with mammillary forms on surface	One perfect, another fair	Silky to dull	3.5 to 4	3.6 to 4	In upper zone of copper deposits generally with azurite, commonly with limonite; secondary ore mineral of copper; green
Pyrite ("fool's gold")	FeS_2	In cubic crystals with striated faces; commonly massive	None, uneven fracture	Metallic	6 to 6.5	4.9 to 5.2	Pale brass-yellow, darker if tarnished; streak greenish-black; widely distributed; used in manufacture of sulfuric acid
Pyrolusite	MnO_2	Rarely in crystals; in coatings on fracture surfaces; commonly in concretions	Crystals have one perfect cleavage	Metallic to dull	2 to 6.5	4.5 to 5	Dark gray or bluish; black streak; important ore mineral of manganese
Rutile	TiO_2	In slender prismatic crystals or granular masses	Good in one direction; has conchoidal fracture	Adamantine to metallic	6 to 6.5	4.2	Red-brown to black; streak brownish to gray-black; abundant in some beach sands; ore of titanium

Mineral	Chemical composition	Form	Cleavage	Luster	Hardness	Specific Gravity	Other properties
Silver (native)	Ag	In flakes and irregular grains	None; hackly fracture	Bright metallic to dull	2.5 to 3	10 to 11	Generally tarnished to dark-gray; cleans to silvery-white; ductile and malleable
Sphalerite (zinc blende)	ZnS	Fine- to coarse-granular masses; crystals common	Six directions	Resinous to adamantine	3.5 to 4	3.9 to 4.1	Color yellow-brown to black; streak white to yellow or brown; principal ore of zinc
Uraninite (pitchblende)	UO_2 to U_3O_8	Massive, with botryoidal forms; crystals cubic or 8-sided	None, uneven fracture	Submetallic to dull	5 to 6	6.5 to 10	Black to dark brown; streak has similar color; a source of uranium and radium

4. Supplementary group, important in scale of hardness

Mineral	Chemical composition	Form	Cleavage	Luster	Hardness	Specific Gravity	Other properties
Apatite	$Ca_5(PO_4)_3(F,Cl,OH)$	In granular masses or as large crystals	Poor, in one direction	Vitreous	5	3.1 to 3.2	Green, blue, violet, brown; accessory mineral in many kinds of rock, especially in crystalline limestones
Corundum (ruby, sapphire)	Al_2O_3	In separate crystals or in granular masses	Two good cleavages, with striations on planes	Adamantine to vitreous	9	About 4	Blue, red, yellow-brown, green-violet; valuable as an abrasive (emery) and as gems
Fluorite	CaF_2	In well-formed crystals and in granular masses	**Good cleavage in four directions**	Vitreous	4	3.2	Colorless, green, blue, or nearly black; commonly in veins with lead and silver ores; also in cavities in limestone and dolostone
Topaz	$Al_2SiO_4(OH,F)_2$	In prismatic crystals; also in granular masses	One perfect cleavage	Vitreous	8	3.5 to 3.6	Colorless to shades of blue, yellow, or brown; found in some pegmatites and quartz veins

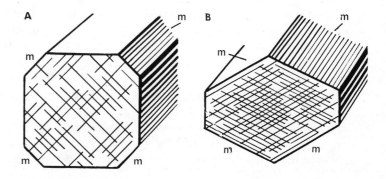

Fig. A–4. A. This pyroxene crystal cut at right angles to its long axis shows two directions of cleavage, each parallel to two faces marked *m* and intersecting the other faces. B. In a crystal of amphibole the two cleavages intersect at oblique angles. Each cleavage is parallel to two faces marked *m*.

APPENDIX B. IDENTIFICATION OF COMMON ROCKS

The three major classes of rocks (igneous, sedimentary, metamorphic) are defined in Chapter 3 and explained with more detail in Chapters 6, 17, and 19. In each class are many distinct kinds, with specific names. Fortunately, fewer than 30 in all make up the great bulk of the visible part of the Earth's crust. These common kinds must be learned well if we are to read correctly the history recorded in the crust. By studying representative specimens of all the important kinds, we can learn the properties some have in common and the distinctive features by which each kind is identified.

Ideally, we should see each specimen in the field as part of an outcrop in which the larger features and relations are clearly shown. The stratification of sandstone or limestone (Fig. 4–1) and the intrusive relation of a dike (Fig. 6–24) tell us at once that the rock is sedimentary or igneous. Some hand specimens in a laboratory may not have clear indications of their general classification. But any systematic description of the common rocks lists them according to class, and we welcome any clue that may tell us at the start whether an unknown specimen is igneous, sedimentary, or metamorphic. A number of such clues are found with practice, and even without them a specimen can ordinarily be traced quickly to its class by a process of elimination.

Texture. We examine a rock specimen closely for the pattern of visible constituents, just as we inspect the weave (texture) in cloth. Many rocks have visible mineral grains, and if these can be made out with the unaided eye over the entire surface the rock has *granular texture* (Fig. B–1), *coarse* if the average grains are as large as peas, and *fine* if the average is about that in granulated sugar. If the grains are so small they can be seen only with the aid of a magnifying glass, the texture is *aphanitic* (p. 39). Some igneous rocks have *glassy* texture; the cooling from magma was too rapid for any grains to form.

Many igneous rocks are porphyritic, with distinct phenocrysts (Fig. 3–15); this proves igneous origin. Certain textures, then, tell us the general classification of some rock specimens as a first step toward their identification.

In examining texture, we are interested not only in the size of grains but also in their shapes and the way they fit together. If the grains are angular and dovetail one into another to fill all the space, they must have been formed by crystallization, and the rock is probably either igneous or metamorphic. If the grains are separated by irregular spaces filled with fine cementing material, probably they are fragments and the rock may be of either sedimentary or volcanic origin.

Mineral composition. Many rocks are identified by their component minerals. The critical minerals are determined by their physical properties, as explained in Appendix A. Grains large enough for clear visibility are required for study without a microscope. A hand lens that magnifies 8 or 10 times is a useful aid in studying the mineral grains, even in coarse-textured rocks.

Other properties. Some limestones look superficially like aphanitic igneous rocks but are much softer. Every rock specimen under study should be tested for hardness.

Some kinds of rocks show characteristic forms on fracture surfaces (Fig. B–3). Other tests are mentioned in the descriptions of specific rocks.

This appendix is devoted chiefly to critical features of igneous rocks. The principal kinds of sedimentary and metamorphic rocks are described briefly in Chapter 3, and in the study of hand specimens reference should be made to pages 41–47 and to Table 17–1, a classification of sedimentary rocks. Short tables of sedimentary and metamorphic rocks (Tables B–2, B–3) are included here to supplement descriptions on foregoing pages.

Table of igneous rocks

In an introductory study igneous rocks can be classified more systematically than others, and details required for satisfactory analysis of laboratory specimens are here separated from the general treatment in the body of the book. Table B–1 supplements Figure 3–17, and the two can be used together with profit. Igneous rocks are grouped in the table according to (1) texture and (2) composition. All rocks in the same horizontal column are alike in texture; those in the same vertical column are generally alike in chemical composition. Any classification for use with hand specimens must be general, and the number of names in the table is reduced to a minimum.

Nature does not draw sharp boundaries, and there are all conceivable gradations in texture and composition. The separating lines in the table, therefore, are somewhat fictitious. We can find a series of specimens that will bridge the gaps in composition between granite and granodiorite, granodiorite and diorite, as in Figure B–2. The few grains of quartz in the specimen between the granodiorite and dior-

ite compartments may be so faint that they will be overlooked; identification as diorite will then be unquestioned. On the border between granite porphyry and rhyolite porphyry small areas of the groundmass may appear aphanitic to one observer and not to another.

In the scheme of the table the minerals of igneous rocks are divided generally into a light-colored group (including the feldspars, quartz, and muscovite) and a dark-colored group (including dark mica, py-

Fig. B–1. In granite all essential minerals are visible. The grains fit snugly together, with angular contacts. The texture is described as *granular*.

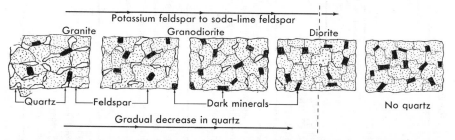

Fig. B–2. There is almost insensible gradation in mineral composition from granite through granodiorite to diorite. The change from dominance of potassium feldspar in granite to soda-lime feldspars accompanies the decrease in content of quartz. (See Fig. 3–17.)

Decreasing content of silica →

Increasing content of ferromagnesian minerals →

Transition from potassium feldspars to soda-lime feldspars →

SUBDIVISIONS BASED ON MINERAL COMPOSITION

DIVISIONS BASED ON TEXTURES	Light-colored minerals, chiefly feldspars, predominant			Dark minerals predominant	Chiefly dark minerals	
Granular, grains nearly uniform in size	**Granite** (largely potassium feldspar, much quartz)	**Granodiorite** (largely plagioclase feldspars, quartz declining)	**Diorite** (plagioclase feldspar, no quartz)	**Gabbro** (coarse-granular) / **Dolerite** (fine-granular)	**Peridotite** (chiefly pyroxene and olivine) / **Pyroxenite** (chiefly pyroxene)	**Dunite** (chiefly olivine)
Granular, with many phenocrysts	**Granite porphyry,** porphyritic granite (much quartz)	**Granodiorite porphyry,** porphyritic granodiorite (less quartz)	**Diorite porphyry,** porphyritic diorite (no quartz)	**Gabbro porphyry, Dolerite porphyry** (not common)		
Aphanitic ground mass, with many phenocrysts	**Rhyolite porphyry** (has quartz)		**Andesite porphyry** (no quartz)	**Basalt porphyry** (not common)	Porphyritic, aphanitic, and glassy textures rare with these compositions	
Aphanitic, phenocrysts rare or absent	**Rhyolite** (has quartz)		**Andesite** (no quartz)	**Basalt**		
Glassy	**Obsidian** (compact glass, vitreous) **Pitchstone** (has dull, greasy luster) **Pumice** (frothy, lightweight, nearly white)					
Pyroclastic	**Volcanic tuff** (cemented volcanic ash) **Volcanic breccia** (cemented coarse volcanic fragments)					

← Decreasing size of grain

TABLE B–2. AIDS IN IDENTIFICATION OF SEDIMENTARY ROCKS
(See Table 17–1)

Rock name	Essential composition	Critical tests
1. Clastic sedimentary rocks		
Conglomerate	Cemented particles, somewhat rounded, considerable percentage of pebble size	Larger particles more than 2 mm. in diameter; smaller particles and binding cement in interstices
Breccia	Fragments conspicuously angular, with binding cement	Large particles of pebble size or larger
Sandstone	Rounded fragments of sand size, 0.02 to 2 mm.; binding cement	Grains commonly quartz, but other rock materials qualify in general classification
Arkose	Important percentage of feldspar grains, sand size or larger	Essential that feldspar grains make 25 per cent or more of rock; some may be larger than sand size
Graywacke	Fragments of quartz, feldspar, rock fragments of any kind, with considerable clay	Poor assortment of several kinds of ingredients, with considerable clay in matrix
Siltstone	Chiefly silt particles, some clay	Surface is slightly gritty to feel
Shale	Chiefly clay minerals	Surface has smooth feel, no grit apparent
2. Rocks of organic and chemical origin		
Limestone	Calcite; may be aphanitic or crystalline	Easily scratched with knife; effervesces in cold dilute HCl
Dolostone	Dolomite; may be aphanitic or crystalline	Harder than limestone, softer than steel; requires scratching or powdering for effervescence in cold dilute HCl
Peat	Obvious fragments of plant materials	
Bituminous coal	Black carbon, layered, blocky	Scratches easily, makes black streak
Salt deposits	Halite, gypsum	See Table A–1

TABLE B–3. AIDS IN IDENTIFICATION OF METAMORPHIC ROCKS

Rock name	Distinguishing characteristics
1. Foliated metamorphic rocks	
Slate	Cleaves into thin, plane plates that have considerable luster; commonly the stratification planes of parent shale make lines on plates; thin slabs ring when they are tapped sharply
Phyllite	Surfaces of plates highly lustrous; plates commonly wrinkled or sharply bent; grains of garnets and other minerals on some plates
Schist	Well foliated, with visible flaky or elongate minerals (mica, chlorite, hornblende); quartz a prominent ingredient; grains of garnet and other accessory minerals common; foliae may be wrinkled
Gneiss	Generally coarse-grained, with imperfect but conspicuous foliation; lenses and layers differ in mineral composition; feldspar, quartz, and mica are common ingredients
2. Nonfoliated metamorphic rocks	
Quartzite	Consists wholly of quartz sand cemented with quartz; outlines of sand grains show on broken surfaces, the breaks passing through the grains; wide range in shades of color
Marble	Wholly crystallized limestone or dolostone; grain varies from coarse to fine; responds to hydrochloric acid test, as do calcite and dolomite; accessory minerals have developed from impurities in original rock
Hornfels	Hard, massive, fine-grained rock, commonly with scattered grains or crystals of garnet, kyanite, staurolite, or other minerals that are common in zones of contact metamorphism

roxene, hornblende, and olivine). As noted previously (p. 41), the light-colored igneous minerals have a high content of silica, whereas the dark-colored ones are lower in silica. Quartz grains in an igneous rock indicate a surplus of silica in the parent magma (p. 40); therefore the presence or absence of quartz grains is a logical basis for drawing a line between granitic rocks and diorite. In the rocks that have no quartz the feldspars divide honors with the dark-colored minerals, and the boundary between diorite and gabbro is drawn where the dark minerals exceed 50 per cent of the total. This boundary is carried through between andesite and basalt on the basis of color. Inspecting thin edges of specimens in strong light is the best test; andesite transmits some of the light, basalt is opaque.

In one respect the table may appear upside down. The coarse-grained rocks, such as granite, are formed deep in the crust, where slow cooling favors crystal growth; the fine-granular and porphyritic rocks are most abundant at shallow depths; the aphanitic and glassy rocks are chiefly volcanic products, chilled quickly on the Earth's surface. Arrangement of the table with fine textures at the top and progressively coarser textures downward would therefore seem logical. But the coarse-grained rocks make the most complete series and are most satisfactory for general study because their mineral composition is on full display. This standard series is a control for the table and serves its purpose best in the top position. If this is kept in mind, the general differences in texture in any column of the table will be readily understood. The same magma would produce granite with slow cooling deep in the crust and rhyolite with rapid cooling in a lava flow. In the same way, diorite is the deep-seated equivalent of andesitic lava, gabbro of basaltic lava. With exceptionally rapid chilling, all three kinds of magma produce glassy lavas, and in explosive eruptions they produce volcanic ash and cinders.

Kinds of igneous rocks

Granite. Feldspar and quartz are the chief minerals in granite. Some biotite usually is present, and many granites have scattered grains of hornblende. The dark minerals commonly are in nearly perfect crystals; this suggests that they formed first, while most of the mass was molten. The feldspar formed next, and the grains crowded against and hampered each other in growth. Quartz, the surplus silica, crystallized last and so is molded around the angular grains of the earlier minerals. This *interlocking arrangement of visible mineral grains* is *characteristic of granite* and is called **granular texture** (Fig. B–1).

Technically, the term granite is applied only to quartz-bearing rocks in which potassium feldspar is predominant, and the name *granodiorite* applies to similar rocks in which plagioclase is the chief feldspar. Without special equipment, the differences in feldspars are not easily recognized, and in a general study the term granite commonly is extended to this whole group of rocks. We sometimes recognize the variation in mineral composition by speaking of the *granitic rocks*. They are widespread in all the continents.

A special kind of granite is *granite* **pegmatite,** or "giant granite," which *has abnormally large grains*. Quarries in pegmatite produce in commercial quantities large sheets of mica and minerals that yield the valuable elements lithium and beryllium (p. 39).

Diorite. In *diorite* the chief mineral is feldspar, mainly plagioclase, though this may not be evident to the unaided eye. Generally the dark minerals are more abundant than in granite. Diorite forms many large masses, but it is not nearly so abundant as granitic rocks.

Gabbro. Dark diorite grades into *gabbro* as the dark minerals exceed 50 per cent of the rock and plagioclase becomes subordinate. The chief dark mineral in gabbro is pyroxene, commonly with some olivine. These minerals are heavier than feldspar, and gabbro is distinctly heavier than granite and average diorite.

Dolerite is fine-grained, intermediate in texture between gabbro and basalt.

Pyroxenite and peridotite. As the dark minerals displace plagioclase entirely, we reach the extreme in composition from that of granite. A granular rock composed almost entirely of pyroxene is *pyroxenite* (pī-rŏx′ĕn-īte). If considerable olivine is present with the pyroxene, the rock is *peridotite* (pĕr′ĭ-dō-tīte). Both these rocks are very dark and heavy and both are commonly associated with ores containing the metals nickel, platinum, and iron. In many masses the pyroxene and olivine have been altered to serpentine, probably by hot water and gases from underlying magma.

A rock consisting almost wholly of the mineral olivine is *dunite* (dŭn′īte; named for Mount Dun, New Zealand). It is not common in exposures at the Earth's surface, but it has particular interest because it is probably the dominant type of rock beneath the Earth's crust (p. 410).

Porphyritic rocks. Both granular and aphanitic igneous rocks commonly have prominent phenocrysts (Fig. 3–15). If these larger grains make up less than about 25 per cent of the rock mass, we say that the rock is porphyritic and give it the name suited to its groundmass (e.g., *porphyritic granite, porphyritic diorite. porphyritic andesite*). If the proportion of phenocrysts is more than 25 per cent, we call the rock a *porphyry* and combine this term with the name that is proper for the groundmass (e.g., *granite porphyry, diorite porphyry, rhyolite porphyry*).

Rhyolite. An aphanitic rock with phenocrysts of quartz is *rhyolite*. The quartz indicates an excess of silica and therefore a close chemical kinship to granite. Rhyolites usually have phenocrysts of feldspar and biotite as well. Colors of the groundmass range from nearly white through shades of gray, yellow, red or purple. Rhyolite commonly has irregular bands made by flowage of stiff magma shortly before it became solid.

Andesite. An aphanitic rock generally similar to rhyolite but lacking the quartz phenocrysts is *andesite*. Usually it has phenocrysts of feldspar and dark minerals. Common colors are shades of gray and green, but some andesites are very dark, even black. Freshly broken, thin edges of dark andesites transmit some light and appear almost white when held before a bright source of light. In this way they are distinguished from basalt, which is opaque even on thin edges. The lighter-colored andesites commonly have irregular banding similar to that of rhyolite.

Andesite is extremely abundant as a volcanic rock, especially around the margins of the Pacific Ocean. The name comes from the Andes of South America.

Basalt. *Basalt* (bă-sält′) is an aphanitic rock that appears dark even on freshly broken thin edges. Common colors are black, dark brown or green, and very dark gray. In the upper parts of lava flows the rock generally is *vesicular*—filled with small openings or *vesicles* made by escaping gases. In many flows these openings have been filled with calcite, quartz, or some other mineral deposited from solution (Fig. 3–16).

Glassy rocks. Quick chilling of magma forms natural glass. *Obsidian* is the highly lustrous kind, and a similar rock is *pitchstone,* which has a dull, greasy luster probably because of somewhat slower cooling. Both kinds of glass produce conchoidal patterns when they are broken (Fig. B–3).

Clear natural glass is not unknown, but most obsidians appear dark, even black. Because many of them correspond in chemical composition to rhyolite and granite, they seem to contradict the rule that rocks with high content of silica are light-colored. But obsidian chipped to a thin edge appears white, even transparent. The dark coloring results from a small content of dark mineral matter distributed evenly in the glass.

Pumice (pŭm′ĭs) is glass froth, full of cavities made by gases escaping through stiff, rapidly cooling magma. Because many of these cavities are small winding tubes, some of them sealed, pumice will float on water for a long time. As the thin walls of the cavities transmit light, pumice is almost white, though it may form the cap of a black sheet of obsidian.

Fig. B–3. Perfect examples of conchoidal fracture are common in broken volcanic glass.

481

Basalt glass forms in the outer parts of some basaltic flows. It is opaque, like ordinary basalt, but has glassy luster.

Pyroclastic rocks. *Volcanic ash,* the fine debris from explosive eruptions, becomes consolidated to form tuff (p. 40). Commonly, the particles of magma are made into froth by the expanding gas, and therefore the flakes making up an ash deposit are in large part pumice, mixed with pieces of older bedrock blasted from the walls of the vent.

The particles of ash in a nuée ardente, similar to those from Mount Pelée (p. 87), are very hot, and when the fast-moving cloud spreads the material in a thick sheet the temperature is high enough to cause partial remelting. *A glassy or aphanitic rock formed by fusion of volcanic ash during deposition is* **welded tuff.** Some natural glasses are now known to be welded tuffs instead of chilled lava flows. Volcanic rocks in southeastern Arizona that strongly resemble flows of rhyolite are now recognized as welded tuffs.

With increase in size of particles, tuff grades into *volcanic breccia* (p. 40). Some breccias made by volcanic explosions contain blocks up to many feet or even tens of feet long. In addition to explosion breccias, many *flow breccias* are *made by the breaking up of* the *solidified lava above and in front of the moving lower part of an active flow* (Fig. 6–1, **A**).

Many volcanic tuffs and breccias are stratified and look much like sedimentary rocks. Successive layers of ash are spread by air currents and become solidified as distinct beds. Furthermore, many explosive eruptions are accompanied by heavy rains, and the ash is swept by the runoff to low ground where it is spread out in thin uniform beds. The loose volcanic debris on steep slopes becomes saturated, and masses of it move down as mudflows and earthflows (p. 142). Some pyroclastic rocks, therefore, are hybrids in classification—partly igneous and partly sedimentary.

APPENDIX C. MAPS

Uses of maps

Nearly everyone has used automobile road maps in planning a trip or in following an unmarked road. A road map of a state, province, or county does the thing that all maps have done since their invention at some unknown time more than 5,000 years ago; it reduces the pattern of part of the Earth's surface to a size small enough to be seen as a whole. For the understanding of geologic relations maps have a special importance because a continent, a mountain chain, and a major river valley are of such large size that they can not be viewed as a whole unless represented on a map.

A map can be made to express much information within a small space by the use of various kinds of symbols. Just as some aspects of physics and chemistry use the symbolic language of mathematics to express significant relationships, so many aspects of geology use the simple symbolic language of maps to depict relationships too large to be observed within a single view. Maps made or used by geologists generally depict three sorts of things: (1) surface forms, (2) distribution and attitudes of rock units, (3) geographic features, such as mountains, rivers, and seas, not as they are today but reconstructed as they are inferred to have been at some time in the past. The first two express the results of direct observation and measurement and are frequently included on a single map. The third expresses concepts built up from whole groups of observations and necessarily is shown on special maps separate from those representing present-day features.

Map making

Base maps and geologic maps. Every map is made for some special purpose. Road maps, charts for sea or air navigation, and geologic maps are examples of three special purposes. But whatever the purpose, all maps have two classes of data: *base* data and *special-purpose* data. As base data most geologic maps show a latitude-longitude grid, streams, and inhabited places; many also have roads and railroads. A geologist may take an existing *base map* containing such data and plot geologic information on it, or he may start with blank paper and plot on it both base and geologic data, a much slower process if the map is made accurately. The plotting of geologic data on a base map is described in Chapter 5.

Two-dimension base maps. Many base maps used for plotting geologic data are two-dimensional; that is, they represent length and breadth but not height. A point can be located only in terms of its horizontal distance, in a particular direction, from some other point. Hence a base map always embodies the basic concepts of direction and distance. The Earth possesses two natural reference points, the poles. Using these two, the ancient Greeks established a grid by means of which any other point could be located. The grid we use now consists of lines of *longitude* (half circles joining the poles) and *latitude* (parallel circles concentric to the poles) (Fig. C–2). The longitude lines (*meridians*) run exactly north-south, crossing the east-west *parallels* of latitude at right angles. The circumference of the Earth at its equator and the somewhat smaller circumference through its two poles being known with fair accuracy, it is possible to define any point on the Earth in terms of direction and distance from either pole or from the point of intersection of any parallel with any meridian.

For convenience in reading, most maps are drawn so that the north direction is at the top or upper edge of the map. This is an arbitrary convention adopted mainly to save time. The north direction can just as well be placed elsewhere, provided only that its posi-

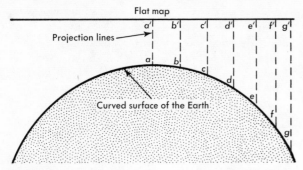

Fig. C–1. Equally spaced points (a, b, c, etc.) along a line in any direction on the Earth's surface become unequally spaced when projected onto a plane. This is why all flat maps are distorted.

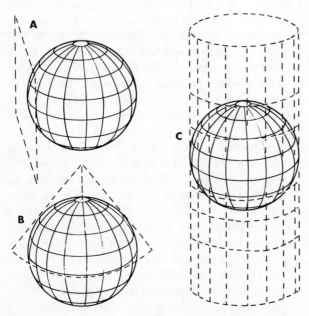

Fig. C–2. The Earth's latitude-longitude grid can be projected onto a plane A, a cylinder C, or a cone B that theoretically can be cut and flattened out.

tion is clearly indicated.

The accuracy with which distance is represented determines the accuracy of the map. *The proportion between a unit of distance on a map and the unit it represents on the Earth's surface* is the **scale** of the map. It is expressed as a simple proportion, such as *1:1,000,000*. This ratio means that one inch, foot, or unit on the map represents exactly 1,000,000 inches, feet, or other units on the Earth's surface; it works out to one inch equals about 16 miles and is approximately the scale of many of the road maps widely used by motorists. Scale is also expressed graphically by means of a lettered bar, as is done on most of the maps in this book. A map that has a latitude-longitude grid does not need any other indication of scale (except for convenience) because the lengths of a degree of longitude (varying from 69.17 statute miles at the equator to 0 at the poles) and of latitude (varying from 68.70 statute miles at the equator to 69.41 at the poles) are known.

Map projections. The Earth's surface is nearly spherical, whereas nearly all maps other than globes are planes, usually sheets of paper. It is geometrically impossible to represent any part of a spherical surface on a plane surface without distortion (Fig. C–1). The latitude-longitude grid has to be *projected* from the curved surface to the flat one. This can be done in various ways, each of which has advantages, but all of which represent a sacrifice of accuracy in that the resulting scale on the flat map will vary from one part of the map to another (Fig. C–2). Examples of cylindrical projections are Figures 15–11 and 15–15. The most famous of these is the Mercator projection; although it distorts the polar regions very greatly, compass directions drawn on it are straight lines. Since this is of enormous value in navigation, the Mercator projection is widely used in navigators' charts.

Figures 6–17, **A**, and 14–29 are examples of conic projections. Some very commonly used varieties are polyconic, in which not one cone, as in Figure C–2, **B**, but several cones are employed, each one tangent to the globe at a different latitude. This device reduces distortion.

Plate 2 (inside back cover) and Figure 22–10 represent two kinds of plane projection, and Figure 7–12 is a projection with certain areas, unimportant for the purpose of this map, eliminated.

In a map of a very small area, such as Figure 10–23, the distortion is of course slight, but it is there nevertheless.

Topographic maps

A more complete kind of base map is three-dimensional; that is, it represents not only length and breadth but also height. Therefore, it shows *relief* (*the difference in altitude between the high and low parts of a land surface*) and also *topography,* defined as *the relief and form of the land. A map that shows topography* is a **topographic map.** Topographic maps can give the form of the land in various ways. The maps most commonly used by geologists show it by contour lines.

Contours. A *contour line* (often called simply a *contour*) is *a line passing through points that have the same altitude above sea level.* If we start at a certain altitude on an irregular surface and walk in such a way as to go neither uphill nor downhill, we will trace out a path that corresponds to a contour line. Such a path will curve around hills, bend upstream in valleys, and swing outward around spurs. Viewed broadly, every contour must be a closed curve, just as the shoreline of an island or of a continent returns upon itself, however long it may be. Even on maps of small areas, many contours are closed curves, such as those at or near the tops of hills. Many, however, do not close within a given map area; they extend to the edges of the map and join the contours on adjacent maps.

Imagine an island in the sea crowned by two prominent isolated hills, with much steeper slopes on one side than on the other, and with an irregular shoreline. The shoreline is a contour line (the zero contour) because the surface of the water is horizontal. If the island is pictured as submerged until only the two isolated peaks project above the sea and then raised above the sea 20 feet at a time, the successive new shorelines will form a series of contour lines separated by 20-foot contour intervals. (A **contour interval** is *the vertical distance between two successive contour lines.*) At first, two small islands will appear, each with its own shoreline, and the contours marking their shorelines will have the form of two closed curves. When the main mass of the island rises above the water, the remaining shorelines or contours will pass completely around the land mass. The final shoreline is represented by the zero contour, which now forms the lowest of a series of contours separated by vertical distances of 20 feet.

As the island is raised, the successive new shorelines are not displaced through so great a horizontal distance where the slope is steep as where it is more gradual. In other words, the water retreats through a shorter horizontal distance in falling from one level to the next along the steep slope than along the gentle slope. Therefore, when these successive shorelines are projected upon the flat surface of a map, they will be crowded where the slope is steep and farther apart where it is moderate. In order to facilitate reading the contours on a map, certain contours (usually every fifth line) are drawn with a wider line. Contours are numbered at convenient intervals for ready identification. The numbers are always multiples of the contour interval and are placed between broken ends of the contour they designate.

Because the contours that represent a depression without an outlet resemble those of an isolated hill, it is necessary to give them a distinctive appearance. Depression contours therefore are *hatched*—that is, they are marked on the downslope side with short transverse lines called *hachures.* An example is shown on one contour in Figure C–4. The contour interval employed is the same as in other contours on the same map.

Ideal example. Figures C–3 and C–4 show the relation between the surface of the land and the contour map representing it. Figure C–3, a perspective sketch, shows a stream valley between two hills, viewed from the south. In the foreground is the sea, with a bay sheltered by a curving spit. Terraces in which small streams have excavated gullies border the valley. The hill on the east has a rounded summit and sloping spurs. Some of the spurs are truncated at their lower ends by a wave-cut cliff, at the base of which is a beach. The hill on the west stands abruptly above the valley with a steep scarp and slopes gently westward, trenched by a few shallow gullies.

Each of the features on the map (Fig. C–4) is represented by contours directly beneath its proper position in the sketch.

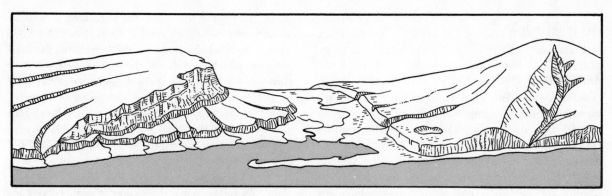

Fig. C–3. Perspective sketch of a landscape. (Modified from U. S. Geol. Survey.)

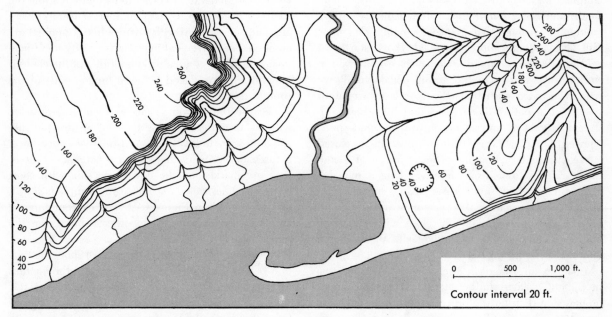

Fig. C–4. Contour map of the area shown in Figure C–3. (Modified from U. S. Geol. Survey.)

Air photographs

Figures 10–7, 10–12, 14–27, and 16–12 are photographs, made from airplanes, with cameras pointing down obliquely at the Earth's surface. Oblique air photographs enable us to see over a much larger area than could be seen from a single point on the ground and are therefore useful in making clear the broad rather than the detailed relations of various geologic features. The figures referred to above were selected for this very purpose. All oblique photographs are "pictorial" in that they show hills and valleys in perspective.

In contrast, Figures 1–2, and 11–16 are photographs made with cameras pointing down vertically at the Earth's surface. Unlike oblique views, vertical photographs do not show perspective; they look "flat." But although distortion is always present, as shown in Figure C–1, they show the pattern of the ground with distortion at a minimum. The vertical air photo-graph, therefore, is one kind of map. It is very widely and generally used as a base map on which geologic data are plotted in the field. Generally, such a photograph must have a scale of 1:20,000 or larger, for it shows so much detail that on a small scale the various features can become blurred.

Used by itself, a vertical air photograph is a two-dimension map. However, two photographs taken in sequence from a flying airplane, so that they overlap by a mile or two, can form a three-dimension map. When viewed through a stereoscope, the relief of the ground surface becomes startlingly apparent. Not only is this a direct aid in plotting geologic data on the photograph, but it also forms the basis of a method of drawing an accurate contour map of the area photographed without the necessity of making a slow, laborious, and costly ground survey. Topographic contour maps are now made largely by methods based on this principle.

REFERENCES

American Society of Photogrammetry, 1952, Manual of Photogrammetry: Washington, American Society of Photogrammetry, 2d. ed., 876 p.

American Society of Photogrammetry, 1960, Manual of photographic interpretation: Washington, American Society of Photogrammetry, 868 p.

Raisz, Erwin, 1948, General cartography: New York, McGraw-Hill Book Co., 2d. ed.

Robinson, A. H., 1960, 2d. ed., Elements of cartography: New York, John Wiley and Sons.

APPENDIX D. SYMBOLS AND CONVERSION TABLES

SYMBOLS USED ON GEOLOGIC MAPS

$\overline{}\llcorner 18°$ Strike and dip of layers (p. 71)

$\times$ 90°   Strike of vertical layers, with tops on side marked 90°

$\oplus$ Layers horizontal

Strike and dip of foliation in metamorphic rocks

Strike of vertical foliation

Anticline; arrows show dips away from axis (Fig. 18-10)

Syncline; arrows show dips toward axis

21°   Plunging anticline, with angle of plunge (Fig. 18-11, **A**)

15°   Plunging syncline, with angle of plunge

Normal fault, hachures on side of downthrow

Reverse fault: arrow shows direction of dip, hachures on side of downthrow

50°   U   D   Dip of fault: D, downthrown side; U, upthrown side

Directions of relative movement along a fault (**Fig. 18-1**)

Low-angle thrust, barbs on side of upthrow

PATTERNS USED FOR COMMON KINDS OF ROCK

In vertical sections
(common symbols)

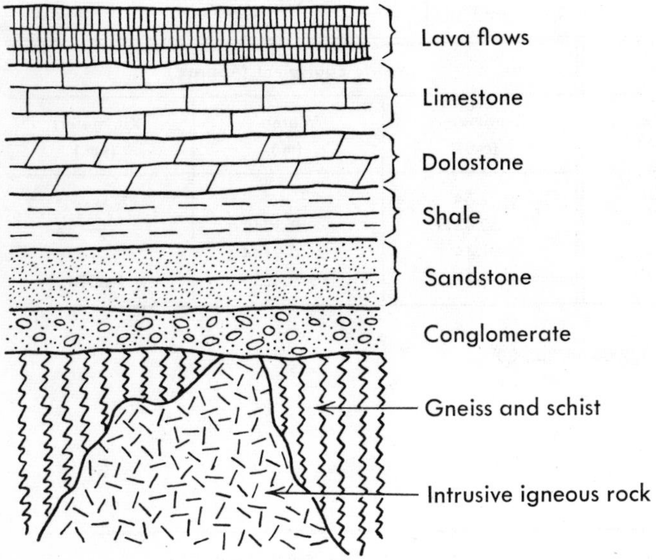

On maps (samples only;
other patterns used as preferred)

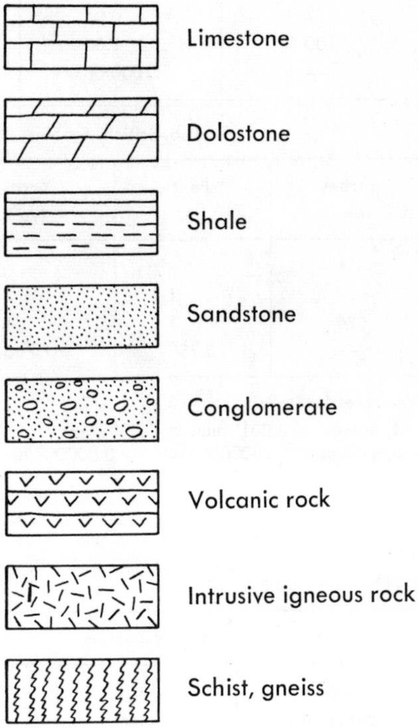

Lava flows

Limestone

Dolostone

Shale

Sandstone

Conglomerate

Gneiss and schist

Intrusive igneous rock

Limestone

Dolostone

Shale

Sandstone

Conglomerate

Volcanic rock

Intrusive igneous rock

Schist, gneiss

UNITS OF LENGTH

Metric System			U.S.-British Equivalent (Approx.)			
Centimeters (cm.)	Meters (m.)	Kilometers (km.)	Inches (in.)	Feet (ft.)	Yards (yd.)	Miles (mi.)
1	0.01	—	0.3937	—	—	—
100	1.00	—	39.37	3.2808	1.0936	—
—	1000.00	1	—	—	1,093.60	0.6214

U.S.-British System				Metric Equivalent (Approx.)		
Inches (in.)	Feet (ft.)	Yards (yd.)	Miles (mi.)	Centimeters (cm.)	Meters (m.)	Kilometers (km.)
1	$1/12$	$1/36$	—	2.54	—	—
12	1	$1/3$	—	30.48	0.3048	—
36	3	1	—	91.44	0.9144	—
—	5,280	1,760	1	—	1609.40	1.6094

Micrometric Scale

1 micron = 0.001 mm. = 0.0001 cm. = 0.000001 m. = 0.00004 in. (p. 30)

1 angstrom = 0.00000001 cm. = 0.000000004 in. (p. 32)

UNITS OF AREA

Metric System			U.S.-British Equivalent (Approx.)			
Square centimeters (cm.²)	Square meters (m.²)	Square kilometers (km.²)	Square inches (sq. in.)	Square feet (sq. ft.)	Square yards (sq. yd.)	Square miles (sq. mi.)
1	0.0001	—	0.1550	—	—	—
10,000	1.0000	—	1550.0	10.7639	1.1960	—
—	1 million	1	—	—	—	0.3861

UNITS OF VOLUME

Metric System			U.S.-British Equivalent (Approx.)			
Cubic centimeters (cm.³)	Cubic meters (m.³)	Cubic kilometers (km.³)	Cubic inches (cu. in.)	Cubic feet (cu. ft.)	Cubic yards (cu. yd.)	Cubic miles (cu. mi.)
1	0.000001	—	0.0610	—	—	—
1 million	1.00	—	—	35.3150	1.3080	—
—	1 million	1	—	—	—	0.2388

UNITS OF WEIGHT

Metric System			U.S.-British Equivalent (Approx.)	
Grams (gm.)	Kilograms (kg.)	Metric tons (M.T.)	Ounces avoirdupois (oz. av.)	Pounds avoirdupois (lb. av.)
1	0.001	—	0.0353	—
1000	1.000	0.001	—	2.2046
—	1000	1.000	—	2204.62

U.S.-British System			Metric Equivalent (Approx.)	
Ounces (oz. av.)	Pounds (lb. av.)	Tons	Grams (gm.)	Kilograms (kg.)
1	1/16	—	28.3495	—
16	1	—	453.5924	—
—	2000	1	—	907.1849

APPENDIX E. THE ELEMENTS

In alphabetic order

Element	Symbol	Atomic Number	Element	Symbol	Atomic Number
Actinium	Ac	89	Molybdenum	Mo	42
Aluminum	Al	13	Neodymium	Nd	60
Americium	Am	95	Neon	Ne	10
Antimony	Sb	51	Neptunium	Np	93
Argon	Ar	18	Nickel	Ni	28
Arsenic	As	33	Niobium (Columbium)	Nb (Cb)	41
Astatine	At	85	Nitrogen	N	7
Barium	Ba	56	Nobelium	No	102
Berkelium	Bk	97	Osmium	Os	76
Beryllium	Be	4	Oxygen	O	8
Bismuth	Bi	83	Palladium	Pd	46
Boron	B	5	Phosphorus	P	15
Bromine	Br	35	Platinum	Pt	78
Cadmium	Cd	48	Plutonium	Pu	94
Calcium	Ca	20	Polonium	Po	84
Californium	Cf	98	Potassium	K	19
Carbon	C	6	Praseodymium	Pr	59
Cerium	Ce	58	Promethium	Pm	61
Cesium	Cs	55	Protactinium	Pa	91
Chlorine	Cl	17	Radium	Ra	88
Chromium	Cr	24	Radon	Rn	86
Cobalt	Co	27	Rhenium	Re	75
Copper	Cu	29	Rhodium	Rh	45
Curium	Cm	96	Rubidium	Rb	37
Dysprosium	Dy	66	Ruthenium	Ru	44
Einsteinium	Es	99	Samarium	Sm	62
Erbium	Er	68	Scandium	Sc	21
Europium	Eu	63	Selenium	Se	34
Fermium	Fm	100	Silicon	Si	14
Fluorine	F	9	Silver	Ag	47
Francium	Fr	87	Sodium	Na	11
Gadolinium	Gd	64	Strontium	Sr	38
Gallium	Ga	31	Sulfur	S	16
Germanium	Ge	32	Tantalum	Ta	73
Gold	Au	79	Technetium	Tc	43
Hafnium	Hf	72	Tellurium	Te	52
Helium	He	2	Terbium	Tb	65
Holmium	Ho	67	Thallium	Tl	81
Hydrogen	H	1	Thorium	Th	90
Indium	In	49	Thulium	Tm	69
Iodine	I	53	Tin	Sn	50
Iridium	Ir	77	Titanium	Ti	22
Iron	Fe	26	Tungsten (Wolfram)	W	74
Krypton	Kr	36	Uranium	U	92
Lanthanum	La	57	Vanadium	V	23
Lead	Pb	82	Xenon	Xe	54
Lithium	Li	3	Ytterbium	Yb	70
Lutetium	Lu	71	Yttrium	Y	39
Magnesium	Mg	12	Zinc	Zn	30
Manganese	Mn	25	Zirconium	Zr	40
Mendelevium	Md	101			
Mercury	Hg	80			

In order of atomic numbers

Atomic number	Element	Symbol	Atomic number	Element	Symbol
1	Hydrogen	H	52	Tellurium	Te
2	Helium	He	53	Iodine	I
3	Lithium	Li	54	Xenon	Xe
4	Beryllium	Be	55	Cesium	Cs
5	Boron	B	56	Barium	Ba
6	Carbon	C	57	Lanthanum	La
7	Nitrogen	N	58	Cerium	Ce
8	Oxygen	O	59	Praseodymium	Pr
9	Fluorine	F	60	Neodymium	Nd
10	Neon	Ne	61	Promethium	Pm
11	Sodium	Na	62	Samarium	Sm
12	Magnesium	Mg	63	Europium	Eu
13	Aluminum	Al	64	Gadolinium	Gd
14	Silicon	Si	65	Terbium	Tb
15	Phosphorus	P	66	Dysprosium	Dy
16	Sulfur	S	67	Holmium	Ho
17	Chlorine	Cl	68	Erbium	Er
18	Argon	Ar	69	Thulium	Tm
19	Potassium	K	70	Ytterbium	Yb
20	Calcium	Ca	71	Lutetium	Lu
21	Scandium	Sc	72	Hafnium	Hf
22	Titanium	Ti	73	Tantalum	Ta
23	Vanadium	V	74	Tungsten (Wolfram)	W
24	Chromium	Cr	75	Rhenium	Re
25	Manganese	Mn	76	Osmium	Os
26	Iron	Fe	77	Iridium	Ir
27	Cobalt	Co	78	Platinum	Pt
28	Nickel	Ni	79	Gold	Au
29	Copper	Cu	80	Mercury	Hg
30	Zinc	Zn	81	Thallium	Tl
31	Gallium	Ga	82	Lead	Pb
32	Germanium	Ge	83	Bismuth	Bi
33	Arsenic	As	84	Polonium	Po
34	Selenium	Se	85	Astatine	At
35	Bromine	Br	86	Radon	Rn
36	Krypton	Kr	87	Francium	Fr
37	Rubidium	Rb	88	Radium	Ra
38	Strontium	Sr	89	Actinium	Ac
39	Yttrium	Y	90	Thorium	Th
40	Zirconium	Zr	91	Protactinium	Pa
41	Niobium (Columbium)	Nb (Cb)	92	Uranium	U
42	Molybdenum	Mo	93	Neptunium	Np
43	Technetium	Tc	94	Plutonium	Pu
44	Ruthenium	Ru	95	Americium	Am
45	Rhodium	Rh	96	Curium	Cm
46	Palladium	Pd	97	Berkelium	Bk
47	Silver	Ag	98	Californium	Cf
48	Cadmium	Cd	99	Einsteinium	Es
49	Indium	In	100	Fermium	Fm
50	Tin	Sn	101	Mendelevium	Md
51	Antimony	Sb	102	Nobelium	No

INDEX

(Numbers of pages on which terms are defined are in **boldface italics**. Asterisks indicate illustrations.)

Aa lava, 98*
Abrasion, *163*
  by surf, 308
  by wind, 269
  glacial, 235
  in streams, 163
  of rock particles, 333*
Absolute time, *58*
Abyssal plain, 287,* *288,* 298
Adjusted stream system, *194*
Age, of the Earth, 60, 63
Air photographs, vertical, for mapping, 66, 68,* 487
Albite, 387, *472*
Alluvial fans, *173,* 258,* 261*
Alluvial fill, *189,* 190
Alluvium, *155,* 181, 259*
  coarse, 258*
Almandite, 387
Alpine geosyncline, 424
Alps, 423, 424,* 425,* 426,* 427*
  arcuate form of, 426*
  development of structure in, 425*
Altimeter, *66*
Amphibole, 387, *471*
Amygdales, *40*
Amygdaloidal basalt, 40*
Andesite, 38,* 42,* 95,* *478,* 481
  porphyry, 40*
Angstrom, *31–32*
Angular unconformity, *371,* 372*
Aniakchak Crater, 89, 90*
Animals, role in weathering, 118
Annual sedimentary layers, 53
Antarctic Ice Sheet, 228, 231*
Antecedent stream, *192,* 193,* 432, 433*
Anthracite, 45, 376, 377,* 378, 445*
Anticline, *357,* 358,* 359,* 449*
Apatite, 470, *475*
Aphanitic rock, 38*
  texture, *39*
Appalachian geosyncline, 420, 421*
Appalachian Mountains, Pl. 1,* 418–422
  block faulting and volcanism in, 430
  erosional history, 432, 433*
  measure of deformation in, 421
  metamorphism, 421
  stream terraces, 432
  structure of bedrock, 418–419,* 421*
  thickness of sedimentary section, 419, 420*
  unconformities, 421*
Aquifer, *200*
Arctic pattern of polygons, 133*
Arete, *238*
Argand, Emile, on Alpine structure, 425
Aristotle, views of, 4
  concept of earthquakes, 395
Arkose, 45, *327*
Artesian springs, 204

Artesian system, 205*
Artesian well, *203,* 204*
Asbestos, fibrous form of, 469*
Ash, volcanic, 83,* *85,* 96*
Assam, earthquake of 1950, 392, 394
Atacama Desert, Chile, 254
Atitlan Volcano, 95*
Atlantic Ocean basin, 286*
  matching of opposed margins, 436*
Atmosphere, circulation of, 120, 121,* 122
Atoll, 300*
Atom, 31
Atomic number, *33*
Atomic patterns of minerals, 35,* 36*
Augite, 387, *472*
Auvergne region, France, 98
Axial plane, of fold, 357,* *358,* 380*
Azurite, *473*

Bacteria, in sea-floor sediments, 448
  in soils, 126, 129
  in swamp deposits, 445
Badlands, 177,* 259,* *260*
Baltic Sea, metamorphic rocks near, 382
  uplift around, 352,* 353
Bank caving, 150,* 170*
Barbed tributary, 193,* *194*
Barchan dunes, *273*
Barite, *472*
Barchan dunes, *273**
Barrier, coastal, 315, 319
Barrier island, 315, *316*
Barrier reef, 300*
Bars, coastal, 315
  in stream, 165*
  point, *168,* 170*
Basalt, 42,* 94, 97,* 98,* 99,* 105,* *478,* 481
  aa, 98*
  amygdaloidal, 40*
  columnar, 99,* 105*
  metamorphism of, 387
  pahoehoe, 98*
Base level, *162,* 186*
  change of, 189
  local, *162**
  ultimate, *162**
Base map, 483
Basin, structural, 356*
Basin and Range Province, Pl. 1,* 348, 430–431*
Basins, classification, 216,* 217
  lake, 213,* 214
Batholith(s), *107,* 108, 456
  in mountain belts, 431, 432,* 439
Bathyscaph, 282
Bauxite, *129,* *473*
  ore, 461*
Bay barrier, 315,* *316,* 320*
Beach, 309,* *310,* 311,* 314,* 315,* 316,* 319,* 320*
  slope of, 312

Beach drifting, *313*,* 333*
Beach dunes, 273
Bed load, *164*
Bedrock, *7*, 29*
  concealed, 70*
  glaciated, 126*
Beds, *328*
Bench, wave-cut, 309*
Bending strain, 396*
Bighorn Basin, Wyoming, 359*
Bighorn River, 359*
Bingham Canyon, Utah, 460,* 461*
Biotite, 46, 117, 387, *471*, 480
Bituminous coal, 376, 377,* 445,* 447*
Black Hills, South Dakota, 39, 73,* 74,* 77
Block-faulting, 430
Blocks, volcanic, *85*
Blowout, *269*
Bombs, atomic, 57
  volcanic, 85*
Botryoidal form, *468*, 469*
Bottomset bed, *174*
Boulder batholith, Montana, 107*
Boulder train, *244*, 249*
"Box canyon," 257, 259*
Braided stream, *172*, 173
Breakers, 306,* 314*
Breccia, fault, 45
  sedimentary, *326*, 327*
  volcanic, *40*
Bristlecone pine, age of, 54
Brunton, *66*, 67*

Calcareous ooze, 291, 292*
Calcareous tufa, *328*
Calcite, 34,* 45, 470, *472*
Caldera, *89*,* 90,* 93*
Caliche, *128*
Capillary fringe, 199,* 200
Capture, stream, *192*, 193*
Carnotite, *473*
Caspian Sea, 221
Cassiterite, *473*
Catastrophists, 4
Caverns, 197,* 208,* *209*
Cementation, 338
Cenozoic column, 62
Cenozoic Era, 60, 63
Chalcedony, *472*
Chalcocite, *473*
Chalcopyrite, *473*
Chalk, *328*
Channel, stream, 157, 160,* 161*
Chemical affinity, *34*
Chemical weathering, 116
  mechanical effects of, 118
Chichen-Itza, Yucatan, 113*
Chile, earthquakes of 1960, 392, 393*
China, earthquake toll, 395
  loess in, 276
Chlorite, *471*
  schist, 46, 479
Chute cutoff, *170*, 171*
Cinder cones, 81,* *96*
Cinders, volcanic, *85*
Cinnabar, *473*
Cirque, *235*, 237,* 238*
Clastic particles and aggregates, *43*
Clastic rocks, *324*
Clastic sediment, *43*
Clay, 115*

Clay minerals, 30,* 116,* 292*
Cleavage, in minerals, *29*, 31,* 34,* 468, 469*
  in slate, 7,* 46, 379, 479
Cleveland dike, 104
Cliffs, recession of, 147*
Climate, *120*
  importance in geology, 254
Climates, desert, 255*
  glacial, 251
  steppe, 255*
Clinton iron ores, 458–459, 462
Coal, 45, *328*, 376, 378
  anthracite, 376, 377*
  as energy, 443
  bituminous, 376, 377*
  cellular structure in, 444
  changed to graphite, 378
  distribution of, 445
  in North America, 446*
  origin, 445*
  seams, 444
  temperatures for metamorphism, 385
Coast and Geodetic Survey, precise locations by, 395
Coast Range batholith, 108
Coast Ranges, Pl. 1,* 354, 415,* 422
Coasts, classification, 317
  sculptural evolution, 318, 319*
Colorado Plateau, 10,* 23,* 51,* 52,* 415*
Colorado River, 10,* 51,* 147,* 159,* 162–163,* 214*
Column, geologic, 62
Columnar basalt, 98, 99,* 105*
Columns (dripstone), 197,* *209*
Compaction, in sediments, 337*
Composite cone, of volcano, *94*, 95,* 100*
Concentration of metals, 454
Conchoidal fracture, *468*, 481*
Concordant intrusive bodies, *106*
Concretion, 335, *336*,* 337,* 461*
Cone of depression, *202*
Confined flow, 203
Conformable strata, 340
Conglomerate, 44, *326*
Connate water, *207*, 208
Connecticut, faults, 365,* 367,* 430
  Triassic rocks, 430*
Consequent stream, *192*
Continent(s), *17*
  altitudes, 17
  map of, Pl. 2* (inside back cover)
Continental drift, hypothesis of, 438
Continental masses, 16,* 418*
  plate-like form, 418*
  structure, 415–418
Continental shelf, *284*, 287,* 288,* 295,* 299*
  sediments of, 294
Continental slope, *288*,* 297*
Contour interval, *485*
Contour line, *485*, 486
Convection currents, hypothesis of, 437–438
Conversion tables, metric and British systems, 490–491
  units of length and area, 490
  units of volume and weight, 491
Copper, *473*
Copper mine, 460,* 461*
Coquina, *328*, 329*
Coral reef, *299*, 300*
Cordillera(s), 17
  American, *415*, Pl. 2*
  North American, *415*, Pl. 2,* 422
Correlation, *342*, 344*
  by isotopes, 344

Corundum, 470, **475**
Crater, volcanic, **84**
Crater Lake, Oregon, 89,* 90*
Crevasses, 231,* **233***
Cross-bedding, 330, 360*
Cross-lamination, 330
Cross-stratification, **330***
Crust of Earth, abrupt movements, 348, 349,* 350*
 average composition, 31
 deformation, 343–376
 equilibrium in, 434*
 general concept, 16
 reality of, 408–409*
 thickness, how found, 408*
 zones of, 22
Crustal warping, **355**
Crystallization, 338
Culebra Cut, Panama, earth flowage, 150
Currents, ocean, 288, 289–291
Cutoffs, 169–171
Cuvier and Brangniart, 77
Cycle of erosion, **185**
 along coasts, 318, 320
 in deserts, 262, 263

DaVinci, Leonardo, 4, 42, 178
Dams, 2, 162–163
 Hoover, 162, 163*
 Imperial, 163*
 Parker, 162, 163*
 St. Francis, 150
Darcy, Henry, 202
Darwin, Charles, 24
Dates, absolute, 56–59
 lead-uranium, 56–57
 potassium-argon, 58
 radiocarbon, 58–59
 strontium-rubidium, 58
Dating, absolute, 56, 63
 relative, 56, 62
Dead Sea, 221
Death Valley, California, 254, 258
 fans, 258*
 faulting, 431
Debris flow, **138**, 139,* 141*
Debris slide, **137**, 139,* 140*
Decomposition, **116**
Deep-sea floor, **288**
Deflation, 261,* **268**, 271, 279
 armor, 268,* **269***
 basins, **269**
Deformation, 348–374
 by bending, 355
 by fracturing, 360–368
 effect of confining pressure, 370
 importance of time, 370
 mechanics of, 368–371
 results in controlled tests, 370–371
Delaware River, 194–195
Delta, **173**, 175,* 214*
Dendritic pattern of streams, **191***
Density currents, 289, **290–291**
Desert, **254**
Desert climate, 255*
Deserts, Australia, 275*
Desmarest, Nicholas, 98, 178
Deuterium, **33**
Diamond, 34, 470, **474**
 placers, Africa, 463
Dickite, 30*
Diffraction pattern, 35*

Dike, 101,* 102,* **103**,* 104*
Diorite, 42,* 477,* **478**, 480
 porphyritic, **478**
 porphyry, **478**
Dip, **71**,* 72*
Disappearing stream, 210*
Discharge, stream, **157**
Disconformable rock units, 340
Disconformity, 372,* **373**
Discordant intrusive bodies, **106**
Disintegration, **116**
Dissection by streams, 183*
Divide, **192**
Dolerite, **478**, 480
Dolomite, 45, **473**
Dolostone, 44, 45, 116, **328**
Dome, in French West Africa, 356*
 structural, 356*
Downwarping, 356*
Drainage, interior, **257**
Drainage system, **183**
Dredge, placer, 463
Drift, glacial, **240**, 249*
Driftless area, 248*
Drilling rig, 452*
Dripstone, **209**
Drowned lands, 354
Drumlin, 242,* **243**, 249*
Dry valleys, 210*
Dunes, **270**, 271*
 ancient, 278*
 classification, 273
 composition, 274
 height of, 272
 migration, 272
Dunite, 42,* **478**, 481
"Dust Bowl", 264,* 279
Dust cloud, 261,* 264*
Dust storms, 264,* 267–268

Earth, age, 51, 60, 63
 core, **406***
 crust, 408,* 409*
 density, 405, 410*
 expanding, 436
 forces acting on, 17–22
 general view of, 13–25
 geothermal gradient, **408**
 interior, 404–412
 major divisions and features, 16, 17
 mantle, 406,* 409,* **410**
 method of weighing, 405
 model, 13*
 outer part, 408–409
 photographed from rocket, 15*
 shape and size, 14, 15*
 shrinking, 435
 temperatures, 407–408
 zones of crust, 22–23
Earthflow, **140**, 142*
Earthquake focus, 397,* **398**
 epicenter, 397,* **398**, 401*
Earthquakes, 392–404
 artificial, 403–404*
 cause, 395–396
 damage, 391,* 393,* 392–395
 deep-focus, **402**
 distribution, 402, 403*
 early views on, 395
 frequency, 404
 human toll, 395

Earthquakes, intensity, *401**
  intermediate-focus, *402*
  magnitudes, *402*
  shallow-focus, *402*
Earthquakes, examples of, Alaska, 392
    California, 348, 350, 392, 394
    Chile, 392
    Greece, 392
    India, 394
    Italy, 395
    Japan, 394–395
    Nevada, 348, 350
    Nova Scotia, 297*
    Portugal, 395
Earthquakes, waves of, in body of Earth, 397*
    long (L) waves, *398*, 399*
    longitudinal waves, *397**
    primary (P) waves, *397*, 399*
    reflected waves, 397,* 401
    refracted waves, 397,* 401
    secondary (S) waves, *397*, 399*
    seismic waves, *399*
    transverse waves, 397*
Echo sounding, 283, 284*
Economic geologists, *25*
El Capitan, 19,* 20
Electric logs of wells, 78*
Electron microscope, 30
Elements, abundance, 31
  alphabetical list, 492
  listed by atomic number, 492
Elm, Swiss Alps, rockfall, 135
Emergence of coasts, 317
End moraines, 229,* 242,* *243,* 249*
Energy consumption, U.S.A., 443*
Epicenter(s), *398*
  distances from, 400*
  distribution, 403*
  location, 400, 401*
Epidote, 387, *471*
Erosion, *22*
  effect of plant cover, 179,* 180*
  glacial, 234, 249
  rate, 184
Erratic, *243,** 244
Eskers, *245,** 246*
Etna, Mount, 87
Evaporites, *328*
Evolution, 24
  indicated by fossils, 343
Exfoliation, *118*
  in Egypt, 119*
  in Mohave Desert, 119*
  of granitic rocks, 119*
Exposure, *28*
Extrusive rocks, *38*

Facies, metamorphic, 385, *387*
  sedimentary, *344,* 345
Falls, 166, 168*
Fan(s), *173,** 258,* 261
  submarine, 298, 299*
Fault(s), *22,* 348–351, 363–368
  abrupt movements, 348–351
  apparent and relative movement, 364
  footwall and hanging wall, *364**
  lateral, 349,* *364*
  normal, 349,* *364,** 365,* 366*
  oblique-slip, *364,* 349,* 350*
  related to monoclinal fold, 368*
  reverse, *364*

Faults(s), San Andreas, 348, 349,* 394*
  special features, 368
  strike-slip, 349,* *364*
  surface expression, 365
  thrust, *364,* 369,* 370*
  varied displacements, 348, 349,* 350,* 364,* 365,*
    366,* 367,* 368,* 369,* 370*
Fault blocks, 430*
Fault scarps, 348, 349,* 350,* 367,* 431*
  after prolonged erosion, 367*
Ferromagnesian minerals, 36, 42*
Field study, 66
Finland, metamorphic rocks in, 388
Fiords, 234,* *238*
Fish, fossil, 6*
Fissure eruption, *97*
Fissure veins, 455,* *456*
"Flash" floods, 257, 258,* 260
Flood, 172*
  Quinebaug River, 165*
Floodplain, *170,* 172,* 182
Flow, of air, 265
Flow breccias, *482*
Fluorite, 470, *475*
Fold(s), *357**
  axial plane, 357,* *358*
  axis, *357**
  closed, *359*
  elements of, 357, 358*
  isoclinal, *359,* 360*
  limbs of, *357**
  open, *359*
  overturned, 360, 361*
  plunging, *358,** 359*
  recumbent, *360,* 361,* 424
Folded belt, erosional features of, 257,* 359,* 420,*
  431, *432,** 433*
Forces acting on Earth, 17–22
  external, 18, 20
  internal, 18,* 19, 20*
Foreset bed, *174,**
Foreset laminae, 317,* 334,* 342*
Foreset layers in a dune, 272*
Formation, geologic, 65,* *66,* 341
Fossil fuels, 443
Fossils, *335**
  and evolution, 343
Fossil trees, 54, 55*
Fracture, conchoidal, *468,* 481*
  of minerals, 468
  of rocks, 476
Frank, Alberta, landslide, 134, 135*
Frenchman Mountain, Nevada, 68,* 431*
Fresh-water limestone, *328*
Fringing reef, *300**
Frost heaving, *145**
Frost wedging, 118, 119,* 234, 238

Gabbro, 42,* *478,* 480
Galena, 34,* 454, *474*
Gangue, *454*
Garnet, 32,* *471*
  replacing limestone, 384,* 385
Geochemistry, *25*
Geochronometry, *59*
Geode, *336,* 337*
Geologic ages, 63
Geologic column, 59–64, 62,* *344–345*
Geologic epochs, 60, 63
  epochs, 60, 63
Geologic eras, 60, 63

Geologic formations, 65,* *66*, 68
  examples on maps, 69,* 73,* 74*
  names assigned to, 66, 68
Geologic maps, 66–78, 69,* 73,* 74,* 75
  basic equipment for, 66
  early examples, 77
  essential features, 66
  of igneous and metamorphic rocks, 75–76
  sedimentary formations on, 66, 69,* 73,* 74,* 75*
  structure sections with, 69,* 73,* 74,* 75*
  symbols, 72,* 488
  use of air photographs with, 66, 68*
Geologic periods, 60, 63
Geologic research, team work in, 77
Geologic series, 60, 62
Geologic stages, 60, 62
Geologic systems, 60–62
Geologic time, 50–64
  general evidence, 51–53
  measurements, 56–59
  scale, 63
Geological Survey, of Canada, 3
  of Great Britain, 2
  of United States, 2
Geology, *2*
  beginnings and growth, 3–5
  early literature on, 11
  physical and historical, 9
  pioneers in, 4
  primary documents of, 5
  profession of, 2
  scientific method in, 24–25
Geomorphologists, *25*
Geophysical exploration, 404,* 449, 450*
Geophysics, *25*
Geosyncline, *420*
  Alpine, 423–425*
  Appalachian, 420, 421*
  Rocky Mountain, 422–423
Geothermal gradient, *408*
Geyser, *109**
  mechanism of, 109*
Giant's Causeway, Ireland, 99*
Gibraltar, Strait of, 290
Glacial ages, 250
Glacial climates, 251
Glacial deposits, 239
Glacial drift, *240*, 249*
Glacial erosion, 249
  of mountains, 238*
Glacial facets on stones, 240,* 270*
Glacial plucking, *235*, 243*
Glacial striations, 235,* 236,* 249*
Glacial transport, 239
Glaciated valleys, 236, 237,* 238,* 239
Glaciation, *233*
  causes of, 251
  effect on sea level, 250
Glacier, *228*
  economy of, 233*
Glacier ice, flow of, 233*
Glacier movement, 232
Glacier National Park, Montana, 105*
Glaciers, former extent, 246
  in glacial ages, 246, 247,* 248*
  piedmont, *228*, 229*
  valley, 227,* *228*, 229,* 238,* 239
Gneiss, *46*, 375*
  granite, *46*, 383*
  injection, 386*
Goethite, 117

Gold, 457,* 462,* *473*
  dredging for, 463*
Graded bed, 297, *331**
Graded profile, of a stream, *181*
Grand Canyon, Arizona, 10,* 51,* 52*
  unconformities, 372*
Grand Coulee Dam, 150
Granite, 30,* 42,* 61,* 477,* *478*, 480
  porphyritic, *478*
  porphyry, *478*
  problem of, 110, 387–389
Granite gneiss, *46*, 383*
Granitic rocks, 477,* 480
Granitization, 110, *388*
  supposed example, 389*
Granodiorite, 42,* 477,* *478*
  porphyritic, *478*
  porphyry, *478*
Graphite, 34, 378, *474*
Gravity, 19,* 20*
Gravity meter, *78*
Gravity spring, 203*
Graywacke, *327*, 479
Great Lakes, 224,* 225,* 226,* 353,* 354
Great Salt Lake, 217,* 218,* 260
Greenland, 146,* 347*
Greenland Ice Sheet, 230*
Groin, *314**
Gros Ventre landslide, 136,* 137*
Ground moraine, 242,* *243*
Ground water, *198*
  as cause of subsidence, 206
  dissolved substances, 207
  distribution, 199
  economic aspects, 205
  finding, 205
  geologic work, 207
  movement, 199, 201*
  origin, 198
  pollution and sanitation, 207*
  pollution and sewage, 206
  recharge, 206, 207*
  runoff, *154**
  zone, aeration, *199**
    saturation, *199**
Guyot, 284,* 285,* 286,* *288*, 299, 321
Gypsum, 45, 470, *473*

Halemaumau, 93,* 94
Halite, 34,* 45, *473*
Hand level, 66, 67*
Hanging valley, 236, 239*
Hardness, of minerals, *470*
  standard scale, 470
Hawaii, Island of, 91,* 92*
Hawaiian Islands, 91, 92*
Headland, 320*
  truncation, 320*
Heim, Albert, on Alpine structure, 424
Helium, 492
  atom, 33*
Hematite, 108, 336, 385, *474*
Henry Mountains, Utah, 106*
Herculaneum, 86*
Hexagonal system, 37
Hibok Hibok, 88
Highlands, southwestern U. S., 415*
Himalaya Mountains, 18,* 416*
  earthquakes, 394
Hinge fault, *368**
Hogback, *71**

Hoover Dam, 162, 214,* 296
  site, 3*
Horn, *238*, 239*
Hornfels, 47, *385*, 479
Hot springs, 109, 454
Hudson submarine canyon, 298, 299*
Humus, *126*, 127*
Hutton, James, 4, 24, 454
Hydraulic action, *163*
  by surf, 307*
Hydraulic plucking, *166*,* 167*
Hydrogen, 492
  atom, 33*
Hydrologic cycle, *20*, 21*
Hydrosphere, 16
Hypersthene, *472*
Hypotheses, use of, 24

Ice, glacier, 232
Ice cap, *228*, 229*
Ice-contact stratified drift, *245*
Ice sheet, *228*, 247*
Idaho batholith, 108
Igneous bodies, 39, 100–108, 456
Igneous geology, 79–111
  problems in, 109–110
  rise of magma, 110
  room problem, 110
  sources of heat, 109
  variations in magma, 110
Igneous rocks, *37*–41
  classification of, 42,* 477–482
  mapping of, 75, 76
  texture of, 40,* 44,* 477*
Imbrication in clastic sediments, 326,* *335*
Industrial minerals, 452
Interglacial ages, 250
Interior drainage, *257*
Intrusive igneous bodies, *39*, 100–108
  concordant *106*
  discordant, *106*
Inyo Range, California, 388
  granite in, 389*
Ion, *33*
Ionic diameters, 33*
Iron ores, 458, 459
  Clinton, 458–459, 462
  Labrador, 459
  Lake Superior, 459*
Island arcs, marine terraces, 428, 429*
  of Lesser Antilles, 428, 429*
  of western Pacific, 417*
Isometric system of minerals, 37
Isoseismal line, *401*
Isostasy, *411*
  evidence for, 352,* 353,* 354, 411,* 412
Isostatic balance, mechanism of, 432–434*
Isotopes, *33*
Italy, earthquakes in, 395

Japan, earthquakes in, 394–395
  pattern of foci, 428*
Jeffreys, Harold, ideas on orogeny, 436
Joint, 362,* *363*
  curved, 363*
  set, 362,* *363*
  system, 362,* *363*
Jura Mountains, 425, 426,* 427*
  complex structure, 425, 427*
Juvenile water, *84*

Kames, *245*
Kame terraces, *245*
Kanchenjunga, in the Himalaya, 413*
Kaolinite, 116,* *471*
Karst topography, *210*
Kettles, *245*
Keystone thrust, Nevada, 369*
Kilauea, 91,* 92,* 93,* 94
Kilauea Iki, 93,* 94
Kyanite, *471*

Labrador iron ores, 459
Laccolith, *104*, 106*
Lagoon, 300,* 301, 315,* *316*, 319*
Lake Agassiz, 224*
Lake Barlow-Ojibway, 224*
Lake basins, 213,* 214
Lake Bonneville, 219, 220*
Lake Mead, 214,* 296
  sedimentary formations near, 65*
Lakes, pluvial, *220*, 221*
  stages in history, 215*
  water economy, 217*
Lakes Michigan and Huron, 353*
  tilted shorelines near, 353–354
Lake Superior iron ores, 459*
Lamar Canyon, Wyoming, 54, 55*
Lamarck, on evolution, 24
Laminae, *328*
Landslide(s), *134*–138, 135,* 136,* 137,* 149*
  during earthquakes, 392, 393*
  of bedrock masses, 134–136
  of regolith, 136–138
  submarine, 297*
La Sal Mountains, Utah, 106
Laterite, *129*
Laue photograph, 35*
Lava, *39*
  flows, *38*, 79,* 81,* 82*
  in form of pillows, 98*
Leaching, *117*
Lead-uranium ratio, 57
Light year, 50
Lignite, 45, 445,* 447*
Limbs, of folds, *357*
Limestone, 44, 45, *328*
  in injection gneiss, 386*
  replaced by garnet, 384,* 385
Limonite, 117, *474*
Lisbon, Portugal, sea wave, 395
Lithification, *337*, 338*
Lithosphere, 16
Lituya Bay, Alaska, 393*
  earthquake and landslide, 392
Load, relation to discharge, 158*
  stream, *157*
Loess, *275*, 276,* 277*
  desert and glacial, 276
Longitudinal dunes, *274*, 275
Long profile of stream, *161*
Longshore bar, 314,* *315*
Longshore trough, 314*
Lost River Range, Idaho, 139*
Lucretius, concept of earthquakes, 395
Luster, in minerals, *469*

Maclure, William, early geologic map, 77
Magma, *39*
  chamber, 86*
Magmas, variations in, 110
Magmatic differentiation, *108*

"Magmatists," 388
Magnetism in rocks, 438–439
  bearing on ancient geographies, 439
  of Tasmania, 438
Magnetite, 450, *474*
Magnetometer, *78*, 450*
Malachite, *474*
Malaspina Glacier, Alaska, 437*
Mantle, of Earth, 406,* 409, *410*
Map projections, 484
Marble, *46*, 479
  in injection gneiss, 386*
Marianas Islands, 417*
  marine terraces in, 429*
Marysville stock, 107*
Mass number, *56*
Mass spectrometer, *57*
Mass-wasting, 133–151, 462
  definition, *134*
  farming problems, 149–150
  in valleys, 180, 181*
  movements of bedrock, 134–136, 147–148;
    of regolith, 136–148
  problems for engineers, 150–151
  rapid movements, 134–143
  role in erosion, 148, 149
  slow movements, 143–148
Matching of strata, 341
Materials of Earth's crust, 27–48
  bedrock and regolith, 28, 29*
  minerals, 28–37
  rocks, 37–48
Matterhorn, 238, 426*
Mauna Loa Volcano, 5,* 91,* 92, 94, 95*
Mayon Volcano, 95*
McDonald Lake fault scarp, 367*
Meanders, *168*, 169,* 170,* 171,* 181*
  migration of, 169
Mediterranean volcanoes, 85
Melting temperatures, of rocks, 384
Meltwater, *233*
Meltwater stream, 243*
Meridians, 483
Mesozoic column, 62
Mesozoic Era, 60, 63
Messina, Italy, earthquakes, 395
Metamorphic facies, 385, *387*
Metamorphic rocks, 7, 46
  principal kinds, 46–47, 479
  texture of, 44*
Metamorphism, 46, *376*–390
  agents of, 378
  beneath a thrust plate, 381*
  by hot fluids, 379
  contact, *378*, 384*
  dynamic, *378*
  dynamo-thermal, *378*
  grades of, 379
  in Alps, 380
  in mountain belts, 385
  in Pennsylvania and Rhode Island, 377*
  of coal, 376–378
  of igneous rocks, 382, 383*
  of sedimentary rocks, 377,* 379,* 380,* 381,* 382,*
    384*
  of shale, grades of, 381
  regional, *379*
  thermal, *378*
  varied effects, 381
Meteorology, *120*

Mica, 31,* 39, 46, *471*, 480
  "dioctahedral," *471*
  "trioctahedral," *471*
Microcline, *472*
Micron, *30*
Mid-Atlantic Ridge, 17, 286,* 287,* 288, 436*
Mid-Indian Ridge, 17
Mid-ocean canyon, 287,* *288*
Migmatite, *388*
Mineral(s), 28–*37*, 468–475
  basic importance, 36
  chemical composition, 31
  cleavage in, *29*, 31,* 469*
  crystal forms, 29, 30,* 31, 32,* 468
  equipment for studying, 468
  ferromagnesian, 36
  formation, 33–36
  general properties, 28
  hardness, 28, 34, *470*
  internal structure, 31–36
  luster, *469*
  physical properties, 468–470
  silicate, 35
  specific gravity, 470
  streak, *469*
  X-ray analysis, 35*
Mineralogists, *25*
Mineralogy, *36*
Mineral resources, 28
Minerals used in industry, 452
Mineral table, 471–475
  use of, 470
Mino-Owari, Japan, fault, 349*
Mississippi River delta, 174, 175*
Mississippi Valley, alluvial fill, 190
Moho, *409*
  drilling project, 409–410
Mohorovičič discontinuity, *409*
Molecular attraction in ground water, 200*
Molluscan shells, 4*
Monadnocks, *187*
Monocline, *360*, 361,* 368*
Monte Somma, 85, 86*
Mont Pelée, 87*–88
Monument Valley, 124*
Moon, sample landscape, 20*
  relation to tides, 289*
Moraines, 229,* *243*
Mt. Evans, Colorado, rubbly slope, 138*
Mt. Everest, 17, 18*
Mt. Katmai, 88
Mt. Mazama, 89*
Mountain, *414*
  chain, range, system, *414–415*
  groups, 414
Mountain belts of Asia and Europe, 416
Mountain histories compared, 422–430
Mountain making, *414*
Mountains, origin and history, 414–440
  ancient records, 434–435*
  of Lesser Antilles, 428, 429*
  of western North America, 422–423*
Mud cracks, 334, *335*, 360*
Mudflow, *138*, 141*
Muir Glacier, 234*
Muscovite, *471*

Natural bridge, 210*
Natural levees, *172*
Nebula in Cepheus, 49*

Neck cutoff, *169*, 171*
Neutron, 32, 33*
Newton's law, 24, 405
Niagara Falls, 168,* 222
Nittany Arch, Pennsylvania, 421
North America, Pl. 2*
    interior lowland, 418
    orogenic belts, 423*
    stable interior, 419
Notch, 310*
Nova Scotia, igneous rocks in, 430
Nuclear energy, 452
Nuée ardente, 87,* 88, *89*, 297, 332
Nuggets, 462*

Obsidian, *38*, 478, 481
Ocean currents, 122, 288–289
Ocean water, complex history, 130–131
Oil, distribution in North America, 451*
    origin, 448
    world reserves, 453*
Oil field, *448*
Oil pool, *447*
Olivine, 387, 410, *471*
Ooze, calcareous, 292*
Opal, *472*
Open-pit mine, 459,* 460*
Ore, *454*
    origin, 455
    relation to magma, 455
Original horizontality of strata, 342
Orogeny, *435*
    possible cause, 435–439
        convection currents, 437–438
        expanding Earth, 436–437
        gravitative movements, 438
        shrinking Earth, 435–436
Orthoclase, *35*, 42,* 409,* 470, *472*
Outcrop area, *71*
Outwash, 242,* 243,* *244,* 245*
Outwash-plain, *244*
Owens Valley, California, earthquake, 348
Oxbow lake, *170*, 171*

Pahoehoe lava, 98*
Paired terraces, 189*
Paleobotany, *71*
Paleomagnetism, 438–*439*
Paleontology, *25*
Paleozoic column, 62
Paleozoic Era, 60, 63
Parallel stratification, *329**
Parícutin Volcano, 80–83, 81,* 82,* 83*
Patterns, for geologic maps and sections, 489*
Peat, 45, *225,* 328, 445*
Pedalfer, *128*
Pediments, 261,* *262,* 264
Pedocal, *128*
Pedology, *126*
Pegmatite, 39,* *480*
Peneplane, *186,* 187*
Pennsylvanian landscape, 125*
Perched water bodies, *203**
Percolation, *200*
Peridotite, 42,* *478*, 480
Permafrost, *250*, 251
Permeability, *199*
Perrault, Pierre, 198
Petroleum, *446* (*see also* Oil)
Petrologists, *25*
Phenocrysts, *40***

Phyllite, *46*
Piedmont glacier, *228*, 229*
Pillow lava, 98*
Pitchblende, 452
Pitchstone, *478*, 481
Placer, *462*, 463*
Plagioclase, *35*, 42,* 387, *471*
Plants, role in weathering, 118
Plateau, 23,* 414, 415*
Plateau basalts, *97**
Playa, *219*, 258,* 261*
Playa lake, *219*, 260*
Playfair, John, 11, 178
Pleasant Valley, Nevada, 348, 349*
Pleistocene Epoch, 60, 63, 250
Pliny the Elder, 37
Plucking, glacial, *235,* 243*
Plunge of fold, *358*
Plunging fold, *358*, 359*
Pluton, *108*
Plutonic rock, *108*
Pluvial lakes, *220*, 221*
Podsol, *128*
Pohutu geyser, New Zealand, 109*
Point bars, *168,* 170
Point Firmin, landsliding, 149*
Pole Star, as datum, 14, 15*
    distance to, 14
Pompeii, 85, 86*
Pool (oil), *447*
Porosity *199*
    of rocks, 337
Porphyritic rocks, *478*, 481
Porphyry, *40,* 478
Potassium-argon dating, 58
Potholes, *166,* 167*
Precambrian, 61, 62, 63
    length of time, 61, 63
Precipitation, world-wide, 122, 123*
Primary ore, 460,* 461*
Projections, map, 484
Proton, 33*
Provo River, 193*
Psilomelane, with botryoidal form, *469**
Pumice, *38*, 478, 481
Pyrite, 32,* *474*
Pyroclastic rocks, 482
Pyrolusite, *474*
Pyroxene, *472*
Pyroxenite, *478*, 480

Quartz, 27,* 32,* *35,* 42,* 457,* 470, *472*
    vein, 457*
Quartzite, *47*, 479
Quaternary, 60,* 62, 63

Radioactivity, *56*
Radiocarbon dating, 58–59
Radio telescope, 50
Rain pelting, 257
Recharge, *206*, 207*
Rectangular stream pattern, 191,* *192*
Recumbent fold, *360*, 361,* 424*
Redwood tree, annual rings, 54*
Regolith, *8,* 29,* 138*
    in a desert, 256
    movements of, 136–148
Rejuvenation, 187,* *188,* 189,* 190
Relief, 485
Remanent magnetism, 438–*439*
Replacement, *208*

Reservoir rock, 447, 448*
Residual concentration, *461**
Residual mountain, *414*
Rhyolite, 42,* *478*, 481
  porphyritic, 481
  porphyry, *478*
Richter scale, earthquake magnitudes, 402
Rills, 260, 262
Ripple marks, 334,* 335, 360*
Ripples, wind, 270, 271*
Rock-basin lakes, 213,* 238*
Rock cycles, 47*–48
Rockfall, *135*
Rock flour, *239*, 241*
Rock lamination, 334*
Rocks, general classification, 5–7, 28–37
  igneous, 5, 37–41, 42,* 478
  metamorphic, 7, 46–47, 479
  sedimentary, 7, 46–47, 325, 479
Rockslide, *134*
Rocky Mountain geosyncline, 422–423
Roof rock, 447, 448*
Rounding of pebbles, 333*
Runoff, *154**
  ground-water, *154**
  surface, *154**
Rutile, *474*

Sahara Desert, 261
St. Elias Range, Alaska, 348, 437*
St. Francis Dam, 150, 165
St. Pierre, 88*
Saltation, *164*
  of sand grains, 266*
San Andreas fault, 348, 349,* 394*
  known extent, 394*
  recent offset along, 394*
  trough-like trace, 367
Sandstone, 45, 278,* *326*, 338*
San Francisco Bay, 354, 401*
San Francisco earthquake, 348, 392, 401*
San Francisco Peak, 100,* 101, 102
Sanidine, *472*
San Juan Parangaricutiro, Mexico, 82*
Santa Monica Mountains, soil creep, 144*
Scale, of map, *484*
  of time, 59–64
Scarps, *see* Fault
Schist, *46*, 479
Science of the Earth, 1–11
Scientific method in geology, 24–25
Sculptural evolution, interruptions, 188
  of a land mass, 184, 186,* 262, 263*
  of coasts, 318
Sea, *282*
  arches, 310*
  caves, 310*
Sea floor, 292*
  sediment, climate and chronology, 294
  sediment, distribution, 293*
  sediments, 291, 295
  topography, 283
  trench, 17, 287, *288*
  trenches, in Pacific Ocean, 417*, 428*
Sea level, 283
  glacial changes, 250
Seamount, 285,* 286,* *288*, 298, 299
Searles Dry Lake, California, 220
Sea wall, *312*
Secondary enrichment, *460,** 461*

Sediment, *43*
  clastic, *43*
  moved by wind, 265*
  offshore, 309
  on sea floor, 291–292,* 293–295, 298
    climate and chronology, 294
    distribution, 293*
Sedimentary facies, 344, 345*
Sedimentary rocks, 6, 41–45, *324*, 479
  characteristic texture, 44*
  classification, 325
  colors, 336–337
  early views on, 41–43
  folded strata, 357,* 358,* 359,* 360,* 361,* 377,*
    380,* 381,* 386*
  present concept, 43
  principal kinds, 44, 45, 325, 479
Seismic belts, *402*, 403*
Seismic prospecting, 403, *404,** 450
Seismic sea wave, 403
Seismic waves, in Earth, 397,* *399*
  artificial, for prospecting, 403, 404*
  changes in velocity with depth, 407*
  speeds of, 399, 400*
Seismogram, *399*
  meaning, 399–400
Seismograph, *398*–399
Seismology, *398*–402
  recording instruments, 398
Sequence of strata, 339,* 341*
Serpentine, 469,* *472*
Severinus, Peter, 4
Shadow zone, seismic, 406*
Shale, 45, 325, *327*
Shearing stress in deformation, 371, 379, 380,* 381*
Sheep Mountain, Wyoming, 359*
Sheep Range, Nevada, 29*
Sheet erosion, *179*
Sheet runoff, *179*, 260, 262
Shield volcano, 89, 91,* *92*, 97*
Shinumo Quadrangle, Arizona, 69*
Shiprock, New Mexico, 101,* 102
Shorelines, abandoned, 219, 220*
Shore profile, 310*
  equilibrium, 312
Shore zone, drowned, 354
  elevated, 347,* 352,* 353*
  tilted, 353*
Sial, *409*
Sierra Nevada, exfoliation in, 119*
  glaciated surface in, 126*
  structural history, 431, 432*
Silica tetrahedra, 35, 36*
Sill, *103*, 104,* 105*
Sillimanite, *472*
Siltstone, 325, *327*
Silver, *475*
Sima, *409*
Sinks, *209*,* 210*
Slate, 7,* *46*, 379, 380,* 381*
Slaty cleavage, 379, 380*
  relation to folds, 380*
Slickensides, 366,* *368*
Sliderock, 115,* *146*, 147*
Slip-face, 271,* *272**
Slumgullion debris flow, 140, 141*
Slump, 143,* 147,* *148*, 150*
William Smith, geologic map, 77
  on stratigraphic order, 342–343
Snow, conversion into glacier ice, 231, 232*
Snowfields, *231*, 236, 238, 243*

Snowline, *231*
Soil, climatic types, 128
  development, 126
  mature, *127*
  pedalfer, *128*
  pedocal, *128*
  podsol, *128*
  rate of formation, 129
  residual, 115,* *117*
Soil-creep, *143*, 144,* 145,* 146, 147*
Soil profile, *127*
Soils, representative compositions, 129
Solar energy, 120
Solid-solution silicates, formulas, 470
Solifluction, *146*
Solution, of rock material, 117
Sorting, *332*, 333*
Space, concept of, 50
Spanish Peaks, Colorado, 102,* 103*
Specific gravity, *470*
Sphalerite, *475*
Spheroidal weathering, 120*
Spits, *315*,* 316,* 317,* 319,* 320,* 486*
Spodumene, 39*
Spotted Range, Nevada, fault, 366*
Spring, *203*
Spring Mountain Range, 6*
Springs, artesian, 204
  gravity, 203*
Stability principle in streams, 175
Stacks, 310*
Stalactites, 197,* *209*
Stalagmites, 197,* *209*
Steppe, 254
Steppe climate, 255*
Stillwater Range, Nevada, mudflow, 141*
Stock, *107*, 455*
  Marysville, 107*
Strata, *see* Stratum
Stratification, 327,* *328*
Stratified drift, *240*
Stratigraphic column, *344–345*
Stratigraphic superposition, 343
Stratigraphy, *338*
Stratum, *328*, 339*
Streak, of a mineral, *469*
Stream, *155*
  bars, 165,* 172
  capture, *192*
  changes in bed, 159*
  channel, 160,* 161*
  dendritic pattern, *191*
  deposition, 164
  discharge, *157*
  economy, *156–157*
  energy, 156
  erosion, 163
  floods, 164
  flow, 155
  gradient, *155*
  load, *157*
  long profile, *161*,* 184*
  patterns, 191*
  solution, 163
  terrace, *188*
  transport, 164
  trellis pattern, 191,* 192
  tributaries, 161*
  velocity, 160*
Streamline flow, *155*
  of ground water, 200

Streams, adjustment, 194
  as geologic agents, 154
  classification, 192
  disappearing, 210*
  geologic activities, 163
  rectangular pattern, 191*
  relation to hydraulic cycle, 154
  relation to valleys, 178
  relation to water table, 201*
  trellis pattern, 191
  unstable systems, 188
Striations, glacial, 235,* 236,* 249,* 332*
Strike, *71*,* 72*
Strip mine, 447*
Stromboli Volcano, 1,* 85
Strontium-rubidium dating, 58
Structural geologists, *25*
Structure section, 69,* 73,* 74,* *75*
Submarine canyons, 250, 287,* *288*,* 298
Submarine fan, 298, 299*
Submergence of coasts, 317
Subsequent stream, *192*
Subsidence, of ground, 206
  during earthquake, 393*
  of land masses, 351,* 354
  under ice caps, 249
Sun-spot "cycle," 54, 329
Superposed stream, *192*, 193,* 433*
Surf, 303,* *306*,* 307*
Surf zone, 306, 308, 313, 314*
Surface ocean currents, *289*
Surface runoff, *154*
Suspended load, *164*
  in air, 267
Swamp, *224*, 225*
Swiss Plain, 426,* 427*
Symbols, on geologic maps, 488*
Syncline, *357*
  overturned, 360*
  plunging, 359*
  recumbent, 424*

Talc, 470, *472*
Talus, *146*, 147,* 257*
Temperature, and pressure, 384
  critical, 109*
  effects in metamorphism, 378
  effects in weathering, 118
  in contact metamorphism, 385
  of fusion, 384
Temple of Serapis, Italy, 351*
Terrace, marine, 354, 355*
  stream, *188*
Tertiary, 60, 62, 63
Texture, of rocks, *39*, 476
  aphanitic, *39*, 476
  glassy, 476
  granular, 476, 477,* *480*
  of pegmatite, 39,* 480
Theophrastus, 4
Thermometer, geologic, 385, 456
Thrust faults, *364*, 369,* 370*
  common type in Nevada, 370*
  relation to folds, 368
Tidal current, 288, *289*
Tidal inlet, 317,* *318*
Tidal marshes, *225*
"Tidal waves," 289, 403
Tides, 288, 289
Till, *240*,* 243,* 250*
  weathering, 250

Tillite, *251*, 332*
Time, absolute, *58*, 59
   concept of, 43
   geologic, 50–64
   measurements of, 56–59
   scale of, 59–64
Time scale, geologic, 63
Tobin Range, Nevada, 348, 349*
Toliman Volcano, 95*
Tombolo, 315,* *316*, 320*
Top and bottom of a stratum, 343
Topaz, 470, *475*
Topographic map, *485*, 486*
Topography, *485*
Topset beds, *174*
Transpiration, *20*, 21*
Transverse dunes, *273*
Trap for oil, 447, 448*
Travertine, *328*
Trellis stream pattern, *192*, 191°
Trenches, sea-floor, 17, 287,° *288*, 417°, 428°
Tributaries, 182,* 184*
Trilobites, 53*
Tritium, in ground water, 199
Troposphere, 16
Troughs, U-shaped, 238
Tsunami, *403*
Tufa, 328
Turbidity current, 88, *290*, 295, 296,* 297,* 298, 331, 332
Turbulent flow, *155*
   of air, 265
Turtle Mountain landslide, 134, 135*

Unconformity, *371*–374
   and Earth history, 373
   angular, *371*,* 372*
   disconformity, 372,* *373*
   proper definition, 373
   surface of, *373*
"Undertow," 306
Uniform bed, *331*
Uniformity of process, *4*
Upwarping, 354, 356*
   in Baltic region, 352,* 353
   in Coast Ranges, 354, 355*
   in Great Lakes area, 353*
Uraninite, 56,* *475*
Uranium atom, 32
Uranium minerals, 452
U-shaped dunes, *274*
U-shaped troughs, 238
U-shaped valley, 238, 239*
Utah Copper Mine, 460,* 461*

Valley, youthful and in rapid growth, 185*
Valley glacier, 227,* *228*, 229,* 238*
Valley of Ten Thousand Smokes, 88
Valleys, cross profile and climate, 257*
   development, 179
   evolution, 181
   glaciated, 236, 237,* 238*
   hanging, 236, 239*
   relation to mass-wasting, 180, 181*
   relation to streams, 178
   U-shaped, 238, 239*
Valley train, *244*
Varve, *330*
Veins, 457,* 462*

Ventifact, *269*,* 270, 271*
Vesicles, *40*, 98*
Vesuvius, 85, 86,* 108
Vitruvius, Marcus, 198
Volcanic action, 83
Volcanic blocks, *85*
Volcanic bombs, *85*°
Volcanic breccia, *40*
Volcanic cinders, *85*
Volcanic cones, kinds, 94
Volcanic crater, *84*
Volcanic mountains, *414*
Volcanic neck, *101*,* 102
Volcanic products, 84
Volcanic rocks, 40, 76,* 97,* 98,* 99*
Volcanic tuff, *40*
Volcano, *84*
   newborn, 80
Volcanoes, distribution, 100
Von Humboldt, Alexander, 415
Von Jolly, value of gravitational constant, 405*
Vulcano, 87

Warping, 354, 356*
   see also Downwarping, Upwarping
Wasatch Range, Utah, 140, 220,* 366,* 430
Water, heavy, 33
   juvenile, *84*
Water finding, 205
Water gap, 190, *191*, 192,* 193*
Water table, *199*,* 207,* 460*
   fluctuation, 202*
   slope, 201*
Wave-built terrace, 310,° *312*
Wave-cut bench, 309, *310*,° 311° 312
Wave-cut cliff, *310*,* 311,* 326*
Wave motion, 304
   lower limit, 305, 306*
Wave period, *304*
Wave refraction, *309*°
Waves, profile of, 305*
   seismic, 397
   seismic sea, 392, 395, 403
   sound, 397*
   "tidal," 289, 403
Waves of oscillation, *304*, 305,* 306*
Waves of translation, *306*°
Weather, effects of, 114
Weathering, *114*, 115*
   affected by climate, 124
   broad appraisal, 130–131
   chemical, 116–117, 126–130, 461
   mechanical, 118–120, 237
   of ferromagnesian minerals, 117
   of granitic rocks, 116, 121*
   part in erosion, 130
   spheroidal, 120*
Weber River, Utah, 193*
Welded tuff, *482*
Wells, artesian, 204*
   contamination, 207*
   ordinary, 202,* 203*
Werner, A. G., 98
Whin sill, 104
Wind, 265
   movement of sediment, 265,* 266, 267
Wind abrasion, 268

Windbreaks, 279*
Wind deposits, 270
Winds, polar easterlies, *122*
    prevailing, 121*
    prevailing westerlies, *122*
    trade, *122*
Wollastonite, as geologic thermometer, 385
Worms and other organisms, in weathering, 118

X-rays, use in mineral study, 35*

Yakutat Bay, earthquake of 1899, 348
Yellowstone National Park, 55,* 109
Yosemite National Park, 363*

Zircon, 35*
Zones of aeration and saturation, *199**